# Understanding Amateur Radio

By
Jay Rusgrove, W1VD
Doug DeMaw, W1FB
and
George Grammer, W1DF

American Radio Relay League, Inc.
Newington, CT 06111

# Foreword

If you're a relative newcomer to amateur radio, then this book can be just what you need! Your advancement from Novice to higher grades of license hinges on your technical knowledge. The information needed is presented in several publications but not always in a thorough nor complete form. *Understanding Amateur Radio* is designed to fill this void. With an accent on understanding, it establishes a technical groundwork for all phases of amateur radio. The basic concepts on which circuits and equipment are built are discussed in depth in a straightforward, leisurely style. This completely revised and updated edition continues the League's policy of providing the best possible instructional and educational material for the radio amateur. Whether you are using this book as a supplement to an organized amateur radio class or for individual study and reference, we know you will find it an effective tool to advance your understanding of amateur radio.

Richard L. Baldwin, W1RU
*General Manager*

# Contents

# Chapter 1

# Some Needed Fundamentals

$\mathbf{A}$t this point you'll probably skip to some more interesting part farther back in the book. Who wants to wade through dry "theory," anyway? Transmitters, receivers, antennas, getting on the air — all are far more interesting and are what attracted you to amateur radio in the first place.

This viewpoint is a reasonable one for the hobbyist, and we have no quarrel with it. What we hope to do in this chapter is to provide you with the answers to questions that, sooner or later, you're going to ask. You'll run into unfamiliar terms, either in reading or in contacts on the air. You'll find that a few concepts thread their way through the techniques of radio communication, and that being familiar with them will save you a lot of head scratching. In other words, you're going to *need* what we have to offer here — not right now, perhaps, but eventually.

In studying for your license examination you have probably acquired at least a speaking acquaintance with the more elementary electrical and radio principles. They won't get more repetition here than is actually necessary.[1] What we want to do is extend them a little farther, so you'll be able to apply them to your own practical problems.

## Polarity

You have learned that there are two kinds of electric *charge*, positive and negative. As applied to practical electric circuits, a negative charge means that the charged object has accumulated an excess number of electrons. A positive charge means the charged body has somehow been robbed of electrons that it normally would have.

The negatively charged body frowns on any attempt to add more electrons to its already swollen total; so, too, the positively charged body looks with disfavor on any effort to dislodge still more of those electrons it has left. This leads to the rule that objects having charges that are of the same kind repel each other.

On the other hand, a negatively charged object is quite willing to lose electrons and get back to normal. Similarly, a positively charged object is eager to acquire some electrons so *it* can get back to normal. Thus, unlike charges attract each other.

This eagerness to get back to normal is described in physics by the word *potential*. In circuits, we're more concerned with the *difference* between the potentials of two charged objects. This difference of potential is expressed in a familiar electrical unit, the *volt*. Since we're dealing with differences, not "absolute" values, there can be a potential difference or voltage between two positively charged (or negatively charged) objects just as readily as between one having a positive charge and one having a negative charge. That is, the *polarity* is *relative*.

A simple example will illustrate. Imagine three charged objects, one (A) having a charge of +5 units, a second (B) having a charge of +8 and a third (C) having a charge of −3. See Fig. 1. The potential difference between A and B is 3 units, with A negative with respect to B although A's charge actually is positive. The potential difference between A and C is 8 units, with A positive and C negative. You can easily work out for yourself the potential difference be-

tween B and C, and the relative polarity.

This isn't just indulgence in simple arithmetic for its own sake. The idea of relative polarity keeps cropping up all the time in radio circuits. Even though the word "relative" isn't often used in circuit discussions where polarity is mentioned, it is always understood.

## Ground Potential

Since we are dealing with differences of potential, or relative potential, it is handy to have something to use as a "reference" potential, to be most useful. This reference should be the same for everybody. Therefore, the "something" that has it must be an object whose potential isn't going to be changed by anything we do. The earth itself is ideal — it's so big that anything we do won't make even the tiniest difference in its electric charge. You'll frequently see and hear the term *ground potential*. When we say something is at ground potential, we mean that it could be put into electrical contact with the earth without being disturbed electrically. It doesn't actually *have* to be in contact with the earth to be at ground potential — just *could* be.

The metal pan or chassis on which equipment is built is usually at ground potential, although there actually may be no direct connection between the chassis and ground. But the equipment would work just the same if we did

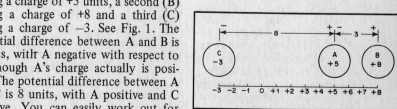

Fig. 1 — Illustrating difference of potential.

[1] It is assumed that the reader has a copy of *Tune in the World with Ham Radio* also published by the American Radio Relay League, Newington, CT and is familiar with the basic material contained in it.

make such a connection. It is, therefore, common to speak of a *chassis ground*, meaning that some part of the circuit is "grounded" to — that is, connected to — the chassis itself. In most circuits a chassis connection is all that is meant when the ground symbol appears. Some confusion can be avoided in this respect if the special chassis-connection symbol is used instead of the earth-connection symbol. The chassis symbol is used in the circuits in this book.

# Direct Current

The distinguishing feature of direct current is that the electrons always move in the same direction through the circuit. If the number of electrons passing some point in the circuit is always the same, the current is a steady one and its value is easily specified. You've learned that the unit of current is the *ampere*, and that the relationship between potential difference and current — that is, between volts and amperes — in such a circuit is summed up in *Ohm's Law*

$$I = \frac{E}{R}$$

where $E$ stands for the number of volts, $I$ for the number of amperes, and $R$ is a property of the circuit itself — its *resistance*. The unit of resistance is the *ohm*. The formula can be transposed to give us two other useful forms

$$E = IR \quad \text{and} \quad R = \frac{E}{I}$$

Going on with a little more review, the power, $P$, in such a circuit is

$$P = EI$$

which, by making a simple substitution, can also be written in two other useful forms

$$P = \frac{E^2}{R} \quad \text{and} \quad P = I^2 R$$

The unit of power is the *watt*.

These expressions, too, can be transposed: In fact, given any two of the four quantities — voltage, current, resistance and power — the other two can always be found. It helps to have the formulas handy, since you'll find a need for them more often than you might think. Fig. 2 summarizes them.

## Power

A word about power: In physics, power is the rate of doing work. (Anything requiring the expenditure of energy is work, in the physical sense; what is done does not have to be useful.) You might guess from the formulas in Fig. 2 that in a direct-current circuit the work done is in overcoming the resistance of the circuit and forcing current to flow. You would be right. Resistance is a

one-way dead-end street. Energy that goes into it never comes back out in the same form. In a resistor such as you buy in a store, the electrical energy put into it comes out as heat energy, raising the temperature of the resistor. The faster the rate at which energy is put in — that is, the greater the power — the more heat generated. "High-power" resistors have to be large in order to handle the heat without reaching a temperature that would burn them up.

An electric heater is a useful device if you want to be warmed by it. In our radio equipment, heat is mostly a nuisance — an unavoidable by-product of resistance in the various circuits. Not that resistance isn't necessary in such circuits; the fact is that it has many legitimate uses. However, the heat it produces is useful only in a few cases, such as in heating the cathode of a vacuum tube.

### The Nature of Resistance

The formulas in the third column of Fig. 2 are really definitions of resistance. The first one ($R = E/I$) must be used with caution, because the name "resistance" is not always applicable. But the other two can be used quite generally. They define resistance as something that has a close relationship with power; that is, as something associated with the expenditure of energy. Energy and power make no distinction between direct and alternating currents. A watt in an ac circuit means just the same thing as a watt in a dc circuit.

Let's look at it by the "black-box" method. In Fig. 3 there is a battery having an output voltage, $E$. When it is connected to a pair of terminals on the box, a current, $I$, flows in the connecting wires. We do not know what is inside the box. But on applying Ohm's Law, we find that it seems to contain a resistance, $R$, equal to $E/I$. Should we conclude that there is an actual *resistor* in the box? It's possible, of course, that there is. But the most that we can say with certainty is that whatever is in the box is consuming energy from the battery in the same way that such a resistor would.

Now it could be that on opening the box we'd find that it actually contained a radio transmitter, and that the dc power from the battery was being converted into radio-frequency power

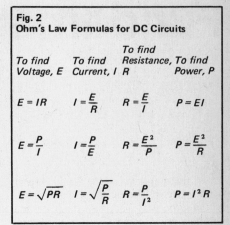

**Fig. 2**
**Ohm's Law Formulas for DC Circuits**

| To find Voltage, E | To find Current, I | To find Resistance, R | To find Power, P |
|---|---|---|---|
| $E = IR$ | $I = \dfrac{E}{R}$ | $R = \dfrac{E}{I}$ | $P = EI$ |
| $E = \dfrac{P}{I}$ | $I = \dfrac{P}{E}$ | $R = \dfrac{E^2}{P}$ | $P = \dfrac{E^2}{R}$ |
| $E = \sqrt{PR}$ | $I = \sqrt{\dfrac{P}{R}}$ | $R = \dfrac{P}{I^2}$ | $P = I^2 R$ |

which in turn was being radiated off into space. The transmitter is certainly not a resistor, although before we knew what was in the box it seemed to act like one. Would it be legitimate to call such a device a "resistance" simply because Ohm's Law seemed to say it was one?

The answer is "yes." A *generalized* definition of resistance is that it is something that uses up power. In using the power it can either convert it to some other form, often one that represents a useful end, or dissipate it internally, usually in the form of heat. It may do both simultaneously. In fact, all electrical devices do dissipate a little of the power themselves. It's just the nature of things for this to happen.

This *apparent* or *equivalent resistance* is a useful concept in dealing with circuits, although it does not physically describe what actually is going on. It is perhaps unfortunate that there isn't some other name given to it. (This isn't the only instance in radio work where you will find one term having several different meanings, or shades of

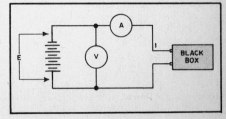

Fig. 3 — What's in the box?

meanings.) But whether resistance is "real," as a resistor, or "apparent," as in the example above, there is one thing you can bank on: In order to qualify as resistance in circuit operation, it has to obey all the laws that govern ordinary resistance.

### Series and Parallel

Throughout your work with circuits you'll be up against *series* and *parallel* connections. These aren't hard to understand. When circuit components are connected in series the current flows through them one after the other. Fig. 4A shows this for a number of resistors connected to a source of voltage, $E$. The same current, $I$, flows through all of them since it has no other path to follow.

If we apply Ohm's Law to such a circuit the voltage measured between the ends of $R1$ will be found to be $R1$ multiplied by the current; that is, $IR1$. This voltage is called the *voltage drop* across $R1$. Similarly, the voltage drop across $R2$ is $IR2$, and the voltage drop across $R3$ is $IR3$. Obviously, the total of all these voltage drops has to add up to the voltage $E$ coming from the source. By some simple mathematics, this leads to the rule that the total resistance of a number of resistances in series is equal to the sum of the individual resistances. That is

$$R_{total} = R1 + R2 + R3 + \text{etc.}$$

for as many resistances as there are in series.

Now look at Fig. 4B. Here the resistances have their terminals connected together. The same voltage, $E$, is applied to each one. The current coming from the source will be divided up among them, some going through $R1$, some through $R2$, and the reaminder through $R3$. The currents in each branch have to add up to $I$, the total current coming from the power source. The current through each resistor will obey Ohm's Law; that is, the current through $R1$ is equal to $E$ divided by $R1$, the current through $R2$ is equal to $E$ divided by $R2$, and so on. If we simply divide $E$ by $I$, we will have a resistance value that will be equivalent to that of all the resistances in parallel. Since the total current is larger than any of the individual resistor currents, this equivalent resistance must be *smaller* than any of the individual resistors. The most important practical case is the one where just two resistances are in parallel. The equivalent resistance can be calculated from

$$R = \frac{R1R2}{R1 + R2}$$

You'll run into many practical applications of resistances in series and parallel. For instance, if you need a certain value of resistance but don't have it all

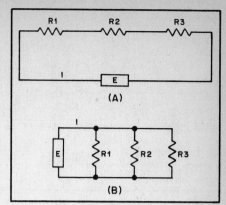

Fig. 4 — Resistances in series (A) and parallel (B).

in one resistor, you can make it up by using two or more smaller resistors whose resistance values will add up to what you want. They will be connected in series in this case, of course. Or you may have a couple of resistors of larger value than you want, but which can be connected in parallel to give you a desired smaller value. Sometimes, too, you may want a certain value of resistance that can dissipate more power than can be handled by any single resistor you have. If you need 500 ohms with a safe power dissipation of four watts, for example, you can connect two 1000-ohm, 2-watt resistors in parallel, or two 250-ohm, 2-watt resistors in series.

# Alternating Current

The problems of alternating current stem from the fact that the current (or voltage) is changing throughout the *cycle*. In a "steady" alternating current each cycle is like the one before it and also like the one that will follow. But within the cycle there is no such peaceful repose as we find in the behavior of direct current. This continual restlessness leads to all sorts of effects that are absent with dc. (That is, absent except during those times when the direct current is being started or stopped, or is otherwise subjected to change. These periods can be, and are, ignored in many situations, although not in all.)

First, there is the question of how to assign a value to an alternating current. If we follow the current throughout a cycle, we may find that at successive instants it is increasing until it reaches, say, one ampere. At that instant it starts to decrease, eventually dying away to nothing. Then it reverses itself to do the same thing while flowing in the opposite direction. Next, it starts the whole

business over again. At no point does it stay still long enough for us to say, "*that's* the value of the current."

### AC Amperes and Volts

The clue to settling on a number to use for the current is found in a statement made earlier: Power makes no distinction between ac and dc. A resistor gets just as hot when current flows from top to bottom as when it flows from bottom to top. Thus the power will be the same regardless of the direction of current flow; and since this is so, it doesn't matter how rapidly the current may reverse direction. It follows that we can say we have one ampere of alternating current when that current heats a given resistor exactly as one ampere of direct current would heat it. If the alternating current has the form of a sine wave when plotted on a graph, as in Fig. 5, it will have an *effective value* of one ampere when its maximum value during the cycle is equal to 1.41 ampere (the exact figure is $\sqrt{2}$). The same relationship holds for the effective

value of voltage. An alternate term for effective is *rms* (*root-mean-square*), this name being derived from the method by which such a wave is analyzed mathematically.

The effects associated with alternating current are intimately related to

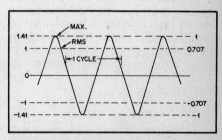

Fig. 5 — If an alternating current or voltage has the sine form shown here, an effective current of 1 ampere exists when the maximum value is 1.41 amp, as shown by the scale at the left. Figures at the right are in terms of 1 ampere maximum current, in which case the rms current is 0.707 ampere. The ratio is the same for all sine waves. Other waveforms will have different ratios, in general.

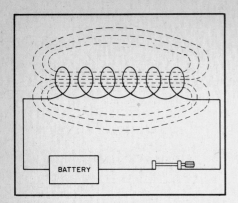

Fig. 6 — Current sent through an inductance sets up a magnetic field around it. The dashed lines represent the paths along which the field exerts magnetic force.

the frequency of the current, or the number of cycles per second. The principal one is reactance, a term you have met briefly in your studies. Since you'll be running into it all the time, it needs a little more detailed consideration. To appreciate reactance, however, you need first to know a little about energy storage in electric circuits.

### Stored Energy

Suppose you carry a stone to an upper floor of your house and place it on a window sill. You probably didn't think of it in these terms, but the fact is that in carrying it up above the ground you have been storing gravitational energy in the stone. The energy stored is equal to the work you did in carrying it up. If you now push the stone off the sill, its stored energy is released, carrying it rapidly back to the ground. This sequence is said to be the result of a gravitational field, an invisible something that has been invented to account for an observed effect.

Electrical energy can be stored, too. If you send a direct current through an inductance, a *magnetic field* comes into being around it (Fig. 6). This field represents stored energy. If you now open the circuit, all the stored energy comes back. It comes back a lot faster than it went into the field, because it has to get back the very instant you open the switch. After that it would be too late, since there would be no circuit. If the returning energy is large, it will make itself visible by a fat spark at the switch contacts.

### Magnetic Energy

Putting energy into a magnetic field also takes work. One definition of work is that it consists of overcoming an opposing force — gravity, inertia, friction, or what-have-you. In storing energy in a magnetic field, the work done consists in overcoming a force generated in the inductance by the very fact that energy is being stored. This opposition

takes the form of an *induced voltage* which bucks the applied voltage. Its value depends not on the actual value of current but on the rate at which the current *changes*. The current changes in value most rapidly at the instant that voltage is applied to an inductance, so at this moment the induced voltage is almost equal to the applied voltage. Then the rate of current change becomes slower and slower, and eventually there is no change that can be measured. At this time the work is complete; the maximum energy is stored in the field, there is no induced voltage, and from then on the resistance of the circuit governs the current flow. Ohm's Law finally prevails.

### Electric-Field Storage

You can store energy in a capacitor, too. In this case the storehouse is an *electric field*, not a magnetic field (Fig. 7). If you apply a dc voltage to a capacitor, there will be an instantaneous rush of current into the capacitor to charge it. The only thing that limits the current at the instant of closing the switch is whatever resistance there may be in the circuit. The capacitor itself acts like a short circuit, at that instant, and all the voltage appears across the resistance. Then as the capacitor "fills up" with electricity — meaning that one set of plates is acquiring an excess of electrons while the other set is being robbed of the same number — the voltage across it rises. Eventually, the voltage at the capacitor terminals is equal to the source voltage and current flow stops. If the source of voltage is then disconnected, the capacitor will remain charged to that voltage. The charge will stay there just as long as there is no path by which electrons can travel from one set of plates to the other. A capacitor with very low leakage will hold a charge for days on end.

If you connect a resistance to the charged capacitor, the energy will dissipate itself in heating the resistor. If the capacitance and resistance are both large, it may take a long time for voltage to disappear entirely from the capacitor terminals. However, the capacitor can be discharged rapidly into a low resistance or a short circuit. If you touch a wire to the terminals of a capacitor of several microfarads charged to a few hundred volts, you'll get quite a spark. (If you touch the terminals yourself you'll get quite a jolt! To avoid danger of this, power-supply capacitors have *bleeder resistors* connected across them to drain off the charge.)

### Time Constant

The time in seconds that it takes a charged capacitor to lose its charge through a resistance is called the *time constant* of a resistance-capacitance cir-

cuit.[2] You'll meet this term every now and then in practical-circuit applications. One example is the automatic gain control used in receivers, taken up in chapter 5. The larger the capacitance and the larger the resistance, the greater the time constant. An easy rule to remember is that the time constant in seconds is equal to microfarads multiplied by megohms.

There is a time constant associated with inductance and resistance, too, but it works the opposite way. That is, the larger the resistance in series with a given inductance, the shorter the time constant. If we want the current to build up in a hurry in an inductive circuit, we have to use a large resistance in series.

### Reactance

Just what does all this have to do with reactance? It goes about like this: From the preceding discussion you've seen that energy is stored in the magnetic field when current through an inductance is increasing, and in the electric field when the voltage across a capacitor is increasing. If the current through the inductance is made to decrease, energy will come back into the circuit. The induced voltage will tend to keep current flowing in the same direction as the original current. By the same token, if the voltage applied to a capacitor is made to decrease, the capacitor will discharge into the circuit, giving back stored energy.

Now an alternating voltage or current is one which not only reverses its direction periodically, but also is one in which the *value* of the voltage or current is continually changing. Because of this continual change, energy will at times be stored in the magnetic field and shortly thereafter returned to the circuit, if the circuit contains inductance. Similarly with the electric field and capacitance. *All of the energy stored during one part of a cycle is*

---

[2] Actually, not all of its charge but 63 percent of it, approximately. There is a mathematical reason for choosing this percentage, but it isn't essential to discuss it here.

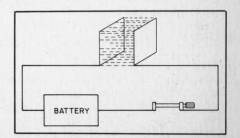

Fig. 7 — An electric field exists between the plates of a capacitor when a voltage is applied. Dashed lines represent paths of the "lines of force."

*returned by the time the cycle is over.*

### Apparent Power

In other words, inductance and capacitance take energy (or power) from the power source only to hand all of it back again. A "pure" inductance or capacitance (i.e., without associated resistance) uses no power. Nevertheless, current does flow in the circuit when voltage is applied. If we multiply the voltage by the current, the same as we do to find power in dc circuits, we get a number which seems to represent power. It only *seems* to do so, because no real work is done unless there is resistance. This power is called *apparent power* or *wattless power*. To distinguish it from real power, a different unit is used — a *volt-ampere*. One volt-ampere is the same as one watt — except that it doesn't do any work, while a real watt does.

You are undoubtedly curious as to how it is that there can be voltage and current but no power. A detailed examination of what goes on in the circuit is beyond the scope of this book. Briefly, however, it is a matter of timing (for which the technical term is *phase*). The voltage and current don't pull together, as they do in a simple resistance. When one is big, the other is likely to be small; or, even, when the polarity of the voltage is positive the current may be negative — that is, flowing in the "wrong" direction. It's something like a tug-of-war in which two teams expend a lot of effort in pulling each other back and forth without making any net progress one way or the other.

### Inductive Reactance

We said earlier that the more rapidly the current changes, the larger the opposing voltage generated in an inductance. A high-frequency alternating current changes more rapidly than a low-frequency one, since there are more cycles per second. Thus the higher the frequency and the larger the inductance, the harder it is for current to flow through the inductance; it meets more opposition. The measure of this opposition is called *inductive reactance*. It is something like the opposition that resistance offers to current flow, and so the unit of reactance is also named the ohm.

Like the wattless watt, though, it is an ohm without resistance. It does act like a real ohm to this extent: Given a fixed frequency, the current through it will be directly proportional to the voltage applied. In other words, we can write for reactance the equivalent of Ohm's Law for resistance

$$I = \frac{E}{X}$$

where $X$ stands for reactance. But for a given value of inductance, reactance increases with the frequency, so it is not a *constant* like resistance is — unless we specify that the frequency stays constant.

### Capacitive Reactance

A capacitor acts in just the opposite way. The more rapidly the applied voltage changes in value, the faster the capacitor stores energy. This means that a high-frequency alternating voltage will put more current into a given capacitor than a low-frequency voltage could. Thus the reactance of a capacitor goes *down* as the frequency increases. Nevertheless, the same formula applies if the frequency stays constant. All we have to remember is that $X$ gets smaller as the capacitance is made larger, and that it also gets smaller as the frequency is made larger.

To distinguish inductive from capacitive reactance, the former is usually designated $X_L$ and the latter $X_C$. Just plain $X$ can mean either one or a combination of both. In the form of equations, the ideas expressed above in words result in

$$X_L = 2\pi f L \qquad X_C = \frac{1}{2\pi f C}$$

In these formulas, $f$ is the frequency, $L$ the inductance, and $C$ the capacitance. The proper units have to be used.[3] We won't attempt to explain the factor $2\pi$ here because that's a whole topic in itself and is chiefly of mathematical interest.

### Reactances Combined

The "oppositeness" of inductive and capacitive reactance has another important effect. When a coil and capacitor are connected in series in a circuit, one tends to undo what the other is trying to do. This is quite different from placing two resistances in series. The resistances both act the same way, and the total resistance is the sum of the two. But if we put inductive and capacitive reactance in series, the total reactance is the *difference*. Conventionally, capacitive reactance is called "negative" and inductive reactance is called "positive." Thus a series circuit might have an inductive reactance of "plus" 15 ohms and a capacitive reactance of "minus" 10 ohms; the total reactance would be only 5 ohms $(15 - 10)$ in that case.

However, reactances of the *same* kind add up just as resistors do. That is, an inductive reactance of 15 ohms placed in series with one of 8 ohms will result in a total of 23 ohms. The same would be true of two capacitive reactances of these same values, except that the sign would be negative.

Also, reactances of the same kind connected in parallel are combined by the same rules that we use for resistances. Not so with reactances of *opposite* kind in parallel! Things begin to get complicated in that case — too much so to be considered in this book, except for one special case, the resonant circuit.

---

[3] The most convenient units in amateur work are megahertz for frequency, microhenrys for inductance, and micromicrofarads (also called picofarads) for capacitance. With these units the formulas are

$$X_L = 6.28 f L$$

and

$$X_C = \frac{1,000,000}{6.28 f C} = \frac{159,000}{f C}$$

in which 6.28 is the approximate value of $2\pi$. The reactance as given by these formulas is in ohms in both cases.

# Resonant Circuits

Since the reactance of an inductance goes up when we increase the frequency, while the reactance of a capacitance goes down, it is reasonable to expect that at *some* frequency the reactances of a given inductance and capacitance will be equal. This is so. The frequency at which it happens is called the *resonant* frequency of the combination.

We're rarely able to ignore resonance in radio-frequency circuits. It's important because at the resonant frequency the inductive reactance is balanced out by the capacitive reactance. This leaves us with only resistance operating in the circuit. There's more to it than just cancellation of reactive effects though, as we shall see.

Fig. 8 illustrates how reactance changes with frequency. In making up this graph we have chosen 5 $\mu$H for the inductance and 50 pF for the capacitance. The scale chosen lets us show a large range of values, of both frequency and reactance, with constant *percentage* accuracy at any point on curves drawn on it. The $X_L$ curve shows that the

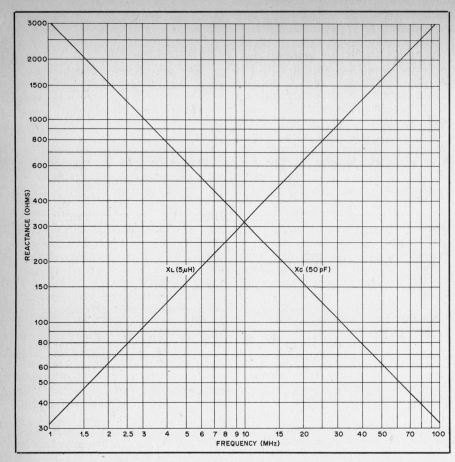

Fig. 8 — Illustrating how the reactances of a typical coil (5 microhenrys) and capacitor (50 pF) vary with frequency.

reactance goes from about 30 ohms at 1 MHz to over 3000 ohms at 100 MHz. The capacitive reactance does just the opposite — it goes from 3000 ohms at 1 MHz to a little over 30 ohms at 100 MHz. Other values of inductance and capacitance would have different actual values, but would behave similarly; the ones picked just happen to be convenient for study.

The striking thing here is that these two curves cross each other at close to 10 MHz. At this frequency their reactances are equal numerically. In other words, the combination of 5 $\mu$H and 50 pF is *resonant* at 10 MHz. Remember that this is only *one* such combination, picked out simply to show graphically how resonance occurs. Theoretically, there is an infinite number of combinations that will resonate at any given frequency. Practically, however, we are confined to certain ranges of inductance and capacitance, because of constructional limitations of actual coils and capacitors.

## Series Resonance

With respect to the circuit in which they are used, the coil and capacitor may be connected either in series or parallel. This is shown in Fig. 9. If we have a source of voltage, $E$, at the resonant frequency and the two are in series, the current is the same all around the circuit. By the Ohm's Law equations for reactance which we gave earlier, the current will cause a voltage to exist across each reactance. These voltages have been labeled $E_L$ and $E_C$ in the series circuit. Strange as it may seem, they can be many, many times larger than the source voltage, $E$. In fact, they are usually at least ten times as large, and may be as much as a few hundred times as large.

This can happen because the two reactances cancel each other's effects, since they are equal at resonance. Thus around the circuit there is zero reactance. There is nothing, then, to limit the flow of current except the resistance in the circuit. Although we haven't shown any resistance in Fig. 9, there is always some, because no components operate without at least a little power loss. Also, the source of voltage will have an *internal* resistance. But if the total resistance is small, the current will be large, by Ohm's Law. And a large current will result in large, but equal, voltage drops across each reactance. The

time or phase of these voltages is such that the voltage across $L$ has its *positive* maximum at the same instant that the voltage across $C$ has its *negative* maximum. The two voltages always add up just to zero.

We can look at this another way, which may make it seem more reasonable: These unusually large voltages can develop because of energy stored in the reactances. The energy going into the magnetic field of the inductance is energy coming out of the electric field of the capacitor, during one part of a cycle. Then when it has all been stored in the magnetic field, it starts coming back into the circuit and goes into the electric field. This means that a lot of energy can be handed back and forth between $L$ and $C$ without making it necessary for the source to supply any. Of course, the energy "bank account" came from the source. But after an initial surge, the source has only to supply the actual power used up in resistance.

## Parallel Resonance

We have a different, but comparable, state of affairs when $L$ and $C$ are connected in parallel. Here, there are two current paths with the same voltage, $E$, applied to both. The two branch currents, $I_C$ and $I_L$, each depend only on the same Ohm's Law formula for a reactive circuit. If the reactance is small and the voltage $E$ is large, each branch current will be large. But the same *voltage* is applied to both reactances (in the series circuit both had the same *current*). So in this case it is the currents that add up to zero around the circuit. Their phase is such that they cancel each other, in the part of the circuit outside the coil and capacitor. In this case, then, there is no current flowing around the circuit as a whole.

A parallel-resonant circuit "looks like" an open circuit to the source of

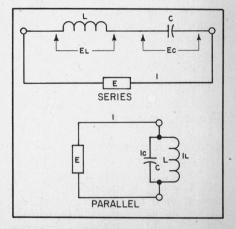

Fig. 9 — Series and parallel circuits formed by inductive and capacitive reactances, together with a source of voltage, $E$.

voltage. Compare this with the series circuit, which "looked like" a short circuit. The reason for this behavior of the parallel circuit is the same as in the series case — stored energy is tossed back and forth between the inductance and capacitance.

These ideas of "short circuit" and "open circuit" must be taken with caution. They would be literally true if we could have coils and capacitors without any losses. But these components always do have losses. If the losses are very small, the series circuit is *approximately* a short circuit, and the parallel circuit is *approximately* an open circuit. Losses mean that the voltages in the series circuit don't quite balance each other, and the currents in the parallel circuit don't quite cancel each other. Some of the energy is lost each time it is handed back and forth. This lost energy has to be supplied continuously by the source, in order to keep things going at an even rate. The source "sees" a resistance, therefore — a very small one in the case of the series circuit, and a very large one in the case of the parallel circuit.

## Impedance

If you've digested what has gone before, you're ready to tackle *impedance*, a word that gets a lot of bandying around in amateur conversations. Its basic definition is simple, but the details are far from being so. In fact, we can't hope to do more than give you a speaking acquaintance with some of them in this book. The inner workings of actual circuits really belong in the field of engineering rather than hobbying. Fortunately, we don't need to know them in order to build and operate amateur equipment.

In broad terms, impedance is a number you get by dividing the voltage applied to a circuit by the current flowing into it. Resorting to the black box again (Fig. 10), suppose we measure the current $I$ flowing into the box and find it to be 1/2 ampere when the applied ac voltage $E$ is 250 volts. Dividing 250 by 1/2 gives 500 as the answer. Although this is not a dc circuit we say that we have 500 "ohms," since the ohm got established as a unit repre-

senting the ratio of voltage to current (that is, $E/I$) in dc work. But we don't know what's in the box, so we can't say that these "ohms" are either resistance or reactance. It would take more than a simple measurement of current or voltage to determine that, because — as we have seen — there is an element of timing or phase that has to be taken into account. The ammeter and voltmeter don't have any information about phase.

The fact is that we could get the same answer whether we have 500 ohms of "pure" resistance or "pure" reactance. But we could also get the same answer if the box contained 500 ohms of something that was a combination of both. Such a combination not only can exist but actually is likely to be more common than either alone. The ohms, then, in this case *could* be either resistance or reactance, but more probably would be impedance, the name for the combination.

You can see why things start to get complicated at this point. In pure reactance they are out of step by exactly one-quarter of a cycle. These are both very special cases. In a *complex impedance* — one made up of both resistance and reactance — the current and voltage may be out of step in any degree between zero and one-quarter cycle. The number of possible cases is infinite.

## Resistive Impedance

It happens that in rf work we are concerned mostly with resonant circuits. These, as we have explained, "look like" pure resistances when they are exactly tuned to the frequency. Off the exact resonant frequency, the resistance is no longer pure, but in many cases the adulteration of resistance by reactance isn't too great. It is customary, therefore, to use the term impedance rather loosely to mean a *resistive* impedance. A resistive impedance is one in which the resistive effects far override the reactive effects — enough so that the latter can be neglected for practical purposes.

You will see references to impedance in amateur publications, with occasional rules and formulas for one or another special case. Don't fall into the trap of thinking that these rules and formulas are wholly accurate. In most cases they won't be. They are nearly always approximations based on assuming that something can be neglected. This is done to simplify them. Properly used, such rules and formulas can be highly useful in practical work. Occasionally, though, they are misused through ignorance of their hidden limitations. Be cautious, therefore, about applying them to cases other than the one they actually are intended to satisfy.

With this warning, we'll have to move

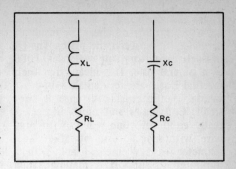

Fig. 11 — The $Q$ of a component is the ratio of its reactance to its resistance.

on to some other circuit functions. Just remember that impedance is the ratio of voltage to current in a circuit, and that the timing or phase of the voltage and current are, in general, such that part of the energy is dissipated in resistance and part is stored in reactance.

## $Q$ – The Shorthand Number

Another thing you'll hear a lot about and read a lot about is $Q$. This is a number tacked on to coils and capacitors, and circuits formed by them, to give some idea of their characteristics. With its help, and with some simplifying assumptions, a good deal of calculation can be saved in gauging the operation of circuits.

One definition of $Q$ is that it is the ratio of reactance to resistance. Thus in Fig. 11 the $Q$ of the combination of $X_L$ and $R_L$ is equal to $X_L$ divided by $R_L$. $R_L$ may be a separate resistor, as shown. On the other hand, it may be the resistance of the coil itself. This internal resistance can't be separated from the coil, of course, but it *acts* just the same as though it were in series with a lossless coil.

The $Q$ of a capacitor is found in the same way — that is, the $Q$ is equal to the reactance, $X_C$, divided by the resistance, $R_C$. Internal resistance here acts the same as in the case of the coil.

Thus the definition of $Q$ applies to components having internal resistance. But it also applies to a circuit, formed by the component and an *external* resistance in series with it. In such a case the internal and external resistance have to be added together to find the value of $R$ that is to be used in the formula. Since added external resistance can only raise the total resistance, the $Q$ always goes down when resistance is added in series. There is no way to lower the internal resistance of a coil or capacitor, and thus raise the $Q$, except by building a better component.

## $Q$s of Components

Capacitors have much better $Q$s than coils, ordinarily. At least, this is true of the types of capacitors used in radio-frequency circuits where $Q$ is important.

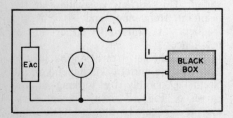

Fig. 10 — Simple measurements of voltage and current don't give a clue to what the unknown impedance may actually be.

These capacitors nearly always are made with either mica or air as the insulator or *dielectric* between the plates. The $Q$s of such capacitors run well over 1000 as a general rule. This means that their internal losses are very small — in other words, the internal resistance is very small. Coil losses run much higher. A really good coil, one wound with large wire, with spaced turns of rather large diameter (a few inches) and with a minimum of supporting material (such as a few thin strips of insulation) may have a $Q$ as high as 500. The $Q$ of a coil wound of small wire on a form a quarter of an inch or so in diameter, with a powdered-iron *slug* for adjustment of the inductance, may be as low as 25 at high frequencies.

You can see that in $Q$ we have a sort of figure of merit for a coil or capacitor. For a given value of reactance, the higher the $Q$ the lower the internal losses. The $Q$ is important not only because of these losses as such but because of its effect on the operation of a resonant circuit.

If you've been wearing your thinking cap, you've caught on to one point we haven't mentioned. Since reactance varies with frequency, the $Q$ of a coil or capacitor can't be expected to be the same at all frequencies. Unless, that is, its resistance changes in exactly the same way as its reactance. It just happens that over a limited frequency range the resistance of a coil made for radio-frequency use does tend to move along with its reactance. Over such a frequency range — which is usually the useful range for that coil — the $Q$ doesn't change a great deal. But it does change some.

## Tuned-Circuit $Q$

Besides its application to inductance and capacitance singly, $Q$ also is used to rate a resonant circuit. Looking again at the resonant series crcuit of Fig. 9, the $Q$ can be defined as the ratio of $E_L$ to $E$; that is, it is the ratio of the resonant voltage to the voltage applied to the circuit. Obviously, the $Q$ is also equal to $E_C/E$, since $E_L$ and $E_C$ are equal (because the reactances are equal) at the resonant frequency.

In the parallel circuit of Fig. 9, the $Q$ is equal to $I_L/I$ or to $I_C/I$, as you can readily see by analogy to the series circuit.

If we change the frequency slightly, either circuit is no longer exactly resonant. In the series circuit the two reactances no longer balance each other completely; there is some reactance left, and it impedes the flow of current. So the current decreases and along with it, the voltages developed across the coil and capacitor. In the parallel circuit, moving the frequency a little away from resonance — say, a little higher — will

cause the current through the capacitor to increase because the reactance of the capacitor becomes slightly lower. But the current through the inductance will *decrease*, because the inductive reactance becomes slightly higher. The two currents no longer cancel each other: thus the *line current, I*, becomes larger.

## Parallel Resonance

We'll be dealing mostly with parallel-resonant circuits in our amateur equipment. There are two common cases. In the first, shown in Fig. 12A, we're interested in the voltage, $V$, that

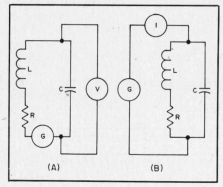

Fig. 12 — Parallel-resonant circuits as seen from the inside (A) and outside (B). These terms refer to the way in which energy is introduced into the circuit.

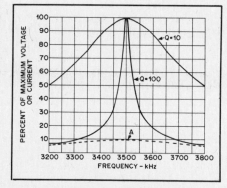

Fig. 13 — Resonance curves showing the effect of circuit $Q$ on the voltage measured by the circuit of Fig. 12A as the frequency of the applied voltage is varied from below to above the resonant frequency of the circuit.

develops across the terminals of the circuit at and near the resonant frequency. The source of energy is assumed to be a generator, $G$, for convenience. (Actually, the energy will be introduced into the circuit by some other means in a practical case.) In the second case, Fig. 12B, the source of energy, $G$, is outside the circuit and the thing of interest is the current, $I$, flowing into the circuit. In both these circuits the $Q$ is determined by the value of the resistance, $R$, in relation to the inductive reactance of $L$, just as though these two formed an independent cir-

cuit. We can forget the capacitor because its losses are so low, in nearly all cases, that practically all the circuit resistance is in the coil. Thus the $Q$ of the circuit at the resonant frequency is the $Q$ of the coil.

Take Fig. 12A first. We will assume a circuit tuned to 3500 kHz. The generator, $G$, has a constant output of 1 volt while its frequency is varied around 3500 kHz. If the $Q$ of the circuit is 100, the voltage $V$ at 3500 kHz will be 100 volts. If we change the frequency to, say, 3600 kHz, $V$ will be only around 17 volts as shown by the $Q = 100$ curve in Fig. 13, although there is still 1 volt coming from $G$. At 3800 kHz, $V$ would be only 6 volts, and so on. Most of the resonant rise in voltage takes place quite near the resonant frequency. This is characteristic of all circuits having fairly high values of $Q$. It means that the circuit "responds" only to frequencies close to resonance. Such a circuit is *sharp*, or *selective*.

(The voltage in this curve is given in relative or percentage terms, since the same ratios will hold for the same circuit no matter what the actual voltage applied through $G$.)

## High- and Low-Q Circuits

Now suppose that we have a circuit tuned to the same frequency, but having a $Q$ of only 10. In terms of *percentage* response, it would look like the one marked $Q = 10$ in Fig. 13. This response is not sharp like that of the $Q = 100$ curve. At 3800 kHz it is still giving 50 percent as much voltage as at resonance, against 6 percent for the circuit having a $Q$ of 100. Such a curve is broad, or "non selective." Both sharp and broad types of response have their uses.

Incidentally, if we had 1 volt from $G$ in both circuits, the resonant voltage in the $Q = 10$ circuit actually would be only one-tenth as large as that from the $Q = 100$ circuit. This is shown by the curve marked A in Fig. 13.

## Parallel Impedance

The circuit of Fig. 11B is supplied energy from the outside rather than the inside, and the generator $G$ is assumed to give a constant output voltage as the frequency is varied. As we saw earlier in the parallel circuit, it is the *line current, I*, that changes when the frequency is varied. This current is smallest at the resonant frequency, and rises as the frequency is shifted to either side of resonance.

We could get a rather good idea of how the line current will depend on the circuit $Q$ simply by looking at the curves of Fig. 13 upside down. However, it is generally more useful to think of the *parallel impedance* of the circuit, in preference to thinking of current variations. To get the relative impedance

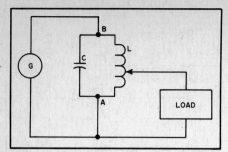

Fig. 14 — A tuned circuit with load connected. The circuit $Q$ can be changed by moving the tap on the coil.

variation, we turn the curves right side up again. In other words, the same curves can be used to show either the resonant voltage rise in a series circuit or the impedance rise in a parallel circuit. As given in Fig. 13, both are on a percentage basis. The actual values of volts in the series case, or ohms in the parallel case, depend on the actual reactance of $L$ and $C$ at the resonant frequency and also on the circuit $Q$.[4]

The impedance of a parallel circuit operated near resonance is usually considered to be purely resistive. Strictly speaking, this is true only at the exact resonant frequency. As soon as we move the frequency from resonance, we get reactive effects. However, in most cases we can ignore them because we operate the circuits so near resonance that the impedance is very close to being a pure resistance.

## Bandwidth

Radio-frequency signals in a form useful for communication do not consist of just one single frequency, even though we usually speak of a signal being "on" such-and-such a frequency. The signal actually occupies a *band* of frequencies. The width, as measured in hertz or kilohertz, depends on the kind of modulation used. An a-m phone transmission occupies a band at least twice as great as the highest audio frequency in the modulation. This highest frequency might be 4000 hertz, in which case the *bandwidth* of the signal would be twice 4000, or 8000 hertz (8 kHz). If such a signal is centered on a *carrier* frequency of 3950 kHz, it actually will use a band of frequencies lying between 3946 and 3954 kHz.

All of the frequencies within such a band must pass through our selective circuits. Otherwise, we wouldn't get the full benefit of the intelligence-bearing

part of the signal. It is, therefore, useful to know just how wide a band a selective circuit will pass. The limits of a circuit *pass band* are generally taken to be those points where the response in voltage is "down" to approximately 70 percent of the response at exact resonance. Seventy percent in voltage represents a 2-to-1 reduction in power, so these points are often called the *half-power* or −3 *dB points*.[5] They have been marked by small arrows on the curves in Fig. 12. By close inspection you can see that the circuit with a $Q$ of 100 has a bandwidth of about 35 kHz while the one with a $Q$ of 10 has a bandwidth of about 350 kHz.

## Circuits with External Loading

To repeat a statement that was discussed at some length earlier in this chapter, resistance is something that uses up energy or power. The object of circuit design is to convey power to a device — the *load* — where some desired use can be made of it. In the tuned circuits so far considered, all the power put into the circuit stayed there. It was used up in the resistance of the circuit itself.

Sometimes the circuit itself actually is the desired load. This is the case with many receiver circuits where — as in supplying signal voltage to an FET or vacuum-tube amplifier — no power is *required* from the circuit. In a case like this the best use is made of the available power when all of it is used to generate the maximum possible resonant rise in voltage.

However, this is seldom the case in a transmitter. Here we want to get power *out* of the circuit. Tuned circuits are always used, for reasons you will meet later. Part of the job of the circuit is to see that an amplifier tube is given the kind of resistance load it wants. The actual load — such as an antenna or transmission line — seldom has the value that the amplifying device would like. We'll take just one simple case at this juncture, leaving further discussion for later.

## Load Resistance and Circuit Q

In Fig. 14 the generator $G$ represents a vacuum-tube amplifier connected to a resonant circuit, $LC$. The generator sees a resistance of a value determined by the $Q$ of the circuit and the reactance of $L$ or $C$. If the $Q$ is low this parallel resistance (between A and B) will be low, as you have seen. Low resistance means that more current will be taken from the generator, assuming that its

voltage output is more or less constant. So the lower the $Q$ of the circuit the more heavily the generator is loaded, and vice versa.

Obviously, if we can vary the circuit $Q$, we can adjust the load on the generator to any value we want, within practical limits. An easy way to vary the circuit $Q$ is to connect the actual load across only part of the coil, as shown. If the number of coil turns between A and the tap is small compared with the number between A and B, the current going into the load will be small. As we move the tap up the coil, the load takes more current. This has the effect of lowering the circuit $Q$ and thus lowering the resistance between A and B as seen by the generator.

This is only one of many ways in which a load can be introduced into a circuit to vary the $Q$ and with it the parallel resistance or impedance of the circuit. You'll meet others in the chapters on practical-circuit applications. One of the important ones is based on the kind of coupling next considered.

## Inductive Coupling

We saw earlier that a changing magnetic field, such as is set up by the rf current flowing through a coil, induces a voltage in the coil. This voltage distributes itself on a per-turn basis, if the field around all turns is the same. (It isn't *always* the same, in the kind of coil used in rf circuits, for a number of reasons — one of which is the fact that there is no way to keep the field from spreading out in the air.) But here is the interesting thing: The field doesn't care whether the turns in which it is inducing a voltage are all part of the same coil or not. We can have two or more coils in the same field and the voltage in each will be in proportion to the number of turns it has.

This means that a load can be connected to an entirely separate coil, L2, as in Fig. 15. The second coil could have about the same number of turns as the number across which the load was connected in the tapped circuit, Fig. 14. However, in that case it would be necessary for L2 to be just as close to

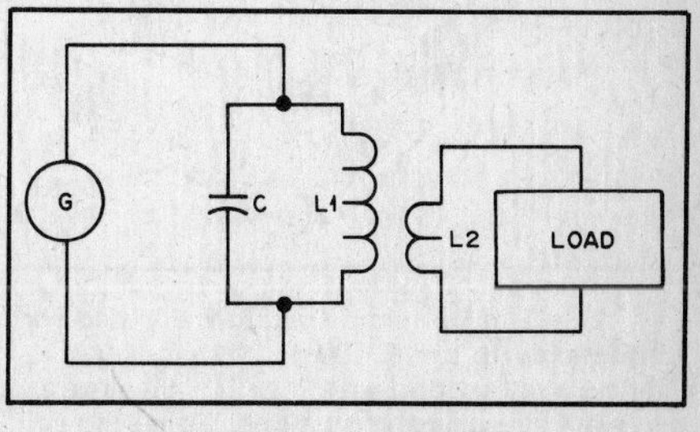

Fig. 15 — Inductive coupling between the tuned circuit and load. This method also offers a way of changing the circuit $Q$.

[4] In the series circuit, the resonant voltage is $Q$ times the applied voltage. In the parallel circuit, the resonant impedance is $Q$ times the reactance of either $L$ or $C$ (they both have the same value of reactance at resonance).

[5] Sometimes the bandwidth is based on a 2-to-1 reduction in voltage; that is, a 4-to-1 reduction in power. This is the "6-dB bandwidth."

L1 as its own turns. This might be done by winding L2 right over the lower part of L1, for example.

The advantage of the two-coil arrangement is that there is no direct connection between the load and the power source. This is often convenient in working with vacuum tubes that have to have large dc voltages applied to them.

A coil *coupled* to a tuned circuit is often called a *link*. It doesn't have to be wound right over the main coil, actually. If the two are somewhat separated and the link is movable with respect to L1, the voltage induced in it will be smaller as we move the link farther away. This is called "varying the coupling." It gives smooth adjustment of the loading on the circuit.

### The Transformer

Two coils used in this way form what is called a *transformer*. The transformer principle — that a coil in a changing magnetic field has a voltage induced in it whether or not there is a direct connection between it and the source of energy — is valid at any frequency. It is widely used at the power-line frequency, 60 hertz, as you no doubt already know.

Low-frequency transformers are made differently from those used in the rf circuits we have been considering up until now. Coils for rf circuits are wound on insulating forms. Coils for 60-hertz transformers, and for frequencies corresponding to the air-vibration rate of sound, up to around 15,000 hertz, are wound on iron cores (Fig. 16). They also have many more turns than we find in rf coils. The iron core and the large number of turns are necessary at such low frequencies. This is because the magnetic field changes slowly at, say, 60 hertz as compared with 7,000,000 hertz (7 MHz). (In fact, the rate at the latter frequency is over 100,000 times faster!) So to get much induced voltage we have to use many

turns and also use iron. The iron increases the strength of the magnetic field many, many times as compared with its strength in air.

### Turns Ratio

The iron has another advantage. The magnetic field finds it much easier to stay in it than to leak out into the air. So all we have to do is wind the coils around the iron core and they are all in essentially the same magnetic field. This means that the voltage per turn will be the same in all of them. Let's see how it works out.

Suppose we have a 60-hertz transformer having two coils, one of 200 turns and the other 400 turns. If we connect the 200-turn coil to a 115-volt source, the voltage induced in it will be 115 volts. But since the 400-turn coil is in the same field and has twice as many turns, the voltage induced in it will be 230 volts. Simply by winding on the right number of turns, we can get any voltage we want within constructional limitations.

### Primary and Secondary Power

But there is another aspect. The transformer can't manufacture power itself. In fact, it will turn some of the power supplied to it into heat — heat in the windings and heat in the core. This is lost power, but it can't be helped; the wire and iron aren't perfect from an electrical standpoint. If they *were* perfect, all the power put into the *primary* winding — the one connected to the power source — could be taken from the *secondary* or output winding. However, for rough estimates we usually assume that we *can* take as much power from the secondary as put into the primary. This is approximately true, because a well-designed transformer will turn only a small percentage of the total power into heat.

Now the consequence of the fact that the secondary power is never more than the primary power is this: If the secondary voltage is larger than the primary voltage, the secondary current has to be proportionately smaller than the primary current, and vice versa. In other words, the current multiplied by the voltage has to be the same in both windings (neglecting those heat losses, of course, which show up as additional power going into the primary). So if the secondary voltage of the transformer in the example above is twice the primary voltage, the primary current will have to be twice the secondary current.

### Impedance Transformation

One thing about transformers of this type that you need to keep in mind is that the currents depend on what is connected to the secondary winding. If a 2300-ohm resistor is connected to the

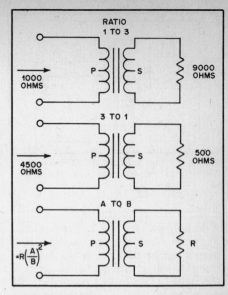

Fig. 17 — Examples of impedance transformation. The name "primary" (P) always is applied to the winding to which the source of power is connected. The secondary, (S) is the winding from which power is taken.

230-volt secondary winding, the current will be 0.1 ampere. The current in the 115-volt primary winding will be 0.2 ampere, by the rule just mentioned. The source of power is "seeing" a load of 0.2 ampere at 115 volts. This load looks like 115/0.2, or 575 ohms, although the actual secondary load is 2300 ohms. If we connect a 230-ohm resistor to the secondary, the secondary current will be 1 ampere and the primary current will rise to 2 amperes. In that case the primary sees a load of 57.5 ohms.

The load "looking into" the primary is not something that is a fixed property of the transformer. It is determined by the *secondary* load resistance and the ratio of turns on the primary and secondary windings.

By choosing the proper turns ratio for the windings, we can make any given load resistance look like some value that is more suitable for our power source. This is summed up in a rule: The impedance ratio of the transformer is proportional to the *square* of the turns ratio. In the transformer used in the example above, the turns ratio was 2 to 1, so the impedance ratio was 4 to 1. (We talked in terms of resistance rather than impedance because it is simpler, and in most cases we do deal with simple resistance rather than impedance generally.)

### Impedance Matching

Fig. 17 shows a couple of examples of impedance transformation and also gives the general rule. Transformers having the required turns ratio are used for changing *impedance levels* in audio-frequency circuits when the actual load

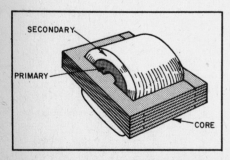

Fig. 16 — The iron-core transformer, used for frequencies up to 15,000 or 20,000 cycles. The coils are wound on a "leg" of the core midway between the outsides. Sometimes the primary is wound over the secondary instead of the reverse order shown. The core consists of thin sheets called laminations.

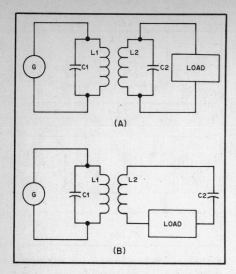

Fig. 18 — Inductively coupled tuned circuits. Circuit A is used for coupling to high values of load resistance — of the order of thousands of ohms. B is used for low load resistances — 100 ohms or less, usually.

does not *match* the resistance that would be optimum for the generator. A familiar example is the output transformer used between an audio power device and a loudspeaker. The speaker will have some low value of impedance or resistance, such as 4 ohms, while the power device wants a load resistance of possibly 5000 ohms for its best operation. The transformer turns ratio would be chosen accordingly, thus bringing about a match between the speaker and amplifying device.

Incidentally, the resistance that is matched is the *optimum* load resistance for the source of power, not the resistance that may be in that source (and all sources of power *do* have internal resistance). We *could* match the internal resistance of the source, and such matching does in fact result in the highest possible power output. However, it also results in poor efficiency and, in the case of devices such as vacuum tubes and transistors, a great deal more distortion than is wanted. The *optimum* load resistance considers these factors and is chosen to give us the best possible all-around compromise.

### Shielding

It is worthwhile at this point to get off the main track of coupling for a moment and take up another aspect of it that you will use continually. This is the matter of *shielding*.

If you put a coil inside a metal enclosure, the enclosure will act like the secondary of a transformer. The coil itself is the primary. The voltage induced in this "secondary" will cause a current to flow in it. The current in turn sets up a field that opposes the primary magnetic field that produced it. If the resistance of the enclosure is low, the

two fields will just about cancel each other *outside* the enclosure. Thus the enclosure is a shield which prevents the coil from being magnetically coupled to other circuits outside it. Preventing such stray coupling is highly necessary in many circuits.

This method works fine at radio frequencies, but to get the same result at audio frequencies the shield would have to be very thick. In this frequency range we depend on the iron core to confine the field by offering it the most favorable path. An iron enclosure, not necessarily one of low electrical resistance, also helps for the same reason.

Electric, as contrasted to magnetic, fields are easily confined inside metal enclosures, even thin ones. This is true at all frequencies if the resistance of the metal is low. The metal simply short-circuits the electric field so it can't get through.

### Coupled Tuned-RF Circuits

In Fig. 15 one rf circuit, that formed by L1 and C, was tuned. The second, L2 and the load, wasn't. The secondary circuit *can* be a tuned one, however. When both circuits are tuned to the same frequency, more current will flow in the secondary, because the reactance of the capacitor cancels the reactance of the coil.

One result of this greater current flow is that the two coils do not have to be so near each other for transferring a given amount of rf power from the primary to the secondary. That is, loose coupling can be used. Another is that two tuned coupled circuits are more selective than one. Both of them have resonant Qs and thus both will respond most strongly to just one frequency. This gives us a way of increasing selectivity in receivers. Extra selectivity is often useful in transmitters, too, because transmitters are prone to generate frequencies we don't want along with the one we do want. These spurious frequencies can't be allowed to go out with the intended signal.

Two common types of inductively coupled resonant circuits are shown in Fig. 18. The arrangement at the top is almost universally used in receivers, where the load often is a very high — almost immeasurably high — resistance. Here, we are interested in getting the largest possible voltage from the secondary circuit. The lower circuit is used when the load is a low resistance. It is often found in transmitting circuits.

### Coupling and Q

The way these circuits operate depends principally on their individual Qs, including the effect of loading on the Qs. If both circuits have high Qs — 50 or 100 or more — the coupling between them can be very loose, indeed, even

when the maximum power is being transferred from the primary to the secondary. The resulting selectivity will be quite high. On the other hand, if the Qs are low — say in the neighborhood of 10 each — the coupling between the two coils must be much tighter for optimum power transfer, and the selectivity will be lower.

The high-*Q tuned transformer* is the kind we want for our receivers. The low-*Q* one is more useful in transmitters, where large amounts of power must be handled and we can't afford to lose much of it in the circuits themselves. A circuit loaded by a useful resistance such as an antenna has to work at relatively low *Q* so that most of the power will go into the load instead of being burned up in heating the coil.

### Coefficient of Coupling

The degree of coupling between two coils is expressed by a number called the *coefficient of coupling*. At this stage it isn't essential for you to know its technical definition. It is sufficient to note that a very small coefficient of coupling will suffice for maximum power transfer if the two coupled circuits have high Qs. That is, the coils can be relatively well separated. If the circuit Qs are low, the coupling coefficient must be larger, meaning that the two coils will have to be rather close together.

### Selectivity of Coupled Circuits

What happens if we vary the coupling between two tuned circuits? If the coupling is very loose, varying the frequency applied to the primary circuit will cause the secondary response to go through the values shown by curve A in Fig. 19. The curve is sharp — good selectivity — but we haven't transferred all the possible rf energy from the primary to the secondary.

If we now increase the coupling to

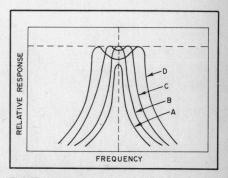

Fig. 19 — Typical response curves obtained at several degrees of coupling when the frequency applied to two coupled circuits is varied. Both circuits are tuned to the same frequency, indicated by the vertical dashed line. The actual shapes of curves like these depend on the circuit Q.

the point where the secondary response is as shown by curve B, we are getting the maximum possible energy transfer. This is called the point of *critical coupling*. The curve has the same general shape as A, but is less selective. If the coupling is increased still farther, the circuits are said to be *overcoupled*. An overcoupled response, shown by curves C and D, always shows two "humps" or points of maximum response. These are about equally spaced from the true resonant frequency. The dip in the center of the curve is small if the circuits are just beyond critical coupling, as in C. The more the circuits are overcoupled, the deeper the dip and the farther apart the humps become.

Overcoupling gives a *band-pass* effect that is often useful. The response curve is approximately flat-topped if the circuits are not too badly overcoupled. This is fine for passing signals that have appreciable bandwidth.

### Other Types of Coupling

In some receivers you may find circuits similar to those shown in Fig. 20. There is no inductive coupling between the tuned circuits L1C1 and L2C2. In fact, they may be shielded from each other. The coupling is through a capacitor, C3, connected between the two circuits.

In A, C3 connects the "hot" sides of the two circuits. The coupling coefficient depends on the value of this capacitance. If the circuit $Q$s are high, C3 will be quite small when the coupling has its critical value. At even very low radio frequencies just a few pF will suffice.

In B, the circuits are coupled at the low-potential side. C3 is common to both circuits, and the voltage developed across it by current flowing through it and C1 introduces energy into the circuit completed by C2 and L2. Only a very small voltage is needed for critical coupling, so the capacitance of C3 in this circuit is very large compared with the capacitances of C1 and C2.

Fig. 20B is probably the one more frequently used. By switching in various

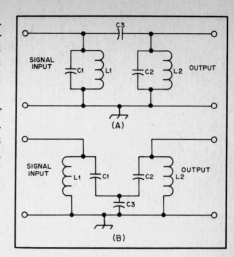

Fig. 20 — Capacitive coupling between tuned circuits. A and B are frequently called "top" and "bottom" coupling, respectively.

values of C3, the coupling — and thus the bandwidth — of the tuned transformer can easily be changed to suit the bandwidths of various types of signals.

# Chapter 2

# Semiconductor and Vacuum Tube Basics

You will be given the essentials of vacuum tubes and their applications a bit later, but first let's examine the newer devices which have in many instances replaced the radio tube. We are speaking, of course, about transistors, diodes and integrated circuits. In nearly all instances where small-signal levels are involved, the transistor or integrated circuit (IC) has replaced the tube. The reason for this is that transistors last longer, consume less overall power, and enable the designer or builder to create a much more compact final assembly than could be realized when using tubes. Another important benefit from the use of semiconductors is reduced equipment heating. This aids frequency stability and helps assure longer life for the equipment.

## Semiconductors Section

As this section is being written, we amateurs are on the brink of seeing power transistors replace power tubes. Rf amplifiers are in common use at 100- and 150-watt output levels, and the amplifying devices are transistors. For that matter, the April and May issues of *QST* for 1976 contained a two-part article which described a 1200-W output solid-state linear amplifier for 1.8 through 30 MHz. Such designs are still a bit complicated and expensive for amateur builders, but it is likely that most commercial ham gear will eventually be 100 percent solid state, regardless of the power level developed.

### Some Practical Differences

In a sense we can equate tubes to transistors, but the manner in which the two kinds of devices operate is quite different. Before we draw any comparisons, let's find out how diodes and transistors are built.

Semiconductors are certain crystalline substances — notably silicon and germanium — which in the pure state have very few free electrons. (An ordinary good conductor has swarms of them.) They are, therefore, normally rather poor conductors. However, by "doping" the material with suitable impurities in the proper amounts, it is possible to do either of two things: (1) release lots of free electrons, or (2) create a myraid of *holes* — spots in the atomic structure where an electron

should be but isn't. A hole, as you can see, is the opposite of a free electron. With external urging from an applied difference of potential, an electron can jump from a "full" atom to a hole in another, creating a new hole when it does. Thus, we can have a sort of chain reaction in which holes move through the substance just as electrons do.

The material with free electrons is called *n-type*, and that with holes is called *p-type*. Neither by itself is much different from an ordinary conductor. But when the two types are formed side by side (during manufacture) to make a *pn junction*, things begin to happen.

We can represent the junction as shown at Fig. 1A. If a battery voltage is applied as in B, the electrons in the n material are attracted to the positive battery terminal and the holes in the p material move toward the negative terminal. Since there is no movement *through* the junction, no current can flow in the circuit. However, if the battery polarity is reversed as in C, holes move across the junction toward the negative battery terminal and electrons move across it toward the positive terminal. With this battery polarity, therefore, a current flows through the junction and the circuit.

The semiconductor rectifier or *diode* is not a perfect insulator when the voltage is applied in the reverse polarity, as in Fig. 1B. A small *reverse current* can flow, when the diode is *back biased*.

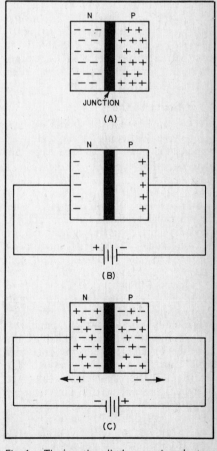

Fig. 1 — The junction diode, a semiconductor rectifier. B shows the nonconducting condition (reverse bias); C shows the conducting condition (forward bias).

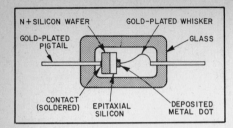

Fig. 2 — Cross-sectional view of a hot-carrier diode.

In the *forward* direction, Fig. 1C, it takes less than a volt to cause very large currents to flow — much less than it does in a vacuum-tube diode.

## Diode Ratings

Aside from the reverse current, which is of the order of a thousand times less than the forward current under normal conditions, the principal limitation of the semiconductor diode is the fact that it cannot stand very high reverse voltages. Diodes suitable for power-supply use can be obtained with reverse-voltage or *peak reverse voltage* (PRV) ratings up to several hundred volts, but in vacuum tubes such ratings may be in the thousands of volts. Also, the semiconductor diode can't stand any overvoltage; it will usually break down and ruin itself if the reverse voltage is just a little over the rating. Its advantages are small size, ability to conduct large currents with low voltage drop, and (as a result of this) very little power loss in the rectifier.

## Point-Contact Diodes

The junction in the diodes we have just been discussing is a region of appreciable area. It can pass large current. Another type of rectifier uses a *point contact* or *cat whisker*, Fig. 2, which shows the inner structure of a hot-carrier type of point-contact diode. In the usual type the semiconductor is n-type material and during manufacture of the diode a very small amount of p-type is formed under the point contact.

The area between the two types of material is so small that the point-contact diode has very low capacitance — generally only about one picofarad. This makes it especially suitable as a rectifier for radio frequencies, since very little current is shunted around the rectifier by the capacitance. This type of rectifier is not used in power-supply circuits except where only small currents — less than 50 mA or so — are needed. Reverse voltage ratings run from 30 to about 100 volts.

Diodes come in a variety of shapes and electrical types. Most of the modern rectifier diodes are the junction type —

a sandwich of semiconductor materials to which the anode and cathode wires are affixed. Many junction diodes are suitable for rf applications well into the uhf region — 1N914s for example. Husky diodes in large metal or epoxy packages are used as rectifiers in power supplies. Some of these semiconductors are titanic by virtue of being able to pass 40 or 50 amperes of current safely with peak-reverse voltage ratings up to 2500. This illustrates their advantage over vacuum-tube rectifiers which might be called upon to provide the same ratings! Power diodes need to be mounted securely on what is called a *heat sink*. The same practice applies to power transistors. A heat sink is a large metal plate — usually with fins — made of aluminum or copper. It conducts heat away from the semiconductor junction to provide a cooling action which prevents damage to the diode or transistor. Some kind of heat-transfer compound is generally used (silicon grease) between the body of the semiconductor and the heat sink to assure maximum transfer of the heat from the device to the heat sink.

## Voltage-Variable Capacitance Diodes (VVC)

Another breed of diode is used frequently in amateur circuits. It is marketed under a host of trade names — Varicap, Epicap and varactor. These diodes are useful as replacements for air variable capacitors in some tuned circuits.

For all practical purposes varactors are junction diodes which have been

manufactured specifically as voltage-variable capacitors (VVC). They are designed to have a high Q at a specific operating frequency. Furthermore, they are built so that a particular change in junction capacitance will occur as the bias applied to the cathode (positive voltage) is at a given level. For example, we might have a varactor diode which is designed to provide 50 pF of junction capacitance when eight volts of dc are applied to the cathode while the anode is grounded. By varying the applied bias voltage, the capacitance will change over a prescribed range, say, 10 to 70 pF. Some varactor diodes are built with two diodes inside the package: The cathodes are joined to a single output terminal, but the anodes have separate connection points. In that manner the bias is applied to the common cathode terminal, but each anode must be permitted to return to dc ground. That type of varactor provides a more uniform change in capacitance than is possible with a single diode. A pair of 1N914 diodes can be connected back to back to obtain the same effect.

The principal advantage realized through the employment of voltage-variable diodes in tuned circuits is that greater miniaturization is possible than with air variables. Also, the builder can ensure short leads in rf circuits (desirable) and control the capacitance change remotely by means of a potentiometer. Several tuned circuits can be controlled by means of a single potentiometer when varactor diodes are used as the tuning elements. Fig. 3A shows the symbol for a conventional diode. A

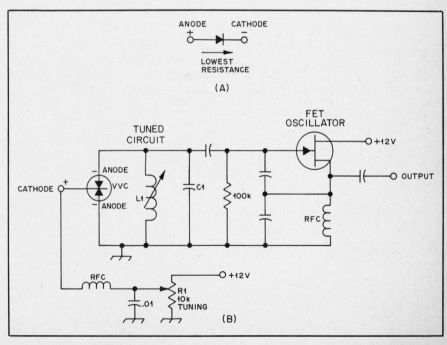

Fig. 3 — A diode symbol is shown at A. At B is a circuit which uses a voltage-variable capacitor diode to tune the oscillator tank.

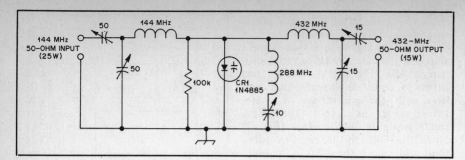

Fig. 4 — A varactor diode can be used as a power type of frequency multiplier.

two-diode varactor element is seen symbolically at Fig. 3B. R1 is the tuning control, and it can be mounted on the equipment panel for easy access. To assure a slow tuning rate, one can use a vernier mechanism to turn the shaft of the control.

Some varactor diodes are used as frequency multipliers. An example of the application can be seen in Fig. 4, where a tripler is depicted. Because of the nonlinear change in varactor-diode junction capacitance during the sine-wave excursion (driving signal), considerable harmonic energy is generated. Since nonlinear conditions are ideal for the creation of harmonic currents, varactors work nicely in multiplier circuits. The change in sine-wave energy as it goes through a complete cycle has the same effect as varying the dc bias on a varactor by the same amount. This causes a constant and predictable change in varactor junction capacitance when a sine wave is used to excite it. Because the capacitance changes nonlinearly, harmonics result.

### Transistors

The earliest and most common of the transistors is called the *bipolar transistor*. The term *bipolar* is explained later on. A major characteristic of the bipolar transistor is that it has three terminals — a base, a collector and an emitter. In the most general of terms the base is similar to the grid of a triode tube. The collector represents a tube plate, and the emitter can be regarded as the cathode of a tube. At this point the resemblance ends, as we shall see shortly.

A significant feature of a single bipolar transistor which is hooked up as an amplifier and operated in the prescribed manner (normal operating voltages and current) is that the input and output impedances of the device are quite low. This results from the fact that low voltage and fairly high currents are found in the base and collector circuits of such amplifiers. Typically, the input impedance of a Class A bipolar-transistor small-signal amplifier (audio or rf) will be between 500 and 1500 ohms. A vacuum-tube triode amplifier operating in the Class A mode would have a grid (input) impedance in the megohm region. Similarly, the collector impedance is quite low compared to that of a vacuum tube which draws small amounts of plate current. In a typical circuit the collector impedance will be somewhere in the range of 1,000 to 10,000 ohms, favoring the lower end of the range.

What does all of this mean to us builders? Well, the text of the message tells us that a different kind of matching technique is needed between stages and between such things as microphones and transistorized amplifiers. Once we adjust our thinking along those lines, we can work with transistors as easily as we can with tubes.

The most common type of *transistor* is formed with two diodes back to back in a three-layer structure as shown in Fig. 5. A sandwich is formed with one type of material as the "meat" and with the other type as the "bread." The in-between material, a thin layer, is called the *base*. The outer ones are called the *emitter* and *collector*. As Fig. 5 shows, the material arrangement can be either pnp or npn. The circuit symbols for the two types are also shown along with the battery polarities that will cause current to flow in the circuit formed by the collector and emitter.

If you compare these arrangements with the simple diode of Fig. 1, you can see that if the battery voltage $E_2$ is larger than $E_1$, the collector-to-base diode is reverse biased and no current can flow between the collector and base. However, current *will* flow through the emitter-base diode with the polarity shown for $E_1$. In the pnp transistor the holes move from the emitter to the base through the diode junction and the electrons move in the opposite direction. Because the base region is very thin, some of the moving holes go right through it to the collector. This gives the collector more holes than it needs, and the extra ones are attracted by the negative voltage on the collector. Thus there is a current flowing directly through the transistor

from the emitter to the collector. It doesn't show up in the external base circuit at all, and it actually is many times larger than the emitter-base current. Furthermore, the *amount* of collector current is directly related to the base current. If the base current is zero, so is the collector current. The larger the base current, the larger the collector current.

The roles of the electrons and holes are interchanged in the npn transistor. Otherwise the explanation is the same. Transistors of either type shown in Fig. 5 are called *bipolar*, because holes (positive) and electrons (negative) both carry the current.

Within limits, the collector current is directly proportional to the base current. Compare this with the vacuum-tube triode, where the plate current is directly proportional to the grid *voltage*. This is one of the differences between transistors and tubes. Another is that all this takes place with very low collector voltages — of the order of 5 to 50 volts with most transistors.

Incidentally, you may wonder how it is possible to tell which is the collector and which is the emitter, since they both have the same type of doping. Actually you couldn't tell, *if* both had the same doping *concentration*. You could wire the transistor into the circuit either way and it would work the same. But such a transistor wouldn't be particularly good, so a different doping concentration is used for the part that is to be used as the emitter. Even so, the device would work after a fashion hooked up backwards.

### Amplification

The fact that the collector-to-emitter

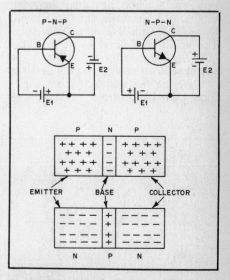

Fig. 5 — The two fundamental types of transistors. Unlike tubes, transistors can be made to work with either polarity of applied voltage, as shown by the symbolic drawings at the bottom. The battery polarities shown are those used for normal biasing in amplifier circuits.

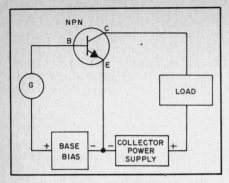

Fig. 6 — The transistor amplifier in bare essentials. If a pnp transistor is used, the bias and collector supply voltages must be negative with respect to the emitter.

current is larger than the base-emitter current, and will have identical waveshape when the base-emitter current (the *signal current*) is alternating, means that the transistor can *amplify*. Here is where some of the similarities between tubes and transistors begin to show.

In order to make use of the collector current (the *output current*), we must have a *load* in the collector-emitter circuit, just as we must have a load in the plate circuit of a tube amplifier. We also must have a suitable bias (called *forward bias*) on the base-emitter diode, just as we must have proper bias on the grid of a tube. But here the bias is a *current* rather than a voltage. Of course, when there is a current there must also be a voltage to cause it, but with the transistor it is the *current* variations in the base that control the collector current. In fact, the signal voltage may have a highly distorted waveshape when the current is varying properly, because the resistance of the base diode doesn't stay put during such variations; it decreases very rapidly when the current increases.

Fig. 6 is the basic amplifier circuit. Compare it with that for a triode tube. The circuit considerations are much the same in the two cases, although the circuit *values* may differ a great deal.

Carrying the analogy further, Fig. 7 shows the base-current variation with

signal when the signal is superimposed on a dc bias (npn transistor) and is supplied from a generator that doesn't mind how the base resistance varies with current. Also, Fig. 8 is a curve of base current vs. collector current which compares with the grid-voltage vs. plate-current curve for a tube. The 20-$\mu$A (total) swing in bias current (Fig. 7) causes the collector current to swing from a bit more than 2 mA to more than 7 mA — a current amplification of more than 250 times. Observe that this curve is noticeably straighter than the curve for a tube, indicating that the collector current can be swung down to zero with very little distortion.

### Temperature and Leakage

We can't take up this subject in great detail, but you need to know a few facts about temperature effects and leakage. The latter is the reverse current mentioned earlier, and in the bipolar transistor the important leakage is from collector to base. It causes a current to flow in the base-emitter diode, and this — like any other base current — is amplified to become larger in the collector circuit.

Unfortunately, leakage and all transistor *parameters* — as the operating characteristics are called — are greatly affected by temperature. Leakage becomes *much* worse with increasing temperature. This causes a drift toward higher currents in turn causing more heating, and the process becomes self-accelerating. If not controlled, it may cause *thermal runaway* and destroy the transistor in circuits where moderate to high amounts of power are involved.

Whatever the transistor type, special care must be used to prevent its dissipation rating from being exceeded. Failure to do so leads to blown-out transistors. Semiconductors don't have the tolerance in this respect that vacuum tubes have.

In passing, it is worth mentioning that temperature effects are much less serious with silicon than with germanium.

### Biasing Circuits

We can minimize temperature effects by using a base-biasing circuit that will resist the tendency of currents to rise with increasing temperature. The circuit of Fig. 9A — probably the simplest of all biasing circuits — does nothing for us in this respect. It simply takes the required base-bias current through a large resistance, R1. It is included here principally to show that the bias current can be obtained from the collector power supply, since the base and collector both operate with the same polarity. The circuit is usable only when the currents are so small that the transistor is operating well below its ratings.

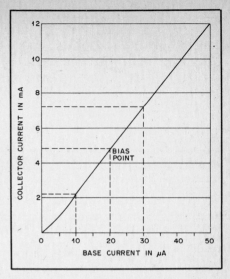

Fig. 8 — Collector current vs. base current. The values are representative of those in a small transistor.

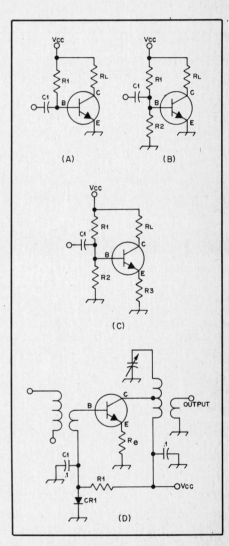

Fig. 9 — Methods of biasing a transistor amplifier. C, which combines voltage-divider base bias with emitter bias, is best for stabilizing the transistor currents against temperature changes, but reduces the gain as compared with the other two. Shown at D is regulated bias which is provided by means of a silicon diode, CR1.

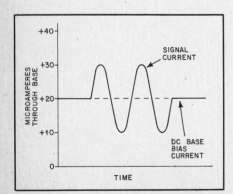

Fig. 7 — Signal current superimposed on base-bias current. Compare this with the negative-grid vacuum tube characteristic.

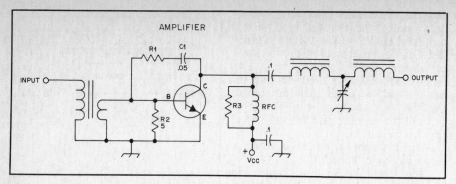

Fig. 10 — A transistor rf amplifier which has negative feedback (R1 and C1). Components R2 and R3 help to assure amplifier stability.

Fig. 9B is a bit better, if R2 can be a relatively low resistance so the voltage across it can't rise appreciably when leakage current flows through it. But the best one is Fig. 9C. Here the collector current flows through R3 just as the plate current flows through the cathode resistor in a tube circuit. An increase in current causes a voltage rise in R3 that bucks the normal bias voltage. This reduces the bias current, so the rising collector current pulls itself down to normal. This is negative feedback, of course, and it will reduce the gain of an amplifier unless R3 is bypassed suitably for the frequency being amplified. To be thermally effective, R3 must be large enough to "lose" at least a few volts of dc in the average case, so the actual voltage between collector and emitter will be less than the supply voltage. This has to be taken into account in the circuit design.

Another means for making the forward bias stay put is illustrated in Fig. 9D. In this example we are taking advantage of the junction barrier potential of CR1 (usually between 0.4 and 0.7 volt for a silicon diode) to maintain the bias voltage supplied through R1. In this application CR1 acts as a voltage regulator, preventing the dc potential at the transistor base from exceeding the diode barrier voltage. The circuit shown is that of an rf power amplifier. Since CR1 is situated below the coil link which feeds rf to the transistor base, and because the diode is bypassed by means of C1, rf clipping will not occur because of CR1. If the diode were connected directly from base to ground, there would be severe clipping of the positive half of the excitation waveform when its level reached beyond the diode barrier voltage. This kind of bias circuit is used frequently in rf linear power amplifiers to establish Class A operating conditions. If higher amounts of forward bias are desired, two or more diodes can be connected in series at CR1.

## Transistor Amplifier Gain

A little earlier, in discussing amplifi-cation with bipolar transistors, we pointed out that *current* is required in the base-emitter diode and that a voltage is necessary to force the current to flow. This means that the base consumes *power*, even when the signal is very small. With the negative-grid vacuum tube, on the other hand, there is no current and no power in the grid circuit; the grid signal voltage does its stuff without causing any loss of power.

With bipolar transistors, we have to think of amplification on a power-gain basis. With tubes, only a few types of amplification (such as Class C operation) demand the same sort of approach. The decibel being a very convenient power-gain unit, it is widely used in rating the gain of transistor amplifiers.

## Capacitances

The transistor, as you can see from Fig. 6, is a triode (three-element) device. And, just as in the case of the triode tube, there are internal capacitances between all pairs of elements. They lead to the same problems in using transistors that we see when using triode vacuum tubes. The base-to-emitter (input) and collector-to-emitter (output) capacitances can be absorbed into tuned circuits when we operate transistors at radio frequencies, so they don't cause much trouble — except that, like all transistor parameters, they are sensitive to temperature. Also — and this is not true of tubes — they are highly sensitive to voltage.

But the capacitance between the collector and base isn't so easily disposed of. There isn't any nice solution here like putting a screen grid into a tube. So other ways of preventing feedback and self-oscillation have to be used. There are several such means, perhaps the most common being the "brute force" method of loading the base and collector circuits so heavily that the amount of rf energy fed back isn't great enough to sustain oscillation. The gain suffers when this is done, of course, because power has to be wasted in the overloads. But the scheme does

work, and we can get away with it because a transistor can produce such a large power gain.

Another technique used to "tame" transistors is called *negative feedback*. In a grounded-emitter (sometimes called "common-emitter") amplifier, the designer will install a resistor and a capacitor between the base and collector elements, as shown in Fig. 10. The collector-signal voltage is approximately 180 degrees out of phase with the drive-signal voltage at the base, so the feedback network, depending on its final value, will cause the collector ac voltage to partially cancel the base ac voltage. This will reduce the stage gain and aid stability. This form of feedback also enhances the broadband characteristics of the amplifier, as it lowers the stage gain more and more as the operating frequency is moved lower. This technique is necessary because transistors exhibit a theoretical increase in gain of 6 dB per octave lower. For example, if a stage had 10 dB of gain at 14 MHz, the theoretical gain at 7 MHz would be 16 dB, and so on. Because of the very high gain occurring at lower frequencies, self-oscillation is a common problem. The negative feedback network (R1 and C1 of Fig. 10) has the least effect at the high end of the

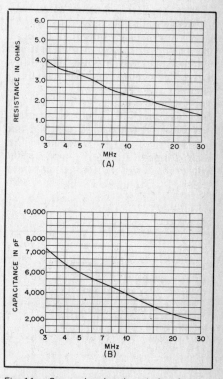

Fig. 11 — Curves showing the relative change in base resistance and capacitance of an hf-band power transistor as its operating frequency is changed. The curves help to illustrate the complexity of input impedance matching versus frequency. The output capacitance and resistance of a power transistor exhibit a similar set of characteristics, but the output capacitance is considerably lower than the input amount.

amplifier operating range, say, 30 MHz. At the low end of the operating range — 1.8 MHz, perhaps — maximum feedback will occur, and the gain will be held down to nearly that seen at 30 MHz. This is because the *RC* feedback network looks like a low resistance (reactance) at the lowest end of the range, and is a high resistance at the upper end of the range. The lower the reactance, the greater the energy fed back to the base from the collector. The actual value of R1 can best be determined experimentally and will depend on the transistor gain and amplifier operating frequency. Values from 50 to 1000 ohms are typical in such a circuit.

It should be said that the input and output capacitances of a transistor also change with the operating frequency, as does the base resistance. The curves given in Fig. 11 show these characteristics. Because of the frequency effects under discussion, rf design work becomes more difficult than when working with tubes, as knowledge of the exact amount of capacitance and resistance is difficult to obtain, even from the transistor manufacturers. The capacitance at a given frequency must be absorbed into the tuned matching network in order to ensure maximum circuit efficiency (power transfer).

**Field-Effect Transistors**

The bipolar transistor we've been discussing isn't the only type, as you know. Another very important variety is the *field-effect transistor* or *FET*. It uses the same materials, but uses them differently. Let's review its operation for a minute.

The arrangement in Fig. 12 is a *junction-type FET*. It has a substrate of p-type semiconductor in which a thin layer of n type — the *channel* — has been formed. Another p-type region, called the *gate*, is formed in the n region. If a voltage is applied across the

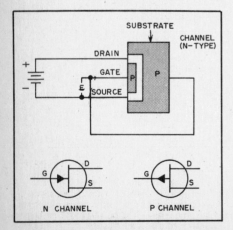

Fig. 12 — The n-channel field-effect junction transistor. Symbols for both n- and p-channel types also are shown.

ends of the channel, electrons will be drawn out of the n-type channel to the positive terminal of the voltage source. This end of the channel is appropriately called the *drain*. Electrons from the battery will enter at the other end of the channel, which is therefore called the *source*. Thus, a current flows through the channel. Incidentally, since the channel is one kind of material only, the current can be made to flow in either direction through it.

Now if the pn junction formed by the gate and channel is back-biased by a voltage *E* which makes the gate negative with respect to the source, the electrons and holes move away from the junction just as they did in Fig. 1B. This is equivalent to squeezing the n channel so that it becomes narrower, so the channel resistance increases and the current becomes less, for the same drain-to-source voltage. The gate voltage, then, controls the drain current. And since the gate-channel diode is back biased, no current flows across the junction. There can be a small leakage current as in any diode, but it is small enough so that the gate-to-source resistance is several megohms, so long as the gate is negative with respect to the source.

The FET, in fact, is pretty much like a triode vacuum tube operated in the negative-grid region. Current *will* flow across the junction if the gate voltage becomes positive with respect to the source, just as grid current flows in a tube when the grid is positive with respect to the cathode.

The n and p materials can be interchanged in the junction FET. This requires that the gate be made positive with respect to the source, and the current is carried by holes. With this difference the two types work alike. The symbols for the two are given in the figure.

The FET is so much like the vacuum-tube triode, in fact, that it is hardly necessary to show the circuits that are used with it. They're the same — except for different values occasioned by the differences in voltage and currents, of course — as for the triode tube circuits given earlier. Just substitute the gate for the grid, the drain for the plate, and the source for the cathode.

The substrate is not shown in the symbols in Fig. 12. It is usually connected to the source inside the transistor enclosure and only three leads are brought out.

**MOSFETs**

The other large family which makes up field-effect transistors is the insulated-gate FET, or MOSFET (metal-oxide silicon field-effect transistor), which is pictured schematically and pictorially in Fig. 13. In order to set up a dc operating condition, a positive

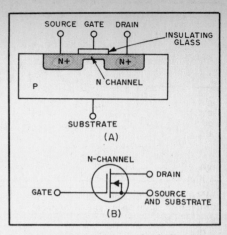

Fig. 13 — The insulated-gate field-effect transistor is seen at A and its electrical symbol is shown at B.

polarity is applied to the drain terminal. The substrate is connected to the source, and both are at ground potential, so the channel electrons are attracted to the positive drain. In order to regulate this source-drain current, voltage is applied to the gate contact. The gate is insulated from the rest of the device by a layer of very thin dielectric material, so this is not a pn junction between the gate and the device — thus the name insulated gate. When a negative gate polarity is applied, positive-charged holes from the p-type substrate are attracted toward the gate and the conducting channel is made more narrow; thus the source-drain current is reduced. When a positive gate voltage is connected, the holes in the substrate are repelled away, the conducting channel is made larger, and the source-drain current is increased. The MOSFET is more flexible since either a positive or negative voltage can be applied to the gate. The resistance between the gate and the rest of the device is extremely high because they are separated by a layer of thin dielectric. Thus the MOSFET has an extremely high input impedance. In fact, since the leakage through the insulating material is generally much smaller than through the reverse-biased pn gate junction in the JFET, the MOSFET has a much higher input impedance. Typical values of $R_{in}$ for the MOSFET are over a million megohms, while $R_{in}$ for the JFET ranges from megohms to over a thousand megohms. There are both single-gate and dual-gate MOSFETs available. The latter has a signal gate, gate 1, and a control gate, gate 2. The gates are effectively in series making it an easy matter to control the dynamic range of the device by varying the bias on gate 2. Dual-gate MOSFETs are widely used as agc-controlled rf and i-f amplifiers, as mixers and product detectors, and as variable attenuators. The isolation between the gates is relatively

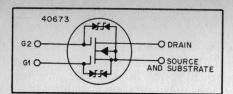

Fig. 14 — Schematic presentation of a gate-protected MOSFET. Back-to-back Zener diodes are bridged internally from gates 1 and 2 to the source/substrate element.

high in mixer service. This helps lessen oscillator "pulling" and reduces oscillator radiation. The forward *transadmittance* (transconductance, or $g_m$) of modern MOSFETs is as high as 18,000 and they are designed to operate efficiently well into the uhf spectrum.

### Gate-Protected FETs

Most JFETs are capable of withstanding up to 80 volts pk-pk from gate to source before junction damage occurs. Insulated-gate FETs, however, can be damaged by allowing the leads to come in contact with plastic materials, or by the simple act of handling the leads with one's fingers. Static charges account for the foregoing, and the damage takes the form of punctured insulation between the gate or gates and the remainder of the internal elements. Devices of the MFE3006 and 3N140 series are among those which can be easily damaged.

Gate-protected MOSFETs are available, and their gates are able to withstand pk-pk voltages (gate to source) of up to 10. Internal Zener diodes are connected back to back from each gate to the source/substrate element. The 40673 and 3N200 FETs are among the types which have built-in Zener diodes. Dual-gate MOSFETs which are gate-protected can be used as single-gate protected FETs by connecting the two gate leads in parallel. A gate-protected MOSFET is shown schematically in Fig. 14.

### Power FETs

Thus far we have directed our attention toward small-signal FETs which are incapable of handling large amounts of power. But, present-day technology has made possible the manufacture of MOSFETs which can deliver as much as 20 watts of rf output at 144 MHz. The term used for these transistors by one company is MOSPOWER FET (Siliconix, Inc.). These FETs can operate in any class (A, AB, B or C) and are useful from audio to vhf.

MOSPOWER transistors are less subject to destruction than power bipolar transistors are. Most bipolar power devices must be protected from a load-mismatch condition when delivering output. If, for example, the last-stage transistor in a transmitter is set up with its matching network to work into a 50-ohm antenna, it should always see 50 ohms, or nearly so. When the load presented by the antenna departs significantly from 50 ohms, the transistor can be ruined. MOSPOWER transistors, on the other hand, can be called upon to look into a dead short or a totally open load, and damage will not take place. This results from the way they are built. They are packaged in a manner similar to bipolar power transistors. The Siliconix VMP-1 and VMP-4 units are for hf and vhf use, respectively. The vhf version has a special case and leads. This minimizes unwanted inductance and capacitance effects.

### Integrated Circuits

When ICs (integrated circuits) were first developed, they seemed to have an aura of black magic surrounding them at least in the eyes of amateurs and the general public. But, there is no mystique connected to ICs, as they are merely solid-state electronics devices which contain a family of transistors, diodes, resistances and capacitances on a substrate (foundation). Manufacturers developed mechanical and electrical techniques which enabled them to put literally hundreds of transistors on a small slice of silicon material, connecting them together on the substrate to perform a host of functions. Because of refined production methods, it is possible to build complex ICs quickly and precisely. As a result, the retail price is much lower for most ICs than it would be for the equivalent number of discrete (separate) bipolar transistors to make up a circuit such as that which is formed on the IC substrate.

There are two principal types of ICs — linear and logic. The latter is intended for operation at low frequencies and dc in such instruments as digital voltmeters, frequency counters, keyers and microprocessors. Linear ICs are used for linear amplification of ac signals, mainly. Therefore, we find linear ICs being employed as receiver mixers, i-f amplifiers, audio amplifiers and a wide variety of other signal applications.

Some of these devices are called IC *subsystems*. A complex IC of that variety might contain all of the essential parts for an a-m or fm receiver, exclusive of the various capacitors, coils, resistors and transformers. That is, the active parts of the receiver (transistors) are manufactured on the IC substrate, and they are hooked together in the proper manner inside the IC to provide an rf amplifier, mixer, i-f amplifier, agc circuit, detector and audio amplifier. Some receiver-subsystem ICs even have transistors within them for the local oscillator. An RCA CA3088E IC is a good example of a subsystem unit for building an a-m radio. The fm-radio equivalent IC is the CA3089E.

The transistors in an IC carry similar ratings to discrete transistors — maximum voltages, currents and operating frequencies. Because of the chummy way that the transistors reside together in an IC, much greater miniaturization of a project is possible than would result if separate transistors were used. Furthermore, many ICs contain resistors and capacitors which are vital to the circuit. These are formed at the same time the transistors are.

A rather complete treatment of logic and linear ICs was given in *QST* in the form of beginner courses. The reader is referred to Hall and Watts, "Learning to Work with Integrated Circuits," starting in *QST* for January, 1976 and DeMaw, "Understanding Linear ICs," starting in *QST* for January, 1977.

# Vacuum Tubes

Although vacuum tubes are fast being replaced in commercial and home-made new-equipment designs, it is worth knowing what they are and how they operate. The demise of tubes is related presently to small-signal (low power) circuits, and this results mainly from the greater efficiency, lower cost, reduced heating and increased miniaturization made possible by transistors, diodes and ICs. In applications where large amounts of power must be generated, say, 150 watts or greater, the vacuum tube still offers the best dollar value. Additionally, special components are needed in a solid-state rf amplifier, many of which are difficult for the amateur to obtain. Even though amateurs and commercial laboratories have successfully developed 1-kW solid-state amplifiers for use from 1.8 to 30 MHz, the overall cost is more than sobering to some constructors. Furthermore, the inexperienced amateur might not be able to cope with the potential instability, impedance-matching problems, heat-dissipation techniques and regulated power-supply requirements attendant to a large solid-state amplifier. In plain language, tubes are a lot easier to work with in many ways. Also, they are less likely to be ruined by temporary periods of careless operation when large amounts of power are being used.

### Diode Tubes

The *diode* or two-element tube is a simple structure, with just a cathode and plate. Its only use is *rectification*. Rectification, the ability to conduct current in one direction but not in the other, has two principal roles in amateur equipment. One is the *detection* of received signals. The second is converting ac into dc in power supplies. Circuits for these purposes are discussed in other chapters. The difference between the two cases is emphasized by the differences in size and construction of the tubes employed in them. These differences in turn result from the large differences in the power levels that the tubes have to handle.

### Power-Handling Ability

A diode used as a detector in a receiver is called on to handle only microscopic amounts of power. It can therefore be quite small. The type 6AL5 tube is a good example — it has *two* diodes in the smallest bulb used for regular receiving tubes. In fact, a couple of diodes often will be found in tubes which are primarily triode or pentode receiving-type amplifiers. The plates are just tiny cylinders surrounding an extension of an indirectly heated cathode.

On the other hand, a diode (or double diode, which is more usual) for a power supply will invariably have a rather large bulb and much bigger plates. We may need 30 or 40 watts of dc power for an ordinary receiver, and often much more for a small transmitter. The rectifier tube has to handle this.

The diode rectifier, whether it is simply detecting a signal or serving to transform ac into dc in a power supply, doesn't do it 100 percent efficiently. Some of the power going into the plate

or plates doesn't go on through to the load. A voltage must exist between the plate and cathode if current is to flow through the tube. If this voltage (called the *tube voltage drop*) is multiplied by the current, we have the power that is lost in the tube itself. This power heats the plate. If the current is large, the power heating the plate will be large, too, especially if there has to be a rather large voltage between the plate and cathode to make the large current flow. To keep the plates at a reasonable temperature it is necessary to make them big. And to get the heat out into the air quickly, the tube has to have a bulb with plenty of surface area.

### Plate Dissipation

You can see what a difference this makes by comparing the 6AL5 with, say, a 5U4G. (The latter is the type of rectifier once used in television receivers where a considerable amount of dc power was needed.) If the tube is to have long life, it must have the ability to get rid of a lot of heat. This ability is summed up in the *rated safe plate dissipation* of the tube.

The safe plate dissipation — meaning the number of watts that can be allowed to heat the plate without damaging the tube — is an important factor in *any* type of tube, not just the diode rectifier. No matter what the tube type, the plate heating comes from the same cause — the tube voltage drop and the plate current. One of the objectives in designing power tubes is to make large plate currents flow with relatively little voltage between the plate and cathode, thus reducing the power lost in the plate.

Fig. 15 may help make this clearer. Although we haven't shown anything connected to the grid, this might be an amplifier circuit. The plate-supply voltage is 400 and the current is 100 mA. The voltage drop in the load is 300 (which means that the load resistance is 3000 ohms, as you can easily figure from Ohm's Law). This leaves 100 volts between the plate and cathode of the tube. The power in the load is 300 volts × 0.1 ampere, or 30 watts. The power lost in the tube plate is 100 volts × 0.1 ampere, or 10 watts. You can easily see why we want to make most of the voltage to be "used up" in the load rather than in the tube. The load power is *useful* power. The tube power just heats the plate.

Fig. 15 is pretty highly simplified in terms of ordinary tube operation. The actual current would be varying — radio or audio frequency — when the tube is amplifying. Also, the load probably won't be a resistor, if any power is being handled. Think of the load as something that *acts like* a resistance in that it consumes energy. For example, it might

be a loudspeaker coupled to the tube through a transformer.

### Plate Efficiency

Whenever an attempt is made to get much power from a tube, the relationship between power delivered to the load and power lost in the plate is very important. The measure of it is called the *plate efficiency* of the amplifier circuit. Plate efficiency is the ratio of the output power to the dc power input to the plate.

In the above example, the dc input is the sum of the plate dissipation and the load power; that is, 10 + 30 = 40 watts. Thus the plate efficiency is 30 divided by 40, or 0.75 (75 percent).

### Tube Characteristics

A *characteristic* is something that tells you what kind of operation you can expect from a tube. Probably the most important of these is one having the rather technical-sounding name of *transconductance*. It simply means the change in plate current for a given change in grid voltage. A tube can amplify because a change in the voltage applied to the grid can cause the plate current to change. Thus the bigger the plate-current change for a given grid-voltage change, the better the tube is as an amplifier. (We really should say "in its intended application," because other things than transconductance can affect the amplification — for example, the frequency at which the tube works.)

Characteristics related to the transconductance are the *amplification factor* and the *plate resistance*. The amplification factor, often called the *mu* ($\mu$), tells us something about the relationship between plate voltage and grid voltage. Suppose we change the grid voltage by one volt and observe how much the plate current changes. Then we change the plate voltage by whatever amount is necessary to bring about the same plate-current change. Perhaps the plate voltage will have to be changed by 40 volts to do it. Then the amplification factor is 40 volts divided by 1 volt, or 40. Triodes can be built with amplification factors running from less than 10 to over 100.

If the plate-cathode circuit of the tube were like an ordinary resistor, the plate resistance would be equal to the plate-cathode voltage divided by plate current it caused. However, that leads only to a "static" value, not of much use. We're more interested in the effect of a *change* in plate voltage on the plate current, since such changes are typical of what goes on in the tube when it is amplifying. So the plate resistance is found by taking current readings at two different plate voltages and dividing the *difference* in plate voltage by the *difference* in plate current. This figure

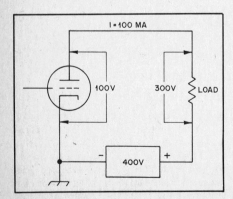

Fig. 15 — Power from the plate supply divides between the tube and the load.

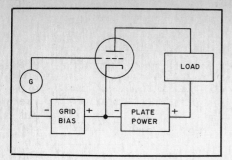

Fig. 16 — Essentials of an amplifier circuit.

corresponds to the internal resistance of a generator. The plate circuit of a tube acts just like such a generator when amplifying.

### Making Tubes Work

Reduced to bare essentials, the tube amplifier circuit is shown in Fig. 16. The source of ac signal to be amplified is represented by the generator G. The amplified signal appears in the load. The dc voltage which is applied to the plate to make it attract electrons from the cathode region is of course essential. Without it, the tube cannot function. The tube itself does not supply power to the load, although it is sometimes handy to think of it as a generator. It simply converts dc power, taken from the plate power supply, into a useful kind of output power in the load. It can do this because the grid is able to control the plate current.

Note that a *grid bias* source is shown in the grid circuit. This bias is a dc voltage applied to the grid. It is needed in the great majority of cases in order to make the tube operate in some desired fashion. It isn't always essential; some tubes are designed so they can operate without it.

When grid bias is required, the dc voltage applied to the grid is always negative. This has the effect of decreasing the plate current, as you already know. The signal voltage to be amplified is an ac voltage, when it rises in the positive direction, it cancels part of the steady bias voltage on the grid. When it swings in the negative direction, it adds to the negative bias voltage. This is shown in Fig. 17. We say that the signal is "superimposed" on the grid bias.

Fig. 17 shows a signal having an instantaneous peak of 10 volts superimposed on a negative dc voltage of 20 volts. At the positive-signal peak the *actual* voltage at the grid is 10 volts negative with respect to the cathode, while on the negative-signal peak it is 30 volts negative with respect to the cathode. At some time during each cycle the instantaneous grid voltage passes through every possible value between —10 and —30 volts. The plate current of the tube follows these changes, being

largest when the grid is at —10 volts and smallest when the grid is at —30 volts.

### Negative-Grid Operation

In this example the grid voltage never reaches zero — that is, it does not reach the point where there is no voltage between the grid and cathode even instantaneously. As you know, a negatively charged electrode in a tube will not attract electrons. So if we always keep the grid negative, no current will flow in the circuit formed by the cathode, grid, signal source and bias source. This is important, because a tube operated in this way does not take any power from the signal source. (Both current and voltage are needed to make power.) This is fine for the purpose of amplifying weak signals, because really weak signals can't supply appreciable power.

The disadvantage of keeping the grid entirely on the negative side is that it limits the range over which the plate current can be made to change. We can illustrate this by a simple graph, Fig. 18. This shows the plate current that will flow for each voltage we put on the grid. (The plate voltage is assumed to have some fixed value suitable for the tube.) If this is the tube which is biased as shown in Fig. 18, you can see that the instantaneous plate current at the positive peak of the 10-volt signal would be about 30 mA, while on the negative signal peak the plate current would be about 5 mA. This is a total change of 20 mA. If we increased the signal voltage to a peak of 20 volts, the instantaneous grid voltage would be just zero on the positive signal peak, at which time the plate current would be almost 50 mA. On the negative peak of such a signal the grid voltage would reach —40 and the plate current would be zero. This almost 50-mA change is the most we can get if the grid is to stay negative all the time. But as the curve shows, the plate current keeps going up when the grid is made *positive* with respect to the cathode.

### Grid Power

If the signal source could drive the grid positive, we could get a bigger swing in plate current and thereby increase the output of the tube. But the instant the grid goes positive, current starts to flow in the grid circuit, as shown by the curve marked "$I_G$." This means that the signal source has to supply real power whenever the grid is positive. If the source can supply the power, well and good. Some sources can and some can't.

### The Cutoff Point

Fig. 18 shows that the plate current gets smaller and smaller as we make the grid bias more negative. At —40 volts

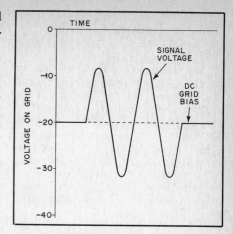

Fig. 17 — How an alternating signal voltage swings the grid voltage up and down about the steady grid-bias voltage.

bias the current is practically zero — that is, it is *cut off*. Making the grid voltage still more negative can't do more than that to the plate current. But there are actually advantages to setting the bias "beyond cutoff" for certain types of operation, particularly in rf power amplifiers.

In still other types of amplifiers there are advantages to setting the bias at, or not quite to, the cutoff point. In either case the benefit lies in increasing the plate efficiency of the amplifier, as compared with the type of operation just discussed in which the plate current flows throughout the signal cycle. Just how this comes about is a rather technical subject which you can find treated in more advanced books. For the present, it is enough to know that operating a tube with bias near or beyond

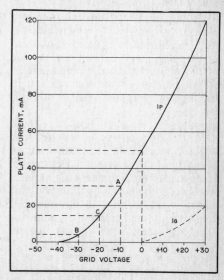

Fig. 18 — A curve such as this shows how the plate current of a tube will change when the grid voltage (that is, the voltage between the grid and cathode) is changed. The plate voltage is assumed to be constant in making up such a curve.

cutoff does help increase the plate efficiency of the amplifier.

## Distortion

The increased efficiency has its price. The output signal can't be exactly like the signal applied to the grid if the plate current is cut off during part of the cycle. In other words, there is *distortion*.

Sometimes, there is a *lot* of distortion. But in many kinds of amplifiers distortion doesn't matter. It matters in an audio amplifier. It does not matter much in many types of rf power amplifiers.

## Voltage and Power Amplification

This brings up the point that there are two kinds of amplification in practical use. In one case we try to get the largest possible *voltage* from the amplifier. This is worthwhile when that voltage is to be amplified, in turn, by a following amplifier stage (*stage* is the name given to one of a number of amplifiers used consecutively; consecutive amplifiers are said to be in *cascade*) *if* the grid of the following tube is never allowed to "go positive."

The second kind is called *power amplification*. Here we're interested in getting as much *power* as possible from the tube. This often requires driving the grid of the tube positive. Thus, power is used up in the grid circuit in order to produce the most output power in the plate circuit.

*Voltage amplification* is the ratio of the output voltage to the signal (grid) voltage that produces it. Power amplification, similarly, is the ratio of the power output to the signal (grid) power that produces it.

## The Decibel

Note that power amplification is a *ratio* of two powers. In communication work you'll find that power ratios often mean much more than the actual value of the power. A signal having a power, or *power level*, of one watt will sound, let's say, twice as loud when its power is increased to two watts. To make it sound twice as loud again we would have to increase the power to four watts. To make it twice as loud again we would have to increase it to eight watts. Each step in the loudness scale requires *multiplying* the power by some constant factor — the factor 2 in this example. There is a mathematical system for changing these ratios into simple numbers that can be added. If we use it, we don't have to go through a lot of multiplication to arrive at an estimate of how much we increase signal strength by increasing power. It is handy to make the unit of such a system one that stands for a just-noticeable increase in signal strength. The unit in use is called

the *decibel*, abbreviated *dB*. It stands for multiplying the power by 1.26, approximately. If the power is increased by 5 decibels, for example, it means that there have been five successive just-noticeable increases in signal strength.

An easy relationship to remember is that a power increase of 3 decibels is almost exactly the same as multiplying the original power by 2. Fig. 19 is a chart showing the number of decibels corresponding to various power ratios.

The decibel works both ways — that is, it gives the ratio of a *decrease* in power level just as readily as it gives the ratio of an increase. All you do is subtract instead of adding. If you cut your transmitter power down to one-half — that is, divide it by 2 — you have decreased it by 3 dB. A number of decibels with a minus sign in front of it means a *loss* of power of that ratio. If the sign is positive, or no sign is shown, a *gain* in power is meant.

## Amplifier Gain

The gain of an amplifier, whether it has just one stage or many, can be expressed either as a simple ratio of voltage or power, or given in decibels. Usually you will have no trouble in seeing what is meant, because it is customary to speak of a *voltage gain* of 1000, or a *power gain* of 250, or a *gain* of 30 dB — using the appropriate actual numbers, of course.

Watch out for gains given in decibels, though, when an amplifier contains voltage-amplifier as well as power-amplifier stages. The decibel measure is sometimes used loosely — and often incorrectly — to express a voltage gain. Always remember that the decibel stands for a *power* ratio.

## Amplifier Classifications

We've mentioned that there are several different types of amplification, and it's appropriate at this point to sort them out. First, there is the kind discussed in connection with Fig. 17. Its distinguishing feature is that plate current flows throughout the signal cycle — the grid is never, even instantaneously, driven negative beyond the cutoff point. An amplifier operated in this way is called a *Class A* amplifier. Since its plate current is driven *down* just as much as it is driven *up* by the signal, the *average* plate current stays just about the same whether or not a signal is on the grid.

Now suppose that the bias is set at cutoff, or slightly to the positive side of cutoff so that just a little plate current flows when there is no signal. During the negative half of the signal cycle the plate current stays cut off. During the positive half, the plate current will be approximately in proportion to the amplitude of the signal. That is, the

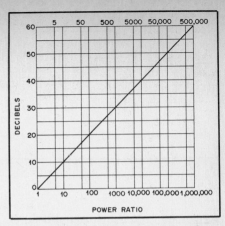

Fig. 19 — This chart shows the number of decibels corresponding to power ratios from one to one (0 dB) to one million to one (60 dB).

average plate current *changes* when the signal is applied, and the bigger the signal voltage the greater the plate current. This is called *Class B* amplification.[1] You'll see applications of it in later chapters.

There is a third general type — the *Class C* amplifier. Here the bias is set well beyond the cutoff point — up to twice the bias required for cutoff, usually. A large grid-driving voltage is used — so large that making it larger wouldn't cause any further increase in plate current. This is called driving the tube to *saturation*.

Class C operation gives the highest plate efficiency that can be obtained. It is useful in rf power amplifiers that are used for code work or are to be modulated for phone. It is used everywhere in transmitters except in one case — where a *modulated* signal must be amplified. Class C operation destroys the amplitude modulation on a signal applied to its grid. A Class A or Class B amplifier must be used for amplifying a modulated signal.

## Screen-Grid Tubes

It would be nice if we could get very large swings in plate current without having to drive the grid positive. This would mean large power output from the tube with no *driving power*. Modern tube design has gone a long way toward this goal. It isn't done with triodes, however. It hinges on having another electrode, the *screen grid*, in the tube.

The screen grid — the name is generally shortened to *screen* — is a grid-like structure placed between the regular grid and the plate. The element we have known so far simply as the "grid" is now called the *control grid* to

[1] An intermediate value of bias also can be used, so that the operation is partly Class A and partly Class B. This is called Class AB operation.

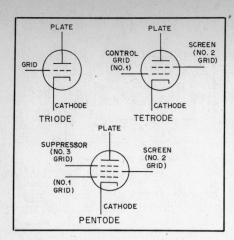

Fig. 20 — Grids in multigrid tubes are numbered in order, starting with the one next to the cathode. In some pentodes the suppressor grid (no. 3) is internally connected to the cathode and does not have a separate base pin. It may be omitted in drawing the symbol in that case, since no wiring is required for it.

distinguish it from the screen. A positive voltage is applied to the screen, and the job of this element is one of attracting as many electrons as possible from the region around the cathode — but to do it in such a way that the electrons will continue on through to the plate and not land on the screen itself. Not all of them do get by the screen, so there is a current in the screen circuit. However, it is small compared with the plate current.

Other than helping along the flow of electrons to the plate, the screen takes no part in amplification in ordinary circuits. This sort of tube structure makes it possible for large plate currents to flow when the control-grid voltage is zero. The presence of the screen, with its positive charge, makes it unnecessary for the control grid to "go positive" to make the plate current large. Thus, the control grid can be operated in the negative region and no power will be taken from the signal source. (You can get still more plate current by making the control grid positive, just as in a triode, but the point is that you don't have to, in order to get a large output.)

### Tetrodes and Pentodes

A tube having a cathode, control grid, screen grid and plate is called a *tetrode*. (If the cathode is indirectly heated, there will be a heater element, too, but it is counted as part of the cathode.) When a screen grid is placed in a tube, the electrons that travel through the screen get up to quite high speed before they reach the plate. In fact, they hit the plate so hard that they often knock electrons loose from the plate itself. These splashed-out electrons are called *secondary electrons*, and the process by which they are released from the plate is called *secondary emission*.

Once free, they often are attracted to the screen because of its positive charge.

The secondary-emission current flowing to the screen doesn't help in maintaining good tube characteristics. To get rid of it a third grid, the *suppressor grid*, is often introduced. This grid is near the plate and is usually operated at the same potential as the cathode. It shields the plate from the screen, so the secondary electrons don't "feel" the positive charge on the screen. As a result, they fall back on the plate for the most part. Tubes of this sort are called *pentodes*.

Modern tetrodes of the *beam* type (where the control-grid and screen-grid wires are lined up so that electrons can pass freely through both) are designed to be relatively free from secondary-emission effects. They usually have *beam-forming plates*, connected internally to the cathode. These plates at least partially shield the plate from the screen and help guide the electron flow *to* the plate in desired paths inside the tube.

### Remote-Cutoff Tubes

In any tube, making the grid bias more negative reduces the transconductance, so the amplification also decreases with larger bias. In an ordinary tube the transconductance decreases almost uniformly with the negative bias, until the plate-current cutoff point is reached. Varying the grid bias offers us a way of controlling the amount of amplification.

However, this method also can cause distortion and associated effects. To get around it, many of the small pentodes made for use in receiver amplifier circuits are given a rather peculiar characteristic. The transconductance "tails off" more and more as the bias is made more negative, so it takes a rather large negative bias to cut off the plate current. For example, a *sharp-cutoff* tube of regular design might reach cutoff with −10 volts on its grid. An otherwise identical tube with *remote cutoff* (or *variable-μ*) might require −40 or −50 volts to cut off the plate current. This characteristic is useful when the tube is required to handle large signals and the bias is varied to control the gain.

### Cathode Bias

In most cases, it isn't necessary to use a separate battery or power supply just to provide negative bias for the control grid. The bias can be stolen from the plate supply by a simple circuit trick. This is shown in Fig. 21. Bias obtained in this way is called *cathode bias*. There will be a voltage drop in resistor R1 because the plate-to-cathode current has to flow through it. The polarity is such that the cathode is "raised above ground" (the negative

terminal of the plate supply is "ground" in this circuit) by a positive voltage equal to the voltage drop of R1.

Note that in the upper drawing the grid is connected back to ground through the signal source, G. But since the cathode is more positive than ground, the voltage from the grid to cathode is negative. Thus the grid is given a negative bias with respect to the cathode.

### The Cathode Resistor

The bias can be set at a desired value by a simple application of Ohm's Law. If you know the bias, you want and also know the total current that will flow to the cathode at that bias, the value of R1 is found by dividing the bias voltage by the cathode current. If you need a bias of 5 volts and the cathode current will be 10 milliamperes at that bias, R1 will be 5 volts divided by 0.01 ampere (10 milliamperes), which is 500 ohms. Note that the plate current must be converted from milliamperes to amperes if you want the resistance to come out in ohms.

Cathode bias isn't entirely free. The voltage between the plate and cathode, which is the *effective* plate voltage, is reduced by the amount of the bias. In most cases the loss of plate voltage is of no consequence; it is only a few volts out of some hundreds.

### Zener-Diode Biasing

Zener-diode voltage regulators can be placed in the cathode circuit of a tube to provide a required amount of bias. The usual cathode resistor is dis-

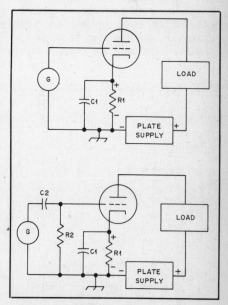

Fig. 21 — Negative grid bias obtained from a resistor between cathode and ground. Two types of "return" circuits for the grid are shown. The lower one isolates the grid (for dc) from the signal source.

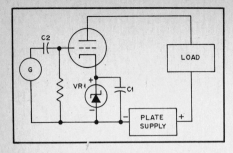

Fig. 22 — A Zener diode can be used to establish a fixed value of bias (VR1).

pensed with and the Zener diode replaces it as shown in Fig. 22. The principle of operation is similar to that of the cathode resistor since the diode places the cathode above ground with respect to power-supply ground, thereby making the grid negative by that amount. The value of bias is determined by the voltage rating of the Zener diode. In other words, if 12 volts of bias were required we would use a 12-volt Zener diode between the cathode and ground.

One must take into account the power dissipated within the diode and select a wattage rating for the diode which will prevent it from being damaged by excessive heating. As an example, if the cathode current of a tube is 10 mA and a 12-volt Zener diode is used, we have a dissipation of 0.12 watt, or 120 mW. A good rule of thumb is to use a Zener diode that is rated for at least twice the power it must dissipate. The nearest standard wattage value is 400 mW, and that will be more than ample. Zener diodes are available for power levels up to 50 watts, permitting their use in high-power rf amplifiers. If a Zener diode can't be found that provides the exact bias voltage required, the nearest value below the desired one can be used. Silicon rectifier diodes can be placed in series with the Zener diode to

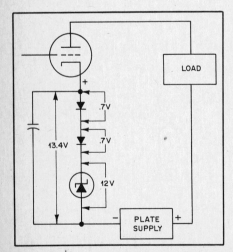

Fig. 23 — Silicon diodes can be placed in series with a Zener diode to increase the bias value.

obtain the exact voltage needed, or nearly so. Fig. 23 illustrates the method we are discussing. Each diode placed in series with the Zener diode will increase the cathode bias by approximately 0.7 volt.

### Grid Return Circuit

The lower drawing in Fig. 21 works just the same way as the upper one. It is used when the signal source, *G*, won't pass direct current, or when for some reason it is not desirable to have it do so. Resistor R2 substitutes for it, so the grid is still at ground potential for dc. The grid is insulated for dc by the *blocking capacitor*, C2. To avoid putting an undue load on the signal source, the resistance of R2 must be large compared with the load resistance that *G* can handle. In many circuits R2 will be as much as a megohm or so. The capacitance of C2 must be large enough so that for the ac signal its reactance is very small compared with the resistance of R2. In rf circuits a few hundred pF is generally enough, but at low audio frequencies it sometimes takes 0.1 microfarad or more.

### Cathode Bypassing

C1 is the *cathode bypass capacitor*. Since R1 is in the plate-cathode circuit, some of the amplified signal voltage will be developed in it, just as dc voltage was. It happens that this amplified signal voltage in R1 *opposes* the signal applied to the grid. This has the effect of reducing the amplification, and is called *negative feedback*. It has its uses, but if it is not wanted we have to prevent any signal voltage from being developed across R1. This is done by bypassing R1 for alternating currents. To be effective, C1 must have low reactance compared with the resistance of R1. Since the R1 resistance usually is fairly small the capacitance must be large. Values of 0.01 $\mu$F are customary if the frequency being amplified is a radio frequency in the 3 to 30 MHz range. Larger values are used at audio frequencies (several microfarads at least), but smaller ones will suffice at vhf.

### Fixed-Value Bias

Cathode bias is especially useful when the average plate current of the tube does not change much, if at all, when a signal is applied to its grid. If the average plate current does change with the strength of the signal, the bias does not stay put at one value but rises as the signal strength increases. In cases like this, it may be necessary to use a battery, Zener-diode bias, or special power supply for bias, so the bias won't change with the signal level. Bias of this sort is called *fixed bias*. But for many applications such as the amplifiers used in receivers and many of those used in

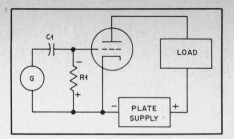

Fig. 24 — Grid-leak bias circuit.

low-power rf and audio stages in transmitters, cathode bias is quite satisfactory.

### Grid-Leak Bias

There is another way of making a tube furnish its own grid bias, shown in Fig. 24. If you look at this circuit without knowing what goes on, you may wonder how there could be any grid bias at all, since no source of bias is shown. The answer is that this method, called *grid-leak bias*, only works when the signal source drives the grid positive with respect to the cathode.

Remember that a current flows in the grid-cathode circuit whenever the grid is positive with respect to the cathode. This current charges the capacitor C1, called the *grid capacitor* or *grid blocking capacitor*. When the signal voltage is making the grid positive, it attracts electrons. These collect on the capacitor plate connected to the grid, giving that side of the capacitor a negative charge. If R1 is large, this charge "leaks" off slowly through it, so the net voltage at the grid is negative. Thus the tube gets an average negative dc bias through its own grid-current flow. The actual bias can be found by multiplying the resistance of R1 by the direct current flowing through it.

Grid-leak bias depends entirely on grid current; there is no bias if the grid isn't getting any signal. This means that the source of signal has to supply power for it. Also, the signal has to be large in order to drive the grid into the positive

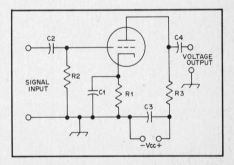

Fig. 25 — Typical resistance coupled voltage-amplifier circuit for audio frequencies. R3 is the plate load resistor, C3 is the plate bypass capacitor and C4 is the output coupling capacitor.

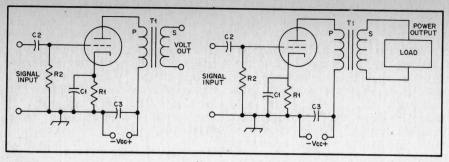

Fig. 26 — Transformer-coupled amplifier. An audio transformer is substituted for R3 and C4 of Fig. 25.

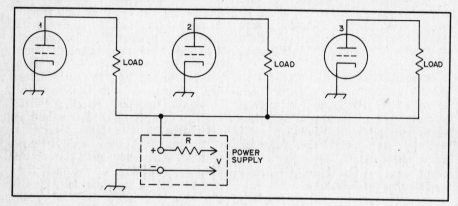

Fig. 27 — Why plate circuits must be bypassed.

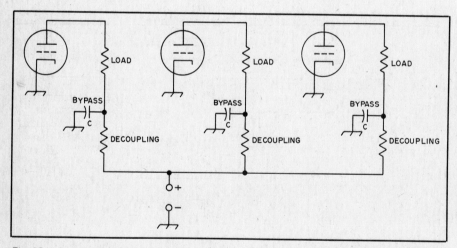

Fig. 28 — A separate bypass capacitor on each stage, backed up by decoupling resistors, will effectively prevent common coupling through the plate supply. The decoupling resistors are not always used, in which case the "brute-force" effect of the bypass capacitors is depended upon to keep the signal currents from wandering into the wrong stages in the amplifier.

region. However, an advantage is that the bias adjusts itself to the signal level. The bigger the signal, the greater the bias. This is just what is wanted in such devices as oscillators, since the bias automatically controls the tube operation to keep it in an optimum region. Grid-leak bias also is found frequently in rf power amplifier circuits, where the automatic feature also is useful.

The resistance of the *grid leak*, R1, could be as low as a few thousand ohms in tube circuits handling a lot of power. Values as high as 100,000 ohms may be used in oscillator circuits of very low power. The value of C1 depends on the frequency being amplified. C1 has to have enough capacitance so that it won't lose much charge during each cycle of the signal frequency. A few hundred pF usually will suffice at radio frequencies, where grid-leak bias is mostly used.

### Voltage Amplifier Circuits

We have been saying right along that the load for a vacuum-tube amplifier doesn't have to be an actual resistor. In fact, it is usually something else — a tuned circuit (which may in turn be loaded, as you have seen earlier in this chapter), a speaker with a transformer, or a variety of other devices. Nearly always, though, it "looks like" a resistance to the amplifier tube. This is necessary for getting power from the tube.

There is one type of amplifier that does use a resistor in its plate circuit. It often has the form shown in Fig. 25 and is called a *resistance-coupled amplifier*. This type of circuit is used almost exclusively for audio-frequency amplification; for reasons explained later it is not useful at radio frequencies. Resistance-coupled amplifiers are always voltage amplifiers, because the power that may be developed in the load resistor can't be taken out.

### Transformer Coupling

Transformers can be used in audio voltage amplifiers, too, as in Fig. 26. The transformer itself often steps up the output voltage by having a secondary winding with more turns than the primary. (This step-up is not considered to be amplification. There is actually less *power* in the secondary than in the primary, since there are losses in the transformer itself.) A transformer step-up is used only when the secondary is connected to a following amplifier tube whose grid is never driven positive.

The amplifiers you find in receivers between the antenna and the detector are also voltage amplifiers.

### Bypassing and Decoupling

You're already familiar with the uses of the components in the circuits of Fig. 25 and 26 except for C3. C3 is a *plate bypass capacitor*. It is used to give the alternating signal current in the plate circuit a good low-impedance path to the cathode. We don't want this current to flow through the B supply if we can avoid it, especially when several amplifier stages are connected to the same supply.

Fig. 27 illustrates why. Just enough detail is given in this figure to show that if the power supply has an internal resistance, R (and all power supplies do have some internal resistance), this resistance will be part of all three amplifier plate circuits. For example, the highly amplified current from amplifier three will flow through R and cause a signal voltage to develop across it. This voltage, in turn, is introduced into the plate circuits of stages one and two. Such *common coupling* can lead to lots of trouble.

Fig. 28 gives the remedy. If the bypass capacitor, *C*, has a reactance of not more than a few ohms at the signal frequency, the signal current in each stage will be confined to that stage and not wander into other stages in the amplifier. Assurance is made doubly sure by connecting a *decoupling resistor* on the power-supply side of the bypass capacitor as shown. Usually this resistance is several hundred times the reactance of the bypass capacitor — values in the neighborhood of 1000 to 5000 ohms are common — so any tendency for the signal currents to get off their proper paths is rather thoroughly discouraged.

### Power Amplifiers

When power is wanted, as for running a speaker, we don't care particularly how much the grid-signal *voltage* is amplified. Here we have to provide a load that represents the optimum resistance for the tube to see as a *power* amplifier. It is done by matching the speaker (or other) load resistance to the optimum value through a transformer, as described earlier.

A typical circuit is shown in the lower drawing of Fig. 26. It looks almost like the voltage-amplifier circuit above it, but a different type of transformer is used. Also, the tube's operating conditions are chosen to give the most power output rather than the most voltage output.

### Push-Pull Amplifiers

A favorite form of circuit where large power outputs at audio frequency are needed is the *push-pull* arrangement shown in Fig. 29. It is so called because what one tube does is always the opposite of what the other tube is doing. The secondary winding of the input transformer, T1, is tapped at the center and the outer ends of the winding connect to the two grids. If the upper end of the winding is positive at some instant, the lower end is negative by exactly the same amount of voltage at the same instant. Thus when the plate current of one tube is increasing because the signal voltage on its grid is going more positive, the plate current of the other tube is decreasing because the voltage on *its* grid is going more negative.

This see-saw action opens the way to getting a great deal of audio power out of a pair of tubes, in relation to the size of the tubes. The reason is that this type of circuit reduces even-harmonic distortion, by a large margin, as compared with a single-tube circuit. Both tubes may still distort, but the distortions are balanced out by the push-pull connection in the output transformer, T2. In fact, the tubes can be biased down practically to the plate-current cutoff point, so that each takes plate current only when the grid is driven by the positive half of the signal cycle, being idle during the negative half cycle. This is an extreme case of distortion, corresponding to half-wave rectification in each tube — yet the two half cycles, one

from each tube, combine to give a composite output with low distortion.

A push-pull amplifier in which the tubes are biased near cutoff is a form of Class B amplifier. It operates at very good plate efficiency. A pair of tubes each rated to give 5 watts audio output as single-tube Class A amplifiers usually can develop 35 to 40 watts of total output when working together in push-pull.

### Interelectrode Capacitances

The circuits just discussed are useful at low frequencies — those through the audio range. At radio frequencies they don't work at all well. To understand why, we have to take a closer look at tube structure.

A triode tube has three elements, all metallic and quite close together. Each pair of electrodes actually has the characteristics of a capacitor. The capacitances are only a few pF, but you will remember that the reactance of a capacitor keeps going down as the frequency goes up. The reactances of these *interelectrode capacitances* are so high at audio frequencies that they usually can be ignored. Not so at radio fre-

quencies. There the reactances are considerably smaller than the load resistance we would need for appreciable voltage amplification. The tube capacitances actually bypass the alternating current around the load resistance. This not only ruins the amplification but introduces other very undesirable effects which are beyond our present scope.

### Why Tuned Circuits are Used

For the moment, consider just two of the interelectrode capacitances — the one between the grid and cathode and the one between the plate and cathode. At radio frequencies the former would tend to short-circuit the input circuit, if it were resistance-coupled and the latter, the output circuit. We can't eliminate the capacitances from the tube, because they are part of its physical structure. So we take the opposite tack, and make them go to work for us. This is done by using *tuned* input and output circuits.

In Fig. 30, $C_g$ represents the grid-cathode capacitance and $C_p$ the plate-cathode capacitance of the tube. You can see that $C_g$ is in parallel with C1, the tuning capacitor of the input circuit. Likewise, $C_p$ is in parallel with C2, the

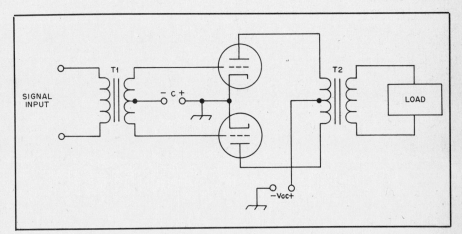

Fig. 29 — Typical push-pull amplifier circuit. This circuit can be varied in a great many ways, depending on whether the tubes operate as Class A, AB, or B amplifiers. If the tubes aren't driven into grid current, resistance coupling can be used to the signal source. In voltage amplifiers the output side may also be resistance coupled, but the transformer T2 is always required if power is to be taken from the circuit.

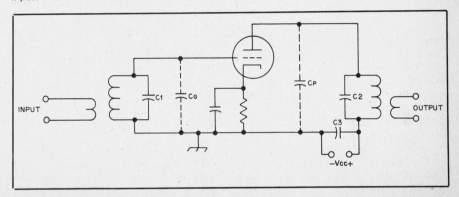

Fig. 30 — How the input and output capacitances of a tube can be absorbed by the input and output tuning capacitances.

tuning capacitor of the output circuit. (C3, the plate bypass capacitor, is so large compared with these last two that it is the same as a short-circuit for the radio frequency.) Thus the interelectrode capacitances become *part of* the tuning capacitances, and they do no particular harm aside from setting a lower limit on the total tuning capacitance that can be used. This is not so important at the lower amateur frequencies, but it does require consideration at vhf.

Using tuned circuits allows us to get normal amplification, besides providing the selectivity that is needed at radio frequencies. We'll have more to say on the latter point in the chapter on receivers.

### Grid-Plate Capacitance

We got around the *input* and *output* capacitances of the tube fairly easily by using tuned circuits. But Fig. 30 ignores one very important capacitance — the one between the grid and plate. Radio-frequency current can and does flow through it. In fact, if the grid and plate tuned circuits are adjusted to about the same frequency — as they have to be to give amplification — the grid-plate capacitance offers an ideal path for the amplified rf energy in the plate circuit to feed back into the grid circuit. When this happens, a sort of merry-go-round action takes place. The fed-back energy

adds to that already present in the grid circuit. This is amplified to give still more rf energy in the plate circuit, and so on. The over all result is that the tube *generates* radio-frequency power instead of just amplifying it. It becomes an *oscillator*. Fig. 30 is in fact an oscillator circuit, not an amplifier circuit. It is known as a *tuned-grid, tuned-plate* oscillator.

### Screen-Grid Amplifiers

Fortunately, the grid-plate capacitance *can* be reduced to negligible size. This is done by placing a shield between the grid and plate, forming a screen-grid tube. Screen-grid tubes, such as are used in the rf amplifiers in receivers, usually also have a suppressor grid; that is, they are pentodes. A screen-grid amplifier circuit is shown in Fig. 31. The suppressor nearly always is connected to the cathode as shown although sometimes it is connected to ground.

The screen grid needs a positive voltage on it if the tube is to work properly. Generally, however, less voltage is needed by the screen than by the plate. The screen voltage is obtained from the plate supply through R1, the *screen dropping resistor*. Screen current flowing through R1 causes a voltage drop across R1 that subtracts from the plate-supply voltage, leaving just the proper voltage on the screen. The right resistance value can easily be found if

you know the current taken by the screen at its operating voltage. For example, say the plate-supply voltage is 250, the screen requires 100 volts, and the screen current is 10 mA under normal operating conditions. (Figures of this sort can be obtained from published tube data.) Then R1 must "drop" 250 − 100 = 150 volts. Its resistance is therefore 150 divided by 0.01 ampere, or 15,000 ohms.

If the screen is to shield the plate from the control grid and thus eliminate the grid-plate capacitance, it must be at the same rf potential as the cathode. The *screen bypass capacitor*, C4, ensures this by short-circuiting to the cathode any rf that might show up on the screen. Like other bypass capacitors, it must have low reactance at the frequency being amplified. A capacitance of 0.01 µF is typical for rf amplifier circuits.

Screen-grid amplifiers are used both in receivers and transmitters. The circuits are basically the same whether the tube is a miniature receiving type or one that can handle hundreds of watts. There may be differences in the way the grid bias is obtained or in the method used to supply screen voltage, but these are details that will vary even in receiver amplifiers.

### Grounded-Grid Amplifiers

The idea of using a grid to shield two elements from each other is used in another kind of rf amplifier circuit. In a triode the grid will shield the plate from the cathode *provided* the grid has no rf voltage on it. It must, like a screen grid, be grounded for rf. (It can still be at some different dc voltage than ground, though, just like the screen grid.)

Of course, if the grid is grounded, the cathode can't be. So the signal voltage must be applied between the cathode and ground, as shown in Fig. 32. This circuit is like Fig. 30 except that the cathode and grid have changed places. The input signal voltage is still *between* the grid and cathode. But now the grid shields the plate (output) from the cathode (input) and very little rf energy can travel from the output side to the input side. Thus there is much less tendency for the tube to go into self-oscillation. The *grounded-grid amplifier* is used in both receivers and transmitters. In receivers it is used principally at vhf and uhf.

One of the peculiarities of this circuit, which is getting to be rather popular in amateur transmitters, is that the plate current has to flow through the input circuit to reach the cathode. Thus the input and output circuits are actually connected together, and a closer study would show that they operate as though they were connected in series. The upshot of this is that the

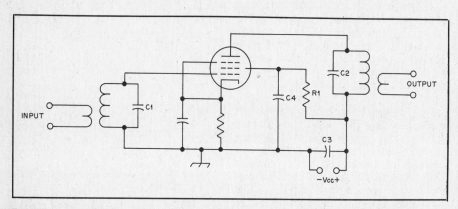

Fig. 31 — Screen-grid amplifier circuit for rf amplification. C1 and C2 are the grid and plate tuning capacitances and C3 is the plate bypass capacitor. Cathode bias is shown. R1 is the screen dropping resistor and C4 is the screen bypass capacitor.

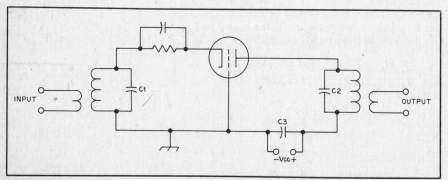

Fig. 32 — Grounded-grid amplifier, using the grid of a triode to shield the output circuit from the input circuit.

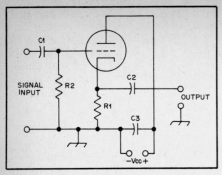

Fig. 33 — The cathode follower, or grounded-plate amplifier.

source of input signal supplies part of the output power. This is quite different from the way an ordinary amplifier operates. The signal source must be prepared to supply quite a bit more power than would be required of it when the amplifier's cathode is grounded.

Only a few types of triodes have been designed with grounded-grid operation in mind. In those that have not been, the grid is not always as good a shield as we might want. Generally, tubes with large amplification factors will be the best in this respect, because the openings in the grid are smaller in such tubes. A number of screen-grid types are useful if the control grid and screen are both grounded for rf; in these, the shielding is likely to be very good.

### Grounded-Plate Amplifiers

The plate of a tube can be grounded at the signal frequency, too. The circuit is as shown in Fig. 33, in a frequently used form. An amplifier operated in this way is usually called a *cathode follower*, because the "hot" side of the output circuit is the cathode of the tube. The plate bypass capacitor, C3, grounds the plate for the signal frequency; the normal dc plate voltage is used.

The output is taken from between the cathode and plate. R1 is thus the plate load resistor as well as the cathode bias resistor. C1 and R2 have the same purpose as C2 and R2 in the lower circuit of Fig. 21. C2 is the output coupling capacitor.

Since the input signal voltage is applied between the grid and ground, it has to be larger than the output voltage. If it weren't, there would be no signal between the grid and cathode. The cathode follower doesn't give any voltage amplification; in fact, there is actually a voltage loss. However, there is *power* amplification.

Earlier, in discussing cathode biasing, we mentioned that the cathode resistor is bypassed in order to avoid unwanted negative feedback. In the cathode fol-

lower we have *all* of the output voltage fed back into the input circuit to oppose the signal voltage. This has its good features, although at the price of a loss in voltage amplification. One benefit is that the amplifier will work over an extremely wide frequency range without tuned circuits — from very low audio frequencies up through several megahertz. Another is that it doesn't require a critical load resistance. The circuit can be looked upon as the equivalent of a transformer for stepping down from a very high impedance to a very low impedance. Suitably designed cathode-follower circuits can work into loads as small as 100 ohms, or even less.

### Oscillators

You already know that a tube can generate power without having its grid circuit driven by an external source. It can do this because more power can be obtained from its plate circuit than is needed by its grid circuit to produce the plate power. To start a circuit oscillating, we need to feed power from the plate back to the grid in such a way as to reinforce the signal on the grid. This is called *positive feedback*, as distinguished from the *negative* feedback that *opposes* the grid signal. With enough positive feedback, any small irregularity in the plate current will supply a signal that will start oscillations going at the frequency to which the tube circuit is tuned.

Positive feedback can be developed in so many ways that we can't begin to cover all of them here. We've already mentioned the tuned-grid tuned-plate oscillator (Fig. 30). Two other general types of circuits are so commonly used that you should be able to recognize them on sight. One, the *Hartley* circuit of Fig. 34A, belongs to the *magnetic* or *inductive feedback* class of circuit. Alternating plate current flowing through the lower part of L1 induces a voltage in the upper part, which is connected to the grid. The second general type, the *Colpitts* circuit of Fig. 34B, uses *capacitive feedback*. Here the plate-circuit energy is fed back by introducing it across C2, which is part of the tuning capacitance of the circuit. This coupling sets up an rf voltage across the whole circuit. The voltage that, as a result, develops across C1 is applied to the grid.

Another circuit you will meet now and then is shown in Fig. 34C. It isn't basically different from the Hartley, but instead of tapping the coil it uses inductive coupling through a *tickler coil* tightly coupled to the tuned-circuit coil.

### The Tank Circuit

The tuned circuit is often called the *tank circuit* of an oscillator or rf power amplifier. The reason is that it stores

several times as much energy as it is called on to give up each radio-frequency cycle. This is necessary if the oscillator is to operate with good stability (the subject of stability is treated in later chapters; it is an extremely important oscillator characteristic). This high ratio of stored to used energy is summed up quite simply by saying that it corresponds to a circuit of high *Q*.

All three of the circuits shown are grid-leak biased. R1 is the grid leak or grid resistor in each case. C2 is the grid capacitor in A and C; in B it is C4.

### Comparing Transistors and Tubes

It can be seen from the foregoing theory sections that tubes and transistors have a great many similarities. If we keep a couple of basic ideas foremost in our minds, we can work easily with either type of device: Tubes amplify voltage and transistors amplify current; tubes use high plate voltage and low plate current, while transistors use low collector or drain voltages and draw fairly high collector or drain current;

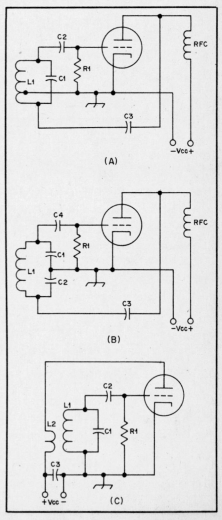

Fig. 34 — Some common oscillator circuits. A — Hartley; B — Colpitts; C — tickler.

and tubes have relatively high input and output impedances, but bipolar transistors have low input and output impedances — comparatively speaking. The greater the power level used with transistors, the more pronounced these characteristics become.

Generally, transistors are more prone to developing unwanted harmonic currents in their collector circuits than is the case with tubes. When grid current is permitted to flow in a tube amplifier circuit, we find harmonic current developing as a result of *envelope distortion*. Transistor amplifiers produce harmonic energy in the same fashion, but the magnitude of the harmonic energy is greater with transistors because of another condition which generates harmonic energy — *nonlinearity*. The latter is brought about by constant nonlinear changes in transistor junction capacitance as the sine-wave signal passes through its 360-degree cycle. The output from a transistor rf power amplifier can be made as clean as that of a tube amplifier if proper harmonic filtering is employed. Fig. 35 shows how a simple half-wave filter can be placed in the 50-ohm output line to prevent excessive amounts of harmonic energy from reaching the antenna. In order for a tube or transistor to function as a frequency multiplier, it is necessary to operate the device in the Class C mode — the condition in which grid and base current flows. Since transistors are more prone to the generation of harmonics they serve well as multipliers. The half-wave filter of Fig. 35 is a low-pass type of network. It passes all frequencies from 7 MHz and lower, but the frequencies above 7 MHz are rejected by the filter. It is necessary to design such a filter for the band of operation, as it is a single-band network. Details on the design of half-wave filters are given in the *ARRL electronics data book*.

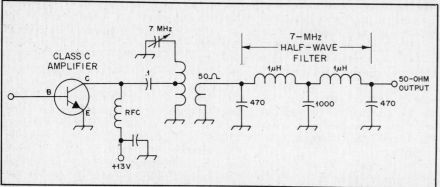

Fig. 35 — Example of how a harmonic half-wave filter is used at the output of a transistor rf amplifier.

### Amplifier Stability

Transistor amplifiers are somewhat harder to tame than is the situation with tube amplifiers. This is because tubes can be neutralized to cancel out the internal feedback capacitance that leads to instability (self-oscillation). When working with transistor amplifiers, we find large amounts of internal feedback capacitance, and the capacitance changes in value during the sine-wave excursion of the driving signal. That condition makes it practically impossible to neutralize a transistor amplifier, except for one part of the drive cycle. Still another transistor characteristic exists to encourage self-oscillation: The gain of a transistor increases as the operating frequency is lowered. The theoretical gain increase is one on the order of 6 dB per octave lower. This means that if a transistor had a gain of 10 dB at 7 MHz, its gain would be 16 dB at 3.5 MHz, and so on. The higher the gain, the greater the occasion for unstable operation. The negative feedback network of Fig. 10 (R1 and C1) will help to keep the stage tamed down, but instability can still occur at low frequencies from the broadcast band down to the audio region — the area where the transistor gain is rather spectacular. Tubes do not exhibit that troublesome characteristic within their rated frequency range, and this makes them a bit easier to work with at radio frequencies.

Many transistor amplifiers will oper-

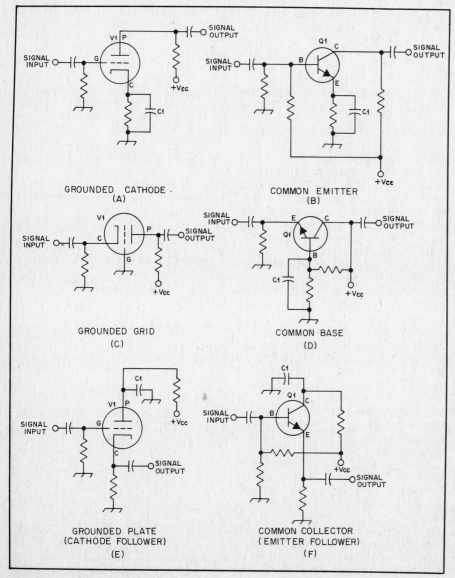

Fig. 36 — Circuits showing the similarity between a triode tube and a bipolar transistor with the various elements grounded for ac.

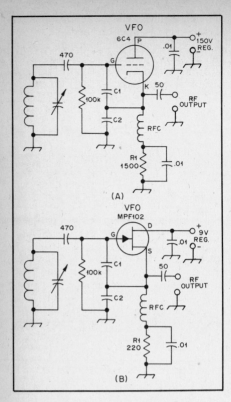

Fig. 37 — Comparison between a triode tube and an FET when used in a Colpitts oscillator circuit.

ate in a stable manner from, say, 1.8 to 30 MHz, but will self-oscillate at some low frequency. The operator may not even realize what is happening unless he listens across the broadcast band and lower to see if he can find signals from his transmitter in that part of the spectrum. The most practical way to prevent unwanted oscillations is to use bypass capacitors at key points — capacitors which are effective at high frequency, medium frequency, low frequency and audio frequency. Fig. 39B shows a 0.01-$\mu$F and a 25-$\mu$F capacitor at the bottom end of the collector rf choke. The combination of those values will be effective in bypassing the circuit from audio to high frequencies. The rf chokes in the base and collector circuits should be the lowest values possible, consistent with the impedances of the transistor elements to which they connect. A good rule is to make the rf choke reactance about four times the impedance of the circuit in which it is used. In Fig. 39B the collector impedance is 1.7 ohms, so four times that value is roughly 7 ohms. For a 7-ohm reactance at 3.5 MHz we obtain an inductance of 0.138 $\mu$H. By keeping the choke inductance as low as possible, the chokes will not combine with the internal and stray circuit capacitances to set up a tuned-base tuned-collector sort of oscillator. In some instances it is helpful to place "swamping" resistors across the chokes to lower their $Q$s (R3

of Fig. 10), as that will further discourage unwanted oscillations.

## Configurations

Earlier in this chapter we discussed grounded-plate and grounded-grid operation of tubes. Field-effect and bipolar transistors can be used in the same fashion. In semiconductor jargon we say that a grounded-base transistor stage is a "common-base" stage; likewise, with the emitter and collector circuits, depending upon which is grounded for ac. The terms *grounded* and *common* mean the same thing in our vernacular, and either is correct. Fig. 36 illustrates how tubes and transistors compare respective to this discussion. In the examples where C1 is specified, it is used to place the related tube or transistor element at ac ground.

As a further illustration of how tube and transistor circuits resemble one another, let's examine Fig. 37. At A is a tube version of an ordinary Colpitts oscillator. C1 and C2 are the feedback capacitors which control the oscillation. At B, a field-effect transistor is used in the same circuit. All of the parts values are the same except for R1, the bias resistor. The only other difference between the circuits is the operating voltage. A field-effect transistor has the same characteristics as a triode tube (high input impedance), and in most instances an FET can be used to replace a tube with only slight alterations of the parts and voltage values.

Bipolar transistors are a bit different in their mannerisms. They differ from tubes and FETs primarily in their input-impedance traits. A single Class A bipolar amplifier has a low input impedance — usually between 500 and 2000 ohms — depending on the base biasing and the value of the base-bias resistors. Fig. 38 shows how a triode tube and a bipolar transistor compare in a microphone amplifier stage. A high-impedance (Hi-Z) microphone is specified in each example. Since the tube grid in the circuit at A is high impedance, the microphone can be connected to it directly or through a blocking capacitor. The 470,000-ohm grid resistor will establish the input impedance of the circuit. It is much lower in resistance than is the tube grid. The latter is in the megohm region, so its value has little shunting effect on the grid resistor. The output impedance of the tube amplifier will be quite high (approximately 15,000 ohms) because of the high plate voltage and low plate current, say, 10 mA.

In order to use the same microphone with the circuit at B in Fig. 38, some type of matching device will be required. If an attempt were not made to provide a reasonable match, there would be two unsatisfactory results. First, the

microphone output voltage would be shunted and lowered by the low-impedance base circuit, and insufficient audio output would exist at the collector of the transistor. Second, the low impedance shunted across the microphone would cause a severe loss of low-frequency audio response. The solution is to include a matching transformer (T1) to step the high impedance of the microphone down to that of the transistor base. A miniature transformer will be satisfactory, as there is no appreciable power in the microphone or base parts of the circuit. Other circuit differences exist, as can be observed in the values of the resistors and capacitors. The larger capacitor values in the transistor circuit are necessary because the impedances are lower at the base, emitter and collector points. (The lower the impedance, the greater the capacitance needed to provide effective bypassing and coupling.)

## Power Amplifiers

Still another comparison between tubes and transistors can be seen by referring to Fig. 39. Both amplifiers are capable of 50 watts of output. However, the component values and the input and output impedances are markedly different. This is because the 6146A tube has an input impedance which is quite high (around 50,000 ohms in this example). Also, the plate impedance is much higher than that of the collector

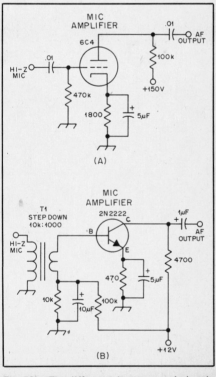

Fig. 38 — The difference between a triode tube and a bipolar transistor are more than subtle in this example of audio circuitry.

in the circuit at B. The tube plate has an impedance of 5000 ohms, but the transistor collector impedance is only 1.7 ohms! It is okay to connect the tube plate to the high end of the plate tank as shown, provided the plate-tank values are chosen for the 5000-ohm characteristic. The transistor collector, on the other hand, is tapped far down on the tuned circuit to enable the collector to be matched to the 50-ohm output load. In effect, L1 and L2 of Fig. 39A serve as a step-down transformer, while L1 and L2 of Fig. 39B provide a step-up action.

The input and output coupling capacitors at Fig. 39B are much larger than those at A in Fig. 39. This is because the impedances are so low in the transistor circuit. If we were to use the capacitance values shown at A, our transistor amplifier would be extremely inefficient, as the input and output circuits would not be coupled tightly enough to their respective loads.

In a transistor amplifier such as that of Fig. 39B, we find a base impedance on the order of one ohm. That is quite a contrast to the input impedance of the 6146A! A 1-$\mu$H rf choke is suitable as a base-return path to ground. No base bias is applied to the transistor for Class C operation, as the driving signal pushes the transistor beyond cutoff. It draws no current during periods when drive is not applied, even though the collector has voltage supplied to it.

Perhaps the most notable difference between the two circuits is the lack of complexity seen in the transistor amplifier. Only one supply voltage is required (13 volts at approximately eight amperes), and the rf chokes are so small in value that they can be made easily by hand. It should be said that the circuit given in Fig. 39B is not representative of the circuit one would use in practice. It has been simplified to make it easier to understand. Fig. 40 shows a more typical 50-watt-output transistor amplifier.

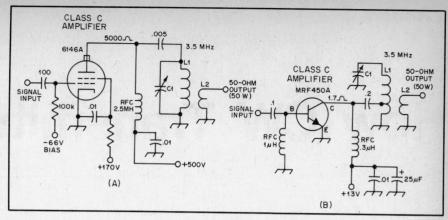

Fig. 39 — Rf power amplifier comparison for a tube and a transistor at the 50-watt output level.

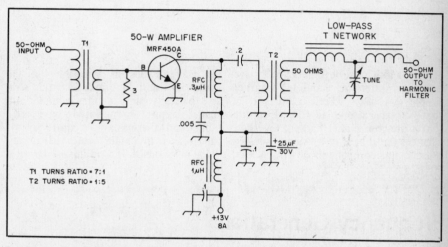

Fig. 40 — A typical transistor rf power amplifier with most of the values shown.

Efficiency for this kind of amplifier is between 50 and 60 percent, so to get 50 watts of output one must run approximately 100 watts of dc input. Driving power to the transistor base will be roughly two watts for the transistor indicated.

The most practical way to match into and out of the transistor is by means of broadband ferrite-core transformers (T1 and T2). An additional rf choke is shown in the collector supply line. It helps to decouple the stage from the other stages in the transmitter, as rf energy can flow along the supply lines. When that happens, a feedback condition will exist, and it will encourage instability in one or more of the transmitter stages. Each stage should contain its own decoupling network.

# Chapter 3

# How CW Transmitters Work

If you're like most beginners you'll have built, or otherwise acquired, a rather simple transmitter. Perhaps it is a kit that you have assembled yourself or one that a previous owner had put together. Chances are that if it is of simple design it is crystal controlled. Most such kits, as well as designs you may see in magazines and in books like this one, are basically similar. The cabinets and panel layouts may not look exactly alike and there may be quite a few differences in detail. More than likely each will consist of a *crystal oscillator*, a *buffer amplifier* and a *final amplifier* stage. There is often provision for voice operation. This mode of operation will be discussed in detail in chapter 4. Let's start our discussion of cw transmitters with how energy on a given frequency is generated.

## Frequency Generation

The first stage in almost all simple transmitters is the oscillator. This stage determines on what particular frequency the transmitter will operate. An oscillator is actually a special type of amplifier, similar in nature to those studied in chapter 1. The transistor or vacuum tube used as the oscillator, amplifies the signal on its base or grid just like any other amplifier. The basic difference is that a portion of the output from the device (collector or plate circuit) is fed back (positive feedback) to the input (base or grid circuit) of the amplifier in such a manner that it aids or adds to the applied signal. For this reason, an oscillator is sometimes referred to as a self-driven amplifier. The frequency at which the amplifier will oscillate is determined primarily by the frequency selective network. In most cases this network will consist of a *quartz crystal* or *tuned LC* circuit.

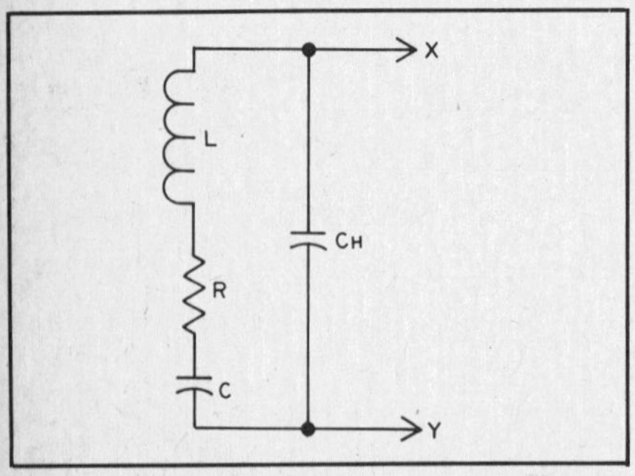

### Crystal Oscillators

A quartz crystal is a mechanical vibrator that behaves like a resonant $LC$ circuit. The electrical equivalent circuit of the quartz crystal is a resonant circuit, consisting of an inductance, capacitance and resistance connected in series. This equivalent circuit is shown in Fig. 1. We have included $R$ to account for the power lost in the crystal when it vibrates. This value of resistance is quite small in comparison to the reactance of $L$ at the operating frequency. Inductances ranging from 100 mH to over 100 H are not uncommon. This yields extremely high $Q$ factors — typical values are between 5,000 and 50,000 with some units as high as a million.

The crystal must be mounted between two metal electrodes in order to be used. These electrodes along with the piece of quartz between them make up the relatively small capacitance $C_H$ which is usually only a few picofarads. The capacitance that is in series with $L$ and $R$ is also on the order of a few picofarads. At frequencies lower than resonance the impedance of the network is high and is capacitive. (See Fig. 2.) The reactance $X_L$ and $X_C$ will be equal at some frequency. This is the so-called series-resonant frequency and corresponds to the natural frequency of the crystal. Slightly higher in frequency, the inductive portion of the circuit becomes the difference between the

Fig. 1 — Equivalent circuit of a crystal resonator. $L$, $C$ and $R$ are the electrical equivalents of mechanical properties of the crystal; $C_H$ is the capacitance of the holder plates with the crystal plate between them.

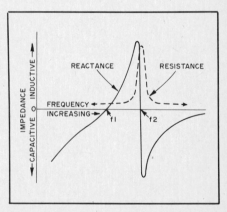

Fig. 2 — Reactance and resistance vs. frequency of a circuit of the type shown in Fig. 1. Actual values of reactance, resistance and the separation between the series- and parallel-resonant frequencies, $f_1$ and $f_2$, respectively, depend on the circuit constants.

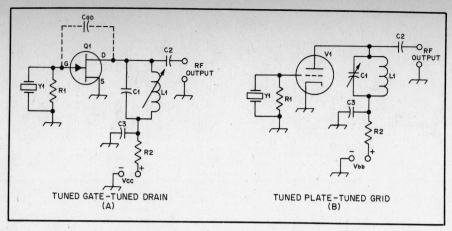

Fig. 3 — Shown at A is an FET tuned-gate tuned-drain crystal oscillator. A vacuum-tube version, a tuned-plate tuned-grid oscillator, is illustrated at B.

reactance of $L$ and the reactance of $C$. The net reactance of this branch becomes inductive and equal to $C_H$. If used in this manner, the crystal is said to be operating in parallel resonance. We haven't destroyed the series resonance by mounting the crystal. Because of the high $Q$ the crystal actually acts almost as a short circuit across $C_H$ at its series-resonant frequency. We can use either resonance by suitable circuit design.

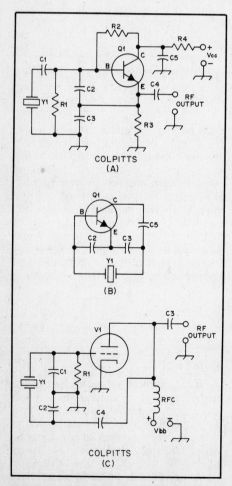

Fig. 4 — At A is a transistor Colpitts oscillator and at B its simplified equivalent circuit. A tube type Colpitts oscillator is shown at C.

There are a number of different types of crystal oscillator circuits. Each circuit has one or more particular traits that distinguish it from the others. One circuit, a *tuned-gate tuned-drain* oscillator is shown in Fig. 3A. The crystal forms the tuned-gate portion of the circuit and the tuned-drain circuit consists of C1 and L1. C3 is a bypass capacitor. Ideally, this capacitor should present a very low reactance at the operating frequency to assure that the bottom of the L1/C1 tank is at rf ground. C2 is a coupling/dc blocking capacitor used to route rf energy from the oscillator to the next stage. Feedback is provided through the interelectrode capacitances within the device. In this example the feedback path is through the capacitance from the gate to the drain — $C_{gd}$. If the interelectrode capacitance does not provide sufficient feedback for oscillation to occur, an external capacitor can be added between the two elements.

The circuit at B is the vacuum-tube equivalent of the circuit shown at A and is called a *tuned-grid tuned-plate* oscillator. Circuit operation is basically the same as in the solid-state version with all numbered components serving the same electrical purpose. The tube circuit has been simplified as much as possible to illustrate the principles. In practice, tetrodes and pentodes are often used instead of triodes. These multi-element tubes will give considerably greater output without driving the crystal any harder.

It is desirable to keep the crystal drive as low as possible because the harder the crystal vibrates, the warmer it will get. Like most circuit components, it responds to a change in temperature with a change in its constants — in this case a change in its resonant frequency. This in turn causes the oscillator frequency to drift. Further, if the crystal is driven too hard, it may shatter. Once cracked or broken it is useless.

A transistor *Colpitts* oscillator is illustrated at Fig. 4A. Feedback is obtained by returning the collector to one end of the tuned circuit (Y1). The amount of feedback is dependent on the relative capacitance values of C2 and C3 since these capacitors are included in the feedback path. A simplified equivalent circuit is shown at B to help illustrate circuit operation. As C3 is made smaller in value the amount of feedback increases. R1 and R2 establish the base bias, R3 is the load resistor, and C1 and C4 are coupling capacitors. Fig. 4B shows the vacuum-tube counterpart of A with a few minor changes. First, the output is taken from the plate circuit, whereas it was taken from the emitter in the solid-state version. For this reason it is not necessary to have the cathode above ground — it is connected directly to ground. Circuit operation for the vacuum-tube and solid-state version is essentially identical.

In Fig. 5A we can see yet another type of oscillator; this one is called a *Pierce*. In this circuit arrangement the crystal is connected between the collector and base of the transistor. R1, R2 and R3 are bias resistors. C2 and C5 are rf-bypass capacitors and RFC is an rf choke. This circuit can actually be considered as a modified Colpitts oscillator as shown in the equivalent circuit at B. C1 and C3 correspond to the same numbered *components* as those shown

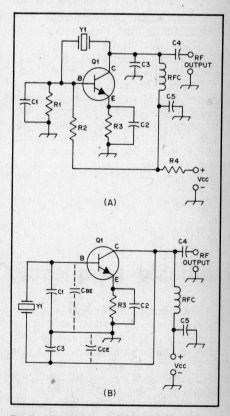

Fig. 5 — Shown at A is a transistor Pierce oscillator. Its equivalent circuit, redrawn to illustrate the feedback path, is shown at B.

at A. The values of these capacitors determine the amount of feedback. $C_{BE}$ and $C_{CE}$ are internal capacitances within the transistor. $C_{BE}$ is the capacitance present between the base and emitter and $C_{CE}$ is the capacitance between the collector and emitter. As shown, these capacitances are in parallel with the external feedback capacitors. If the internal capacitances are of a large enough magnitude at the operating frequency, C1 and C3 may be omitted.

So far we have only discussed oscillators that provide power output on the crystal series or parallel resonant frequency. This is fine for many applications but not for all. The highest frequency that ordinary fundamental-mode crystals are available for is approximately 30 MHz. Many pieces of equipment, especially vhf types, require oscillator power at much higher frequencies. There are two basic ways of obtaining higher frequency output from these basic oscillator circuits. For frequencies above 30 MHz or so, *harmonic* or *overtone* oscillators are generally used.

Harmonic oscillators make use of the fact that harmonic currents flow in addition to fundamental (crystal frequency) currents in the collector or plate circuit. The crystal oscillates at its fundamental frequency, but the output circuit is tuned to the desired harmonic frequency. The higher the order of the harmonic, the lower the output compared to what could be obtained at the fundamental frequency. Second harmonic (twice the fundamental frequency) and third harmonic (three times the fundamental frequency) energy is quite usable with most crystal oscillators. If higher order harmonics are needed, it is customary to use a series of frequency-multiplier stages rather than attempting to obtain the output directly from the oscillator. A frequency multiplier in its simplest form, is an amplifier with its output circuit tuned to a particular harmonic of the input frequency.

An *overtone oscillator* uses a special

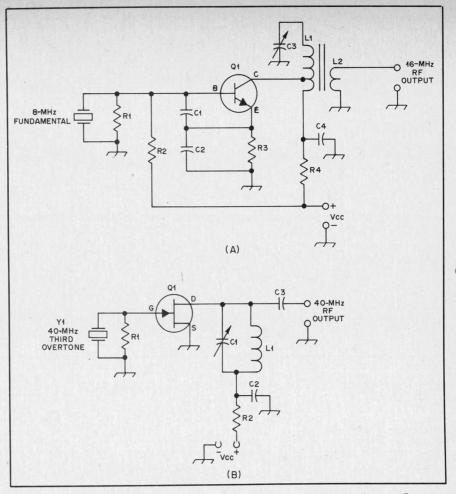

Fig. 6 — An example of a harmonic oscillator at A. An overtone oscillator is shown at B.

type of crystal called an *overtone crystal*. It is different in design from an ordinary fundamental type of crystal in that oscillations at certain odd harmonic frequencies are possible. This is brought about primarily through a different crystal cut than that used with a fundamental crystal. For example, a 36-MHz third-overtone crystal will oscillate at 36 MHz in a properly designed circuit. By proper design we mean a circuit that provides the correct amount of feed-

back at 36 MHz and a circuit that also has a tuned output network resonant at the overtone frequency (36 MHz in this case). Circuits that do not meet these requirements will not provide appreciable power output at the desired frequency. In an improperly designed circuit the crystal would oscillate at 12 MHz. Very little 36-MHz energy would be present at the output. Examples of harmonic and overtone oscillators can be seen in Fig. 6.

# Variable–Frequency Oscillator (VFO)

Thus far we have limited ourselves to a discussion of crystal-controlled, single-frequency oscillators. It should be fairly obvious that a handful (or even a sack full) of crystals will not give us complete coverage of any amateur band. For that reason it is desirable to replace the crystal with a continuously variable frequency-determining network. Remembering what we talked about a few pages back, the crystal equivalent circuit

is nothing more than a series or parallel resonant circuit. In a variable-frequency type of oscillator the crystal has been replaced with a discrete coil and capacitor. In most VFO circuits either the capacitance or inductance of the tuned circuit is made variable, thereby making the frequency of oscillation adjustable. It is difficult to obtain VFO frequency stability as good as that of a crystal. However, we can come reasonably close.

It may surprise you to know that the particular type of circuit used is less important than how you use it. There are three main areas of concern as far as VFO stability is concerned: instantaneous frequency change due to a change in supply voltage, a slow change in frequency (drift) caused by component heating, and a shift in frequency due to a change in oscillator load. A properly designed VFO can come very close to eliminating each of these problems. At this point we should discuss some design criteria for all VFO circuits regardless of the particular type.

## The Tank Circuit

The tuned circuit of an oscillator should have a high operating $Q$. For this reason the amplifying device, be it an FET, transistor or vacuum tube, should be lightly coupled to the tuned circuit so as not to load the network down and destroy the $Q$. Additionally, a large capacitance-to-inductance ratio is in most cases desirable.

High-$Q$ capacitors in the frequency determining portion of the circuit are essential. Capacitors using air for the dielectric are best for the variable-capacitor position. Fixed-value capacitors at frequency-determining positions should be polystyrene or silver mica, as these types exhibit better stability in the presence of rf current. Low-$Q$, disk ceramic types should be avoided at these positions in the circuit. Disk ceramic types are entirely suitable for bypass applications or for drift compensations.

Like the capacitors, the coils must also be of high $Q$. Additionally, they must be mechanically stable. Most capacitors, because of their inherent makeup, exhibit no mechanical stability problems under normal conditions. As good a coil is not quite as easy to find. Those most suitable for use in a VFO circuit will be wound with fairly heavy gauge wire on a low-loss form. Air-wound coils (some use plastic strips for support) have lower losses than any of the form-mounted coils. They are more susceptible to mechanical vibration, though, and must be mounted carefully on that account. Toroidal coils wound on ferrite cores are better and are almost immune to such vibration effects when coated with $Q$ dope. Changes in core characteristics are quite pronounced as the ambient temperature varies. Good results can be obtained with powdered-iron toroids, but they are best suited to environments where the room temperature is relatively constant. If the coil must be adjustable, either to set the VFO to the proper frequency range or to perform the actual tuning of the oscillator, it should be tight wound on a slug-tuned ceramic form. The form should have a tight fitting slug so that it won't rattle in the presence of vibration, or move with heating.

Actually, protecting the circuit against mechanical vibration and heating effects may be even more important than extreme attention to reducing the electrical losses. Mechanical vibration of any kind will cause minute changes in the electrical constants of the components. This would cause the frequency to be modulated accordingly. If the hum from a power transformer vibrates the coil or capacitor, the output from the oscillator may sound as though it came from a poorly filtered power supply. Or, if the table on which the oscillator is sitting happens to get a bump, the frequency may be "wobulated" in a rather annoying fashion. We can reduce effects of this sort through rigid construction and by isolating the oscillator from sources of vibration.

## Heating Effects

Heat, or rather a change in temperature, is another factor that will influence the stability of a VFO. This was a particular problem during the vacuum-tube equipment era because tubes, no matter what type, get hot. As a change in temperature causes a change in the value of components, it was necessary to keep the frequency-determining components as far away from the heat-producing tube as possible. This is only one type of heating — let's call it "direct heating." Another form of heating caused by rf circulating currents, is within the components themselves. To minimize these effects temperature-stable components must be used.

With transistor and FET oscillators direct heating of other components is not usually a problem since these devices run relatively cool. It is not necessary to keep the tuned circuits far removed from the active device. Instead, they can be mounted in close proximity, on the same circuit board for example. One heating problem that does exist is within the FET, transistor or tube itself. As all amplifiers must dissipate some amount of power, so must all oscillators. Power dissipation is in the form of heat. This problem can be reduced by keeping the power input to the device low; however, the problem cannot be completely eliminated. Heating of this sort causes small changes in capacitance inside the device. Since these capacitances are unavoidably a part of the oscillator circuit, the frequency will shift accordingly. The heating-up process is fairly slow, so the frequency drifts — maybe for only minutes, if conditions are favorable, but more likely for a longer period of time.

One of the best ways to combat the effect of heating is to make the device "see" a large value of shunt capacitance in the tuned circuit. The bigger these shunt capacitances, the smaller the percentage change in circuit capacitances when the device heats up. This is because the internal changes are a function of the actual temperature and thus are the same (for the same power input) regardless of the circuit constants.

Frequency drift is hard to stop if the oscillator is being continuously turned on and off during receive and transmit

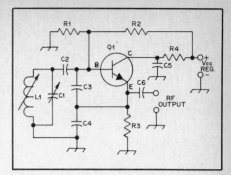

Fig. 7 — Here is a circuit of a Colpitts variable-frequency oscillator. Rf output is removed from the emitter connection.

conditions. The ideal situation would be for the oscillator to run continuously for the entire operating period and shut off when the station is closed down for the day. Although we have painted a somewhat bleak picture of VFO stability, through modern design techniques it is possible to obtain VFO frequency stability almost as good as that of a crystal. Many commercial and home-made pieces of equipment have "rock solid" VFOs.

## VFO Circuits

A *Colpitts* VFO is shown in Fig. 7. Note the similarity between this VFO and the Colpitts crystal oscillator we looked at earlier. The circuits are almost identical except that the crystal has been replaced with a tuned circuit. Variable capacitor C1 tunes the oscillator to the desired frequency. L1 may be made adjustable in a practical circuit so that it can be used to set the VFO exactly on the lowest frequency of the range the oscillator is to cover. This would be done with the tuning-capacitor plates fully meshed. As in the crystal circuit, R1 and R2 are biasing resistors and C2 is a dc blocking capacitor. If C2 had not been included, the low dc resistance of the tank coil would place the base of Q1 at dc ground potential. This would short the base bias to ground — something we do not want in this circuit. All other components function in the same manner as that of the Colpitts crystal oscillator.

Another type of VFO, a *Hartley*, is illustrated in Fig. 8A. This type of oscillator can be distinguished from most other types because it uses a tapped coil. The feedback path, though it may be somewhat obscure in this example, is from the drain, through C3 back to the bottom of L1. C2 and C4 are coupling capacitors and R1 establishes the correct amount of base bias. The circuit is sometimes seen as in Fig. 8B in which the feedback circuit is a bit more obvious. Operation is exactly the same; however, this arrangement does

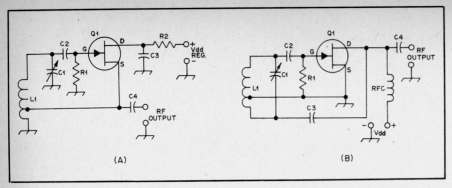

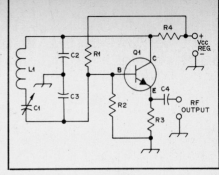

Fig. 8 — Shown at A is an FET version of the Hartley oscillator. Note that tuning capacitor C1 is grounded. At B is the same circuit not making use of a common-ground connection.

Fig. 9 — Here is the Clapp VFO. The frequency-determining components, C1 and L1, are connected in series in this configuration.

not allow for the bottom of C1 to be grounded. This is usually desirable because it simplifies the mounting of most variable capacitors and can aid the mechanical stability.

A *Clapp* oscillator is shown in Fig. 9. We can see through close analysis that it is actually a version of the Colpitts oscillator. In this circuit fixed-value capacitors are used for C2 and C3 and an additional capacitor is used in series with the inductive branch to adjust the frequency of oscillation. Feedback still depends on the relative values of C2 and C3. Since these capacitors are made much larger in value than C1, the frequency of the tank circuit is essentially dependent on L1 and C1. The large value of these capacitors tends to mask changes of capacitances within the device.

All of the oscillator circuits we have discussed thus far can be built around a transistor, FET or vacuum tube, not just those shown in a particular diagram. Circuit modifications are necessary with each different device used, which we would expect, since each device has its own operating parameters and characteristics.

### Oscillator Loading

It's possible to ruin the stability of a good oscillator by the way you remove power from it. No matter how you couple to the oscillator, be it a link or small-value capacitor, or no matter how lightly you couple to the oscillator, the mere fact that you are removing power from the oscillator will affect its frequency stability. Any variation in the load will change the frequency of oscillation to a degree which is dependent on the tightness of the coupling, as well as the load itself.

It's fairly obvious that the load on the oscillator should be as light and as constant as possible. This can be accomplished through the use of a *buffer amplifier* between the VFO and the remainder of the circuitry. The ideal buffer is one that operates with very little driving power and offers good isolation between the input and output. Not all devices make excellent buffers. FETs and vacuum tubes have an edge over transistors in this regard because of their high input impedance and low interelectrode effects. Bipolar transistors typically have low input impedances and rather high interelectrode capacitances.

The buffer amplifier would provide maximum output if its drain, collector or plate circuit were tuned. Unfortunately, even in the best of buffer amplifiers tuning the output circuit through resonance would affect the input of the device (cause a phase shift) and ultimately the oscillator frequency stability. To eliminate this problem, most buffers use an untuned output circuit.

Dc voltage is supplied to the circuit through an rf choke or resistor. Although the buffer efficiency is reduced, oscillator stability is enhanced. If more power output is required, an additional buffer stage can be used. Actually, the use of two buffer stages after the oscillator is common practice in many pieces of commercial and homemade equipment.

A two-stage buffer amplifier is shown in Fig. 10. It is suitable for use after almost any VFO. Q1, a junction FET, presents a high-impedance load to the VFO. R1 is typically 100 k$\Omega$ or more. Signal energy is removed from the source of Q1 and fed to a bipolar output stage. Q1 produces no voltage gain in the source-follower configuration, but does offer a fair degree of isolation between the input and output. C2 couples energy to Q2, and Q2 supplies a small amount of gain. The output is taken from the collector through C3.

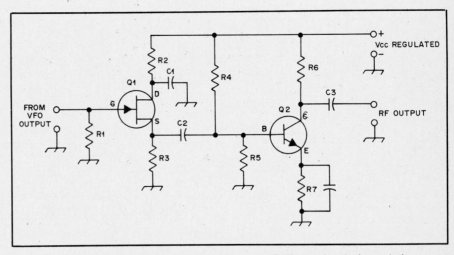

Fig. 10 — Illustrated here is a two-stage VFO buffer. An FET is used as the input device because of its high-input impedance characterisitcs.

# Power Amplification

In a simple transmitter it is likely that a series of power-amplifier stages will follow the oscillator circuit. They boost the power from the relatively low-level oscillator up to some higher level. The final output power may be a few milliwatts, or watts, or even a few hundred watts. Each amplifier stage is basically the same as any other. The more power we want, the larger the voltages and currents, and therefore the larger the tube and associated components. Though the fine details of each circuit will differ, the basic idea still remains — that of amplifying a signal to obtain greater output.

## Efficiency and Dissipation

Efficiency and dissipation are important factors in amplifier design. Efficiency can be expressed as the ratio of two powers. The first is the useful power output of the device and the second is the power input that produced the output. The equation looks like this.

$$\text{Eff. (in percent)} = \frac{\text{power output}}{\text{power input}} \times 100$$

For example, say we have an amplifier that is operating at the 80-watt input level and the useful power output is 50 watts. Efficiency, according to the formula, is 62.5 percent. The difference between the 80 watts of input and the 50 watts of output power is lost or dissipated in the amplifying device. If the device happens to be a vacuum tube with a rated plate dissipation of 30 watts, all is well and good. If the device is of the solid-state variety, transistor or power FET, you might be in trouble! It is common practice to design solid-state amplifiers well within their rated power-dissipation factors. The reason for this is that many solid-state devices can not handle overloads without suffering damage. Tubes are not quite so critical, and can usually take temporary overloads without sustaining permanent damage.

For an example, let us assume that we are using a transistor with a collector-dissipation rating of 30 watts. A conservative rule of thumb suggests that a factor of 1-1/2 to 2 be used when determining the maximum safe dissipation for most solid-state devices. This means that a device rated for 30 watts would be used in a circuit requiring 15 to 20 watts of collector dissipation. In our example we need a 30-watt dissipation device. There are two ways to solve our problem — either replace the device with one that has a higher rating or lower the power dissipation so that it will be within the safe operating range of the existing device. For the sake of working through the example let's take the second route.

There are two ways that we can lower the power that the device must dissipate. One way would be to keep the same amount of input power but raise the efficiency so that the dissipation would be only, say, 15 watts. Working back through the efficiency equation, we find that in order for the device to dissipate only 15 watts, the efficiency would have to be raised to approximately 80 percent. This high an efficiency could only be obtained if the amplifier were running Class C. Even then 80 percent efficiency is difficult, at best, to attain.

The other method would be to keep the same efficiency and reduce the input power. This will automatically reduce the amount of power the device is called upon to dissipate. If the input power is reduced to 40 watts and the efficiency remains at 62.5 percent, the amount of power to be dissipated would be lowered to 15 watts. This level is acceptable with the device we are using. Needless to say, one should use a device within its ratings. Once a solid-state device or vacuum tube is ruined, there is no way the user can repair it.

## Device Load

For reasonably efficient operation the amplifying device must have the proper collector, drain or plate-load resistance. The value of the load is dependent on several factors including the voltages and currents used and the class of operation. One equation is generally used to calculate the load resistance for a transistor. The equation is not dependent on the class of operation. It looks like this

$$R_L = \frac{V_{CC}^2}{2P_O}$$

where $V_{CC}$ is the collector voltage and $P_O$ is the power output required from the stage. This formula provides us with a close approximation of the load resistance.

When calculating the load resistance for a vacuum tube, the class of operation must be taken into account. The following formulas are expressed for each class of operation

Class A tube:

$$R_L = \frac{\text{plate volts}}{1.3 \times \text{plate current}}$$

Class B tube:

$$R_L = \frac{\text{plate volts}}{1.57 \times \text{plate current}}$$

Class C tube:

$$R_L = \frac{\text{plate volts}}{2 \times \text{plate current}}$$

where plate volts is the dc plate potential and plate current is the plate current under key-down conditions.

A transistor stage operating at low supply voltage (12 volts) and operating at the several-watt level will have a collector impedance of something less than 50 ohms. Conversely, a vacuum tube operating at the high power level, with a high-voltage potential (200 volts) applied to the plate, will have a plate impedance on the order of 10,000 ohms.

It has become common practice to design transmitters to operate into 50- and 75-ohm load impedances. The final transistor in a transmitter running at least several watts of power must have a collector network that will transform its low collector impedance up to 50 to 75 ohms. This would be a step-up network or transformer looking at it from the collector side. The final tube in a transmitter would require just the opposite, since its plate impedance is going to be much larger than 50 or 75 ohms.

Several types of impedance-matching networks suitable for use with transistor circuits are shown in Fig. 11. At A, a broadband 4 to 1 transformer (T1) is used to elevate the collector impedance of an output stage. When properly designed, this type of transformer is capable of providing a step-up or step-down impedance transformation of four over a wide range of frequencies. The double pi-section filter after the transformer acts as a low-pass filter, attenuating harmonic energy that appears at the output of Q1. We can think of the double pi section as two separate sections joined together at C4 as shown in the inset drawing. C4 is actually a combination of two capacitances — that which is required for the first portion of the filter (C3/L1) and that which is required by the second part of the filter (L2/C5). Let's assume that the collector impedance is 12.5 ohms. The 1 to 4 transformer would elevate this value of resistance to 50 ohms. The filter would be designed for an input and output impedance of 50 ohms.

The filter used in the example above can be used to transform impedance levels. For an example, let's say that the collector impedance in the circuit we just discussed is changed to 10 ohms. The 1 to 4 transformer would step this value up to 40 ohms. In this case the filter network can be designed for a 40-ohm input impedance and a 50-ohm output impedance. You might ask why not just design a filter network to go directly from the 10-ohm collector impedance to the 50-ohm antenna impedance level, and eliminate the broadband transformer. The reason that we don't do this is that a transformation as large as this and to such a low impedance will require component values that are very awkard — either very large or very small. It is much more practical to include a step-up transformer between the collector and the filter.

A slightly different system is shown at Fig. 11B. In this example a broadband transformer not necessarily of the 4 to 1 variety is used. A transformer of this sort can be designed for almost any impedance ratio. This ratio is determined by the number of turns of wire used for the primary and secondary. For this example let's assume that the collector impedance is 5.6 ohms. An impedance step-up of 9 is needed to step up the collector impedance to 50 ohms (50/5.6 = 9). In a transformer, the impedance ratio is the square of the turns ratio. Shown mathematically

$$(N \text{ ratio})^2 = R \text{ ratio}$$
or
$$N \text{ ratio} = \sqrt{R \text{ ratio}}$$

where N ratio is the wire turns ratio and R ratio is the impedance ratio. In the example above we know the required impedance ratio, but need to know the proper turns ratio. Substituting the

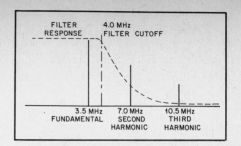

impedance ratio in the second equation we find that the turns ratio we need is 3. A transformer with these characteristics is shown in the diagram. A 50-ohm input and output harmonic filter is used between the transformer and the antenna connection. Broadband transformers of the types that we have just discussed are good for several bands of operation, 80 through 10 meters, for example. The filter networks used after the transformers are not. The filter cutoff frequency, the highest frequency that will pass unattenuated, is designed for a frequency just above the highest frequency in the particular band being used. A filter designed for use with a transmitter operating on the 80-meter band (3.5 to 4.0 MHz) may have a cutoff frequency of 4.5 MHz. The second harmonic of 3.5 MHz is 7.0 MHz. This frequency would be attenuated by the filter. A drawing of the fundamental, harmonics and frequency response of the filter is shown in Fig. 12. It should be obvious that additional filters will be required for each higher band of operation. If the same filter were used for 40 meters little or no energy would reach the antenna!

A T network is shown in Fig. 11C. Component values are calculated to provide the proper impedance transformation from collector to output terminal. This network has a low-pass response so a harmonic filter is not required. Assuming the collector impedance is not extremely low, this network can be used directly between the collector circuit and the antenna without the aid of a transformer.

An example of link coupling is shown in Fig. 11D. The impedance step-up or step-down ratio is again determined by the primary and secondary turns ratio. C1 tunes the primary of the transformer to resonance at the operating frequency.

Illustrated in Fig. 13 is a tube amplifier stage with its associated output matching network. This network is called a pi network and performs the task of impedance matching and at the same time provides a low-pass frequency response. It is perhaps the most popular

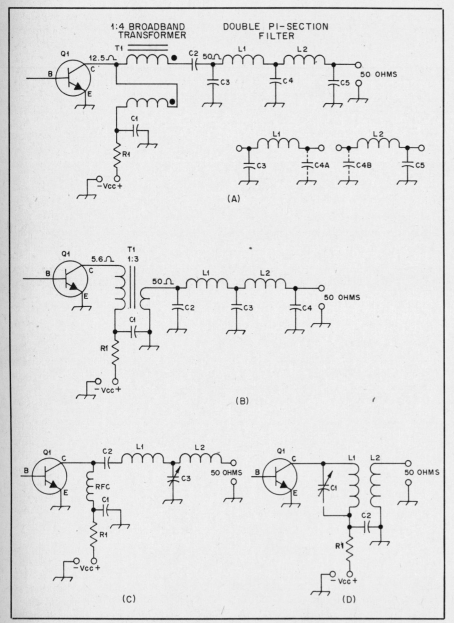

Fig. 11 — The method of impedance matching shown at A makes use of a 4 to 1 broadband transformer. The inset drawing illustrates how two single pi sections are connected together. The circuit at B uses a broadband transformer not of the 4 to 1 variety. A low-pass T network is shown at C. Link coupling is illustrated at D.

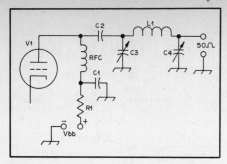

Fig. 13 — Illustrated is the popular pi network as used with a vacuum-tube amplifier. For multiband operation L1 is tapped with the proper amount of inductance selected by the band switch.

matching method used in tube type transmitters because band switching can be accomplished easily by using a tapped coil for L1. C3 and C4 are air variable capacitors and are made large enough in value to cover the lowest frequency of operation. An equivalent circuit is shown in Fig. 14 to make it a bit easier to visualize circuit operation. C1 and C2 can be considered in series across L1. These three components form a tuned circuit that should always be adjusted for resonance at the operating frequency. The amount of coupling to the load is dependent on the ratio of C1 to C2. As C2 is made smaller in value (C1 is made larger to retain resonance), the coupling to the load is greater as more current will flow through the load. Conversely, as C2 is made larger (C1 is made smaller to retain resonance), the coupling to the load is less and a smaller amount of current will flow through the load. Both capacitors will have an effect on the tuning of the amplifier. Each time either capacitor is adjusted, the other must be tuned to keep the circuit at resonance.

Most of the impedance-matching devices that we have looked at can be used with solid-state devices or vacuum tubes. It's a matter of which is best suited for each particular circuit. A network that works fine with a vacuum tube may not be usable with a solid-state circuit because the component values may be prohibitively high or low.

## Class of Operation

We've said nothing up to this point as to which class of operation should be used for cw transmission. Actually, any Class A, AB, B or C can be used. Cw transmission does not require the use of linear amplifier stages. Class A is seldom used because of its low efficiency. AB and B are more popular, but Class C offers the best efficiency.

In Class C operation the collector or plate current flows in relatively short pulses, not like the input which is a sine wave. The output tank circuit is responsible for turning these pulses back

into a single-frequency sine-wave signal. Making the collector or plate current flow in this manner will give us a large amount of output, compared to the dc input. Class B would be the next logical choice for cw operation after Class C. In B, collector current flows for nearly 180 degrees, or one half of the input cycle. Good efficiency can be obtained with this class operation, but it won't be as high as Class C.

## Tank-Circuit Considerations

As we just mentioned, with Class C operation collector or plate current flows in pulses that are short compared to a complete rf cycle. The collector or plate current bears no resemblance to a sine wave. This means that the signal is rich in harmonic energy since the only waveform that contains a single frequency is a sine wave. Steps must be taken to remove these harmonics so that they won't interfere with other amateur or commercial frequencies. There are several ways of accomplishing this: The most common is through the use of a selective circuit placed in the collector or plate lead.

The selectivity of this tuned circuit depends on the $Q$ of the circuit. If the circuit is handling an appreciable amount of power, the $Q$ of the circuit is determined more by the loading than by the resistance of the coil itself. In other words, the operating loaded $Q$ ($Q_L$) is the $Q$ that counts, not the $Q$ of the coil alone. The tuned circuit is shunted by the load resistance that the transistor or tube sees. In most cases the operating $Q$ is low in comparison to the $Q$ of the coil.

In practice the operating $Q$ of the circuit is determined by two things. The first is the ratio of the collector or plate voltage, current or power, this being closely related to the load impedance for the device. The second is the amount of output capacitance across the device. For a given voltage/power or voltage/current relationship, the larger the capacitance the higher the $Q$. Tank $Q$s on the order of 10 to 12 are sufficient for reducing harmonics to an acceptable level. This 10 to 12 figure applies to resonant tuned circuits. Circuits such as the half-wave low-pass filter (nonresonant) function with $Q$ values as low as one and still provide adequate harmonic rejection.

## Flywheel Effects

The tank circuit of an amplifier has often been compared to the flywheel on an engine. Both the tank circuit and the flywheel are driven by short, regularly timed bursts of energy from the primary source of power. The flywheel converts the pulsating mechanical power into a smooth rotating motion. It does this by storing up energy (in inertia) during the

power bursts, and releasing it uniformly during the in-between periods. The heavier it is the greater the energy storage and the smoother the resulting motion. A heavy flywheel has high $Q$.

The same is true with the tank circuit. It stores electrical energy during the bursts of collector and plate current and releases it uniformly during periods when the current is cut off. (The stored energy is represented by rf currents circulating around the tank formed by the coil and capacitor.) The result is a smooth output that can be expressed as a single frequency, just as the power from the flywheel can be expressed in terms of so many smooth rotations per minute.

## Neutralization

A certain amount of capacitance exists in any active device between the output and input circuits. In the bipolar transistor it is the capacitance between the collector and the base. In an FET it's the capacitance between the drain and gate. In vacuum tubes it is the capacitance between the plate and grid circuit. We have assumed thus far that this capacitance has little effect on the amplifier operation. In fact, it doesn't at the lower frequencies, however, at the higher hf frequencies, and above, the capacitive reactance may be low enough to cause complications. Oscillations can occur when some of the output signal is fed back in such a phase so as to add to the input (positive feedback). As the output voltage increases so will the feedback voltage: The circuit adds fuel to its own fire and the amplifier is now a self-fed oscillator. The output signal is no longer dependent on the input signal, and the circuit is useless as an amplifier. In order to rid the amplifier of this positive feedback, it is necessary to provide a second feedback path (negative feedback). This path should supply equal and opposite voltage to that causing the oscillation.

One neutralization technique is

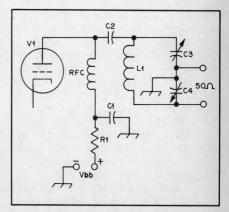

Fig. 14 — Here is the pi network redrawn. C3 and C4 are actually in series across L1.

shown in Fig. 15. In this circuit the supply voltage is fed to a tap on the tank coil. The power supply is bypassed so it is at rf ground. At an instant when the top of the coil is positive with respect to ground, the bottom of the coil must be negative with respect to ground. The feedback path is through $C_{FB}$ which feeds the base a signal that is oppsite that being fed back through $C_{CB}$.

## Parasitic Oscillations

Oscillations can occur in an amplifier on frequencies that have no relation to those intended to be amplified. Oscillations of this sort are called "parasitics" mainly because they absorb power from the circuits in which they occur. Parasitics are brought on by resonances which exist in either the input or output circuits. They can occur below the operating frequency which is usually the result of an improper choice of rf chokes and bypass capacitors. High-$Q$ rf chokes should be avoided as they are most likely to cause a problem.

Parasitics are more likely to occur above the operating frequency as a result of stray capacitance and lead inductances along with interelectrode capacitances. In some cases it is possible to eliminate such oscillations by changing lead lengths or the position of leads so as to change the capacitance and inductance values. Another effective method is to insert a parallel-resistor/small-coil combination in series with the grid or plate lead. The coil serves to couple the vhf energy to the resistor and the value of the resistor is chosen so that it loads the vhf circuit so heavily that the oscillation is prevented. Values for the coil and resistor have to be found experimentally as each different layout will probably require different suppressor networks.

## Transmitter Controls

A simple cw transmitter control panel is shown in Fig. 16. Although the one that you own may not look exactly like this one, it probably has many of the same controls. Before we discuss how to actually tune the transmitter, let's take a look at what each of the controls does.

The band switch selects the tuned circuits for the various stages in the transmitter. Each band switch position selects the proper amount of $L$ and $C$ so that each transmitter circuit can be tuned to the frequency of operation. The tuning and loading controls are associated with the final output stage. These are the two variable capacitors in the output pi network. The tuning control is the capacitor connected from the collector or plate of the amplifying device to ground. The loading control will be the variable capacitor connected

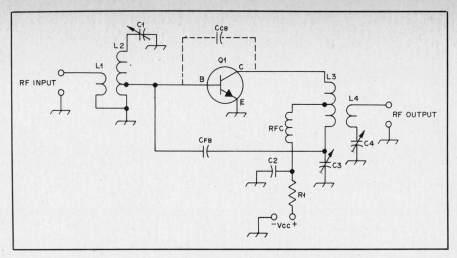

Fig. 15 — This drawing shows one method of neutralizing an amplifier. $C_{CB}$ is the feedback path within the transistor and $C_{FB}$ is the feedback path used to oppose the internal path.

across the output.

If your transmitter has a control labelled DRIVE TUNE it more than likely adjusts a variable element in the tuned circuits of the low-level stages. After the exact frequency of operation has been selected, either by the crystal frequency or by the setting of the VFO, it is adjusted for maximum permissible drive to the final. This ensures that all of the stages ahead of the final are tuned to resonance and maximum power is fed to the output stage. A DRIVE LEVEL control is used to adjust the amount of power that is fed to the output stage for amplification. Since in most transmitters it is possible to overdrive the output stage (most transmitters have a surplus of drive available), this control should be set for the proper amount of drive in accordance with the tube or equipment manufacturer's specifications. Nothing is gained by overdriving an amplifier stage. The output device may be driven beyond its ratings, in which case shortened device life or destruction may occur. Chances are that increased amounts of harmonic energy and other spurious undesired output will be transmitted along with the main signal. This will increase the chances of interference to other radio services and increase the possibility of television interference. The best motto is to keep the signal clean and this can only be done by running the amplifying devices within their specifications.

Meters and what they measure will vary from transmitter to transmitter. Whatever the meter is wired to measure one thing is strived for — proper tuning of the final amplifier. This is because the output stage is normally the one running the highest power. We saw earlier that if an amplifier is not running properly, the efficiency will decrease and the power "lost" will be dissipated within the amplifying device. The meter

may have a VOLTS position which would indicate the supply voltage to the output stage. There may also be a position for CURRENT which would be a measure of the amount of current drawn by the final stage. Additionally there may or may not be a position for RELATIVE RF OUTPUT. This position is helpful for tuning the output stage by adjusting the tuning and loading controls for a maximum reading on the meter. If the transmitter is of the vacuum-tube variety it might have a GRID CURRENT position. The drive tune and drive level controls are adjusted for a specified amount of current according to the manufacturer's suggestions.

If a crystal is to be used as the frequency-determining device, it should be plugged into the socket marked crystal. In some transmitters a VFO may be plugged directly into this socket; some others have a separate jack for this purpose. A hand key, semiautomatic bug or electronic keyer should be plugged into the socket marked key.

The FUNCTION switch in most

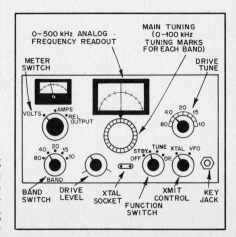

Fig. 16 — Typical controls that are found on most simple transmitters.

transmitters will have at least several positions. The OFF position should remove all power from the transmitter. STANDBY position places the transmitter in a standby mode. Some or all of the operating voltages are removed from the active devices. TUNE position allows the operator to make preliminary adjustments of the transmitter at reduced power levels. The OPERATE position allows the transmitter to function in a normal fashion.

## Tuning Procedure

If you own a commercial piece of transmitting equipment, it is always best to follow the manufacturer's instructions on how to tune the transmitter. The outline given here is a general one at best, but, will give you an idea of how it's done.

It is a good idea to operate the transmitter into a dummy load while learning the ropes of transmitter tuning. The best dummy load is a high-power noninductive resistor submerged in an oil bath. The value of resistance used is normally 50 ohms, the same as the output impedance of most transmitters. If this type is not available, a substitute can be made from an ordinary light bulb with a wattage rating approximately the same as that of the power output expected from the transmitter. See chapter 10. Turn the function to the standby position. If the transmitter is all solid state, it will not require a warm-up period. If it is of the vacuum-tube variety, a warm-up period of a minute or so should be sufficient. The band switch must be placed in the proper position for the intended band of operation.

Place the meter switch in the GRID position (RELATIVE OUTPUT if your transmitter has no grid-switch position), turn the function switch to tune and key the transmitter. With the drive level advanced to the approximate midrotation position, adjust the drive-tune control for a maximum reading. Let up on the key and place the meter in the CURRENT or PLATE position and turn the function switch to the operate position. With the loading control set for maximum capacitance, again key the transmitter and quickly adjust the tuning control for a dip in plate current. Advance the final-amplifier loading control an eighth turn or so and redip the final-amplifier with the tuning control. Continue this procedure until the transmitter is operating at the specified amount of current. If you are using a tube type of transmitter, it is advisable to check the grid current after this procedure as it has likely changed during tuning. It should be adjusted by means of the drive control to the manufacturer's specification. Never run the transmitter outside the ratings specified by the manufacturer!

# Chapter 4

# How Phone Transmitters Work

Most amateurs will think of single sideband or frequency modulation when they hear the words "phone transmission." These two forms of voice transmission are the most popular at present as far as amateur radio is concerned. This has not always been the case as not too many years ago amplitude modulation (a-m) was the order of the day. Just as the transistor has replaced the vacuum tube in most low-power applications, single sideband has all but eliminated amplitude modulation. Each form of voice transmission has its own characteristics and advantages, and as you might have guessed, disadvantages. In this chapter we'll examine the fine points of the various methods used for transmitting voice signals.

### The Voice Band

It is possibly easier to grasp the essence of modulation when it is put in terms of phone. You are aware of the fact that sound is a vibration in the air, a vibration usually made up of many frequencies lying within the range we call *audio frequencies*. The lower and upper limits of this range are not the same for all listeners; what you can hear depends on the condition of your hearing apparatus. The extremes are usually taken to be about 15 or 20 hertz at the low end and 15,000 to 16,000 hertz at the high end.

But long experience, backed by many tests, shows that a frequency range of about 200 to 3000 hertz will contain all the frequencies needed for making your voice understandable to a receiving operator. The actual range generated by a person talking may be much greater, but if those frequencies below about 200 and above about 3000 hertz are eliminated — filtered out — there is little, if any, loss in the speaker's ability to make himself understood. That is, voice *intelligibility* is high when the frequencies are kept within that range.

### Microphones

In phone transmission the first step is to translate the air vibrations into electrical vibrations having the same form. The device that does this is the familiar *microphone*.

Piezoelectric microphones make use of the phenomena by which certain materials produce a voltage by mechanical stress or distortion of the material. A diaphragm is coupled to a small bar of material such as Rochelle salt or ceramic made of barium titanate or lead zirconium titanate. The diaphragm motion is thus translated into electrical energy. Rochelle-salt crystals are susceptible to high temperatures, excessive moisture or extreme dryness.

Ceramic microphones are impervious

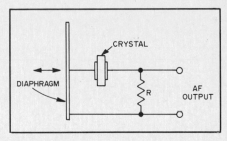

Fig. 1 — Representative circuit of a crystal microphone.

to temperature and humidity. The output level is adequate for most modern transmitters.

The crystal or ceramic microphone generates only a few hundredths of a volt. Because this voltage is effectively in series (internally) with a capacitance of around 0.03 $\mu$F, the frequency response depends on the load resistance, $R$, Fig. 1, into which the microphone works. A resistance of 1 to 5 megohms is generally used when a tube or FET follows the microphone. With bipolar transistors the load is necessarily low — a few thousand ohms — which means that the lower audio frequencies are attenuated. The amplifier must boost these frequencies if "flat" overall response is wanted.

# Amplitude Modulation

Although the use of *amplitude modulation* has steadily declined to the point where very few amateurs use this form of voice communications, it is worth studying as it will lay the groundwork for some of the more complex forms of voice transmission.

Amplitude modulation is perhaps the most basic method for inserting audio information on a carrier wave. In the previous chapter we learned how to generate a pure carrier wave (A1) on a given frequency in any of the amateur bands. This carrier wave contained no

audio information. The manner in which a message was transmitted consisted of turning the carrier on and off forming short dots and longer dashes to form letters and words. With amplitude modulation (a-m) the carrier is left on for the entire transmission. Audio in-

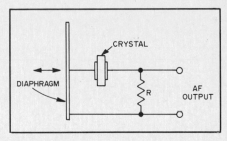

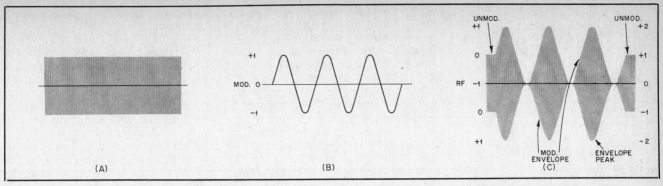

Fig. 2 — At A is the carrier waveform with no modulation. The audio-frequency waveform in the middle drawing is superimposed on an rf signal, as shown by the outline, or modulation envelope. Note that the modulation envelope is duplicated on the lower side of the rf axis.

This isn't really a separate envelope; it just looks that way because when the rf amplitude is changed, it changes symmetrically both above and below the zero axis. The positive and negative half cycles of rf have to be equal.

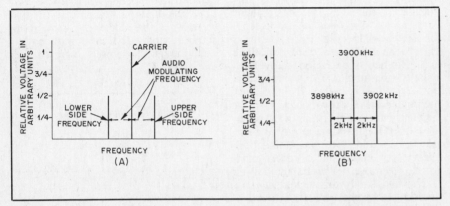

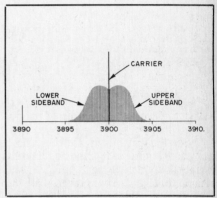

Fig. 3 — Shown at A is an example of a 100-percent modulated carrier waveform. At B is the 3900-kHz carrier and two side frequencies, 2 kHz removed from the carrier frequency.

Fig. 4 — Modulation with a band of audio frequencies sets up two sidebands, centered on the carrier frequency.

formation from the microphone, after amplification, is used to vary the amplitude of the *envelope* — thus the name amplitude modulation. A series of waveshapes are shown in Fig. 2 to help illustrate this point. At A is an unmodulated waveform, the type you would expect from an ordinary cw transmitter. It is a pure sine wave and therefore contains only one distinct frequency.

Let's assume that we want to modulate this rf wave with an audio-frequency sine wave. Normal speech is not a sine wave but rather a complex waveform made up of many frequencies. An audio sine wave can be closely approximated by whistling a single-frequency tone into the microphone. An audio sine wave is shown in Fig. 2B. In the amateur bands, the carrier frequency is thousands of times greater than the audio modulating frequency, so the carrier will go through a great many cycles during one cycle of even the highest audio frequency we want to transmit. We couldn't begin to draw in all the actual rf cycles because there would be far too many to be printed. We will have to keep in mind that there are many, many more rf cycles than audio for any given period of time. When the envelope is modulated or

controlled by the audio frequency, the resulting rf waveform looks like the one shown in Fig. 2C. As we can see, the rf carrier (A) is modulated with the audio sine wave (B) to form the new waveform at C.

**Modulation Sidebands**

It may not be obvious after examining the waveform of Fig. 2C that frequencies other than the rf carrier frequency are present. New frequencies are generated through the modulation process and are located above and below the carrier frequency. These new frequencies are called *side frequencies* (sidebands). A frequency generated above the carrier is called an *upper side frequency* and one below is called a *lower side frequency*. As we will see, when an rf carrier is modulated by a pure sine-wave tone, an upper and lower side frequency will be generated. Side frequencies are always generated in pairs symmetrically about the carrier frequency. They are sum and difference frequencies obtained by either adding the audio frequency to the carrier frequency or subtracting the audio from the carrier frequency. This can be illustrated as in Fig. 3.

To help visualize this, let's assign the

frequency 3900 kHz to the carrier and 2 kHz as the audio modulating frequency. As we can see in Fig. 3B two new frequencies, the upper and lower side frequencies, are generated at 3902 kHz and 3898 kHz (3900 kHz + 2 kHz and 3900 kHz − 2 kHz). Fig. 3B is representative of an a-m transmitter output with a sine wave used as the modulating source. As we said earlier, the human voice is made up of a number of different frequencies — not just one discrete frequency. Fig. 4 illustrates what the output of an a-m transmitter looks like if a human voice is used for the modulating source. A band of frequencies rather than one discrete frequency are present on each side of the carrier. If the highest frequency we let modulate the transmitter is 3 kHz, the upper and lower sidebands will extend 3 kHz above and below the carrier for a total signal bandwidth of 6 kHz.

**Modulation Percentage**

One of the things that it's easier to visualize by the carrier idea is *percentage of modulation*. In Fig. 5 the modulation has just the right value to make the carrier amplitude go to zero on the audio downswing and to twice its unmodulated value at the peak of the

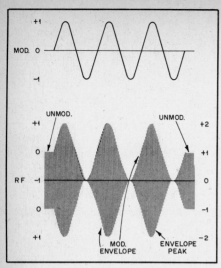

Fig. 5 — Here, the carrier is 100 percent modulated. This is shown by the fact that the envelope peak is exactly twice the unmodulated amplitude while the valley just reaches the zero level.

upswing. This is "100-percent" modulation.

Now look at Fig. 6. Here, we have the same carrier, but the modulating signal is only half as big as in Fig. 5. The rf amplitude goes down to one-half the unmodulated value on the downswing and up to 1.5 times the unmodulated value on the upswing. This is 50-percent modulation. The percent modulation is the ratio of the maximum swing of the modulation (either up or down) to the amplitude of the unmodulated carrier. With voice the modulation percentage is continually varying, because some sounds are loud and others are not, all within a word; also, everyone raises and lowers his voice volume within a sentence.

## Overmodulation

Can there be more than 100-percent modulation? Obviously, the rf output

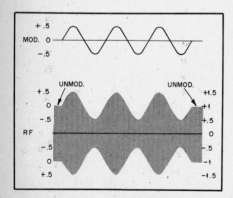

Fig. 6 — In this case the carrier is not fully modulated, as shown by the fact that the envelope peak is not twice the unmodulated-carrier amplitude while the "valley" in the envelope does not reach zero.

can't be reduced below zero. All we can do is make it *stay* at zero for a more-or-less long period of time. Fig. 7 illustrates this. There is a gap during which there is no output. This is bad. The outline of the rf signal — the *modulation envelope* — now differs considerably from the waveshape of the modulation. (In Figs. 5 and 6 the modulation envelopes were identical to the modulating signal.) One result of this is that the signal heard by the receiving operator isn't the same as what was intended to be transmitted. In other words, the modulation is distorted.

Worse, the bandwidth of the transmission has been made greater by this *overmodulation* in the downward direction. This doesn't show in the drawing, of course, because the drawing doesn't show the *frequency* aspects. A simple way of looking at it, however, is that because there is distortion there must be new modulation frequencies present — harmonics. You've been introduced to these in earlier chapters. Since harmonics are always *multiples* of the frequency from which they were generated, they are the same as *higher* audio frequencies added to the modulation. Higher frequencies mean greater bandwidth. Downward overmodulation increases the bandwidth beyond what is necessary — sometimes far beyond — and thus can lead to unwarranted interference with other stations.

You can modulate upward as far as your transmitter can go. Theoretically there is no limit. Practically, though, most transmitters can't go very far upward, and when they can't the peaks of modulation become *flattened*. The overall result, in its effect on the bandwidth, is just about the same as equivalent overmodulation downward.

## Power in Amplitude Modulation

The reason why most transmitters can't be modulated very far upward will become clear on examining what happens to the power in a modulated signal. Suppose that the transmitter output without modulation is 100 watts. What is it when the signal is modulated 100 percent as in Fig. 5? By inspection, you can see that the power will be zero at the bottom of the downswing. And since the amplitude at the peak of the upswing is twice the unmodulated amplitude, the power at this instant is *four times the unmodulated amplitude* or 400 watts. (Remember that amplitude refers to current or voltage; when the voltage doubles, the current also doubles in an ordinary circuit.) When the power is averaged over one or more cycles of the modulation frequency, a mathematical study will show that the power in a 100-percent modulated signal is 1.5 times the unmodulated power. Thus the 100 watts without modulation

increases to 150 watts with 100-percent modulation.

### Voice Power

The figure of 1.5 times is actually true only of single-tone modulation — that is, modulation by a sine wave. Voice waveforms are not sine waves. For the same *peak* amplitude as a sine wave, an average voice waveform will contain only about half as much power as the sine wave. It would be nearer the truth to say that with voice modulation the average power in a 100-percent modulated signal is about 1.25 times the unmodulated power. *But*, the power at the top of the envelope (called the *peak-envelope power*) of a 100-percent modulated signal is always four times the unmodulated power. Any two waveforms that have the same peak amplitude have the same peak power, even though the powers averaged over

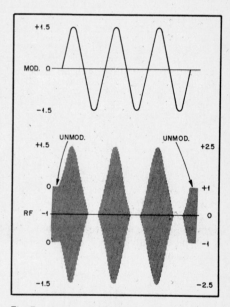

Fig. 7 — Attempting to modulate more than 100 percent gives a modulation envelope that is only a distorted reproduction of the original. It also leads to greater signal bandwidth and "splattering" into adjacent channels.

one complete cycle may differ widely. It is these peaks that we must be prepared to furnish during modulation.

The extra power in the modulated signal doesn't come out of nowhere. It has to be supplied somehow in the modulation process. The extra power required is proportional to the square of the modulation percentage. Thus the 50-percent modulated signal of Fig. 6 would have only one-fourth as much extra power as the 100-percent modulated one of Fig. 5. The latter, for the 100-watt unmodulated power in the example, required 50 extra watts when modulated; modulated as in Fig. 6, only 12.5 extra watts would be needed. On

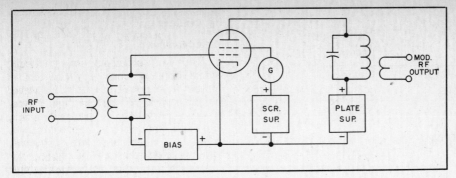

Fig. 8 — Stripped-down screen-modulator circuit.

the other hand, the overmodulated signal of Fig. 7 is hitting an up-peak that is 2.5 times the amplitude of the unmodulated signal. The peak power needed here is 2.5 squared, or 6.25, times the unmodulated power. Few transmitters are designed to have that much extra power capability!

All the message content of a signal is in the modulation. The higher the modulation percentage the more *talk power* we transmit to the receiving end. The goal is 100 percent — but without overshooting!

## Modulation Circuits

Since modulation is really a mixing process, any of the mixer or converter circuits we've studied could be used for generating a phone signal. Instead of introducing two *radio* frequencies into a mixer circuit we simply introduce one radio frequency (the carrier frequency) and the voice band of audio frequencies.

Mixer circuits used in receivers are designed to handle a small signal and a large local-oscillator voltage. This means that the percentage of modulation is low. In a transmitter we want to get as close as possible to 100-percent modulation, and we also want more power output. For these reasons modulator circuits differ in detail from receiving mixers, although much the same in principle.

## Screen Modulation

One method that is used in some low-power kit transmitters is *screen modulation*. The circuit shown in Fig. 8 is reduced to the bare essentials on purpose. You can easily get lost in the details of the various screen modulation circuits in use, and thus not be able to see the forest for the trees. The rf circuit is that of an ordinary rf power amplifier — any type so long as it uses a screen-grid tube. The difference is in the way the tube is *operated*.

If we had a perfect screen-grid tube the output amplitude (voltage or current to the load, not the power) would be perfectly proportional to the voltage

on the screen. If we should double the screen voltage, for example, the output amplitude also would double; if we reduced the screen voltage to zero the output would go to zero. This sort of operation is shown graphically in Fig. 9. The relative amplitude of the rf output voltage or current is shown along the lefthand scale. Up to the point marked A, the plot of amplitude versus screen voltage is a straight line, a fact that leads to calling such a characteristic *linear*. The corresponding power output, which varies with the square of the amplitude, is shown by the second curve.

## Flattening

In practice, the amplitude characteristic won't be a perfectly straight line. However, if the tube's operating conditions are properly chosen the characteristic will be reasonably linear. But if the screen voltage is increased too far, the line will start to bend over horizontally. In this region, to the right of A in the figure, the modulation will begin to be distorted. Therefore we have to operate in such a way that the screen voltage doesn't get into this flattening region. In the graph shown, this would mean that the screen voltage shouldn't go over 400 volts.

Now let's relate this to what we learned earlier about power in a modulated signal. If we are to modulate 100 percent, *point A represents the modulation up-peak*. It is *not* the unmodulated level. Without modulation, the amplitude can only be one-half the peak-envelope value, as shown in Fig. 5. So without modulation we have to reduce the dc screen voltage to point B on the graph, that is, to 200 volts. The power is now down to one-fourth of its peak value, which is where it should be.

Now if a source of audio-frequency power is connected in series with the dc screen supply as shown by generator *G* in Fig. 8, the audio voltage will add to the 200 volts dc on the screen. If the audio voltage has a peak value of 200 volts, it will swing the screen from B to A, back to B, then down to zero, and

back to B during each af cycle. This modulates the signal 100 percent, just like in Fig. 5.

## Carrier vs. Talk Power

But suppose we try to set the unmodulated amplitude somewhere between B and A — at point C, say — in order to fool ourselves into thinking we have a bigger signal. If we do, we can no longer modulate 100 percent, because we can't swing the screen voltage beyond A without flattening. At point C the dc voltage on the screen is 300, so we can swing up only 100 volts without going beyond the flattening point, A. This is only half the swing we had from point B, meaning that we have only half as much amplitude variation and only one-fourth the talk power. The *unmodulated* power has increased in the ratio of $(300)^2$ to $(200)^2$, or 9 to 4 — over twice as much. There is a bigger carrier, to be sure, but to get it we've had to sacrifice the thing we want — talk power.

## The Plate Meter

Unfortunately, talk power doesn't show on the transmitter meters. Usually, the meter reads the modulated amplifier plate current, which only gives an indication of dc input to the plate. Don't be misled by the meter; it has an innocent face but a lying tongue when it comes to modulation.

Actually, the dc input to a normally operated amplifier *doesn't change* when it is modulated. It stays just the same at any modulation percentage up to 100 if the *modulation characteristic* is linear. This is because the plate current swings

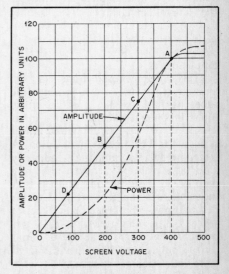

Fig. 9 — Idealized screen-modulation characteristic. This shows the relationship between screen voltage (which varies instantaneously with the voice signal), output rf voltage and current amplitude, and output power.

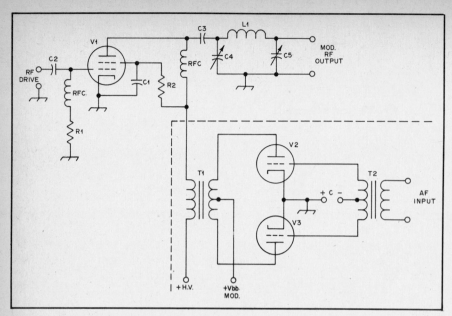

Fig. 10 — Plate modulation of a Class C rf amplifier.

down just as much as it swings up, during each audio cycle, so the *average* current doesn't change.

## Power

Look again at Fig. 9. Point A on this curve represents ordinary cw operation. Point B, half the cw screen voltage, is where we set the operating point for 100-percent modulation. Now at this point the output amplitude has dropped to one-half its cw value. Although the graph doesn't show plate current, the plate current also will drop to one-half its cw value. So the dc input also is cut in half, since the plate voltage remains the same. But the power *output* is only *one-fourth* the cw value. This means that the rf amplifier plate efficiency at the unmodulated-carrier level is only half what it was at the full cw level. The plate of the tube actually may have to dissipate more power at half the dc input.

This unhappy result limits us in the amount of power we can put into the tube. We have to take a licking on dc input in order to keep the tube in its socket while we get the peak power needed for 100-percent modulation. A screen-modulated amplifier can only work at a plate efficiency of 30 to 35 percent, in those periods which it isn't modulated. In round figures, 2/3 of the dc input power is burned up in the plate while 1/3 is converted into rf carrier output. This means that the dc input can be only about 1.5 times the rated plate dissipation of the tube.

One way or another, you pay a price for modulation. That extra power in a modulated signal has got to come from *somewhere*. In screen modulation — or

any system where the modulation is applied to a grid — the price is reduced efficiency, at the unmodulated-carrier level, in the rf amplifier.

In a moment we'll look at a system that doesn't penalize us in plate efficiency. First, however, there is something you need to know about the modulator.

## Modulator Power

As we saw earlier, the modulator must swing the screen voltage, at an audio rate, from zero to twice the dc voltage. The screen takes some current, although it is not large compared with the plate current. The dc source supplies the current that flows at the unmodulated level. As the af voltage swings the screen between zero and the peak voltage, the screen current will change more or less in proportion. This means that the power input to the screen varies when we modulate. On the average, the screen takes *more* power during modulation.

The difference in power between modulation and no modulation is mostly audio-frequency power superimposed on the dc power. It has to be supplied by the modulator tube. The amount is small and it can be supplied easily by a receiving-type tube. However, the screen isn't a good load for the modulator tube, because the screen current isn't exactly in proportion to the screen voltage. In other words, the load that the screen offers to the modulator isn't constant. This can cause distortion if the modulator tube isn't capable of supplying several times the power actually needed. A receiving power pentode or tetrode that can develop a couple of

watts without undue distortion is recommended.

## Plate Modulation

The low efficiency of grid-type modulation systems very drastically limits the rf power output that can be obtained with 100-percent modulation. If we could get the cw plate efficiency and still modulate 100-percent, we could get much more carrier output without going over the plate rating.

It can be done with a different system — plate modulation. This system, too, has its price — not in reduced output, but in demanding more audio power from the modulator. The 50-percent increase in power that is needed for 100-percent modulation can be added to the carrier power in the form of audio-frequency power. This means that the modulator has to deliver to the rf amplifier audio power equal to half the dc power input to that amplifier.

Such a modulator will cost more than a screen modulator, obviously. However, when you calculate the cost of getting the same rf output by both modulation methods you're likely to find that it's cheaper in the long run to use plate modulation.

In Fig. 10, the rf amplifier circuit is the same as in Fig. 8, with one exception. The screen voltage is taken from the rf amplifier high-voltage supply through a dropping resistor, and the audio-frequency power from the modulator now goes to *both* the plate and screen. The value of the dropping resistor is chosen so that the dc screen voltage is right for cw operation, or close to it. (Operating conditions are not entirely rigid, and any suitable values can be used so long as tube ratings are not exceeded.) In other words, the rf amplifier circuit itself, and the voltages and currents at which the tube operates, are about the same as those that would be used for cw. This gives us the highest possible rf output from the tube.

The modulator is the part shown below the dashed line. Don't take the circuit details too literally; they will vary with the type of tube used in the modulator, how the tubes are operated, and so on. However, plate modulators are always push-pull in any except flea-power transmitters; only the push-pull audio amplifier will give enough power output without excessive distortion.

## The Modulation Transformer

An important element in the plate-modulation system is the *modulation transformer*, T1. The modulator has to supply the af power to the rf tube at the right voltage for 100-percent modulation. The peak af voltage must be equal to the dc plate voltage on the rf stage.

The modulator tubes and their operating conditions determine the af power available for modulation, and the turns ratio of T1 determines the af voltage applied to the modulated amplifier plate — and also the screen, since the plate and screen are supplied from the same sources. However, you won't ordinarily find much mention of voltage in modulator discussions. The reason for this is that the modulator needs some specified load resistance into which it can deliver its power. This is given in the tube data as the plate-to-plate load resistance in push-pull operation. As you have seen earlier, the turns ratio of a transformer establishes an impedance ratio as well as a voltage ratio, so both ratios come out to the same thing in the end. In this case it is convenient to talk of the impedance ratio. The impedances we are dealing with actually are resistances.

## Modulating Impedance and Transformer Ratio

The modulating impedance or resistance of the plate-and-screen circuit of the rf tube is easily calculated — just divide the dc plate voltage by the sum of the dc plate and screen currents. For example, if a 6146 tube is operated at 600 volts with a plate current of 125 mA and a screen current of 10 mA, the total current is 135 mA (0.135 ampere) and the resistance is 600 divided by 0.135. This is 4450 ohms, close enough. The dc power input to the plate and screen is 600 times 0.135, or 81 watts, so we

need 40.5 watts of audio power for 100-percent modulation. The modulator tubes we choose might need a plate-to-plate load resistance of 9000 ohms in order to develop 40.5 watts of audio power. Then the primary-to-secondary impedance ratio of the modulation transformer would have to be 9000/4450, or slightly over 2 to 1. A ratio of 2 to 1 would be plenty close enough in practice, because the values aren't so critical that a difference of a few percent will matter.

The modulation transformer has to be able to handle the audio power, of course. In addition, the transformer has to be designed so that the dc plate and screen current can flow through its secondary winding without adversely affecting its operation.

It is always good practice to use a modulator that can generate a little more power than actually is needed for 100-percent modulation. Be generous, rather than skimpy, in your design. It pays off in lower distortion and a cleaner signal, as well as ensuring full modulation even if the transformer ratio isn't exactly right.

## Linear Amplifiers

Since the audio-frequency power needed for plate modulation is expensive, how about amplifying a phone signal *after* it has been modulated? Then the modulation could be done at a very low power level, where audio power is cheap.

It is perfectly possible to amplify a modulated signal. It's done all the time in receivers, for example, before the signal reaches the detector. The amplifier has to be one that will not distort the modulation envelope, which must be preserved in just the form that it had in the modulated stage. A Class B amplifier will do this.

Unfortunately, an amplifier that won't distort the modulation envelope — called a *linear amplifier* — has rather poor plate efficiency when amplifying an amplitude-modulated signal. Low distortion and high plate efficiency just don't go hand in hand in this case.

In fact, the linear amplifier has to operate in just about the same way as the screen-modulated amplifier. With the linear amplifier, the modulation envelope of the signal applied to the control grid has to swing up and down about the carrier level, to produce an amplified modulated signal in the plate circuit. In the screen modulator the audio voltage on the screen has to swing up and down about the carrier level to produce a modulated signal in the plate circuit. In both cases the plate efficiency at the unmodulated-carrier level is about 33 percent.

Whether you screen-modulate a tube or use it as a linear amplifier, you can run just the same input and get the same rf output. There is no power advantage one way or the other. Screen modulation is the preferable system because it is easier to adjust.

# Double– and Single–Sideband Transmission

At this point you might be asking yourself "Why double or single sideband? What's wrong with a-m? After all, it does get the intelligence through and isn't that all that matters?" To best answer these questions let's take a closer look at the a-m signal analyzing where the actual usable voice power is located.

## Carrier and Sideband Relationships in A-M

To keep things on a simple basis at first, assume that an ideal a-m transmitter has a carrier *output* of 100 watts. We know that when this carrier is modulated, sidebands are generated in proportion to the strength of the modulating signal (until we reach 100-percent modulation), and that the carrier strength itself is not affected *at all* by modulation. A plot of the frequency spectrum (voltage *versus* frequency) of the simple case of steady 100-percent modulation of the carrier by a single tone (sine wave) of 1000 cycles would look like Fig. 11. The envelope (a plot of voltage *versus* time) would, of course,

have the appearance of Fig. 12. All right, so far? We know that in a resistive circuit where the resistance stays constant the power is proportional to the square of the voltage applied. In the case we are talking about, three voltages are applied; one is the carrier, and the other two are the upper and lower sidebands, respectively, in accordance with Fig. 11.

The voltage of each of the sidebands is half that of the carrier. Therefore, the power in each sideband is $(1/2)^2$ times that of the carrier. Since it was assumed that the carrier output was 100 watts, the power in each sideband is 25 watts, and the *total* sideband is 50 watts. This, incidentally, is the maximum single-tone sideband power that can be generated by amplitude modulation of a carrier of 100 watts. No one has ever been able to do better, because it just isn't possible to do so. (It doesn't help to over-modulate! This *cuts down* the desired sideband power and generates spurious sidebands called splatter.)

We can represent the information in

Figs. 11 and 12 by means of a vector diagram. In Fig. 13 the carrier voltage is given one-unit length. Therefore, the upper- and lower- sideband voltages have one-half unit length, and are so indicated. Now, watch out for this one: In

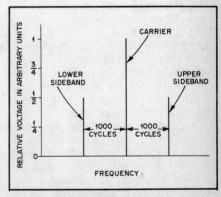

Fig. 11 — Example of 100-percent modulation of a carrier by a single tone of 1000 cycles per second.

Fig. 13 the carrier vector is assumed to be standing still, though actually it makes one revolution per cycle of carrier frequency. Imagine you are standing at the origin of the carrier vector and are spinning around with it at carrier frequency. What you would see are the upper and lower sideband vectors rotating in *opposite* directions at the modulation frequency in such a way that the terminus of the last vector in the chain of three lies along the line of the carrier, bobbing up and down at 1000 cycles per second. As far as you could tell, the carrier vector does not move or change at all, and that is the impression Fig. 13 is intended to convey. At the instant of time ($T_o$, Fig. 12) chosen for Fig. 13, the three vectors are all in line and add up to two voltage units. One two-thousandth of a second later the side-

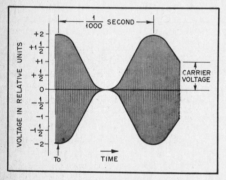

Fig. 12 — Envelope of carrier 100 percent modulated by a 1000-cycle sine wave.

band vectors have rotated one-half turn each, and the three vectors add to zero, since $1 - 1/2 - 1/2 = 0$. This should make it easier to understand the relationship between Figs. 11 and 12 without too much trouble.

Now, here is the point of all this: The carrier vector is one voltage unit long — corresponding to a power of 100 watts. At the instant of time shown in Fig. 13, the total voltage is two units — corresponding to $(2)^2$ times 100, or 400 watts. One two-thousandth of a second later, the answer is easy — the voltage and power are zero. Therefore, the transmitter *must* be capable of delivering 400 watts on peaks to have a carrier rating of 100 watts. Stated differently, the excitation, plate voltage and plate current must be such that the output stage can deliver this peak power. What about this? We are already up to 400 watts on a 100-watt transmitter! Yes, we are, and if the transmitter won't deliver that power we are certain to develop sideband splatter and distortion.

Under the very best conditions that

can be imagined we need a transmitter which can deliver 400 watts of power on peaks to transmit a carrier power of 100 watts and a total maximum sideband power of 50 watts. What does this 100-watt carrier do *for* the transmission? The answer is it does nothing — for the simple reason that it does not change at all when modulation is applied.

### Removing the Carrier

Suppose we remove the carrier and double the amplitude of each of our sidebands. This will still run our transmitter at its peak output capacity of 400 watts, all it can do. Well, the sideband power goes up all right. The sideband voltages are doubled, so our sideband power is four times what it used to be. That means each sideband is 100 watts, and our transmitter is not overloaded on peaks. The total sideband power is, of course, 200 watts. But this sideband power doesn't do much for us if it can't all be put to work. That is the situation with two sidebands and no carrier; the sideband power is in such a form that it doesn't lend itself readily to full utilization.

What if we remove one of the sidebands, too? If we do, we can increase the voltage on the remaining one to two units and run our transmitter at its maximum peak power output of 400 watts. This time it is *all* sideband power. It so happens that sideband energy in this form is usable. It is similar to cw and we can receive it in much the same way. All that is necessary is to set the BFO in our receiver so that it is at the same frequency as the carrier we removed.

We put out 400 usable watts with a transmitter that could put out only 50 usable watts in the form of amplitude modulation.

Expressed in decibels, the ratio of 400 watts to 50 watts (8:1) is 9 dB. But this isn't the complete story. The transmission covers only half the spectrum of the a-m transmission and isn't blowing a loud whistle in the middle of it all. This kind of 9-dB gain doesn't bother the other fellow as much as if it were obtained with antenna gain on a-m transmission.

### Transmitter Ratings

We might worry about the little 100-watt transmitter straining itself to put out 400 watts, for that is what we said we wanted it to do for a short percentage of the time. It might burn up if we kept that one sideband generated by the 1000-cycle tone pumping through it steadily. Fortunately, speech waveforms have a high ratio of peak to average power. It is average dissipated power that burns up tubes or transistors, so there is nothing to worry about

on this score until we can learn how to talk with waveforms having a much lower ratio of peak to average power. Actually, the steady 100-watt carrier of an a-m signal causes most of the dissipation in the 100-watt transmitter, but it was built to stand up under that kind of treatment.

While shrouded in theory, we were talking about *output* power and managed to show that we could get 400 watts of sideband power output with single sideband at the same peak power that gave only 50 watts of sideband power in the case of a-m. That's fine for comparison purposes on a theoretical basis, but there is the practical matter of efficiency to consider. Let's lean over backward and say that a *good* Class C plate-modulated amplifier such as the one in our ideal 100-watt a-m trans-

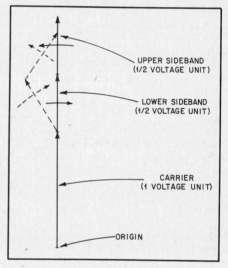

Fig. 13 — Vector diagram of 100-percent modulation of an a-m carrier at the instant (corresponding to $T_0$ in Fig. 12) when peak conditions exist. The broken vectors show the relationships of an instant when the modulating signal is somewhat below its peak.

mitter runs with an efficiency of 80 percent. Neglecting the fact that the total input under modulation with speech is somewhat higher than the carrier input (which is $100/0.08 = 125$ watts), the dissipation in the output stage is 25 watts. Let us say, however, that the modulation still drives the transmitter to its peak output power of 400 watts, but has very low average power. Therefore, the peak sideband power output is 50 watts, with very low average power. Here is a strange way of rating things, but it means something: The peak *useful* sideband power is 50 watts obtained with a final-stage dissipation of slightly over 25 watts in the a-m transmitter. The peak input power is, of course, $400/0.80 = 500$ watts, since the efficiency of 80 percent is pretty nearly constant with this type of operation. You have already guessed what the next thing is. The peak useful efficiency is

$$\frac{\text{peak useful power output}}{\text{peak input}}$$

or 50/500 = 10 percent. Who says high efficiency? This figure is not the true efficiency of the output stage — that's the assumed 80 percent — but it is the "communication" efficiency. The transmitter, of course, cannot tell the difference between carrier and sideband signals it deals with, so we must be satisfied with 10-percent "communication" efficiency as we have defined it. Now let's look at the single-sideband situation. The output stage must be a linear amplifier. This linear amplifier will have characteristics quite similar to Class B modulators used, for instance, in the little 100-watt plate-modulated a-m transmitter. Suppose we put into this transmitter the same speech waveform we used in the example above. This wave had a high peak-to-average power ratio, if you recall, and we were concerned only with conditions during the peak period. Things are adjusted so that the peak *output* is 400 watts in order to fall into our theoretical pattern. The theoretical maximum peak efficiency of a linear amplifier is 78.5 percent, but nobody ever got that much out of such an amplifier. However, with modern tubes we can get 70-percent peak efficiency quite comfortably, so let's use that figure in our calculations. All right, the peak power input is 400/0.70 = 572 watts, which, if sustained, would get some tubes mighty hot at 70-percent efficiency, if they could dissipate only 25 watts. This signal isn't sustained, however, for we assumed a speech input wave having a high peak-to-average power ratio, and it is average power that makes plates incandescent. Well, all of this 400-watt peak output is useful "communication" power, and it is obtained at 70-percent efficiency. Thus we can say that the "communication" ef-

ficiency of the final stage of this single-sideband transmitter is 70 percent.

All this does sound wonderful. What about dissipation in the final stage? If we neglect the average dissipation during modulation with our speech wave, then one might say that the total dissipation is close to zero. It certainly would be if we had vacuum tubes with linear $I_p$ vs. $E_p$ curves right down to cutoff. But there are plenty of tubes that make good linear amplifiers, and they do not have linear $I_p E_p$ curves at all. This generally means that the linear amplifier is operated in such a way that there is dc input even though there is no signal input. This dc input power, of course, heats the tubes when no signal is there, and represents most of the dissipation that the tubes are called upon to stand under conditions of speech modulation. In most cases good linearity is obtained when the no-signal input plate current is about 5 percent of the maximum-signal plate current. This means that the no-signal dissipation is about 5 percent of the maximum input power, since the dc input voltage is held constant. Therefore, the total dissipation would be something close to 572 X 0.05 = 28.6 watts.

That's close to the 25 watts which our a-m transmitter burned up in the plates of its tubes. You have guessed it again; the output stage of the single-sideband transmitter delivering 400 watts peak communication output can use the same tubes that are necessary in the 100-watt-carrier-output a-m transmitter which delivers 50 watts peak communication output.

The foregoing comparison isn't absolutely accurate, since the actual waveform of speech input is unknown. But it is a fair comparison, and experience and tests support the argument. That is what really proves the point.

### Generating the SSB Signal

There are at least two basic systems for generating an ssb signal. The two that we will concentrate on here are called the *filter* and *phasing* methods. Most every piece of present-day ssb equipment uses the filter method for ssb

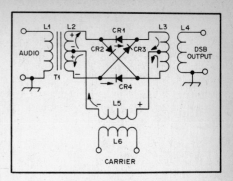

Fig. 15 — A diode-ring balanced modulator. Arrows indicate the direction of current flow with only the carrier applied and with the polarity shown across L5.

generation. One reason for this is that it requires no further adjustments once it is set for proper operation. Also, high-quality crystal or mechanical filters are readily available.

### The Filter Method

As we have learned, in order to have an ssb signal, we must remove the carrier and one of the sidebands from an ordinary a-m signal. The block diagram shown in Fig. 14 shows how it is done. The rf oscillator generates a carrier wave which is injected into the balanced modulator. Audio information, after it is amplified by the speech amplifier, is also applied to the modulator. It is the job of the balanced modulator to take these two inputs and supply as its output both sidebands minus the carrier. This meets the first requirement for the generation of an ssb signal — removal of the carrier.

Let's see how the balanced modulator accomplishes this. There are many different types of balanced modulators and it would be impossible to show them all here. One of the more popular types is illustrated in Fig. 15. This particular circuit is called a diode-ring balanced modulator. Audio information is coupled into the circuit through transformer T1. The carrier is injected through coils L5-L6 and the double-sideband suppressed-carrier output is taken through L3-L4. To better understand the circuit operation, let's first analyze the circuit with only the carrier applied. The polarity of voltage shown across L5 will cause current to flow in the direction indicated by the arrows. CR1 and CR4 will conduct. The current that flows through each half of L3 is equal and opposite causing a cancelling effect. Output at L4 will be zero. During the next half cycle, the polarity of voltage across L5 will reverse, CR2 and CR3 will conduct, and again the output at L4 will be zero.

Now, for a moment, let's remove the carrier signal and connect an audio

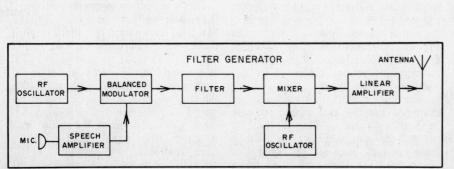

Fig. 14 — A basic system for generating a single-sideband suppressed carrier signal.

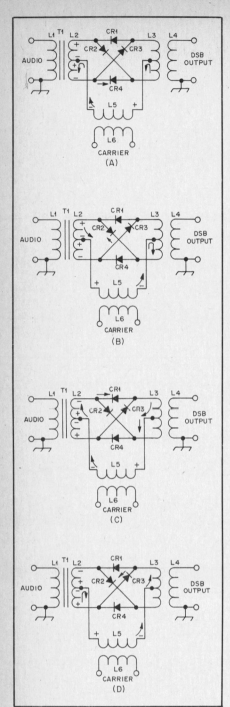

Fig. 16 — Shown here are the four possibilities of polarities of voltages of the modulating source and carrier. Arrows indicate the direction of maximum current flow.

source to the terminals marked audio. During one half of the audio cycle CR2 and CR4 will conduct and the output will be zero. On the other half cycle of the audio signal, CR1 and CR3 will conduct and again the output at L4 will be zero. We can see that if either the carrier or the audio is applied without the other, there will be no output.

Both signals must be applied if the circuit is to work as intended. In practice, the carrier level is made much larger than the audio input. Conduction of the diodes is, therefore, determined by the carrier. There are basically four conditions that can exist as far as the polarity of voltage of the carrier and audio signals are concerned. We must keep in mind that the carrier is going through many, many cycles while the audio sine wave goes through only one. Let's look at the drawing at Fig. 16A. With the polarities indicated, the major current flow will be through CR4 since the audio and carrier voltages are aiding (adding together) in this path. Since the balance through L3 has been upset (the bottom half of L3 has more current flowing through it than does the top half), there will be an output present at L4. At B, the polarity of the carrier has reversed while the audio polarity has remained the same. This is the order in which the polarities would change since the carrier is reversing polarity at a much quicker rate than the audio signal. At C, the carrier polarity is back to what it was at A; however, now the audio is on the negative portion of its sine wave and so its polarity is reversed. Maximum current flow under these conditions is through CR1 and again an output signal appears at L4. The fourth condition that will exist is shown at D. The audio signal polarity is the same as in C, but the carrier is reversed. This time, diode CR3 will be the main path for current flow. As you have probably guessed, there is output at L4 under these conditions.

Fig. 17 shows a composite drawing of the audio and carrier waveforms. The shaded-in areas represent the double-sideband suppressed-carrier output from the balanced modulator.

Another type of balanced modulator is shown in Fig. 18. Two balancing controls are provided so that the circuit can be adjusted for optimum carrier suppression (50 dB is a practical amount). The principle of operation in this circuit is the same as that of the one we previously discussed. With either the audio or carrier applied separately, the circuit is balanced and there will be no output. With both the audio and carrier applied, the balance is upset and output will be present at T1. We won't go into the detail that we did in the previous circuit. The reader can determine which diodes are conducting for the different polarities of voltage presented by the audio and carrier signals.

The two circuits that we have just examined can be classified as passive balanced modulators. That is, they do not provide gain (amplify) but actually cause a small amount of signal loss (insertion loss). Balanced modulators can be built using active devices. One

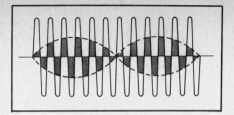

Fig. 17 — Superimposed audio and rf waveform. The shaded-in area represents the double-sideband suppressed-carrier output from the balanced modulator.

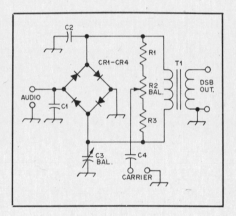

Fig. 18 — Here is another common form of balanced modulator. C3 and R2 are adjusted for maximum carrier suppression.

such modulator is shown in Fig. 19. This circuit makes use of two FETs as the active devices. As was true with the two other modulators, the circuit is in a balanced condition if either the audio or carrier are applied separately. In this circuit the tuned output network (C5/L1) is adjusted for resonance at the rf (carrier) frequency. At audio this circuit represents a very low impedance allowing no audio to appear at the output. Consider the carrier input for a moment. Injection voltage is supplied to each gate in a parallel fashion. Since the input to each gate is of equal amplitude and of the same phase and the output circuit is connected for push-pull operation, the currents flowing through each half of the tank are equal and opposite. The signals will effectively cancel and the output will be zero.

Let's analyze the circuit with both the audio and carrier energy applied. Since we have a push-pull input arrangement for the audio information, the bias for the FETs varies at an audio rate. The audio signal applied to one gate is 180 degrees out of phase with the other. While one of the devices is forward biased, the other is reverse biased. The input to each device is the audio signal plus the carrier signal. Sum and difference frequencies are developed at the output (double-sideband suppressed carrier).

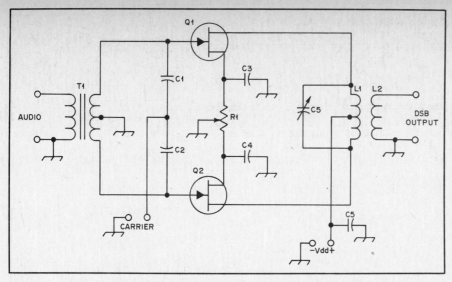

Fig. 19 — This circuit is an active balanced modulator using two FET devices. R1 is adjusted for maximum carrier suppression and C5 is adjusted for maximum double-sideband output.

## Removing The Unwanted Sideband

We now have a signal that contains both the upper and lower sidebands of what was an a-m signal. The next step in generating our ssb signal is to remove one of the sidebands. Looking back at Fig. 14, we see that the next stage after the balanced modulator is the *filter*. This circuit does just as its name suggests — it filters out one of the sidebands. There are two basic forms of filters commonly used for this purpose. They are called *crystal filters* and *mechanical filters*.

An example of a simple *crystal filter* is shown in Fig. 20. The two crystals would be separated by approximately 2 kHz to provide a bandwidth suitable for passing one sideband and not the other. More elaborate filters using four and six crystals will give reduced bandwidths farther down the slopes of the response without affecting the bandwidth near the top of the response. The curves to the right of the filters show this. As we can see, the filter with more crystals has a narrower response at the −60 dB point. The filter at B has better "skirt selectivity" than that at A. Two half-lattice filters of the type shown at A are connected back to back to form the filter at B. Crystal-lattice filters of this type are available commercially for frequencies up to 40 MHz or so.

*Mechanical filters* can be built at frequencies below approximately 1 MHz. Most are made up of three basic sections: an input transducer, a mechanically resonant filter section and an output transducer. Fig. 21 illustrates a typical mechanical filter. The transducers use the principle of magnetostriction to convert the electrical signal

to mechanical energy, than back again. The mechanically resonant section consists of carefully machined metal disks supported and coupled by thin rods. Each disk has a resonant frequency dependent upon the material and its dimensions. The effective $Q$ of a single disk may be in excess of 2000.

As we have seen, either type of filter can provide the narrow response we

need to filter out one of the sidebands. Fig. 22 illustrates the frequency response of a filter along with the position of the two sidebands and the suppressed carrier. We can see that in this case the lower sideband will be passed and the upper sideband greatly attenuated.

Referring back to our block diagram in Fig. 14, we now have an ssb signal present at the output of the filter. This ssb signal is now injected into a mixer stage. An rf oscillator, perhaps a VFO, is used as the other input to the mixer. This stage combines these two inputs, either by subtracting one from the other or by adding them together, to provide as its output an ssb signal at some new frequency. For the sake of working through an example, let's say that we generated the ssb signal at 1 MHz. As we know, we cannot put this on the air directly since there are no ham bands in that frequency range. By using a VFO with a frequency output of from 6.0 to 6.3 MHz we can convert the 1 MHz signal to cover the 40-meter amateur band (6.0 MHz + 1 MHz = 7.0 MHz and 6.3 MHz + 1 MHz = 7.3 MHz). As we said, this can be done by either adding or subtracting the frequencies. We could also cover the 40-meter band using 8.0 to 8.3 MHz for the VFO frequency range (8.0 MHz − 1 MHz = 7.0 MHz and 8.3 MHz − 1 MHz = 7.3 MHz).

At the output of the mixer we have an ssb signal that can be placed anywhere in the 40-meter amateur band.

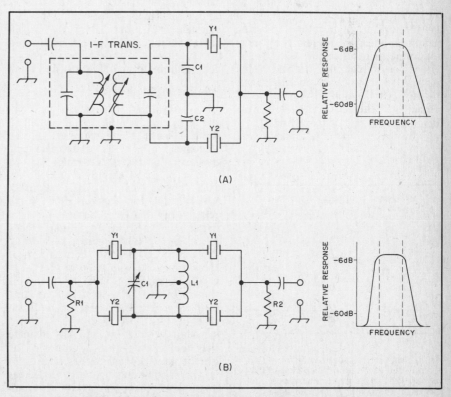

Fig. 20 — A half-lattice band-pass filter at A; B shows two half-lattice filters in cascade.

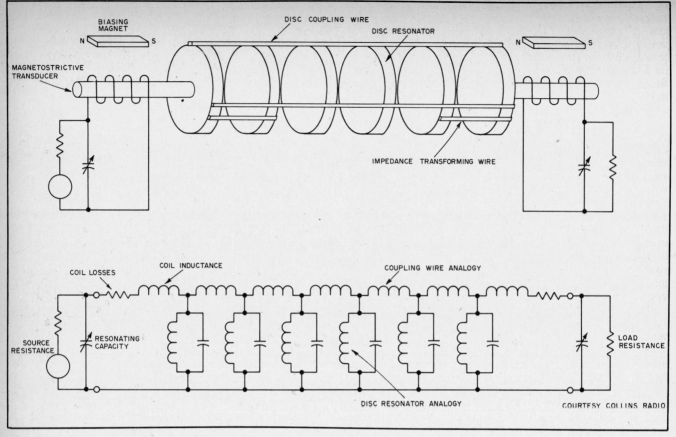

Fig. 21 — Basic diagrams of mechanical filters.

The last stage shown in the block diagram is the linear amplifier. Since the modulation process occurs at low power levels in a conventional transmitter, it is necessary that all of the amplifiers following the balanced modulator be linear. At the low-power level stages of the transmitter, high voltage gain and maximum linearity are quite a bit more important than efficiency. Class A amplifiers are normally used. At the higher power levels it would be nice to be able to use Class C amplifiers for improved efficiency. The distortion level, unfortunately, is rather high. Distortion is in the form of odd-order inter-

modulation products that are close to the desired frequency and cannot be filtered out by the resonant tank circuit. This results in an increase of transmitted signal bandwidth either side of the normal signal. Since linearity is very important, high power amplifiers are normally run Class AB or B. The no-signal resting plate current is adjusted for the lowest plate dissipation consistent with an acceptable distortion level.

### The Phasing Method

Fundamentally, the "phasing" method of generating a single-sideband signal consists of removing one of the sidebands by means of a balancing process rather than by filtering.

The principle employed may be explained by reference to Figs. 23A and B, which are vector diagrams showing the relationship between carrier and sidebands produced in amplitude modulation. In Fig. 23A a carrier is shown in "reference" phase, and the positions of the sideband vectors indicate that peak-envelope conditions exist at the instant shown. In Fig. 23B a carrier of the same frequency but 90 degrees away from that of Fig. 23A is shown. The two sideband vectors in Fig. 23B indicate that the envelope has a value (at the instant shown) equal to the carrier; that is, the modulating signal is 90 degrees away from that which gave the conditions shown in Fig. 23A.

If the conditions shown in Fig. 23A exist at the output of one modulating device at the same instant that the conditions indicated in Fig. 23B exist at the output of another modulating de-

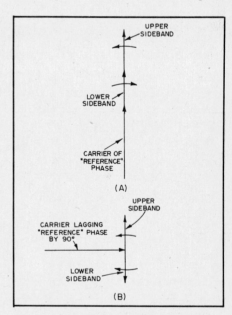

Fig. 23 — The carrier and sideband relationship required to generate a single-sideband signal by the "phasing" or "balancing" method. The modulating signal in B leads the modulating signal in A by 90 degrees. When the two signals represented by A and B are combined, the upper sidebands add and the lower sidebands cancel out, resulting in a single-sideband signal.

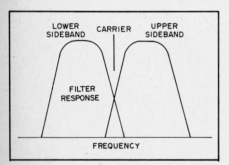

Fig. 22 — Here is a drawing of a crystal or mechanical-filter response with respect to the position of the other sideband and the carrier. We can see that only one sideband will be let through unattenuated while the other will not.

vice, and if the sideband frequencies and magnitudes are the same, the simple sum of Figs. 23A and B will consist of carrier and upper sideband only. It can be seen that the lower-sideband vectors are equal in magnitude and opposite in direction, and hence would cancel one another. How can this result be obtained in practice?

The vector diagram of Fig. 23A might be said to represent the output of a modulated amplifier where a carrier of reference phase is modulated by a tone of reference phase. Thus, Fig. 23B would represent the output of a second modulated amplifier where a carrier of the same frequency but 90 degrees displaced from reference phase is modulated by a tone that is also 90 degrees displaced from its reference phase. To make the whole thing work, the frequencies of all corresponding signals represented in the two vector diagrams must be exactly the same. This would suggest an arrangement such as Fig. 24, which would operate satisfactorily if the 90 degrees phase-shift devices held amplitudes and phases of the respective signals to agree with the requirements indicated in Figs. 23A and B. The carrier phase-shifter is easy to build, since the carrier frequency is constant, but the modulating signal phase-shifter might not be, since it must work over a wide range of frequencies. The arrangement of Fig. 24 works in principle but not in practice, for any wide range of modulating frequencies.

It so happens that two phase-shift networks having a *differential* phase shift of 90 degrees can be inserted between the source of modulating signals and the modulating devices to

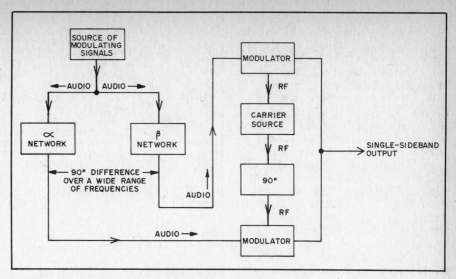

Fig. 25 — The system outlined in Fig. 24 becomes practical by using two audio channels (∝ and β networks) with a constant phase *difference* of 90 degrees.

generate sets of sidebands which can be combined to cancel one of the sidebands as indicated earlier. This leads to an arrangement such as that shown in Fig. 25, where the symbols "∝" and "β" indicate the two networks that have a *difference* in phase shift of 90 degrees over any desired range of modulating signal frequency.

### Examination of an Actual Circuit

Now that we have most of the theory concerning cw and ssb transmission under our belts, let's take a look at an actual circuit diagram. The circuit shown in Fig. 26 is a simplified version of the "real thing" so that we can more easily observe the main points of interest. Let's start by analyzing the circuit for single-sideband operation. Located at the upper left of the diagram is the speech amplifier. As we discussed earlier, it is the duty of this stage to amplify the level of the microphone. With a microphone connected to J1, audio information is coupled to the base of Q1 through C1, a 1-μF capacitor. The base bias is determined by the values of R1, R2 and R3 and is set for Class A operation. Amplified audio energy is coupled to S1B through C3. With the switch in the ssb position, audio is injected into the balanced modulator. The modulator consists of L1 through L4 and CR1 through CR4 and is of the type we studied in detail earlier. As we have learned, a carrier signal is also required in order to produce ssb. Q4 and its associated components supply this energy. With S1A in the ssb position the oscillator generates a carrier on 8.9985 MHz. This signal is routed to the balanced modulator through C19. Output from the balanced modulator (at L4) under these conditions is double-

sideband suppressed carrier. The filter after the modulator attenuates the unwanted sideband. Output from the filter is a 9-MHz ssb signal. This signal is, in turn, applied to the 40673 mixer stage. VFO energy is also fed to this mixer. Q8 and the rest of the VFO circuitry is designed to generate a signal on any frequency between 5.0 and 5.5 MHz. The setting of C24, the tuning capacitor, determines exactly what frequency the VFO will produce. The 9-MHz ssb signal and the VFO energy are mixed in a subtractive fashion to produce ssb output energy on any frequency between 3.5 and 4.0 MHz (9.0 MHz − 5.5 MHz = 3.5 MHz and 9.0 MHz − 5.0 MHz = 4.0 MHz). Since the ssb energy is fixed at 9.0 MHz, the VFO controls the output frequency.

C9, C10, C11, L7, L8 and L9 comprise a band-pass filter which lets through, unattenuated, signals in the 3.5- to 4.0-MHz range. Harmonic energy along with unwanted mixing products are attenuated before reaching the power amplifier. The amplifier simply boosts the power output of the mixer stage. A T network, of the type that we have already studied, is used between the collector of the 40082 transistor and antenna.

Now let's take a look at how the transmitter works in the cw mode. We can see that with S1A in the cw position, the crystals are switched and the output of the carrier oscillator will be on 8.999 MHz. In this circuit we change crystals when switching to the cw mode. This is so that the carrier oscillator will be centered in the mechanical or crystal filter passband, or nearly so. During ssb operation we want the carrier to be located partway down the slopes of the filter response. This

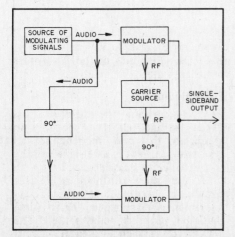

Fig. 24 — A block diagram showing the circuits required to generate a single sideband by the method of Fig. 23. This is an impractical method because there is no known means for obtaining the 90 degrees audio shift over a wide range of frequencies.

gives us additional carrier suppression. In cw we are interested in retaining the carrier and do not want to attenuate it. Some transmitters use the same crystal for ssb and cw operation. Those circuits have enough carrier energy in reserve to make up for the loss through the filter.

With S1B set for cw, output from the speech amplifier is open circuited. The center connection of L2 is connected to R13 and R14. As we remember from our study of balanced modulators, if either audio or carrier energy is applied alone there will be no output — the circuit is balanced. In order to obtain output from the balanced modulator, we must upset this balanced condition. By supplying a small amount of dc voltage to the center connection of L2, we can do just that. R13 controls the amount of dc fed to the winding and, therefore, the amount of balance upset. The greater the upset, the greater the carrier output from the modulator. Output from the balanced modulator is in the form of cw and occupies the frequency of 8.999 MHz. This signal passes through the crystal or mechanical filter essentially unattenuated and on the mixer. From thereon in, the signal is processed in the same manner as ssb. Q5 is a keying transistor used to supply the cw drive-level control with keyed positive voltage.

Q6, Q7 and associated components form a break-in delay system. We won't examine this in detail here because we will take a close look at a similar system in the chapter on transmitter accessories. Basically, the circuit pulls in relay K1 whenever the key is closed, holds it in during and between code characters, and then allows it to drop out after a period of time. The amount of delay is governed by the setting of R18. The relay is used to transfer the

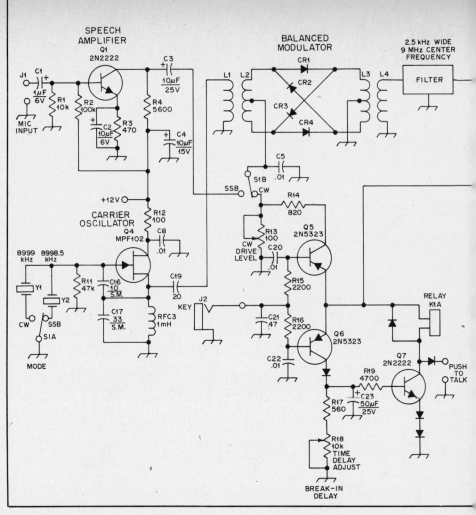

Fig. 26 — Schematic diagram of a simplified ssb/cw transmitter designed for 80 meters.

station antenna from the transmitter to the receiver. With a system like this one it is not necessary to throw a switch when changing from receive to transmit. When you're ready to transmit, just start sending — the circuit will do the rest!

# Frequency and Phase Modulation

We can transmit voice information by modulating any property of a carrier. These properties are amplitude, frequency and phase. Since we've already studied amplitude modulation, let's move on to frequency and phase modulation. If the frequency of the carrier is varied in accordance with the variations in a modulating signal, the result is called *frequency modulation* (*fm*). Similarly, varying the phase of the carrier current is called *phase modulation* (pm).

Frequency and phase modulation are not independent, since the frequency cannot be varied without also varying the phase, and vice versa.

### Frequency Modulation

Fig. 27 is a representation of frequency modulation. When a modulating signal is applied, the carrier frequency is increased during one half-cycle of the modulating signal and decreased during the half-cycle of opposite polarity. This is indicated in the drawing by the fact that the rf cycles occupy less time (higher frequency) when the modulating signal is positive, and more time (lower frequency) when the modulating signal is negative. The change in the carrier frequency (*frequency deviation*) is proportional to the instantaneous amplitude of the modulating signal, so the deviation is small when the instantaneous amplitude of the modulating signal is small, and is greatest when the modulating signal reaches its peak, either positive or negative. That is, the frequency deviation follows the instantaneous changes in the amplitude of the

modulating signal. As we can see in Fig. 27C, the amplitude of the signal does not change during modulation.

### Phase Modulation

To understand the difference between fm and pm it is necessary to appreciate that the frequency of an alternating current is determined by the *rate at which its phase changes*.

If the phase of the current in a circuit is changed, there is an instantaneous frequency change during the time that the phase is being shifted. The amount of frequency change, or deviation, depends on how rapidly the phase shift is accomplished. It is also dependent upon the total amount of the phase shift. In a properly operating pm system the amount of phase shift is

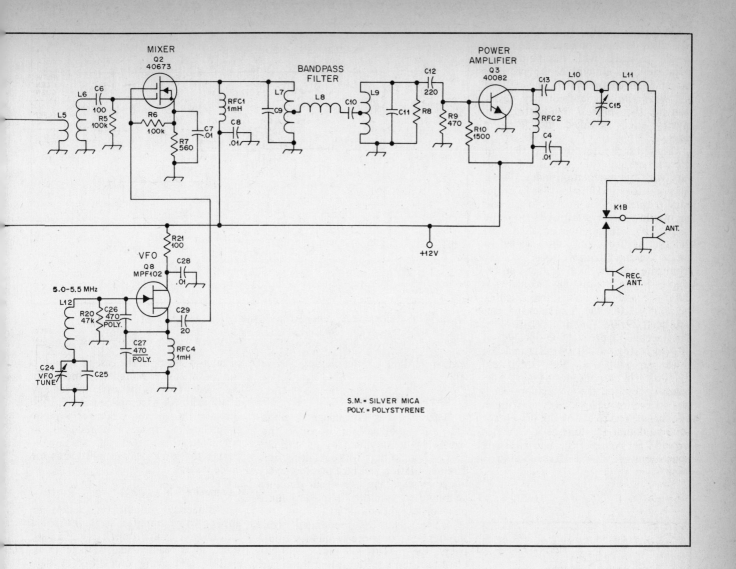

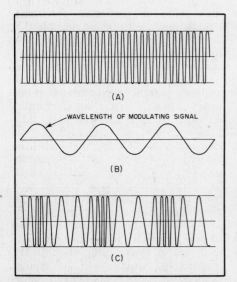

Fig. 27 — Graphical representation of frequency modulation. In the unmodulated carrier at A, each rf cycle occupies the same amount of time. When the modulating signal, B, is applied, the radio frequency is increased and decreased according to the amplitude and polarity of the modulating signal.

proportional to the instantaneous amplitude of the modulating signal. The rapidity of the phase shift is directly proportional to the frequency of the modulating signal. Consequently, the frequency deviation in pm is proportional to both the amplitude and frequency of the modulating signal. The latter represents the outstanding differences between fm and pm, since in fm the frequency deviation is proportional only to the amplitude of the modulating signal.

## FM and PM Sidebands

The sidebands set up by fm and pm differ from those resulting from a-m in that they occur at integral multiples of the modulating frequency on either side of the carrier rather than, as in a-m, consisting of a single set of side frequencies for each modulating frequency. An fm or pm signal therefore inherently occupies a wider channel than a-m.

The number of "extra" sidebands that occur in fm and pm depends on the relationship between the modulating

frequency and the frequency deviation. The ratio between the frequency deviation, in cycles per second, and the modulating frequency, also in cycles per second, is called the *modulation index*. That is, the modulation index can be calculated as follows

$$\text{Modulation index} = \frac{\text{carrier frequency deviation}}{\text{modulating frequency}}$$

In order to work through an example let's assume that the maximum frequency deviation in an fm transmitter is 3000 Hz either side of the carrier. The modulating frequency is 1000 Hz. To find the modulation index we use the equation as follows

$$\text{Modulation index} = \frac{3000}{1000} = 3$$

In pm the modulation index is constant regardless of the modulating frequency; in fm it varies with the modulating frequency, as shown in the previous example. In an fm system the ratio of the *maximum* carrier-frequency deviation to the *highest* modulating frequency used is called the *deviation ratio*.

Fig. 28 shows how the amplitudes of the carrier and the various sidebands vary with the modulation index. This is for single-tone modulation; the first sideband (actually a pair, one above and one below the carrier) is displaced from the carrier by an amount equal to the modulating frequency, the second is twice the modulating frequency away from the carrier, and so on. For example, if the modulating frequency is 2000 Hz and the carrier frequency is, say, 29.5 MHz, the first sideband pair will be at 29.498 MHz and 29.502 MHz. The second pair will be located at 29.496 MHz and 29.504 MHz and the third pair will be at 29.494 MHz and 29.506 MHz. Amplitudes of these sidebands depend on the modulation index, not on the frequency deviation. With an a-m signal, regardless of the percentage of modulation (so long as it does not exceed 100 percent) the sidebands will appear only at 29.498 MHz and 29.502 MHz.

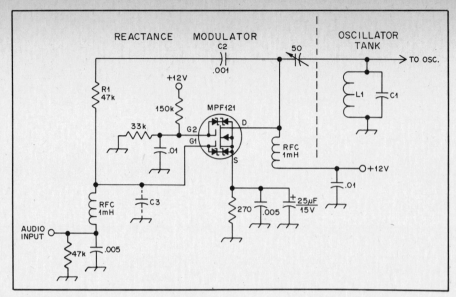

Fig. 29 — Reactance modulator using a high-transconductance MOSFET.

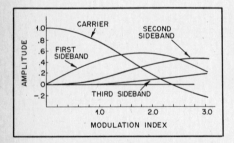

Fig. 28 — How the amplitude of the pairs of sidebands varies with the modulation index in an fm or pm signal. If the curves were extended for greater values of modulation index, it would be seen that the carrier amplitude goes through zero at several points. The same statement also applies to the sidebands.

Note that, as shown by Fig. 28, the carrier strength varies with the modulation index. (In amplitude modulation the carrier strength is constant; only the sideband amplitude varies.) At a modulation index of approximately 2.4 the carrier disappears entirely. It then becomes "negative" at a higher index, meaning that its phase is reversed as compared to the phase without modulation. In fm and pm the energy that goes into the sidebands is taken from the carrier, the *total* power remaining the

same regardless of the modulation index.

## Frequency Multiplication

Since there is no change in amplitude with modulation, an fm or pm signal can be amplified by an ordinary Class C amplifier without distortion. The modulation can take place in a very low-level stage and the signal can then be amplified by either frequency multipliers or straight amplifiers.

If we pass the modulated signal through one or more frequency multipliers, the modulation index is multiplied by the same factor that the carrier frequency is multiplied. For example, if the modulation is applied on 18 MHz and the final output is on 144 MHz, the total multiplication is 8 times. If the modulation frequency is say 500 Hz at 18 MHz, it will be 4 kHz at 144 MHz.

Frequency multiplication offers a means for obtaining practically any desired amount of frequency deviation, whether or not the modulator itself is capable of giving that much deviation without distortion.

## Narrow-Band FM and PM

"Narrow-band" fm or pm, the only type that is authorized for use on the lower frequencies where the phone bands are crowded, is defined as fm or pm that does not occupy a wider channel than an a-m signal having the same audio modulating frequencies. Narrow-band operation requires using a relatively small modulation index.

If the modulation index (with single-tone modulation) does not exceed about 0.6, the most important extra sideband, the second, will be at least 20 dB below the unmodulated carrier level, and this should represent an effective channel width about equivalent to that

of an a-m signal. In the case of speech, a somewhat higher modulation index can be used. This is because the energy distribution in a complex wave is such that the modulation index for any one frequency component is reduced, as compared to the index with a sine wave having the same peak amplitude as the voice wave.

## Comparing FM and PM

Frequency modulation cannot be applied to an amplifier stage, but phase modulation can. From that we can see that pm is readily adaptable to transmitters employing oscillators of high stability such as the crystal-controlled type. The amount of phase shift that can be obtained with good linearity is such that the maximum practicable modulation index is approximately 0.5. Since the phase shift is proportional to the modulating frequency, this index can be used only at the highest frequency present in the modulating signal, assuming that all frequencies will at one time or another have equal amplitudes. Taking 3000 Hz as a suitable upper limit for voice work, and setting the modulation index at 0.5 for 3000 Hz, the frequency response of the speech-amplifier system above 3000 Hz must be sharply attenuated to prevent sideband splatter. Also, if the "tinny" quality of pm as received on an fm receiver is to be avoided, the pm must be changed to fm, in which the modulation index decreases in inverse proportion to the modulating frequency. This requires shaping the speech-amplifier frequency-response curve in such a way that the output voltage is inversely proportional to frequency over most of the voice range. When this is done the maximum modulation index can only be used at some relatively low audio frequency,

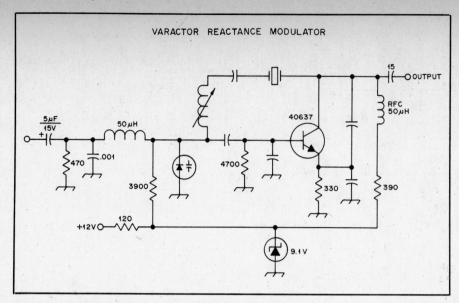

VARACTOR REACTANCE MODULATOR

Fig. 30 — Reactance modulator using a varactor diode.

## Generating an FM Signal

perhaps 300 to 400 cycles in voice transmission, and must decrease in proportion to the increase in frequency. The result is that the maximum linear frequency deviation is only one to two hundred cycles, when pm is changed to fm. To increase the deviation for nbfm requires a frequency multiplication of eight times or more.

It is relatively easy to secure a fairly large frequency deviation when a self-controlled oscillator is frequency-modulated directly. True frequency modulation of a crystal-controlled oscillator results in only very small deviations and requires a great deal of frequency multiplication.

The chief problem is to maintain a satisfactory degree of carrier stability, since the greater the inherent stability of the oscillator, the more difficult it is to secure a wide frequency swing with linearity.

### Generating an FM Signal

There are two general categories into which most methods of producing fm will fall. They are *direct fm* and *indirect fm*. As you might expect, each has its advantages and disadvantages. Let's look at the direct-fm method first.

## Direct FM

A simple and satisfactory device for producing fm in the amateur transmitter is the reactance modulator. This is a vacuum tube or transistor connected to the rf tank circuit of an oscillator in such a way as to act as a variable inductance or capacitance.

Fig. 29 is a representative circuit. Gate 1 of the modulator MOSFET is connected across the oscillator tank circuit, C1L1, through resistor R1 and blocking capacitor C2. C3 represents the input capacitance of the modulator transistor. The resistance of R1 is made large compared to the reactance of C3, so the rf current through R1C3 will be practically in phase with the rf voltage appearing at the terminals of the tank circuit. However, the voltage across C3 will lag the current by 90 degrees. The rf current in the drain circuit of the modulator will be in phase with the gate voltage, and consequently is 90 degrees behind the current through C3, or 90 degrees behind the rf tank circuit. This lagging current is drawn through the oscillator tank, giving the same effect as though an inductance were connected across the tank. The frequency increases in proportion to the amplitude of the

lagging plate current of the modulator. The audio voltage, introduced through a radio-frequency-choke, varies the transconductance of the transistor and thereby varies the rf drain current.

The modulated oscillator usually is operated on a relatively low frequency, so that a high order of carrier stability can be secured. Frequency multipliers are used to raise the frequency to the final frequency desired.

A reactance modulator can be connected to a crystal oscillator as well as to the self-controlled type as shown in Fig. 30. However, the resulting signal will be more phase-modulated than it is frequency-modulated, for the reason that the frequency deviation that can be secured by varying the frequency of a crystal oscillator is quite small.

The sensitivity of the modulator (frequency change per unit change in grid voltage) depends on the transconductance of the modulator transistor. It increases when R1 is made smaller in comparison with C3. It also increases with an increase in $L/C$ ratio in

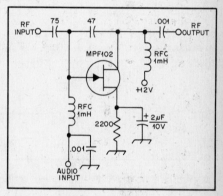

Fig. 32 — Phase modulator using an MPF 102 JFET.

the oscillator tank circuit. However, for highest carrier stability it is desirable to use the largest tank capacitance that will permit the desired deviation to be secured while keeping within the limits of linear operation.

A change in *any* of the voltages on the modulator transistor will cause a change in rf drain current, and consequently a frequency change. Therefore, it is advisable to use a regulated power supply for both modulator and oscillator.

The circuit shown in Fig. 31 consists of a reactance modulator which shifts the frequency of an oscillator to generate an fm signal directly. Successive multiplier stages provide output on the desired frequency, which is amplified by a PA stage. This system has a disadvantage in that, if the oscillator is free running, it is difficult to achieve suf-

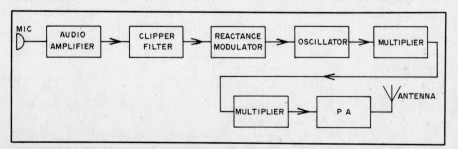

Fig. 31 — Block diagram of a direct-fm transmitter.

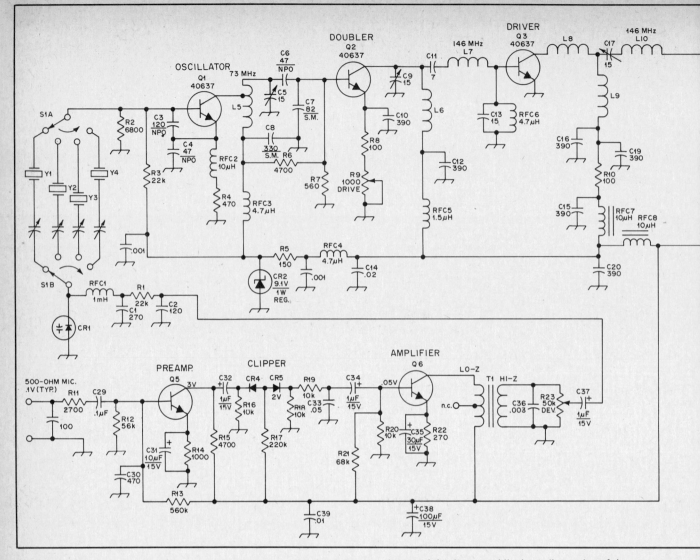

Fig. 33 — Here is the schematic of an actual fm transmitter. The rf circuitry is at the top of the diagram while the audio portion of the transmitter is at the bottom.

ficient stability for vhf use. If a crystal-controlled oscillator is employed, unless the amount that the crystal frequency is changed is kept small, it is difficult to achieve equal amounts of frequency swing.

### Indirect FM

The same type of reactance-tube circuit that is used to vary the tuning of the oscillator tank in fm can be used to vary the tuning of an amplifier tank and thus vary the phase of the tank current for pm. Hence, the modulator circuit of Fig. 29 or 32 can be used for pm if the reactance transistor or tube works on an amplifier tank instead of directly on a self-controlled oscillator. If audio shaping is used in the speech amplifier, as described above, fm instead of pm will be generated by the phase modulator.

The phase shift that occurs when a circuit is detuned from resonance depends on the amount of detuning and

the Q of the circuit. The higher the Q, the smaller the amount of detuning needed to secure a given number of degrees of phase shift. If the Q is at least 10, the relationship between phase shift and detuning (in kHz either side of the resonant frequency) will be substantially linear over a phase-shift range of about 25 degrees. From the standpoint of modulator sensitivity, the Q of the tuned circuit on which the modulator operates should be as high as possible. On the other hand, the effective Q of the circuit will not be very high if the amplifier is delivering power to a load since the load resistance reduces the Q. There must, therefore, be a compromise between modulator sensitivity and rf

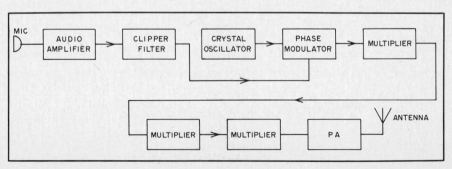

Fig. 34 — Block diagram of an indirect-fm transmitter.

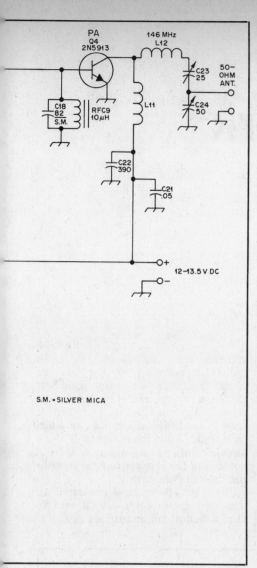

S.M. = SILVER MICA

power output from the modulated amplifier. An optimum figure for $Q$ appears to be about 20; this allows reasonable loading of the modulated amplifier and the necessary tuning variation can be secured from a reactance modulator without difficulty. It is advisable to modulate at a low power level.

Reactance modulation of an ampli-

fier stage usually results in simultaneous amplitude modulation because the modulated stage is detuned from resonance as the phase is shifted. This must be eliminated by feeding the modulated signal through an amplitude limiter or one or more "saturating" stages; that is, amplifiers that are operated Class C and driven hard enough so that variations in the amplitude of the input excitation produce no appreciable variations in the output amplitude.

For the same type of reactance modulator, the speech-amplifier gain required is the same for pm as for fm. However, as pointed out earlier, the fact that the actual frequency deviation increases with the modulating audio frequency in pm makes it necessary to cut off the frequencies above about 3000 Hz before modulation takes place. If this is not done, unnecessary sidebands will be generated at frequencies considerably away from the carrier.

The indirect method of generating fm shown in Fig. 34 is currently popular. Shaped audio is applied to a phase modulator to generate fm. As the amount of deviation produced is very small, a large number of multiplier stages is necessary to achieve wide-band deviation at the operating frequency. In general, the system shown at A will require a less complex circuit than that at B, but the indirect method (B) often produces superior results.

### An Actual FM Transmitter

Now that we have covered the essentials of transmitting an fm signal, let's look at an actual fm transmitter circuit. This particular one is designed to operate in the amateur 2-meter band (144 to 148 MHz).

### RF Circuitry

Six low-cost bipolar transistors are used in the circuit of Fig. 33. Q1 is the oscillator, which uses 18-MHz fundamental crystals ground for a load capacitance of 20 pF. Output from the first stage is taken at 73 MHz, a frequency multiplication of four. The second stage, Q2, doubles the frequency to 146 MHz. The remaining stages operate as

amplifiers at 146 MHz.

Frequency modulation is effected by applying audio to a voltage-variable diode (Varicap) CR1. As the amplitude of the audio varies, the junction capacitance of CR1 changes, and this change pulls the crystal frequency above and below its preset frequency to provide fm. The amount of deviation, or swing, is determined by the audio level impressed across CR1. Normally, this will be set for 5- or 15-kHz deviation, depending upon the bandwidth in vogue for a given area. Approximately 1.5 volts of reverse bias is developed within the circuit and appears across CR1. This eliminates the need to provide back bias from the 12-volt line.

Crystals Y1 through Y4 are adjusted to the desired frequency by means of trimmer capacitors. Approximately 3 kHz of shift is possible with the value given. Regulated voltage is supplied to Q1 (and to the bias line of Q2) by means of Zener diode CR2. This measure helps insure against oscillator instability.

A drive control, R9, is connected in the emitter lead of Q2 to permit the operator to reduce power to the minimum amount needed. This measure helps to prolong the life of dry batteries during portable operation.

### The Modulator

Only a few peak-to-peak volts of audio are needed to provide fm. A two-stage audio channel is shown below the rf circuitry. This circuit amplifies the microphone output to a suitable level for clipping at diodes CR3 and CR4. A small amount of forward bias is used on the diodes to permit clipping action at relatively low audio level. The 10,000-ohm resistor and .05-$\mu$F capacitor used after the clipper diodes serve as a filter to reduce the harmonics caused during clipping. Output stage Q6 amplifies the clipped audio to a maximum level of 20 volts peak to peak. The deviation control, R23, is adjusted to provide the amount of frequency swing needed. A value of approximately 3 volts pk-pk is typical for 5-kHz deviation with the circuit shown.

# Chapter 5

# How Receivers Work

Perhaps the single most significant part of an amateur's station is his receiver. No matter how big the transmitter's on-the-air voice, permitting its signals to be heard around the world, the effectiveness of the station will depend mainly on the receiver and its ability to separate the stations and respond adequately to weak signals. There's a popular cliche among radio amateurs which goes something like, "If you can't hear 'em, you can't work 'em."

Let's look into the business of receivers by considering how to select a suitable one for your needs, and how to operate one correctly after it becomes a member of the equipment family in your ham shack. As you have learned already, radio signals are forms of energy sent into the ether so that they can be collected on a receiving antenna and converted by means of a detector (receiver) into something that the human senses can recognize. Typically, we are dealing with aural (sound) or visual (vision) presentation of the converted radio-frequency energy that our receivers have made coherent for us. The notable exception to aural and visual recognition of the signal energy would be seen in the case of a deaf amateur relying on his sense of touch to copy Morse code (placing his finger tips on the cone of a loudspeaker).

## Basic Signal Detection

Chances are that you've played with "crystal sets" at some time in your life. A crystal set is a fundamental type of radio-wave detector that is used to convert amplitude-modulated broadcast-band signals ("standard a-m") to energy that the human sense of hearing will relate to. The basic parts of so simple a receiving system are a long length of wire (antenna) to collect some of the broadcast station energy from the air, a crystal-diode detector made from silicon or germanium minerals, and a transducer (earphones or loudspeaker) to permit one to hear the converted rf energy. The crystal detector rectifies the rf signal to provide electrical current that varies at an audio rate. The transducer responds to the rectified energy and produces sound waves that our ears can pick up. Fig. 1A shows the simplest form of crystal receiver. Only three components are necessary — a diode, an antenna and headphones. An earth ground is necessary to complete the circuit. Such a receiver will respond best to the strongest radio station in the general area of the receiver, but if several a-m broadcast stations are nearby it is likely that the listener will hear a jumble of voices and music, as there is nothing in the receiver to help separate the stations (selectivity).

At Fig. 1B we have illustrated an improved circuit for a crystal set. We have added a coil and tuning capacitor

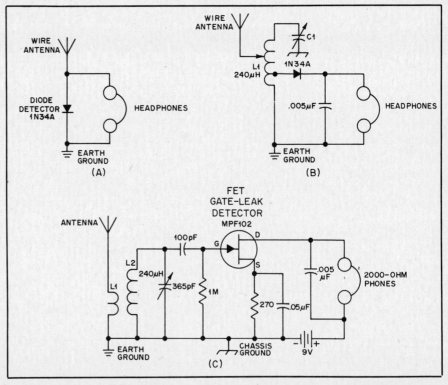

Fig. 1 — Examples of simple detectors. At A we find the most basic of a-m receivers. An improved version is seen at B, where some tuned-circuit selectivity has been added. The detector at C offers selectivity and signal amplification.

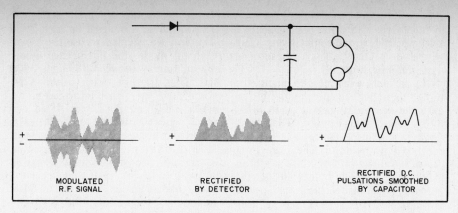

MODULATED R.F. SIGNAL

RECTIFIED BY DETECTOR

RECTIFIED D.C. PULSATIONS SMOOTHED BY CAPACITOR

Fig. 2 — The operation of the diode rectifier in detecting a modulated rf signal. The rf signal itself makes no impression on the headphones, but rectifying it gives us a direct current that varies just in the same way that the modulation varied the strength of the original signal. The high-frequency pulsations in current that result from rectification are filtered out by the capacitor, leaving only the audio-frequency variations in the direct current to actuate the phones. Another way of looking at it is that the high-frequency pulsations are bypassed by the capacitor, but since the more slowly varying direct current cannot pass through the capacitor, the current flows through the headphones to produce a sound.

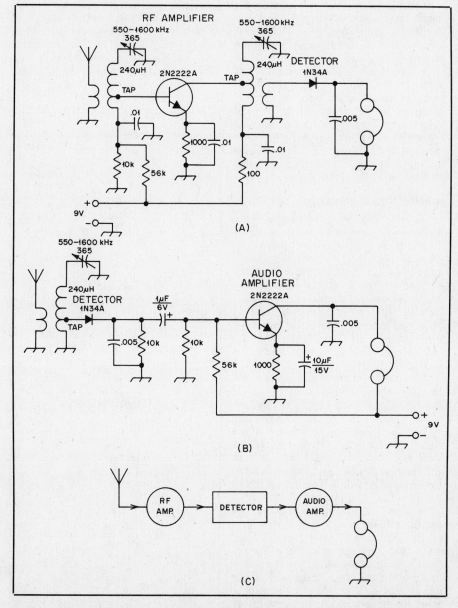

Fig. 3 — An a-m diode detector is enhanced at A by the addition of an rf amplifier stage. At B we have added an audio amplifier stage instead of an rf one. The effects in circuits A and B are similar. A block diagram is given at C to illustrate how the rf and audio amplifiers could be added to our diode detector to provide added overall circuit gain.

(L1 and C1). These components form a *tuned circuit* which can be adjusted to the frequency of the broadcast-band signal of interest. Not only will this make the detected signal somewhat louder in the earphones, it will favor the desired station and tend to reject other nearby station signals if they are on a different frequency than the one being listened to. The end of the wire antenna is moved up or down on the coil as shown by the arrow. The best spot for the wire will be that which produces the loudest signal response with a minimum of interference from the stations apart from the one of interest. The diode detector is connected to the coil a few turns above the end of the coil where the earth ground is attached. If the diode is moved too high on the coil it will *load* the tuned circuit too heavily and spoil its ability to separate the stations.

In either circuit (Fig 1A and 1B) the detector is really a rectifier: It changes radio-frequency current into dc (direct current) in the same manner that power-supply rectifiers convert 60-Hz ac energy into dc. The intelligence in the received signal (voice or music) is carried by the *variations* in the signal strength (amplitude), and the direct current provided by the diode detector follows these variations at an audio-frequency rate. The principle is shown in Fig. 2. Once the dc-current variations are converted into sound by the headphones, the signal becomes *intelligent*, or suitable for the sense of hearing.

A more elaborate detection scheme is illustrated at C in Fig. 1. Here we have what is known as a gate-leak detector. A field-effect transistor is used to convert the rf energy into dc current for application to the headphones. The gate-source diode junction in the FET acts as the rectifier, and the pulsating dc current is increased in magnitude by the transistor to provide signal amplification. Since operating voltage (9 V) is applied to the detector, we call the FET an *active* device. The detectors at A and B of Fig. 1 have no dc operating voltage applied, so they are called *passive* devices in electronics vernacular. The .005-$\mu$F bypass capacitor across the headphones is used to shunt the high-frequency energy to ground, but it is small enough in value to have minor effect on the audio-frequency energy in that part of the circuit. Since there is nothing other than the bypass capacitor to restrict the audio response of the circuits at Fig. 1, the fidelity of the voice and music will be excellent.

The basic detectors we have discussed can be considered as the nuclei of most communications receivers. Everything else is built around them — rf amplification, selectivity circuits and audio amplifiers, in the case of a TRF

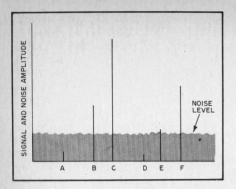

Fig. 4 — The amount of amplification that can be used is eventually limited by noise. The strengths of the signals at A and D in this drawing are below the strength of the noise and would be heard poorly, if at all. The signal at C is well above the noise and would be easily "copied."

(tuned radio-frequency) receiver. A superheterodyne receiver has additional circuits to go with the detector, and we will discuss that kind of unit later on.

The need for additional circuitry relates to our dealing with many signals on numerous radio frequencies — all coming in on the antenna at one time. Also, the signal we may want to listen to could be very weak while the unwanted ones were strong. Therefore, we need amplifiers to go ahead of and after the detector, plus some special circuits to provide selectivity for separating the myriad signals entering the input terminal of our receiver.

## Amplification

The simple receivers shown in Fig. 1 must depend on the strength of the bc-band signal for the loudness of the energy heard at the headphones. It is understandable, therefore, that even though weak-signal energy may reach the detector, the resulting dc current will be too low in amount to activate the phones. The solution to such a problem is *amplification*. We can approach this from two directions, or we can employ a combination of the methods to build up the audio at the phones. We have the option of using an *rf amplifier* between the antenna and the detector, or we can use an *audio amplifier* between the detector and the headphones. Either system will increase the amount of signal current arriving at the phones. Alternatively, rf *and* audio amplification can be used to make the intelligence louder at the phones. Fig. 3 shows the kinds of circuits we might use to accomplish the desired effect.

## How Much Amplification?

The energy taken by the receiving antenna as radio waves pass over it is very low in level — microvolts in most instances. Therefore a considerable amount of amplification is needed within the receiver to bring the signals to a level which is suitable for driving headphones or a loudspeaker — a factor of some millions, normally.

In an ideal example one might continue to amplify the energy indefinitely, until the desired signal was loud enough to be heard comfortably. There is a significant limiting factor that we must contend with — noise. There are three primary sources of this noise — atmospheric noise which comes in on the antenna, manmade electrical-impulse noise caused by such things as light dimmers, electric razors, vacuum cleaners and nearby power lines and finally the noise which is generated within the receiver. Tubes and transistors create their own noise, just as some of the passive circuit elements do.

In designing a receiver the objective is to have circuits which will amplify the signal energy as much as possible while amplifying the noise by the least amount. Certain circuit additions can be used to minimize the effects of the noise, but it is not possible to get rid of noise totally. Noise occurs at all frequencies from audio well into the rf spectrum. A well-designed receiver will exhibit a minimum amount of internal noise. The noise trait is called the *signal-to-noise ratio*. Fig. 4 illustrates the relationship between noise and signal energy.

## A Better Receiver Concept

Thus far we have talked about the simplest of receivers for a-m signal detection. But in today's amateur world there is very little a-m work being done, and the decline in that mode is expected to continue. Most voice communication is carried out by means of single sideband in the range from 1.8 to 29.7 MHz. In such a system the carrier is suppressed by 50 dB or more within the transmitter, and the voice energy is converted to rf current, the latter of which changes in amplitude at an audio rate. Since no carrier is transmitted with the signal, it is necessary to supply one at the receiver in order to convert the signal to an amplitude-modulated one so that it can be detected properly. If this were not done, the signal coming from the loudspeaker would have an unintelligible, mushy sound. The circuit which handles the function of *carrier reinsertion* is called the *beat-frequency oscillator* (BFO).

By the term "single sideband" we mean that only one sideband of consequence exists either side (upper or lower sideband) of the center frequency of the signal. That is, if we were to transmit a conventional a-m signal, the same information would be present on each side of the carrier, even though only one sideband would be needed to extract intelligence from the signal. Thus, if we transmitted an ssb signal on, say, 3900 kHz, and we decided to use the lower-sideband mode, the intelligence would appear roughly between 3898 and 3900 kHz. (Fig. 5). For upper sideband we would find the signal information between 3900 and 3902 kHz. If an a-m signal were transmitted on 3900 kHz, the intelligence would spread from 3888 to 3902 kHz (two sidebands) or greater. It can be seen from this explanation that ssb takes up half the spectrum space that a-m does — an aid to QRM reduction. Furthermore, the ssb transmitter is more efficient than an a-m one because no high-power modulator and power supply are required. Also, it is much more efficient overall to generate just one sideband.

The BFO used during ssb reception is not on exactly the same frequency as the signal to which it supplies a carrier. The frequency must be offset slightly in order to provide the correct relationship for detection. That is, our 3900-kHz lower-sideband signal would have the BFO operating at roughly 3898.3 kHz to assure the most natural voice sound

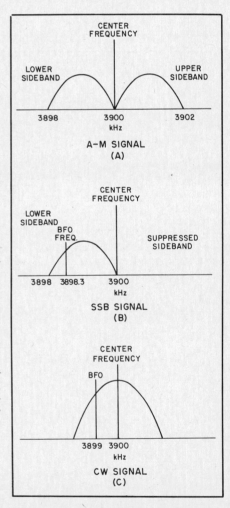

Fig. 5 — Illustrations of a-m, ssb and cw signal bandwidths. Illustrations B and C indicate the proper placement of the BFO frequency.

in the loudspeaker. In a superheterodyne receiver, which we will discuss later on, the detection usually takes place at the intermediate frequency (i-f) — 455 kHz, 3300 kHz or 9 MHz in most modern receivers. The BFO operates at the i-f also, but is offset from the signal frequency roughly 1.7 kHz.

A BFO is necessary for continuous-wave (cw) reception also. Without it one would hear only thumps for each code character, and that would be extremely difficult to decipher. If an a-m receiver were used to copy cw, that's the kind of sound that the operator would hear. Since a carrier already exists during cw transmissions, there is no need to reinsert one in the receiver as we did for ssb reception. What the BFO does do for us is to cause a beat note (frequency difference) in the audible range, and we can copy that without difficulty. So, if we transmitted a cw signal on 3900 kHz we would set our BFO at 3899 or 3901 kHz to cause a beat frequency of 1 kHz (1000 Hz). In other words, the *difference* between 3900 and 3899 or 3901 kHz is 1000 Hz. Some operators like a lower-pitched note, so they will offset the BFO less than one kHz. Thus, if you preferred a 600-Hz cw note you would adjust your BFO to 3900.6 kHz or 3899.4 kHz to get the desired effect. An a-m signal can also be copied on such a receiver. There are two ways that it can be done: (1) disable the BFO and, (2) tune the BFO to exactly the same frequency as the a-m signal (zero beat). This means that an a-m signal which was transmitted on 3900 kHz would provide a BFO frequency of exactly 3900 kHz to provide intelligibility. If the two frequencies were not set at zero beat, an annoying heterodyne would be heard in the speaker, as the BFO would be beating against the a-m signal carrier, as was the situation during ordinary cw reception. Of course, the receiver would need to have a detector which was meant for a-m detection, if the BFO was turned off. Conversely, most a-m detectors will work satisfactorily for cw and ssb reception by merely adding a BFO circuit.

## A Simple SSB/CW Receiver

Now that we have a general idea about the electrical characteristics of an ssb/cw type of receiver, let's examine a simple circuit which can be used to copy signals for those modes. Fig. 6 shows in the most basic form what is known as a *synchrodyne* or *direct-conversion* receiver. C1/L2 are tuned to the frequency of interest (e.g., 3900 kHz). Signal energy from the antenna is coupled to the detector-tuned circuit by means of a coil link, L1. The BFO, Q2, oscillates over the range covered by C1 and L2, and its precise frequency is determined by the setting of C2, the

main tuning control. For cw reception the BFO would be set at roughly 3899 or 3901 kHz. For lower-sideband reception we would set it at approximately 3898.3 kHz, and for upper sideband at 3901.7 kHz. In practice we would not monitor the BFO frequency. Instead we would merely tune the dial until the ssb signal had a natural voice sound, or to obtain the desired pitch during cw reception.

In practical terms we can regard the detector as a mixer and the BFO as a VFO (variable-frequency oscillator). The main difference is that rf or i-f energy would come from a mixer, and audio energy emerges from a product detector. The term "product detector"

is used to signify that the detector output is the product (difference frequency) of the incoming received signal and BFO frequency.

Although the circuit of Fig. 6 would work fine when strong signals were received, it would not produce ample headphone volume for weak signals. Direct-conversion receivers normally require between 80 and 100 dB of audio amplification to be suitable for the very weak signals. A more sophisticated direct-conversion receiver would also contain some means for establishing audio selectivity between the detector and the headphones. This might take the form of an audio band-pass filter made from 88-mH toroid coils and

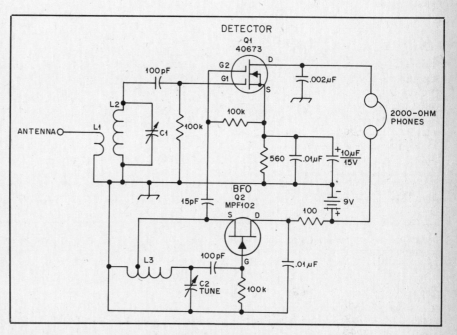

Fig. 6 — Circuit example of a simple direct-conversion receiver. The BFO is heterodyned with the incoming signal at Q1 to produce the desired audio output frequency for cw and ssb reception.

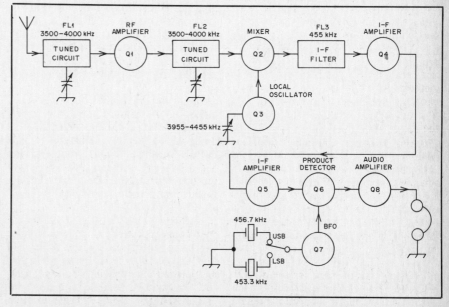

Fig. 7 — Block diagram which illustrates the superheterodyne receiver principle.

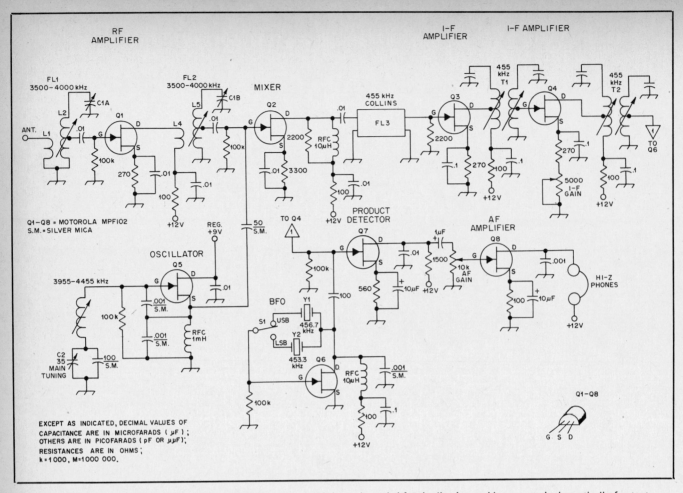

Fig. 8 — Example of an all-FET superheterodyne receiver. The circuit is not intended for duplication and is presented schematically for text-discussion purposes only.

0.47-µF paper capacitors, or an *active filter* could be fashioned by using op-amp ICs, resistors and capacitors. More on that subject later in the book. The filter would shape the audio response for ssb or cw reception, thereby providing receiver selectivity for better separation of the signals. A filter will also reduce noise in a receiver to some extent.

## Overall Receiver Selectivity

In the previous section we touched upon the matter of *audio selectivity* in a simple direct-conversion receiver, but in a typical modern communications receiver of the superheterodyne variety the selectivity is obtained in a different manner. The points of principal interest in the receiver, respective to selectivity, are the receiver front end and the i-f system. So that we may illustrate the foregoing in the least complicated manner, let's find out how a *superheterodyne receiver* functions. Fig. 7 shows a block diagram of such a circuit. Q1 performs as an rf amplifier to boost the signal energy coming from the antenna. On each side of Q1 we find circuits

which are tuned to the desired signal frequency (FL1 and FL2), which are really tunable filters. The peaking control for these filters is usually called a *preselector* control. The name implies that this is a selectivity circuit which is used ahead of the receiver mixer, and rightly so: These filters establish the receiver *front-end selectivity*. Unfortunately, it is not possible to make these tunable filters narrow enough in response — at least not in a practical receiver for hf-band operation and higher — to separate all of the signals properly. But front-end selectivity is desirable to keep commercial signals outside our ham bands from entering and overloading the receiver to cause reception problems. We might have a tuned circuit with a bandwidth of, say, 10 kHz at 350 kilohertz, but a comparably good tuned filter at 3500 kHz (ten times the frequency) would have the same *percentage bandwidth,* or 100 kHz (10 × 10 = 100). As we go higher and higher into the amateur spectrum the bandwidth becomes greater and greater. Therefore it is difficult to build an all-band hf receiver (160 through 10

meters) and have the same front-end selectivity on each band. Fortunately, the bandwidth of the received signals does not increase as the operating frequency is made higher. A phone signal requires no more actual bandwidth at 420 MHz than it does at 4 MHz, or at any frequency lower than 4 MHz. Its bandwidth is determined by the audio frequencies in the human voice, not by the radio frequency at which the signal goes out over the air. Therefore, we can use exactly the same selectivity (in kHz) at 420 MHz as at 4 MHz. In the circuit of Fig. 8 FL1 and FL2 determine the receiver front-end selectivity. They are tuned simultaneously to the desired frequency by means of C1A and C1B, which are two sections of a single variable capacitor. The C1A/C1B combination, along with L2 and L5, comprise the preselector circuit.

We have learned that the front-end selectivity becomes less and less as we move higher in frequency. Therefore, we need to enhance the *adjacent-channel selectivity* in some manner so that it will be the same on all of the amateur bands covered by the receiver.

The practical solution lies in the selection of some frequency where a narrow response can be established. The incoming signal must, therefore, be converted to that ideal frequency. Here is where the superheterodyne concept pays off!

The principle is seen in Fig. 8 where a 3.5-MHz signal is fed to a mixer (Q2), then heterodyned with the local-oscillator energy from Q5 to produce a *difference frequency* of 455 kHz. The latter is an *i-f* (intermediate frequency) at which better selectivity can be obtained. The *primary frequency* in the receiver is 3.5 MHz, and the *ultimate frequency* is at audio, as heard in the headphones. Fig. 8 shows a 455-kHz i-f filter, which by itself will establish the receiver selectivity. Various bandwidths are available for crystal or mechanical filters — 200 Hz, 400 Hz, 2.1 kHz and the like. The narrower filter responses are used for cw work, but for ssb reception a 2.1- to 2.4-kHz filter is necessary in order to provide sufficient bandwidth for voice signals. The audio output from the receiver would be difficult to decipher if a 400-Hz cw filter was used for ssb work.

We could replace FL3 with an i-f transformer, such as we find at T1 and T2. The transformers by themselves, because they are at 455 kHz, would provide reasonably good selectivity for phone-signal reception. Most early day amateur receivers had no complex i-f filters: They relied upon the selectivity characteristics of the i-f transformers to provide the adjacent-channel selectivity needed. Some receivers used an i-f of 100 kHz, while others employed conversion schemes that provided an intermediate frequency of 250, or even 50 kHz. In all cases a low i-f was chosen because better selectivity could be obtained than if some high i-f were used.

Because all of the incoming primary signals — 28 MHz, 7 MHz, 1.8 MHz or whatever are converted down to a low i-f (455 kHz in Fig. 8), the resultant signal bandwidth is the same for each case, regardless of the bandwidth characteristics of the tuned circuits at the input of the receiver (FL1 and FL2). To summarize, the adjacent-channel selectivity obtained is a measure of receiver ability to single out one of a group of signals that are very close to one another in frequency. If the band occupied by one signal just touched the band occupied by another, the two signals would be on adjacent channels. Having suitable i-f selectivity will help us to copy one of the signals without undue interference from the other.

### Selective I-F Filters

Modern receivers do not rely on the selectivity characteristics of ordinary tuned circuits, such as the transformers in Fig. 8 (T1 and T2). Crystal or mechanical filters are employed in the i-f amplifier circuit of the receiver to establish a desired bandwidth. These filters can be manufactured or home-made for a desired selectivity trait. A quality crystal i-f filter may have two, four, six or even eight crystals working together. Generally speaking, the more crystals used, the greater the sharpness of the filter. Quartz crystals have an extremely high inherent $Q$, and that is why they are ideal for i-f filtering. Crystal filters enable the designer to use a high i-f that would be impractical if

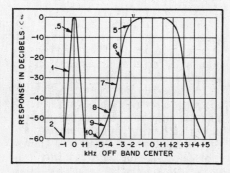

Fig. 9 — Two selectivity curves. The narrow one at the left is very good for code reception but does not pass a wide-enough band of frequencies for good reproduction of voice signals. The curve at the right is a band-pass type intended for phone-signal reception.

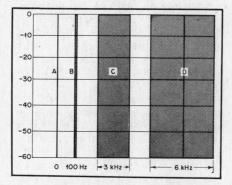

Fig. 10 — Bandwidths of ideal signals of various types. A — unmodulated carrier; B — keyed cw signal; C — signal-sideband signal; D — amplitude-modulated phone signal. This drawing and Fig. 9 are to the same scale, and you can use them as described in the text.

*LC* filters (ordinary tuned circuits) were employed. This means that we can ignore the rule that we must go lower in frequency to obtain adequate selectivity. Crystal filters are built for use in i-f systems that operate from 10.7 MHz down to as low as 100 kHz.

A mechanical filter is one that contains a series of disks which are coupled together with wires. As the i-f signal is passed through the filter, the disks vibrate at their natural resonant frequencies (as crystals do) to establish the

center frequency of the filter. Since they are *mechanically resonant* in nature, the i-f energy must be converted to mechanical energy, then back to i-f energy at the output of the filter. Transducers are used to effect the energy transformation. Mechanical filters have a high-$Q$ characteristic also, and that is why they are able to provide the selectivity we need in a receiver. This type of filter is not practical for use above 500 kHz because of physical problems encountered in the manufacturing process.

### Visualizing Selectivity

The workings of selectivity are not always understood. You may have heard a fellow ham remark that "so and so's carrier is broad as a barn door" — usually about some nearby station with a powerful signal. The fact is that an unmodulated carrier has no width at all. It is just one single frequency. How, then, does the idea get abroad that an unmodulated signal can be "wide"?

Fig. 9 shows two selectivity curves that are reasonably typical of a modern superhet receiver. At 6 dB down from the maximum response, one has a width of 500 hertz (0.5 kHz) and the other has a width of 5000 hertz (5 kHz). The numbers along the sides of the curves show the bandwidth in kilohertz at the point indicated; for example, the bandwidth of the righthand curve is 6 kilohertz at 20 dB down.

Fig. 10 shows the transmitted bandwidths of "ideal" signals of various types. Actual signals would not be confined entirely within the bands shown, but if the transmitter is well-designed and properly operated nearly all of its emission should be inside the limits. Perhaps the single-sideband signal at C is too ideal in this respect. However, a practical ssb transmitter should not have any components less than 30 dB down in the "other" sideband. Such a signal is represented at D by the dashed line cutting off at −30. There should be nothing above this line in the transmitted signal.

### Cardboard "Tuning"

These two figures will give you the basis for an instructive and possibly amusing half hour. Trace Fig. 9 on a piece of paper and paste the tracing on a card. Then cut out the parts *inside* the selectivity curves. Place your tracing on Fig. 10 so that its −60 axis is on top of the −60 axis of Fig. 10. Now slide the tracing sidewise, keeping the two axes together. As the openings pass over the "signals" of Fig. 10, you can see the response build up, as the leading edge of the curve slides over the "signal"; it reaches a maximum at the center of the curve, and then decreases as the trailing edge of the curve passes over it. Finally

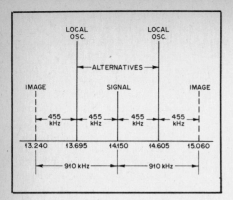

Fig. 11 — In converting to an intermediate frequency we have two choices for the local oscillator frequency, as shown. But either one will bring about response to an undesired frequency or image.

it disappears altogether from the cut-out, and that signal is "tuned out."

This is a representation of what actually happens as you tune through a signal with your receiver. Tuning is simply the process of moving the pass-band of the receiver across a signal (or series of signals, when more than one is present). If you repeat this experiment a number of times with each selectivity curve on each type of signal and observe carefully what is happening to the response, you will soon get a good idea of what selectivity really means. You will see, for instance, that the unmodulated carrier at A "seems" to have width; it appears to be 10 kHz wide with the broad curve but only 2 kHz wide with the sharp curve. In other words, what you observe in tuning across an un-modulated signal is not the width of the signal itself. Its width is zero. What you actually observe is the response curve of the selective circuits of your receiver.

## Bandwidth and Skirt Selectivity

In tuning across a phone signal you can see that the sharp curve will not bring in the entire signal by any means. You need greater bandwidth for receiving phone. Note, however, that although the a-m phone signal is actually 6 kHz wide, it will *seem* wider as you tune through it because you can still hear (that is, see) part of it even when you're far from having it centered in the wider curve.

One other thing this little experiment will do for you is give you some appreciation of the importance of the *shape* of the selectivity curve. Some curves drop off relatively slowly on the sides or *skirts*. You'll hear a signal over a wider arc of the tuning knob with such a curve. If the skirts drop down almost vertically the signal comes in quickly and goes out quickly as you tune through it. Try making up a few curves of various skirt shapes, each with the same bandwidth at 6 dB down, and see

for yourself. You'll soon come to realize the value of *skirt selectivity*.

## Frequency Conversion

Now back to the superhet and frequency conversion. There is another advantage to the frequency-conversion process besides the constant selectivity. An amplifier having a given number of stages operating at a relatively low radio frequency — below 500 kHz, say — can be designed for considerably more gain, with stability, than a similar amplifier at high frequencies. High selectivity and high gain go hand in hand at low frequencies. Thus the superhet solves a major receiving problem in high-frequency reception.

However, frequency conversion also brings in some new problems that weren't there before. They aren't insurmountable, but they do demand care in design and construction.

There is only one known method of frequency conversion that is at all useful for the purpose. This is the process known as *heterodyning* or *beating*. To get a desired new frequency — known universally as the *intermediate frequency* in a superhet receiver — it is necessary to "mix" a third frequency with the signal frequency. The *mixing* process (which differs considerably from ordinary amplification) leads to an interesting result: Two new frequencies appear, one equal to the difference between the original two, and one equal to the sum of the original two. These are in addition to the two original ones, which also appear in the output of a mixer. In the superhet receiver the one we almost always want is the *difference* frequency.

Here is an example: Let us say that our intermediate-frequency amplifier operates at 455 kHz. There is a signal on 14,150 kHz that we want to convert to 455 kHz. Thus 455 kHz will be the difference between 14,150 kHz and a new frequency that we have to introduce in order to effect a conversion. You can readily see that there are *two* frequencies — 13,695 kHz and 14,605 kHz — that will meet the specification. Either one is 455 kHz from 14,150 kHz. The former is 455 kHz lower and the latter 455 kHz higher in frequency. We can use whichever we choose of these two *local-oscillator* frequencies. (They are called local-oscillator frequencies because they are generated by an oscillator in the receiver itself and do not come from outside as the signal does.)

## Image Frequencies

The fact that such a choice exists is one source of trouble in a superhet. For if either of two frequencies will produce a desired output or i-f (intermediate-frequency) signal, it is also true that

each local-oscillator frequency can generate the same difference from two frequencies, one above and one below it. For example, if we should choose 14,605 kHz for the local-oscillator frequency in the case mentioned above, a signal on 15,060 kHz also would be 455 kHz from the local oscillator. Thus we have a new source of interference — so-called *image* signals, or signals on the other side of the local-oscillator frequency (Fig. 11). As you can see from the example, these image signals are always spaced from the desired signal by exactly twice the intermediate frequency (15,060 − 14,150 = 910 kHz, which is twice 455 kHz).

So the superhet solves the problem of uniform selectivity at all frequencies at the cost of introducing a *new* problem in selectivity — that of image rejection.

Here we have to face some hard facts. These image signals are always the same number of kilohertz from the desired signals, regardless of the signal frequency. In percentage, therefore, the image gets closer to the desired signal the higher we go in the spectrum. Unfortunately, there is no way to reject the image signal except by using enough selectivity at the desired-signal frequency. It might seem that we're right back where we started from when we went to the superhet arrangement. And indeed we are, except for one thing: The image interference is always distant, in frequency, from the desired signal by twice the intermediate frequency. It is signals on that frequency *only* that can interfere. And we can have considerable

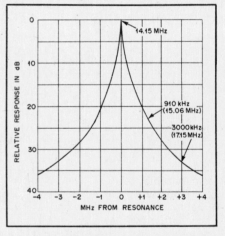

Fig. 12 — This is typical of the selectivity of a single circuit using a good coil at a signal frequency of 14.15 MHz. An image signal at 15.06 MHz (455-kHz i-f) will get through, because the response of the circuit at that frequency is only a little over 20 dB below the response to a desired signal on 14.15 MHz. Changing to a 1500-kHz i-f will add 10 dB to the suppression of the undesired image. In practice, a receiver using either of these i-fs would have at least two such tuned circuits, theoretically doubling the suppression (in decibels) in either case.

control over their rejection. Obviously, the farther the image is from the desired signal the less response a given tuned circuit will have to it, since the response drops off as you move away from the resonant frequency. So we can put the image frequency as far away as possible, by using an intermediate frequency that is fairly high.

### Front-End Image Response

Fig. 12 shows relative response of a typical circuit to signals 900 kHz and 3000 kHz off the resonant frequency of 14,150 kHz. The two i-fs, of course, would be 450 kHz and 1500 kHz. There is a 10-dB improvement in image rejection at the higher intermediate frequency, just because of the way a tuned circuit responds to off-frequency signals.

Actually, at least two such circuits in cascade would be needed to give adequate image rejection at high frequencies, even with the 1500-kHz intermediate frequency. It is for this reason, among others, that receivers of any pretensions at all always have an rf amplifier stage preceding the mixer. There will be one such tuned circuit associated with each of these stages.

### Double Conversion

But again, we've arrived at a happy answer only at the price of new difficulties. Intermediate-frequency amplifiers at 1500 kHz and higher can't be built to have the same selectivity and gain per stage as at frequencies below 500 kHz — at least, not when conventional tuned circuits are used. So we generally find that still *another* frequency conversion is needed — from a first intermediate frequency that is used because it results in good image suppression, to a second intermediate frequency that gives us the close-in or adjacent-channel selectivity we want. This is known as the *double-super* or *double-conversion* arrangement.

Of course, still another local oscillator is necessary, operating on the right frequency to give the appropriate difference. Taking again the signal on 14,150 kHz and assuming a first i-f of 1500 kHz, we need a first local-oscillator frequency of 14,150 + 1,500 = 15,650 kHz. Out of the mixer comes 1500 and suppose we want to convert this to 455 kHz. To do so we need a local oscillator at either 1500 + 455 = 1955 kHz or at 1500 − 455 = 1045 kHz. Usually the higher frequency would be used, because of the next crop of troubles that the superhet brings with it — *spurious responses.*

### Birdies

The image signal we talked about above is a prime example of a spurious response — so called because it is not wanted, even though it is quite legitimately generated. Unfortunately there are still other types. Each of the local oscillators generates harmonics along with the frequency we want from it. If there are two such oscillators, there are endless possibilities for harmonic combinations that will mix to give a difference frequency equal to the i-f, or perhaps to give a spurious signal at the actual frequency to which the receiver is tuned. These birdies can show up in any tuning range, and usually do. They can be kept to a minimum in the ham bands by a judicious choice of the first intermediate frequency. But the more oscillators there are going simultaneously in the receiver, the more birdies there are — and it is not just a simple proportion!

Altogether, the superhet receiver would seem to be a kind of Pandora's box, with all sorts of undesirable things popping out of it. Nevertheless, the advantages in selectivity and gain, over a very wide tuning range, do outweigh these side effects — provided care is used in design and construction to minimize the spurious responses of various sorts. A good receiver will reduce them to the point where they are rarely noticeable. We have emphasized them here to make you appreciate the fact that they do exist, that no receiver is *wholly* free from them. A little knowledge on this point may save you the embarrassment of having to eat your words after complaining vociferously about some station being off frequency or invading a ham band — when the signal actually was a "phantom" conjured up by the receiver itself!

### Identification

There are ways of recognizing birdies and images for what they are, although sometimes it takes a good deal of experience. Spurious signals generated by the receiver itself will be unmodulated (or nearly so — sometimes there may be a little hum on a birdie) and will be there all the time. They will not usually be affected by the antenna, so if you take off the antenna and the signal is still there as big as ever, you can blame it on the receiver.

Images, of course, are signals coming from outside, and will disappear along with the "legitimate" signals when you disconnect the antenna. However, you can often spot them. If the image signal happens to be close enough in frequency to an actual signal to make an audible beat tone or heterodyne, there is an easy test. Vary the receiver tuning back and forth slightly. If the beat tone changes, one of the signals is an image. If the tone does *not* change, both signals are "legitimate." Of course, the character of the signal can be a clue, too; we don't expect to find commercial or

broadcasting stations working in bands that are exclusively amateur worldwide. But in other parts of the world some sections of the amateur bands are shared with commercial and government users, so unless you know your frequency assignments pretty well, and can measure frequency pretty accurately, you can't always depend on the nature of the signal itself to tell you whether it is real or spurious.

### Controls on a Typical Receiver

Fig. 13 shows the front panel of an imaginary modern receiver. The controls are labeled to identify their functions. The preselector we discussed in the foregoing section of text should be adjusted at the front panel for maximum signal response at the frequency of interest. Thus, if we wanted to listen to a QSO on 3900 kHz we would set the band switch to 80 meters, adjust the main tuning dial to 400 (3900 kHz), put the mode switch in the lsb (lower sideband) position, tune in the signal for best audio quality, then adjust the preselector control for a maximum S-meter reading as the operators talked. If no signals were present at the time you set the receiver up for reception at some chosen frequency, the preselector could be set fairly close by adjusting it for maximum noise in the speaker. On 160, 80, 40 and 20 meters there is usually enough noise coming in on the antenna to make this easy to do. On 15 meters and higher the greater part of the noise may come from *within* the receiver, but the preselector can be peaked while using receiver noise. You may have to listen a bit more carefully for the peak if the latter technique is used.

Most up-to-date amateur receivers cover only the ham bands — 160, 80, 40, 20, 15 and 10 meters. A general-

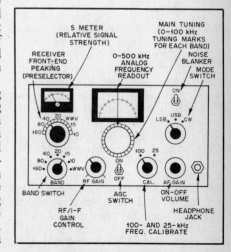

Fig. 13 — This is the front panel of a typical modern amateur receiver. The labels identify the control functions (see text).

coverage type of receiver will provide continuous frequency coverage from, say, 550 kHz to 30 MHz, and will have two tuning dials. One is for fast tuning across a spread of several megahertz and is called the *bandset* control. The remaining dial is the *bandspread* control. It is used to provide a slow tuning rate for a small portion (kilohertz usually) of the range covered by the bandset dial. Most older amateur receivers were of the general-coverage variety, and the bandspread dial was calibrated for the amateur bands so that the operator would know what frequency his receiver was tuned to. Therefore, if one wanted to listen to 3900 kHz, the bandset dial was adjusted to 4 MHz, and the bandspread dial would provide a frequency readout of 3500 to 4000 kHz, usually in rather broad frequency increments (5 or 10 kHz per dial mark).

The divisions on the main tuning dials of most modern receivers provide 1-kHz increments. This is known as the *frequency resolution*. A dial with only 10-kHz markers would be considered as one with low resolution; a 5-kHz dial would provide moderate resolution; the 1-kHz increments would give the operator high resolution. The latter is preferred by the modern amateur because it enables him to find a frequency of interest more precisely than was possible with older receivers.

The dial mechanism shown in Fig. 13 provides two frequency scales or indicators. The dial plate in the rectangular window at the upper center is usually marked off in 25-kHz increments, and tunes a range of 500 kHz. The main tuning knob below it has 1-kHz divisions. The low end of each band is at 0 on the upper dial plate, and the high end of the band will be somewhere near 500 on the dial — depending upon how many kHz are available for amateur use in a given band. For example, on 80 meters we would find 3500 kHz at 0 on the dial, and 4000 kHz would appear at 500 on the main dial. The skirt on the tuning knob would provide 100 kHz of tuning-range calibration in 1-kHz divisions. This being the case, if we wanted to tune the receiver to 3725 kHz, we would first adjust the main dial to read 200 (3700 kHz), and the skirt on the tuning knob would read 0. Next, we would adjust the knob until the skirt plate read 25. Our receiver would now be set for operation at 3725 kHz. The accuracy would depend, of course, on how well the manufacturer designed the receiver VFO (linear response) and the accompanying dial mechanism with its frequency markers. A well-designed unit will hold its calibration within a hundred hertz over the complete tuning range of a given amateur band. But, some receivers need to be recalibrated as

the operator moves the dial from one part of an amateur band to another. Calibration is done by turning on the frequency calibrator within the receiver — a crystal-controlled oscillator which provides 100- and/or 25-kHz beat notes. The oscillator is adjusted for zero beat with WWV several times a year to assure its accuracy — a simple task. Most modern receivers have a friction-fit dial plate on the main tuning knob, and to calibrate the dial for 1-kHz accuracy it is necessary only to turn on the calibrator oscillator, grasp the knob of the main tuning control, and slip the 1-kHz dial skirt so that it reads zero at the frequency where the 100-kHz beat note is heard. The dial mechanism we have just discussed is known as the *analog-readout* type.

Many of today's receivers use *digital frequency readout*. Instead of having dial plates with numbers, the receiver has an LED 7-segment type of electronic display, which when illuminated, has numbers that light up in red or blue to show the exact frequency of the receiver within 0.1 kHz (100 Hz). The display window usually has six significant numbers. Therefore, if we were to tune the receiver to 14,250 kHz exactly, the display would read 14,250.0, and if we were not quite on frequency it might read something like, 14,250.2. This would mean that the receiver was set approximately 200 Hz or 0.2 kHz too high. When digital frequency readout is employed there is no need to recalibrate the receiver when moving about within an amateur band: The frequency counter which drives the digital display keeps accurate track of the frequency for us and tells the LED display what to indicate numerically! It is necessary, however, to check the accuracy of the frequency counter within the receiver from time to time. It has its own crystal oscillator (time base), and with aging the crystal accuracy may change. The crystal usually has a frequency trimmer which the operator can adjust so that the counter and its display can be set precisely to the frequency of WWV, the National Bureau of Standards station.

## Other Receiver Controls

The illustration of Fig. 13 shows an *agc* switch at the lower center of the panel. All manufactured receivers have an automatic gain control (agc) circuit. The purpose of agc is to prevent loud signals from being too loud in the speaker or headphones. That is, the stronger the signal, the harder the agc works to lower the signal strength before it reaches the speaker. A well-designed agc system will make an S-1 signal and an S-9 signal sound the same in the speaker, in terms of loudness. The weaker signal might have more noise in it, but the loudness will be the same as

that of the stronger signal. Agc is primarily a convenience feature for the operator — to keep him from being uncomfortable when he suddenly tunes across a loud signal while the audio level of the receiver is at a high setting. Many good homemade receivers have no agc circuit, but with equipment of that type the operator must keep his hand close to the rf or af gain control most of the time. If the receiver has an agc on-off switch (some don't), the user can disable the agc to aid reception of very weak signals. Also, some very strong signals tend to overload a receiver, and by turning off the agc and reducing the setting of the rf-gain control the reception can be improved. Both the agc and rf-gain control affect the gain of the receiver rf and i-f amplifier stages. The rf gain can be considered a *manual gain control* (mgc), while the agc is *automatic* in nature.

In a typical situation, where the agc is disabled, the operator will set the af gain fairly high and will use the rf gain as his volume control. When this is done the af gain is ignored and remains at its original high setting.

At the right center of the panel in Fig. 13 we have a mode switch. It provides lsb, usb and cw positions. The lower-sideband (lsb) mode is used on 160, 80 and 40 meters by most amateurs. On 20, 15 and 10 meters they prefer the upper-sideband mode (usb), although usb or lsb is suitable on any amateur band. This peculiar choice of modes is the result of early-day ssb designs in which simplified circuitry caused the lsb mode to appear on the lower bands, and the usb mode to occur on the higher bands. Even though modern transmitters and receivers are designed to accommodate both modes on all bands, the effect from yester-year's equipment remains to haunt us.

A *noise-blanker* switch can be seen at the upper right in Fig. 13. Some modern receivers have a blanker built in, and it is a useful feature when noise pulses of short duration (spark-plug noise for one) impair reception. However, few noise blankers have a worthwhile effect on ordinary hash types of noise or atmospheric QRN. Noise blankers are used in the i-f amplifier section of a receiver, and in some designs they actually impair receiver performance when they are turned on: receiver overloading can take place. Noise blankers are useful during mobile operation on 20, 15 and 10 meters, and in situations where the amateur lives near a highway when passing cars cause QRN.

The last significant item on the panel of our imaginary receiver is seen at the upper left. It is an S meter (signal-level meter). This is no doubt the most *used and abused* adornment on a receiver. An

S-meter face plate contains markings in S units and decibels, neither of which can be relied upon when issuing signal-strength reports to other stations. Yet, many amateurs — new and old — consider the meter reading as the gospel truth.

In bygone days, at least one receiver manufacturer made an effort to calibrate his S meters so that each S unit was equal to 6 decibels, and so that the S-9 reference point was equivalent to 50 microvolts of signal strength. The markings above S9 were rendered in decibels — usually up to 40 over S9. Although it is possible to calibrate a meter in that manner, the accuracy will hold over just one amateur band. This is because the receiver has different overall gain characteristics for each band. This is brought about by differences in the performance traits of transistors, ICs and tubes versus the operating frequency. The front-end tuned circuits differ from band to band also, and are more lossy at some frequencies than at others, depending upon how much care was put into the circuit design.

It can be realized from the foregoing discussion that an S meter is primarily a gimmick for the operator to use as a topic of discussion in a QSO. Its usefulness can be utilized, however, while making comparative readings (relative reading) when some station operator switches antennas or power levels, or when one wants to give comparative signal reports to two or more stations in a round-table QSO. But to rely on what the meter face indicates is pure folly. A signal that reads 20 dB over S9 might be only S8 in a *real* situation, or vice versa.

## Receiver Circuits

At this juncture you are acquainted with how basic receivers operate — simple detectors to superheterodynes, inclusive. This book would be an enormous one if we went into all of the details of all of the subjects covered, but we should look a bit more closely at receiver circuits in a superhet before moving along to the next chapter. A detailed discussion of receiver design, written for beginners, was presented in six installments during 1974 in *QST* by DeMaw and McCoy. The fine points were covered in that series, and you may wish to study that material for additional information.

Meanwhile, let's examine the workings of a simple superheterodyne receiver of the type illustrated in the block diagram of Fig. 14. The schematic diagrams which follow in numerical sequence are representative of typical circuits which one could equate to our block diagram. It should be stressed that all of the circuits shown are intended as tutorial aids rather than being suggested as material for practical duplication.

The diagram of Fig. 14 shows a receiver which tunes the 75- and 80-meter bands. Regardless of the hf amateur band of interest, the circuit layout would be essentially the same. We start at Q1, where the signal energy from the antenna system is fed to an rf amplifier. Q1 builds up the signal level and supplies the increased energy to the mixer, Q2. At this point we develop our intermediate frequency of 9 MHz. This is done by beating some energy in the 5.0- to 5.5-MHz range with the 3.5- to 4.0-MHz signal from the antenna and rf amplifier. The mixer output is *sum* of the two frequencies — 9 MHz in this case. We chose 9 MHz as the i-f because it is possible to purchase i-f filters for use at 9 MHz. Other i-fs could be used just as easily, provided the amateur could build his own filter, or buy one for the frequency of interest.

Output from the mixer is routed through FL1 so that we can establish a selectivity characteristic for our receiver that fits our needs (2.4 kHz for ssb, or 500 Hz for cw work). In Fig. 14 we have used a filter and BFO crystal that will provide the necessary features for cw reception.

Now that we have "laundered" the incoming (primary) signal by passing it through an i-f filter, we must amplify it to make up for the loss in the filter (usually 5 to 10 dB of loss, depending on the type of filter employed). This reduction in signal level is referred to as *insertion loss*.

Before we move ahead to the i-f amplifier stages (Q5 and Q6), let's stop along the way and look at the local-oscillator section of the receiver, Q3 and Q4. Our variable-frequency oscillator, Q3, provides the necessary tuning range at 75 and 80 meters by generating an injection voltage for the mixer which runs from 5.0 to 5.5 MHz. If we were to connect the output of Q3 to the mixer directly, we would probably experience a condition known as "pulling." The effects of such a condition are observed when one tunes the preselector (tuned circuits for the rf amplifier stage). The tuning process changes the load that the oscillator looks into, and that causes a slight change in oscillator frequency. So that we might lessen that effect to a degree that makes it unnoticeable we have added a *buffer* stage, Q4. The buffer tends to isolate Q3 from Q2, and that practically eliminates the pulling condition. The more stages used as buffers, up to a practical point, the better the isolation between the oscillator and the mixer. The greatest number of buffer stages found in a typical circuit is three.

Our circuit contains two i-f amplifiers: Q5 and Q6 build up the level of the signal after it emerges from FL1. So that the weak signals will sound similar in strength to the stronger ones, we have included an agc circuit (Q11 and Q12). The higher the strength of the incoming signal from the antenna, the more the agc circuit reduces the gain of the two i-f stages, which in turn tends to level the output of the receiver in the headphones.

Output from the i-f amplifiers is routed to a product detector (CR1 and CR2), which converts the i-f energy to

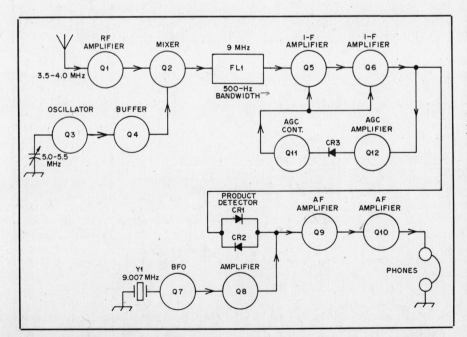

Fig. 14 — Block diagram of a typical single-conversion superheterodyne receiver. The arrows indicate the direction the signal voltages move.

audio-frequency intelligence which the human ear can discern. The i-f energy is heterodyned by the 9.007-MHz voltage generated at Q7 to produce a 700-Hz frequency product in the audio range. This gives us a 700-Hz audio note while copying cw. An amplifier is used after the BFO to build up the developed energy to a level that is suitable for the product detector.

A two-stage audio amplifier (Q9 and Q10) follow the product detector. These amplifiers bring the audio-frequency energy up to a level that is adequate for driving our headphones.

## RF Amplifiers

Some modern receivers do not feature an rf amplifier stage between the antenna and the mixer. In the past some manufacturers left the rf stage out of their receivers in an effort to cut the cost of the product. A receiver of that type is thought to be an "inexpensive" or "cheap" one, and indeed that was often the case. The major shortcoming in a receiver of that kind was insufficient rejection of out-of-band signals, poor sensitivity (especially on 20, 15 and 10 meters), and noisy performance on the higher bands. Mixers generate a considerable amount of internal noise and have less gain than most rf-amplifier stages do. The real purpose of an rf-amplifier stage is to build up the incoming signal so that it overcomes the noise generated in the mixer.

A properly designed modern receiver should not require an rf amplifier on 160, 80, 40 and 20 meters if the remainder of the circuit is designed correctly in terms of noise and gain distribution. The advantage in feeding the signals to the mixer directly (through a front-end filter) is an improvement in receiver *dynamic range*. In simple terms, high dynamic range can be defined as that characteristic which prevents the circuit from being overloaded in the presence of strong signals which are on or apart from the frequency to which the receiver has been tuned. If the dynamic range is poor, the receiver can be desensitized by strong signals that may be many kilohertz away from the frequency we are interested in. The effect is one of having the overall receiver gain decrease, and that is especially troublesome during weak-signal reception. Another effect is seen as *IMD* (intermodulation distortion). The strong unwanted signal or signals will appear at many places in the receiver tuning range, and that is caused by unwanted mixer products being generated and passed along to the remainder of the receiver. A high-gain rf amplifier, when used ahead of a mixer, can cause the mixer to perform poorly with regard to dynamic range. Therefore, with some types of mixers it is better to avoid

using an rf amplifier. Another effect of overloading is called *cross-modulation*. This phenomenon is observed as we find one signal in a band being superimposed on a weaker one. In ssb reception it can sound as though two stations are talking at the same time, and neither signal will be easy to understand. During cw reception we may find two cw signals blending together, with the strongest one chopping up the lesser one, or an ssb signal may become superimposed on the weak cw signal. Some inexperienced amateurs have been known to accuse the owner of the interfering station of having a "dirty" transmitter or of over-modulating the carrier. The truth of the matter is that the receiver being used had poor dynamic range. The cure for overloading — aside from redesigning the receiver — is to put a resistive attenuator between the antenna and the receiver, or by using a short piece of wire as the receiving antenna. The net effect during either cure is a reduction in the level of the signals coming into the receiver. This represents a sacrifice in receiver performance, however, as it will impair weak-signal performance.

A poorly designed rf amplifier stage can produce its own IMD, so if care is not taken in that part of a receiver the bad effects we have discussed concerning mixers can be compounded by those of an inferior mixer. We must be careful not to overload the rf amplifier in the presence of very strong signals. Furthermore, the rf amplifier should be set up so that it delivers only the gain needed to override the noise of the mixer. In broad terms this is known as *gain distribution*. The latter is applicable throughout a receiver — careful gain distribution in the interest of low noise and adequate overall receiver gain, right on out to the speaker or headphones!

Fig. 15 shows two types of rf amplifiers for use ahead of a receiver mixer. The circuit at A uses a dual-gate MOSFET which has been configured for moderate gain. Although Q1 could be made to provide up to 25 dB of signal gain, the amplification capability has been degraded purposely to a level of approximately 15 dB. Here we have resorted to an intentional mismatch. We have tapped the gate-1 and drain elements of Q1 at a low point on the tuned circuits. Therefore, the amount of signal appearing on gate 1 will be considerably lower than would be the case if gate 1 were attached to the top of L2. This practice will help prevent Q1 from being overloaded in the presence of strong signals. The closer we tap gate 1 near ground, the lower the stage gain. We

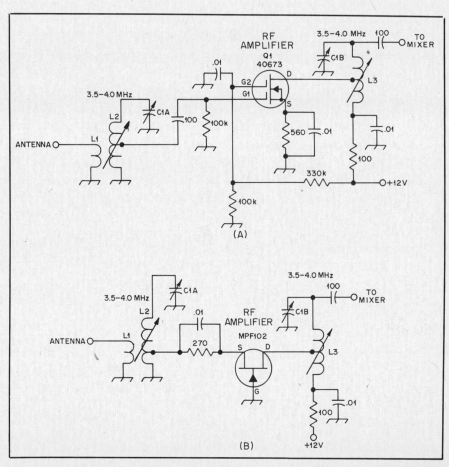

Fig. 15 — Diagrams of two FET rf amplifier stages. The one at A is a common-source, dual-gate MOSFET amplifier. At B is a junction FET amplifier operating in the common-gate mode.

have also tapped the drain of Q1 at a low point on the coil (L3) to lower the stage gain. A secondary effect of doing that is an improvement in the *Q* of the tuned circuit (reduced loading on L3), which helps improve the selectivity of the output-tuned circuit.

At Fig. 15B we find a common-gate JFET rf amplifier. It has a maximum gain capability of around 15 dB. With the source tapped well down on L2 and with the drain connected near the mid-point of L3, an intentional mismatch results. The gain of this amplifier is approximately 10 dB — adequate for most receiver designs. A common-gate FET amplifier has two advantages over the type shown in Fig. 15A: It is less apt to self-oscillate, and will exhibit good IMD characteristics. Either amplifier in Fig. 15 is suitable for use with the mixer shown in Fig. 16.

The two tuned circuits of the rf amplifier, L2/C1A and L3/C1B, act as tunable band-pass filters to help reduce images, and to keep out-of-band signals from entering the receiver. C1A is a two-gang variable capacitor which would be accessible at the receiver front panel as the preselector control.

## Mixers

Mixers are also called *converters*, because they convert the incoming signal in a superhet receiver to an intermediate frequency. For our discussion, however, we will label them as mixers. There are several kinds of mixers, and each has its advantages and disadvantages. There are single-ended mixers (Fig. 16A), single balanced mixers and doubly balanced mixers. Also, we have *active* and *passive mixers*. Fig. 16B shows a passive mixer of the doubly balanced variety.

An active mixer is one that requires a dc operating voltage. It usually has at least *unity gain* (a gain of 1), or considerable gain (*conversion gain*). A passive mixer, on the other hand, has no operating-voltage requirement, and exhibits a signal loss — *conversion loss*. An active mixer can have a conversion gain from unity to perhaps 15 dB, whereas a passive mixer may have a conversion loss as great as 10 dB. The gain of the rf amplifier, which precedes a mixer should, therefore, be set in accordance with the mixer gain. As a general rule of thumb, we should ensure that the circuit gain between the antenna and the mixer output is at least unity, and preferably somewhat more than unity. This will permit us to realize an acceptable noise figure for the receiver, while providing workable sensitivity.

A single balanced mixer is one that is arranged to have a push-pull input and push-pull output characteristic. The circuit can employ diodes (passive) or transistors (active). The advantage is one of cancellation (within the mixer) of the oscillator energy which is fed to the mixer. In other words there is less chance for the oscillator energy to appear at the mixer output (unwanted) than in the case of a single-ended mixer.

When a doubly balanced mixer is employed, the three mixer terminals are rather well isolated from one another, which helps to keep the mixer output pure. Balanced mixers can offer as much as 50 dB of internal cancellation of the rf-input and oscillator energies.

The principle disadvantages of diode mixers are that they are lossy and require considerably more oscillator injection voltage than is necessary with active mixers. There are many devices that are suitable as mixers — diodes, bipolar transistors, FETs and integrated circuits. Of the active devices an FET is usually the better choice as it will be less prone to overloading than a bipolar transistor. Mixer types of integrated circuits contain bipolar transistors, so they are also more subject to overloading than FETs.

In Fig. 16A we have specified a dual-gate MOSFET as a mixer. It can be thought of as a tetrode tube, with the source acting as a cathode, the drain as the plate, gate 2 as the screen grid and gate 1 as the control grid. R1 is chosen to generate enough bias to bring the operating point near drain-current cutoff. Then the positive swings of the signal at gate 1 cause the drain current to increase more than the negative swings cause it to decrease. The amplification will not be the same for signals of all strengths but will vary with the amplitude of the signal.

The oscillator (Fig. 17) generates and supplies injection voltage to the mixer at gate 2. Because the gate-to-gate capacitance of Q2 is very low, the isolation between the oscillator and the incoming rf signal will be quite good, and that will greatly minimize pulling effects when the preselector is adjusted, or when strong signals are present. The local-oscillator energy is mixed at Q2 with the incoming rf signal to produce the desired i-f, which in this example is 9 MHz.

Unlike a straight-through amplifier, the mixer drain circuit amplifies only the i-f energy. Therefore, the drain circuit is arranged so that only the desired i-f beat is selected and passed along to the i-f amplifier stages. Remember, in this example there are two beats available at the mixer output — 9 MHz and 1.5 MHz. Because we are interested only in the 9-MHz beat, we have included a filter, FL1, at the mixer output. FL1 will pass only the desired 9-MHz i-f signal and will establish the receiver selectivity at the same time. FL1 will also reject the oscillator frequency (5.0 to 5.5 MHz) and the signal frequency (3.5 to 4.0 MHz). In receivers which don't contain complex i-f filters the unwanted signal and mixing components must be rejected by the tuned i-f transformers which follow the mixer.

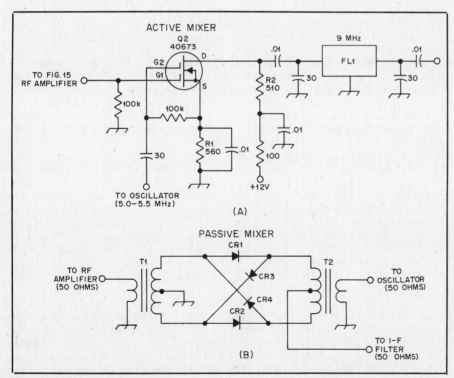

Fig. 16 — Circuit examples of active and passive mixers. R2 at A is chosen to match the characteristic impedance of the i-f filter (FL1). At B, we see a doubly balanced diode-ring passive mixer (see text).

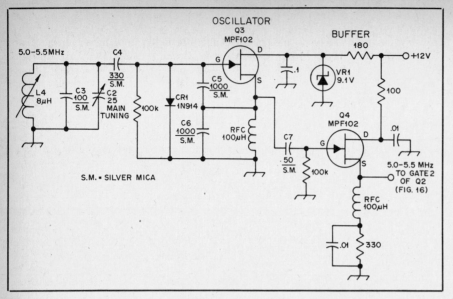

Fig. 17 — Schematic diagram of a typical local oscillator which provides stable operation.

Many early day receivers were built in that manner. A good modern amateur receiver will contain a high-grade i-f filter after the mixer.

The main advantage in using a fairly high i-f (9 MHz as opposed to 455 kHz, for example) is that the opportunity for image problems is greatly diminished because the signal is separated by a considerable amount from the i-f. Also, the oscillator and incoming signal frequencies are spread quite far apart, and that minimizes the pulling effects we talked about earlier.

The doubly balanced diode-ring mixer seen in Fig. 16B is preferred by many designers. It will assure good receiver dynamic range and excellent mixer balance. However, it would require some matching networks at its three terminals in order to make it compatible with the filter at Fig. 16A, the rf amplifier in Fig. 15, and the oscillator of Fig. 17. The mixer has a characteristic impedance of 50 ohms at all three terminals, which requires that it be matched to the circuits with which it is used. Furthermore, the oscillator of Fig. 17 would not provide sufficient injection voltage for the diode-ring mixer: An additional amplifier stage would be required. Also, a well-designed receiver would probably have a low-noise i-f amplifier between it and FL1 to compensate for the approximate 8-dB conversion loss of the mixer.

### The Local Oscillator

Perhaps the most important feature of a local oscillator is its stability. Our primary objective is to have it stay put once it has been tuned to the desired frequency. An otherwise good receiver can be a "disaster machine" if the oscillator is mechanically and/or electrically unstable. The more selective the receiver, the more pronounced the effects of instability.

Electrical instability results mainly from heat changes within the oscillator components, or from temperature changes in the general area of the oscillator circuit. Rf currents flowing within the various parts of the circuit — resistors, coils, capacitors and transistors — cause component heating, however minor. The heating causes changes in component values, and that leads to a shift in operating frequency. Rf and dc current within the transistors causes changes in internal capacitance (junction capacitance) and resistance. For these reasons it is important to design an oscillator which is relatively immune to heating effects. Some capacitors are less subject to temperature changes than others, so for use in the frequency-determining part of the actual oscillator stage it is best to employ silver-mica or polystyrene capacitors (C3 through C7, inclusive, Fig. 17): Polystyrene capacitors are somewhat more stable than silver-mica ones.

Half-watt resistors are better than 1/8- or 1/4-watt ones because they are less apt to go through changes in resistance from heating if they are physically large. Furthermore, the distributed capacitance across the larger resistors is less than it is with small resistors: Reducing stray capacitance will aid stability.

By keeping the power level of the oscillator as low as possible, we can reduce the dc and rf currents within the device, and that will greatly improve stability. It is always better to keep the oscillator power low, then build up the power amount by means of amplifier stages after the oscillator.

Another important step toward stability is the use of regulated supply voltage at the oscillator — or at all stages in the oscillator chain (VR1 of Fig. 17). Changes in supply voltage, although they may be minor, will cause the operating frequency to change. The dc voltage supplied to the oscillator should be pure (free of hum and noise). If it is not, the hum or noise will be injected into the mixer along with the desired energy, and the output signal of the receiver will sound mushy or buzzy. A high-$Q$ oscillator tuned circuit (L4-C2-C3) will help assure a low noise bandwidth within the oscillator itself. The greater the tuned-circuit $Q$, the lower the oscillator-noise bandwidth.

Mechanical instability is caused by vibrations of component parts in the circuit. The pigtails on capacitors and resistors should be kept as short and rigid as possible to minimize that effect. Similarly, the coil and variable capacitor leads should be short and stiff. A well-built variable capacitor and dial mechanism should be employed, and the double-bearing type of variable is preferred for best mechanical stability (a bearing at each end of the rotor shaft). The chassis or circuit board upon which the oscillator circuit is built should also be rigid. Any flexing of the chassis or related parts will cause shifts in oscillator frequency. The entire oscillator circuit should be housed in a metal shield compartment. This will keep unwanted rf energy from getting into the oscillator circuit and will reduce the effects of ambient temperature changes within the immediate area of the oscillator (drafts and such).

In the circuit of Fig. 17 the operating frequency is determined by the combination of capacitances presented by C2 through C6, inclusive, and L4. Our main tuning control is C2, a variable capacitor that is accessible at the receiver front panel. A vernier drive mechanism is normally used to slow down the tuning rate of the oscillator. A 5:1 to 10:1 reduction ratio is suitable for most amateur work.

In our circuit we have added a gimmick to help the stability of Q3 — a diode, CR1. By adding the clamping diode to the gate of an FET, we achieve two desired results: We lessen the harmonic output of the oscillator and reduce the changes in transistor junction capacitance during oscillation. CR1 must be a high-speed rf unit (switching diode), and a 1N914 suits the need. It clamps the positive-going rf sine-wave peak at approximately 0.7 volt (the barrier voltage of the silicon diode), which limits the FET transconductance. Although the diode does not stop oscillation, it does reduce the change in junction capacitance considerably. This aids stability and reduces the harmonic

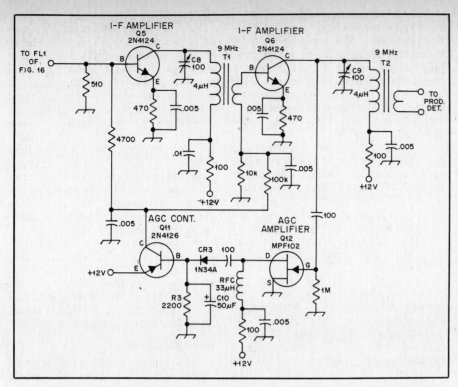

Fig. 18 — Example of a bipolar-transistor i-f amplifier. An agc circuit is shown also. See text for a discussion of this circuit.

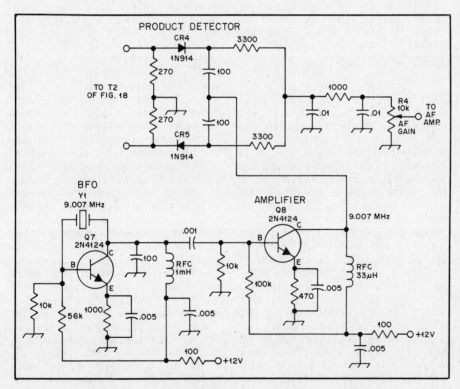

Fig. 19 — Circuit diagram of a two-diode balanced product detector and BFO chain.

output of the oscillator. The harmonic currents are reduced because the change in FET junction capacitance during the sine-wave excursion occurs in a non-linear manner, and nonlinearity in any active or passive device encourages harmonics.

Output from Q3 (Fig. 17) is routed to a source-follower buffer stage, Q4. An FET is used at Q4 to minimize loading effects on the oscillator. The gate of an FET is of very high imped-ance (megohms), making it an ideal ·device for the purpose. Coupling capaci-

tor C7 is small in value to help reduce loading at the output of Q3. The 100-kΩ resistor at the gate of Q4 establishes the impedance of the circuit because it is much lower in resistance than the natural impedance of the FET gate. Output from the oscillator chain is taken across a 100-μH rf choke, which is broadly self-resonant at 5 MHz. A source follower does not provide a voltage gain, but a slight power gain is realized.

## I-F Amplifiers

When we get to the i-f strip of a receiver, we have a small duty to per-form — that of building up the signal level from the output of the i-f filter. I-f amplifiers can be built from tubes, bipolar transistors, FETs, or ICs. For the purpose of simplified illustration we have selected two bipolar transistors, Q5 and Q6 of Fig. 18, for the purpose. The operating principle is the same, regard-less of the active device used.

It is necessary that an i-f filter be terminated in its characteristic imped-ance if it is to function as a filter. Therefore, we have used a 510-ohm resistor in the base-bias network of Q5. We shall assume that FL1 of Fig. 16 is a Spectrum International KVG filter, which has a terminal impedance of 500 ohms. The 510-ohm base resistor gives the filter a suitable load to work into.

The i-f signal is amplified consid-erably by Q5 (roughly 20 dB), then is fed to Q6 for further amplification. T1 is designed to transform the 10,000-ohm collector impedance (approximate) of Q5 to a base impedance of 1000 ohms at Q6. This will assure maximum transfer of signal energy. T2 is used to transform the collector impedance to approximately 500 ohms, which is suit-able for looking into the product de-tector of Fig. 19. Toroidal transformers are ideal for the purpose, as the builder can wind them to yield the turns ratios necessary for proper impedance matching (the impedance ratio is the square of the turns ratio). Q5 and Q6 have been biased for Class A linear amplification. T1 and T2 are peaked at the center frequency of i-f filter FL1. Trimmer capacitors C8 and C9 are used for this purpose.

## Applying AGC

We have lauded the virtues of agc earlier in this chapter, but let's look more closely at how agc functions. A greatly simplified agc circuit is shown in Fig. 18, but it is satisfactory for illus-trative purposes.

Amplified i-f energy is sampled at the output of Q6 through a 100-pF coupling capacitor. Q12 is used to in-crease the i-f signal level before it is rectified by means of CR3. An FET is used at Q12 to minimize loading of the tuned circuit formed by C9 and the primary of T2.

Q11 is operated as a pnp-transistor attenuator. At low signal levels it is switched to an *on* mode by means of the 2200-ohm base resistor which goes to ground. This permits full dc voltage to flow from the Q11 emitter to collector, and in turn to the base-bias circuits of Q5 and Q6. In this condition the i-f amplifiers are operating at full gain, which is really what we want when the incoming signal from the antenna is weak. As the received signal becomes stronger, the rectified i-f voltage at CR3 increases in level, thereby bringing Q11 out of its fully on mode. As the positive bias at the base of Q11 increases, Q11 moves farther toward nonconduction. This causes the base bias for Q5 and Q6 to lessen, and the i-f strip gain drops. Through this process we realize a gain-leveling effect at the headphones or speaker — the main purpose of agc. A good communications receiver will have an agc range between 60 and 100 dB. The actual range will depend upon how much gain the i-f strip has in the first place, plus the control capability of the agc system.

Agc does not have to be developed from the output of the i-f strip. Alternatively, audio-frequency energy can be sampled at some point ahead of the audio-gain control, rectified and supplied to a control stage such as Q11.

Whether the agc is rf or audio derived, a time constant must be included in the agc system to smooth out the agc action. No two operators seem to prefer the same delay time for an agc circuit, so the absolute time constant is rather arbitrary. A discharge time of one second seems popular for cw and ssb work, and that can be effected by means of a parallel resistance and capacitance just after the agc rectifier (R3 and C10 of Fig. 18). The greater the capacitance at C10, the longer the delay period, and vice versa.

### The Product Detector

Product detectors function essentially as mixers do. That is, they are supplied with two rf energies so that a third, or product frequency, can result. The primary distinction between the two is that a product detector provides an audio-frequency output rather than an i-f output. As is true of mixers, product detectors can be of the active or passive variety. The same gain and loss rules apply.

But now that we have greatly amplified the signal level by means of an i-f strip, there is no real need for an active type of detector. The remaining amount of receiver gain can be obtained with audio amplifiers. Our choice is the circuit of Fig. 19, wherein a pair of diodes (CR4 and CR5) function as the detector. The diodes rectify our i-f energy and convert it to audio information. However, without a BFO (beat-frequency oscillator), we would hear only thumps in the speaker during cw reception or mushy voice sounds while copying ssb. Therefore, we must insert a carrier of the appropriate frequency (9 MHz) by means of a BFO such as the one shown in Fig. 19.

A pair of 270-ohm resistors are connected across the secondary winding of T2 in Fig. 18 to create a center tap for the balanced detector. A capacitive divider is formed by placing two 100-pF fixed-value capacitors in series after the diodes. The BFO energy is injected at the junction of the capacitors. A value of 7 to 10 volts peak is about right for the detector circuit shown. It is necessary to keep the BFO energy out of the audio amplifier, and that measure is assured by the two 3300-ohm resistors, the 1000-ohm one, and the two .01-$\mu$F bypass capacitors just ahead of the af gain control, R4. The resistors and capacitors act as an rf filter at the detector output. There will be some reduction in the available detector-output signal because of the series resistors ahead of R4. The three fixed-value resistors and R4 comprise a resistive divider, and that will effectively tap the audio amplifier down on the detector output. However, there is ample gain available to prevent a degradation in receiver performance.

### The BFO Circuit

In order to obtain maximum performance from a product detector, it is necessary to supply considerably more BFO energy to the detector than is available from the i-f amplifier. Some designers feel that a ratio of 10:1 is a good ball-park figure between the i-f signal and the BFO injection voltage. If the BFO injection level is too low, the signals will not sound clean in the headphones or speaker. Furthermore, the conversion loss of the detector will increase with reduced BFO injection.

Modern receivers employ crystal-controlled BFOs, and that results in good frequency stability. Most older receivers used a BFO circuit that was similar to a tunable local oscillator, and a *pitch control* was available on the front panel of the receiver. The operator was required to set the BFO frequency precisely if he was to obtain proper usb, lsb or cw reception. Some amateurs never did get the hang of setting the frequency correctly, and it was a pain in the neck to get things adjusted properly. The crystal-control technique is much better, as it requires only a panel-mounted switch for selecting the correct BFO crystal for usb reception, a second one for lsb use, and a third crystal for cw applications. This assures good sta-

bility and ease of operation.

At Fig. 19 we find a single crystal, Y1, for controlling Q7. The frequency listed is for cw reception, providing an audio beat of 700 Hz. If single-sideband reception is desired, the circuit can be modified to include two additional crystals — one for usb and another for lsb reception. A single-pole, three-position switch would be used to connect the desired crystal to the BFO circuit.

A Pierce oscillator is used at Q7. Its output is supplied to an untuned amplifier, Q8. The latter builds up the BFO voltage to a suitable level for injecting the product detector. The 33-$\mu$H collector choke at Q8 is broadly self-resonant at 9 MHz. Although it should not be necessary to do so, the designer may apply regulated voltage to his receiver BFO as an aid to stability. A well-designed crystal oscillator should not require a regulated supply voltage.

### Audio Amplification

It is seldom practical to design a receiver which has enough audio output available from the product detector to drive a pair of headphones — at least when copying weak signals. Therefore, an audio amplifier always follows the detector. The circuit of Fig. 20 provides approximately 40 dB of gain, and that is more than adequate for good headphone volume with the collection of circuits we have been discussing.

Q9 and Q10 operate as Class A amplifiers. Distortion will be low because the stages operate in a linear manner. A pair of 2000-ohm phones will provide the most audio output, but lower-impedance phones will work okay with the circuit at some sacrifice in gain.

If a speaker is to be used with a circuit of this kind, it will be necessary to add an audio power amplifier after Q10 in order to drive a loudspeaker. Such an amplifier should be capable of providing 0.5 to, say, 5 watts of output across an 8- or 16-ohm voice-coil impedance.

FETs or ICs could be used in place of Q9 and Q10, and there are a lot of circuits that would perform well in this part of our superhet receiver. Bipolar transistors are shown here for the purpose of simplifying this discussion.

No attempt has been made in the circuit of Fig. 20 to shape the audio response. Unwanted high frequencies can be attenuated by using bypass capacitors from bases and collectors of Q9 and Q10 to ground. Values in the .001- to .05-$\mu$F range are typical of those which one might add. It is helpful to roll off all audio frequencies above 2500 Hz. This will lessen the annoying effects of high-pitched QRM and hiss noise. The low-frequency response can be improved by restricting the passage of

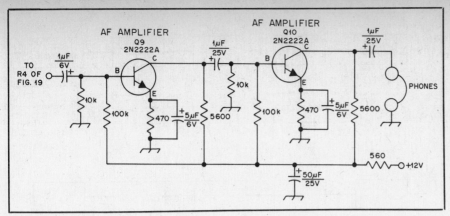

Fig. 20 — Schematic diagram of a simple two-stage audio amplifier for driving headphones. Overall circuit gain is approximately 40 dB.

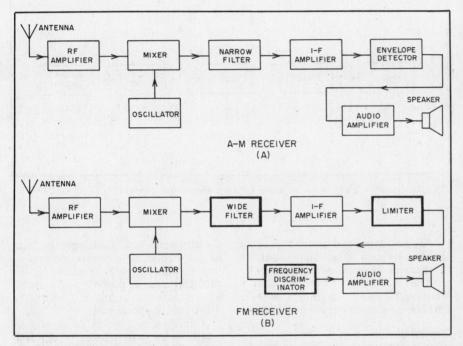

Fig. 21 — Block diagrams of (A) an a-m (B) an fm receiver. Dark borders outline the sections that are different in the fm set.

energy below 300 Hz. This can be achieved by making the three 1-$\mu$F coupling capacitors lower in value — 0.1 to .005 $\mu$F, typically. An audio band-pass characteristic of 300 to 2500 Hz will greatly improve receiver performance by rejection of QRM above and below the audio band-pass range.

**Other Considerations**

Thus far, we have dwelled exclusively on the single-conversion superheterodyne concept. We have done this primarily to make our circuit illustrations as straightforward as possible. It should be said, however, that there are double- and triple-conversion receivers being built and sold for amateur use. They differ mainly from single-conversion types in the number of mixers and local oscillators used. That is, for every conversion carried out it is necessary to employ a mixer and oscil-

lator, and a new i-f results each time. The concept was quite popular many years ago so that a very low last i-f could be obtained (typically 50 kHz). The low i-f made it possible to obtain narrow-selectivity characteristics for cw and ssb work without the expense of a complex i-f filter. A triple-conversion receiver might have a first i-f of 1500 kHz, a second i-f of 455 kHz and a third i-f of 50 kHz. It all gets rather involved when it comes to designing and building a receiver, and the effort is hardly worth it by present-day standards. Multiple-conversion receivers usually suffer from poor dynamic range, and the probability of unwanted spurious responses (birdies) greatly increases with the number of conversions.

**Audio Selectivity**

Weak-signal reception can often be improved by adding a selective audio

filter (passive or active) to a receiver. A passive filter would consist of inductors and capacitors tuned to give a desired band-pass characteristic for cw or ssb reception. An active filter would probably be one made with two or four poles of band-pass filtering and designed for a specific shape response. Operational amplifiers are used for most RC active audio filters at the present time. Audio filters enhance the signal of interest, bring it up out of the noise, and reject QRM from signals that are nearby in frequency.

**FM Reception**

The fm mode has become the most popular one from 144 MHz to 450 MHz. Generally speaking, the receiver is similar to the type used for hf-band reception of cw and ssb signals. Selectivity and stability — the desirable characteristics of any receiver — are needed in an fm unit. In addition, the fm receiver should respond only to frequency-modulated signals — any traces of amplitude modulation on a signal should not be detected. Because the fm signals used in amateur communications are broader than a-m or ssb transmissions, careful design is needed in the i-f portion of the receiver to assure that the overall bandwidth is wide enough to allow detection without distortion, but not as wide that adjacent-channel interference becomes troublesome.

Block diagrams of an a-m/ssb and an fm receiver are shown in Fig. 21. Fundamentally, to achieve a sensitivity of less than one microvolt, an fm receiver requires a gain of several million — too much total gain to be accomplished with stability on a single frequency. Thus, the use of the superheterodyne circuit has become standard practice. Three major differences will be apparent from a comparison of the two block diagrams. The fm receiver employs a different detector, has a limiter stage added between the i-f amplifier and the detector, and uses a somewhat wider filter. Otherwise the functions, and often the circuits, of the rf, oscillator, mixer and audio stages will be the same in either receiver.

In operation, the noticeable difference between the two receivers is the effect of noise and interference on an incoming signal. From the time of the first spark transmitters, QRM has been a major problem for amateurs. The limiter and discriminator stages in an fm set can eliminate a good deal of impulse noise, except that noise which manages to acquire a frequency-modulation characteristic. Accurate alignment of the receiver i-f system and phase tuning of the detector is required to achieve good noise suppression. Fm receivers perform in an unusual manner when QRM is present, exhibiting a characteristic known as the *capture effect*. The loudest signal received, even if it is only two or three times stronger than other stations on the same frequency, will be the only transmission demodulated. By comparison, an S9 a-m or cw signal can suffer noticeable interference from an S2 carrier.

## FM Receiver Design

Until recently, fm receivers have followed the design shown in block-diagram form in Fig. 22. One or two rf amplifier stages and a double conversion frequency scheme were used. Greater band occupancy has inspired both commercial and amateur receiver designers to work on the dynamic range and strong-signal handling capabilities of fm receivers. As cross-modulation and overload effects are primarily caused by the rf amplifier and mixers, a good deal of research has gone into the application of various solid-state devices for use in receiver front ends. The result of this work has been a vast improvement in fm receiver signal-handling capability.

Two devices, the FET and the hot-carrier diode, are responsible for the revolution in front-end circuits. Both devices can be operated to provide square-law response as mixers. The sensitivity of either type is such that the rf amplifier can be eliminated in many cases. Although the hot-carrier diode has been used by the amateur fraternity, the device hasn't been popular with fm receiver designers for two reasons. To assure linear mixing, the level of oscillator injection to a diode mixer must be at least 10 dB above the strongest signal to be received. Even with a balanced bridge of hot-carrier diodes, the power required from the local oscillator is considerable. Also, the diode mixer must be followed by a low-noise i-f preamplifier for best overall receiver noise figure, introducing a new area for cross-modulation effects to appear. FET devices exhibit a slightly better noise figure (by 1 to 3 dB), and thus, are usually chosen over hot-carrier diodes.

The designer has a choice of two basic approaches to the layout of a new fm receiver. He can use single conversion (Fig. 22B). But, to provide sufficient gain before the limiter, he must employ an rf amplifier, and worse, use a bipolar-transistor mixer to achieve high conversion gain. Even with an rf amplifier stage, getting sufficient i-f gain with stability can be a problem. Alternatively, a dual-conversion scheme can be employed where sufficient overall gain can be obtained in the i-f stages. With this design, Fig. 22C, the rf stage can be eliminated if sufficient rf selectivity can be achieved before the first mixer, without seriously degrading the sensitivity of the receiver.

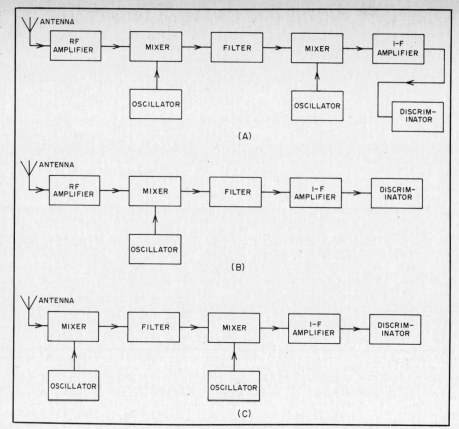

Fig. 22 — Block diagrams of the fm receiver designs discussed in the text.

As we mentioned earlier, some of the circuits used in an fm receiver are the same as those in an a-m receiver (rf amplifier, oscillator, mixer and audio). We should focus our attention on those parts of the circuit that are different.

## Bandwidth

As we already know, an fm signal swings above and below a center frequency with voice modulation. The amount of peak swing allowed in the fm transmitter is called the *deviation*. Three deviation amounts are now standard practice: 15, 5 and 2.5 kHz, which in the current vernacular of fm users, are known as wide band, narrow band, and sliver band, respectively. The 2.5- to 3-kHz deviation (called nbfm by OTs) was popular for a time on the vhf bands and 10 meters after World War II. Deviation figures are given for the frequency swing in one direction. The bandwidth required in an fm receiver is approximately 2.4 times the deviation — 36 kHz for wide band and 13 kHz for narrow.

Most fm receivers are dual-conversion designs. The second mixer should be located after a high-selectivity filter if spurious and image responses are to be kept to a minimum.

For the average ham, the use of high-selectivity filter in a homemade receiver offers some simplification of the alignment task. Following the techniques used in ssb receivers, a crystal or ceramic filter should be placed in the circuit as close as possible to the antenna connector — at the output of the first mixer, in most cases.

One item of concern to every amateur fm user is the choice of i-f bandwidth for his receiver, as both 15- and 5-kHz deviation are now in common use on the amateur bands. A wide-band receiver can receive narrow-band signals, suffering only some loss of audio in the detection process. However, a wide-band signal will be badly distorted when received on a narrow-band rig. At this point it seems reasonable to assume that increasing fm activity and continued production of commercial narrow-band transceivers will shift amateur operation to a 5-kHz deviation standard. But, as with the a-m operators, the wide-band enthusiasts will be around for some time to come, lured by inexpensive surplus wide-band gear.

## Limiters

When fm was first introduced, the main selling point used for the new mode was the noise-free reception possibilities. The circuit in the fm receiver that has the task of chopping off noise and amplitude modulation from an incoming signal is the *limiter*. Most types of fm detectors respond to both fre-

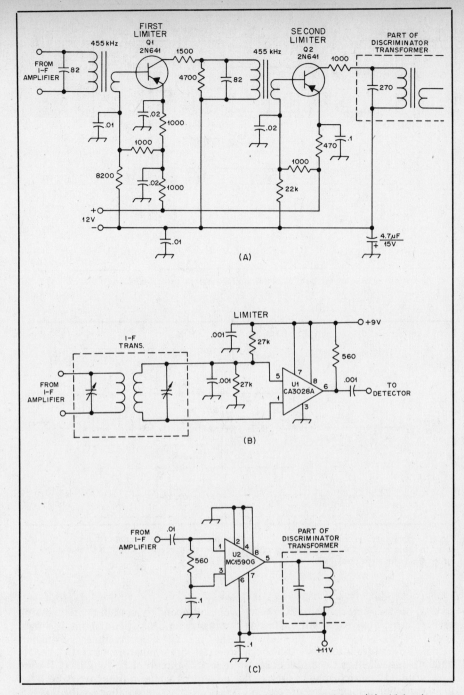

Fig. 23 — Typical limiter circuits using (A) transistors, (B) a differential IC, (C) a high-gain linear IC.

quency and amplitude variations of the signal. Thus, the limiter stages preceding the detector are included to "cleanse" the signal so that only the desired frequency modulation will be demodulated.

Limiter stages can be designed using transistors, ICs or tubes. Fig. 23A has transistors in two stages biased for limiter service. The base bias on either transistor may be varied to provide limiting at a desired level. The input-signal voltage required to start limiting action is called the *limiting knee*, referring to the point at which collector current ceases to rise with increased input signal. Modern ICs have limiting knees of 100 mV for the circuit shown in Fig. 23B, using the CA3028A or MC1550G, or 200 $\mu$V for the Motorola MC1590G of Fig. 23C. Because high-gain ICs such as the CA3076 and MC1590G contain as many as six or eight active stages which will saturate with sufficient input, one of these devices provides superior limiter performance compared to a pair of tubes or transistors.

### Detectors

The first type of fm detector to gain popularity was the frequency discriminator. The characteristic of such a detector is shown in Fig. 24. When the fm signal has no modulation and the carrier is at point 0, the detector has no output. When audio input to the fm transmitter swings the signal higher in frequency, the rectified output increases in the negative direction. Over a range where the discrimination is linear (shown as the straight portion of the line), the conversion of fm to a-m which is taking place will be linear.

A practical discriminator circuit is shown in Fig. 25. The fm signal is converted to a-m by transformer T1. The voltage induced in the T1 secondary is 90 degrees out of phase with the current in the primary. The primary signal is introduced through a center tap on the secondary, coupled through a

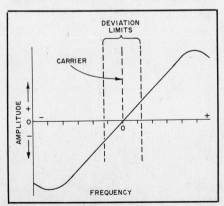

Fig. 24 — The characteristic of an fm discriminator.

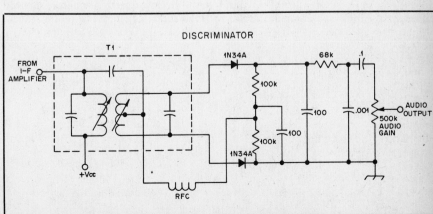

Fig. 25 — Typical frequency-discriminator circuit used for fm detection.

capacitor. The secondary voltages combine on each side of the center tap so that the voltage on one side leads the primary signal while the other side lags by the same amount. When rectified, these two voltages are equal and of opposite polarity, resulting in zero-voltage output. A shift in input frequency causes a shift in the phase of the voltage components that result in an increase of output amplitude on one side of the secondary, and a corresponding decrease on the other side. The differences in the two changing voltages, after rectification, constitute the audio output.

In the search for a simplified fm detector, RCA developed a circuit that has now become standard in entertainment radios and which eliminated the need for a preceding limiter stage. Known as the *ratio detector*, this circuit is based on the idea of dividing a dc voltage into a ratio which is equal to the ratio of the amplitudes from either side of a discriminator transformer secondary. With a detector that responds only to ratios, the input signal may vary in strength over a wide range without causing a change in the level of output voltage — fm can be detected, but no a-m. In an actual ratio detector, Fig. 26, the dc voltage required is developed across two load resistors, shunted by an electrolytic capacitor. Other differences include the two diodes, which are wired in series-aiding rather than series-Opposing, as in the standard discriminator circuit. The recovered audio is taken from a tertiary winding which is tightly coupled to the primary of the transformer. Diode-load resistor values are selected to be lower (5000 ohms or less) than for the discriminator.

The sensitivity of the ratio detector is one half that of the discriminator. In general, however, the transformer design values for $Q$, primary-secondary coupling, and load will vary greatly, so the actual performance differences between these two types of fm detectors are usually not significant. Either circuit can provide excellent results. In operation, the ratio detector will not provide sufficient limiting for communications

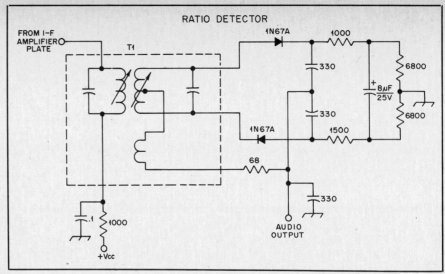

Fig. 26 — A ratio detector of the type often used in entertainment radio and TV sets.

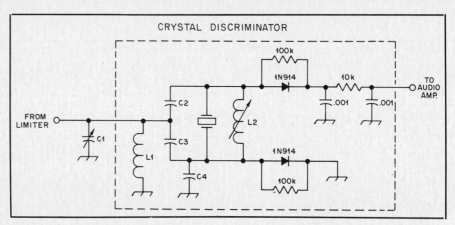

Fig. 27 — Crystal discriminator. C1 and L1 are resonant at the intermediate frequency. C2 is equal in value to C3. C4 corrects any circuit imbalance so that equal amounts of signal are fed to the detector diodes.

service, so this detector also is usually preceded by at least a single limiting stage.

The difficulties often encountered in building and aligning LC discriminators have inspired research that has resulted in a number of adjustment-free fm detector designs. The *crystal discriminator* utilizes a quartz resonator, shunted by an inductor, in place of the tuned-circuit secondary used in a discriminator transformer. A typical circuit is shown in Fig. 27. Some commercially made crystal discriminators have the input-circuit inductor, L1, built in (C1 must be added) while in other types both L1 and C1 must be supplied by the builder. Fig. 27 shows typical component values; unmarked parts are chosen to give the desired bandwidth.

# Chapter 6

# Antennas and Feeders

Some years ago a widely used text-book on radio engineering began a chapter on antennas with this statement: "An understanding of the mechanism by which energy is radiated . . . involves conceptions which are unfamiliar to the ordinary engineer." Obviously, radiation must be a stiff subject. So in this book we simply ask you to accept the well-known fact that energy *is* radiated in the form of electromagnetic waves. We won't attempt to explain why.

In studying for the Novice license you were introduced to wavelengths and frequency. The formula is

$$\text{Wavelength in meters} = \frac{300}{\text{frequency in MHz}}$$

In Fig. 1 the transmitter is generating a radio-frequency voltage, indicated by the sine wave in the upper drawing. When the voltage is applied to an antenna, energy is radiated into space and travels away with the speed of light. As shown by the lower drawing, it covers a certain distance — one *wavelength* — in the time the voltage takes to go through one cycle.

## Current in a Wire

This relationship between wavelength and frequency has a very practical use. Suppose we connect an rf ammeter in the center of a wire having a length $L$, as in Fig. 2. Further, suppose that by some means we introduce rf energy of adjustable frequency into the wire. If the frequency is gradually raised, it will be found that the current indicated by the ammeter will also rise, at first. But after reaching a maximum at some frequency, $f$, the current will start to go down again if we continue to raise the frequency. This is the sort of thing we found to happen in an *LC* circuit as discussed in chapter 1. The wire, in fact, acts like a resonant circuit. It is tuned to the frequency, $f$, for which its length is equal to one-half wavelength. If the wire is 40 meters long, for example, it would be resonant at the frequency for which 40 meters is one-half wavelength. From the formula above, this would correspond to a resonant frequency of 300/80, or 3.75 MHz.

A wire such as this is called a *dipole*, when its length is of the order of a half wavelength, or less. One exactly a half-wavelength long is called a *half-wave dipole*. Very often, the simple term "dipole" is used when a half-wave dipole actually is meant.

## Two Practical Points

Before going farther, it is well to translate this into a more familiar unit of length, the foot. Converting units and changing to a *half* wavelength gives us

$$\text{1/2 wavelength in feet} = \frac{492}{\text{frequency in MHz}}$$

or

$$\text{Resonant frequency in MHz} = \frac{492}{\text{length in feet}}$$

The second point is this: These formulas are not quite accurate for an actual wire. They apply only to a wave traveling in space. In a practical half-wave antenna the difference amounts to about five percent, on the average. Thus an *average* formula for resonant length would be

$$\text{1/2 wavelength in feet} = \frac{468}{\text{frequency in MHz}}$$

Remember that this is only an average. In a particular case actual resonant length might differ by a few percent from the length given by this formula. The difference is usually small enough to have little practical effect.

## Electrical Length

*Electrically,* the length given by the last formula is a half wavelength because it is a *resonant* length, even though it is physically short of being a half wavelength in space. We can account for the difference in length by the fact that energy does not travel quite as fast along a wire as it does in *free space*.

In some cases, as you will see later

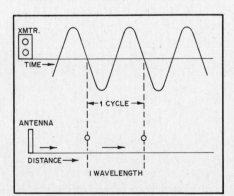

Fig. 1 — One wavelength is the distance that radiated energy will cover, traveling at the speed of light, during one cycle of the radiated frequency.

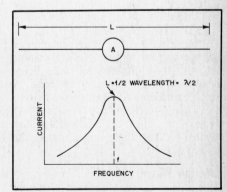

Fig. 2 — The rf current at the center of a wire is highest when the wire length is equal to one-half wavelength. The Greek letter λ stands for wavelength.

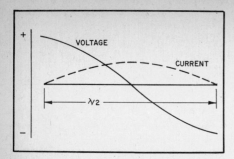

Fig. 3 — The current and voltage along a half-wave wire have different values at all points along the wire. When plotted as shown above, the graphs are wave-like in shape, and since their positions are fixed with respect to the wire, they are called standing waves.

when we get to transmission lines, there can be quite a marked difference between electrical wavelength and free-space wavelength. When you see the length of an antenna or line expressed in terms of wavelength, you can safely assume that an electrical measure is being used, unless it is made plain that free-space measure is meant.

### Enter Time

In chapter 1 we dealt with circuits that offered a complete path around which electrical energy could move. A wire such as is shown in Fig. 2 doesn't offer any such path. How is it that current can flow in it?

In the "closed" circuits of chapter 1 it was assumed, without our having said it in so many words, that electrical energy traveled around the circuit so rapidly that its action could be taken to be instantaneous. In the circuits we use in transmitters and receivers for frequencies up to 30 MHz, at least, this is a satisfactory assumption. As long as the circuit is small compared with the wavelength (the wavelength corresponding to the frequency we happen to be using), the action is instantaneous, for all practical purposes.

But an antenna such as the wire in Fig. 2 is *not* small compared with the wavelength. If the length *L* is one-half wavelength, a length of time equal to one-half cycle of the applied frequency is needed for energy to go from one end of the wire to the other. Imagine a voltage applied to the left-hand end of the wire at an instant when the voltage is at the positive peak of the cycle. A voltage impulse will go along the wire to the right, reaching the end one-half cycle later. But at this instant the *applied* voltage has moved on to its *negative* peak.

### Standing Waves

In other words, when the left-hand end of the wire is negative, the right-hand end is positive — and vice versa. Also, when the voltage reaches the end

of the wire, it comes to the end of the track. There is no place for it to go except back over the same path. The energy is *reflected* from the end. In going back, it combines with energy — from a later part of the cycle — that is going out.

Fig. 3 shows what happens in a wire one-half wavelength long. All the components of voltage, those traveling out and those reflected back, add up to make a *standing wave* of voltage. If we could go along the wire with a meter for measuring rf voltage, we should find that the voltage is highest at the ends of the wire and is practically zero at the center. Between the ends and the center it gradually decreases. When plotted against length, as in Fig. 3, it is like part of a sine wave.

### Polarity

The plus and minus signs on the scale at the left can be somewhat misleading. One end of the antenna isn't always positive, and the other end isn't always negative. In fact, both ends alternate between positive and negative each rf cycle. What the picture tries to show is that *when* the left-hand half of the wire is positive the right-hand half is negative. The reverse is also true. The voltages in the two halves of the antenna always have opposite polarity.

On the other hand, if we went along the wire with a meter for measuring rf current, we should find that the current is zero at the ends. This you might expect, since current can't flow off the wire into space. The current gets larger as we move toward the center, and is largest right in the middle of the wire. In the drawing, the current is shown entirely on the plus side of the scale. Again this shouldn't be taken literally; it actually goes from positive to negative and back again each cycle. The picture means that the current is always flowing in the *same* direction, at any given instant, throughout the entire length of a half-wave wire.

### Nodes and Antinodes

The point where the amplitude of a standing wave passes through zero is called a *node*. Thus in Fig. 3 the standing wave of voltage has a node at the center of the antenna. The standing wave of current has two nodes in this figure, one at each end of the wire.

A point of maximum amplitude is called an *antinode* or, sometimes, a *loop*. (Properly, the term loop refers to the entire segment of the standing wave between two nodes.) The standing wave of voltage has antinodes at the ends of the wire in Fig. 3, while the current antinode is at the center.

Note that where there is a current antinode, there is a voltage node, and where there is a current node, there is a

voltage antinode. Also, an antinode of current is one-quarter wavelength away from a current node; similarly with the voltage. These two statements are true, in general, of all standing waves along wires.

### Longer Wires

The tuned circuits you met in chapter 1 were resonant at just one frequency, that for which the inductive and capacitive reactances were equal. An antenna isn't quite so simple. If the things shown in Fig. 3 happen when a wire is a half wavelength long because of the *time* it takes energy to surge back and forth, it seems reasonable to expect that another half wavelength of wire added to the first will see a repetition of these same events. And so it is. There will be a repetition each time a half wavelength is added.

Fig. 4 shows the *current* and *voltage distribution* when the wire is two half-waves (or one wavelength) long and three half-waves (1-1/2 wavelengths) long. At the ends of each half-wave section the voltage is high and the current is zero. In the middle of each such section the current is high and the voltage is zero. But there is a difference between two adjacent half-wave sections. You can see that when the voltage at the left end of the first section is positive, as shown, the voltage at the left end of the second section is negative. It has to be the same as the voltage at the right-hand end of the first section, of course, since the two sections are connected together. Also, when the current in the first section is positive, as shown, the current in the next section will be negative. That is, the currents in adjacent half-wave sections flow in opposite directions. This is called a *phase reversal*.

### Phase

In the third section, shown in the bottom drawing of Fig. 4, there is again a phase reversal. This brings the phase relationships in this section back to exactly what they are in the first section. In other words, *alternate* half-wave

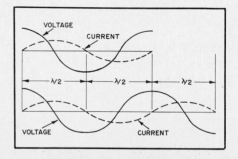

Fig. 4 — Harmonic resonance. The upper drawing shows the standing waves on a wire one wavelength long; the lower shows them on a wire 1-1/2 wavelengths long.

sections have identical standing waves of current and voltage on them. They are said to be *in phase. Adjacent* sections are *out of phase.* This goes on no matter how many half-wave sections are added to the wire.

### Harmonic Resonance

Each of these sections is just as much resonant to the applied frequency as another. In effect, we have two resonant antennas end-to-end in the upper drawing of Fig. 4, and three in the lower drawing. These are called *harmonic resonances,* since they occur at the same frequencies as the harmonics of a fundamental frequency. That is, they are integral (whole-number) multiples of the fundamental.

In the case of an antenna, the fundamental frequency is the one for which the entire wire length is equal to one-half wavelength. For example, an antenna that is a half wavelength long at 7150 kHz will be two half-waves long at 14,300 kHz (second harmonic), three half-waves long at 21,450 kHz (third harmonic), and so on up the scale. The actual multiples are approximate, not exact, integers. The resonant frequencies will differ slightly from exact harmonics. The reasons are the same as given earlier in the discussion of the length of a practical antenna.

### Grounded Antennas

A half wavelength is the shortest length of wire that will be resonant to a given frequency, if the wire is simply considered by itself. However, if we connect one end of the wire to earth, the grounded end is no longer "free." We can't raise the potential of the earth itself, so the voltage at the grounded end has to be zero. On the other hand, we *can* make current flow into the earth. Thus the earth can be made to act as a substitute for one half of the half-wave antenna.

Fig. 5 shows this. The current is large at the earth connection, and decreases to zero at the open end of the antenna. The voltage is zero at the bottom and has its greatest value at the top. But the length $L$ for this antenna is

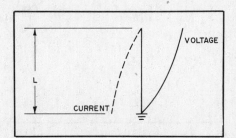

Fig. 5 — Grounding one end of the antenna chops off one-half of the standing wave; that is, the length $L$ need be only a quarter wavelength for the antenna to be resonant.

only a *quarter* wavelength, at resonance. So a grounded antenna need be only half as long as a dipole antenna to be resonant at the same frequency.

### Antenna Impedance

Impedance, as it was defined in chapter 1, is equal to voltage divided by current. When the current and voltage both change as we move along the antenna, as they do in Fig. 3, the impedance also is different everywhere along the antenna. Therefore, if we want to talk about antenna impedance we have to specify the point at which it is measured.

The customary place to measure the impedance of a simple antenna is at the center of the wire. In Fig. 6 an rf generator, $G$, is inserted in series with the antenna at its center. The voltage from the generator will cause a current, $I$, to flow; this current has the same value on both sides of the terminals. The antenna behaves like a circuit having resistance, inductance and capacitance in series. At the resonant frequencies of such a circuit the inductive and capacitive reactances cancel each other, as you saw in chapter 1, leaving only the resistance. This is also true of the antenna. Thus, at its resonant frequency the antenna "looks like" a simple resistance, and it is at this frequency that the current is largest. A half-wave antenna has a resistive impedance, measured at this point, in the neighborhood of 70 ohms. It is rarely exactly 70 ohms in any practical case, because the actual resistance depends on the same factors that affect the resonant frequency.

If the frequency is moved off resonance the impedance rises, just as it does in a series $LC$ circuit. It also becomes complex — there is reactance, now, along with the resistance.

Now suppose the rf generator to be connected to one end of the antenna, as in Fig. 6B, with one ammeter at the end and the other at the center. As the frequency is varied the current $I_2$ will reach its highest value at resonance, where the antenna is a half wavelength long. But the current $I_1$ at the terminal where the generator is connected will be *smallest* at this frequency. As seen by the generator, the antenna is just like a parallel $LC$ circuit. That is, at resonance its impedance is maximum and is a simple resistance. As the frequency is moved away from resonance the current $I_1$ increases; the impedance at this point becomes smaller and is again complex, containing both reactance and resistance.

### Impedance Values

Antennas are usually fed with rf power either at the center or the end. Thus, the two cases illustrated by Fig. 6

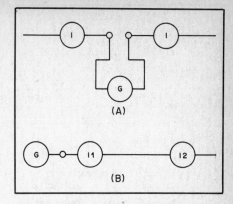

Fig. 6 — A half-wave wire driven at the center behaves like a series-resonant circuit. One driven at the end acts like a parallel-resonant circuit.

have some practical importance. The resonant impedance at the end is much more dependent on the thickness of the antenna conductor and other such factors than is the impedance at the center. Values can range from a few hundred to several thousand ohms. The thicker the conductor, the lower the resistance as viewed from the end. At the center, the effect of conductor thickness on the resistance, at resonance, is relatively minor.

The impedance of a grounded antenna usually is measured between the earth and the bottom of the antenna. Like the center-fed antenna with free ends, the grounded antenna acts like a circuit having $L$, $C$ and $R$ in series. As the antenna is only half as long, for the same resonant frequency, the resistance is only half as great. That is, it is in the neighborhood of 35 ohms, for an antenna a quarter wavelength long.

This assumes a "perfect" ground — one that has extremely low losses at the operating frequency. Ordinary ground is far from perfect, and the earth connection usually adds quite a considerable amount of resistance to the system — often as much as 25 ohms. The ground resistance can be reduced by burying a large number of wires, having a length of about a half wavelength, going out from the base of the antenna like the spokes of a wheel. To be effective, though, a really large number of them — several dozen — has to be used.

### The Nature of Antenna Resistance

In chapter 1 it was emphasized that resistance, as defined in broad terms, is something in which power is used up — usefully or otherwise. The resistance of an antenna divides into two parts, one useful and one not. The useful part is called *radiation resistance.* The power used up in this resistance is the power actually radiated into space from the antenna. The nonuseful part of the resistance is represented by losses,

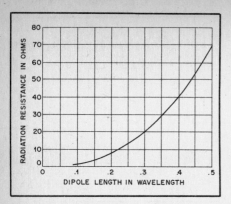

Fig. 7 — Radiation resistance measured at the center of an antenna as the length of the wire is varied. Lengths here are in terms of free-space wavelength.

partly in the conductor (because of its ordinary resistance at the operating frequency), partly in insulation associated with the wire, and partly in conductors and dielectrics close enough to the antenna to be in a strong electromagnetic field. These are lumped together and often called the *ohmic* resistance. Power dissipated in ohmic resistance is turned into heat.

Since only power used up in the radiation resistance is useful, we want the radiation resistance to be much larger than the ohmic resistance. It is the *ratio* of the former to the latter, rather than the actual values in ohms, that is of interest. We may measure different values of total resistance at different points along a given antenna, but the ratio of the two components of the resistance does not change. In other words, it does not matter where power is introduced into the antenna; the same proportion will be radiated, and the same fraction lost, in every case.

### Why Impedance Is Important

Since it is only the *ratio* of radiation resistance to ohmic resistance that counts, you would be justified in concluding that the actual value of resistance is unimportant. This is so in the antenna itself. But another factor must be taken into account. Somehow, rf power must be put into the antenna before there can be any radiation. In feeding power to the antenna the actual antenna resistance — or impedance — *is* important.

Rf circuits using practical components work at best efficiency when the impedance level is between perhaps 25 and 2000 ohms. These are not exact limits by any means, but do indicate the general range. If the impedance is only an ohm or two, or is many thousands of ohms, the losses in the circuits themselves may be far greater than the power that can be delivered through them to a load. And between the plate of the

transmitter and the antenna itself, there must be circuits — often several of them. Each exacts its toll of power.

The resistance of a half-wave antenna is about 70 ohms, as we have mentioned. This value is well within the optimum range for minimizing the losses in any circuits we may use to match the antenna to the final amplifier. Furthermore, it is nearly all radiation resistance. Ohmic resistance amounts to only a few percent of the total if the antenna is mounted in a clear spot. However, the radiation resistance decreases if the antenna is shortened. For example, if a dipole is a quarter wavelength long, its radiation resistance as measured at the center is only about 14 ohms, as shown in Fig. 7. If the length is shortened to one-eighth wavelength the resistance drops to around four ohms.

### Coupling Losses

If the same power can be put into all these values of resistance, all of the power will be radiated. However, the "if" is a big one. The half-wave antenna is resonant, and so needs no tuning. The shorter antennas are not resonant; their impedances have large amounts of reactance along with resistance. In order to put power into a short antenna, the reactance has to be "tuned out" by adding the same value of reactance, but of the opposite kind, at the antenna terminals. A short antenna has capacitive reactance, so inductive reactance has to be added to cancel it, as in Fig. 8. But coils inherently have resistance, and a coil of the size needed for tuning a 1/8-wave antenna, for instance, will have more resistance than the radiation resistance of the antenna itself. As a result, more power is used up in heating the coil than is radiated by the antenna.

Aside from considerations such as these, there is nothing sacred about the resonant length. The antenna will radiate just as well whether or not it is resonant. However, it will not *get* all the power output of the transmitter if it is so far off resonance that the tuning apparatus uses up an appreciable portion of the power.

Beginners often take antenna resonance far more seriously than it warrants. A small departure from the resonant length is of little consequence. The resistance and reactance change rather slowly around the resonant point, so there is no observable increase in loss if the antenna isn't exactly resonant. As a matter of fact, an antenna can't be resonant at more than one single frequency. Yet, it isn't by any means necessary to use different antennas for each frequency in an amateur band.

### Directivity

Offhand, you might think that the

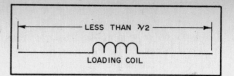

Fig. 8 — Inductive loading of a short antenna to make it resonant. The shorter the antenna the greater the inductance required. The term *loading*, as used in this connection, has nothing to do with the type of loading (for power transfer) discussed in chapter 2. It dates from early radio times and refers to tuning a circuit — usually by adding inductance — to a lower frequency than the one to which it is naturally resonant. The natural resonance in this case would be that of the wire without the coil.

strength of a signal radiated from an antenna would be the same in all directions —up, down and to all sides. It isn't. The radiation is stronger in some directions than in others. This comes about because the ends of the antenna always have opposite polarity, and because the antenna is not just a point but has a length that isn't small compared with the wavelength.

You can think of it as a case of timing, or phase. The electromagnetic field from one part of the antenna

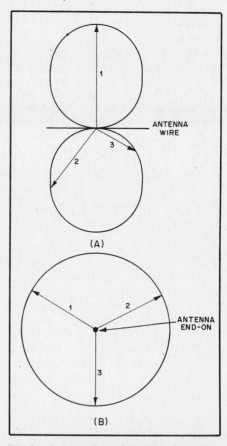

Fig. 9 — Cross-sections of directional pattern of a half-wave antenna. A — in the plane in which the wire lies; B — in a plane cutting through the center of the wire at right angles to it.

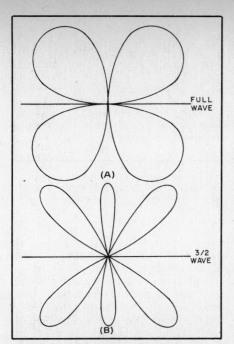

Fig. 10 — Cross-sections of directional patterns of (A) a full-wave antenna and (B) one having a length of 1-1/2 wavelengths. The cross-sections correspond to the one in Fig. 9A, in relationship to the antenna wire.

doesn't reach a distant point at the same time as the field from another part. In an extreme case, the fields reaching such a distant point may even get there with the same amplitude but *opposite* polarity. Then they add up to zero; there is no radiation in that direction, or, in another direction, the fields may reach the distant point with the same amplitude and the *same* polarity. Being "in phase," they add together to give the strongest field the antenna is capable of producing. In still other directions, neither of these conditions is met completely, so the strength of the signal has an intermediate value.

### Directive Patterns

This rather complex operation is summed up in what is called the *directive pattern* of the antenna. The pattern is a graph showing the relative strength of the radiation in all directions. We can't show a pattern completely on a sheet of paper, since the paper has only two dimensions, while the antenna actually radiates into all the space surrounding it. Antenna patterns usually are a "slice" or cross section of the full pattern.

Fig. 9A shows typical cross-sectional patterns for a half-wave dipole. The arrows marked 1, 2 and 3 show, by their length and direction, the relative strength of the radiated field. Don't forget that this drawing is a slice; in order to visualize the complete pattern you would have to imagine that the pattern rotates around the antenna wire,

in and out of the paper, to form a doughnut with a point, not a hole, in the middle. Then when you turn the antenna on end, as in B, a slice at right angles would give you just a circle, as shown.

Taking these two patterns together, you can see that a *horizontal* half-wave antenna will radiate best directly upward and downward (if you are looking at the antenna from the side) and won't radiate at all directly off the ends. If you imagine yourself *over* the antenna in A, it radiates best at right angles to the direction in which the wire runs. On the other hand, if you are looking directly down on a *vertical* antenna, as in B, the antenna is radiating equally well in all directions. These last directions, of course, are along the ground, going around the compass.

If the antenna is shorter than a half wavelength, the pattern will still have much the same shape. However, if the length is two or more half wavelengths, there are rather drastic changes. Figs. 10A and 10B show, respectively, the patterns for the "full-wave" and "three half-wave" antennas whose current and voltage distribution are shown in Fig. 4. The maximum radiation is longer broadside to the wire but goes off at an angle, as you can see by comparing these drawings with Fig. 9A. These, too, are

cross sections of a solid pattern that you can visualize by imagining the cross-section drawing to be rotating around the antenna.

### The Earth's Part

Since the antenna radiates in all directions, some of the energy must go toward the ground. The earth acts more-or-less like a huge reflector for radio waves. The rays hitting it bounce off much like light rays from a mirror. These reflected rays combine with the direct rays from the antenna at a distance. The result is that the directive pattern of the antenna is modified by the presence of the earth "mirror." Just what the mirror does depends on the height of the antenna above it, and whether the antenna is horizontal or vertical.

Fig. 11 shows a couple of typical cases for a half-wave antenna. The patterns at the left show the relative radiation when you view the antenna from the side; those at the right show the radiation pattern you would "see" when you look at the end of the antenna. Changing the height from one-fourth to one-half wavelength makes quite a difference in the upward radiation — that is, the radiation at high angles. The *radiation angle* is measured from the ground up.

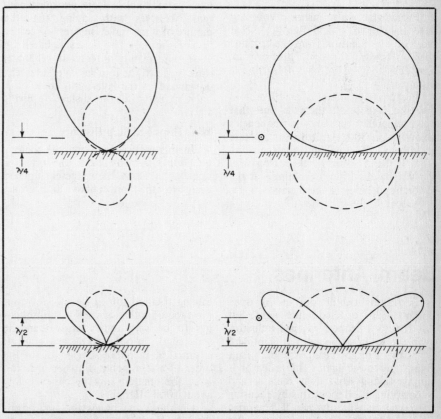

Fig. 11 — Effect of the ground on the radiation from a horizontal half-wave antenna, for heights of one-fourth and one-half wavelength. Dashed lines show what the pattern would be if there were no reflection from the ground.

Fig. 12 — Effect of the ground on radiation from a half-wave vertical antenna. In the absence of the ground, the pattern would be like the dashed line.

Fig. 12 shows what happens to the patterns of a vertical half-wave antenna sitting on the ground. Here the maximum radiation is along the ground.

Lest you take these pictures too seriously, we have to warn you that the ground isn't like the mirror on your wall. It's pretty foggy, as a matter of fact. In other words, it isn't by any means the perfect reflector that these pictures assume it to be. The fogginess is principally the result of energy losses; a fairly husky proportion of the wave energy striking the ground is used up in the ground resistance. The principal effect of this is that you don't get the radiation at very low angles that Fig. 12 would lead you to expect. Practically, there isn't a great deal of difference between horizontal and vertical antennas in this respect if the horizontal is a half wavelength or more above the earth.

### Wave Paths

From what we've just said you may have concluded — and rightly — that most of the radiation from the antenna goes up toward the sky. This being so, how does a signal get back to earth at a distance?

Fortunately, there is a reflector in the sky. At least, there is one that operates pretty regularly at frequencies below about 30 MHz. It doesn't operate at vhf except now and then on the 50-MHz band. This is the reason why the vhf bands differ from those at the lower frequencies in the distance ranges

that normally can be covered. Vhf requires highly developed equipment for working very far beyond the optical horizon as determined by the antenna heights. (It can be done, though.) But on those frequencies for which the sky reflector works, communication is possible over very long distances even with low power.

### The Ionosphere

The sky reflector is really not a reflector, technically speaking. It is a region in the upper atmosphere where the paths of radio waves are bent so the signals come back to earth. This region is known as the *ionosphere*. In the ionosphere, energy from the sun breaks up or *ionizes* the thin atmosphere into electrically charged particles which collect in several separate layers. The two principal ones are at heights of about 60 miles and 150 miles, respectively. These layers have the same effect as mirrors, but mirrors of a special kind. They are better mirrors for longer wavelengths than for short ones, and are also better for waves striking them at a glancing angle than for waves hitting them head on.

Even an elementary recital of the various effects that are associated with the ionosphere would occupy a good-sized chapter. Wave propagation is a whole subject in itself — a fascinating one, too, and one that accounts for much of the charm of operating your own radio station. Here we must content ourselves with saying that the picture of wave travel, in simplest terms, is like Fig. 13. The waves radiated by your transmitting antenna travel up at some angle to the ionized layer, are bent downward in the layer, and come back to earth at the distant receiving station.

### Wave Hops and Skip Distance

In this picture the signal got there in one *hop*. In many cases the returning signal hits earth, is reflected upward again to the ionosphere, and comes

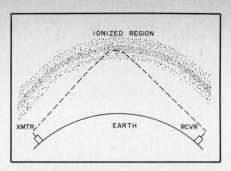

Fig. 13 — A wave entering the ionosphere is bent back toward earth, when suitable conditions exist, to reach a distant point.

down again still farther away. This can be repeated a number of times — enough times to carry the signal to the most distant parts of the earth, if you pick the right transmitting frequency and the right time of day. The time of day is important because the ability of the ionosphere to reflect signals depends on the sun.

The fact that a signal leaving the transmitting antenna at a low angle is more readily reflected than one going more-or-less directly upward leads to an interesting result. There are times (depending on the transmitting frequency again) when signals don't come back at short distances from the transmitter. This no-signal region around the transmitter is called the *skip zone*, because signals skip over it before coming back to earth. When there is "skip," you can work the longer distances with relative ease, but not the shorter ones. The skip zone may extend out for as much as 2000 miles from your station when you're using the very highest frequency that can be reflected at all. The *skip distance* is much shorter on lower frequencies such as 7 and 3.5 MHz. For much of the time, on these frequencies, there is no skip zone at all. As a rule, you can work the longest distances most easily on those frequencies for which the skip distance is greatest.

# Beam Antennas

A flashlight bulb out in the open doesn't seem to shed much light. But put it into a properly shaped reflector, as in the ordinary pocket flashlight, and it throws a bright beam. The bulb isn't giving any more light. The reflector is simply taking what light there is and intensifying it. It does this by focusing the rays into a narrow pencil. The price paid for the "gain" in this beam is *less* light in all other directions.

The radio rays from an antenna, too,

can be focused into a beam. However, the type of reflector used in a flashlight has to be very much larger than the wavelength, in order to do any good. It is practical in radio wavelengths of the order of a few inches, but becomes too large for amateur use in bands below about 1000 MHz.

On the lower bands the focusing is done by combining the individual radiations from a number of dipoles. The waves from the dipoles are timed so that

they add together when going in the desired direction, and tend to subtract (*interfere* with each other) in other directions. The subtraction means a *decrease* in intensity in those other directions. The total power must remain the same, since the antenna can't manufacture power itself. It can only rearrange it.

### Types of Beams

A dipole in such a system is called an

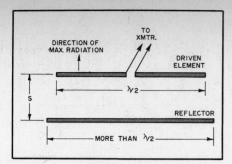

Fig. 14 — A two-element parasitic beam. The lengths in wavelengths shown are to be understood to be electrical rather than physical lengths.

*antenna element*. It may or may not be exactly resonant, depending on the kind of system. A combination of antenna elements is called an *array*. There are two general types of arrays. In one, all the elements are connected to the transmitter through a system of transmission lines. This is called a *driven array*. However, it isn't *necessary* that all elements be driven directly. If an element is close to and more-or-less parallel with a second element that does have rf power in it, some of the power in this second element will be coupled into the first through the electromagnetic field. There is a resemblance here to inductive or capacitive coupling between ordinary circuits. Elements that get their power by this means are called *parasitic elements*, and arrays in which they are used are called *parasitic arrays*. One or more of the elements in a parasitic array has to be driven, of course; power has to be introduced into the system before any electromagnetic-field coupling can take place.

Besides multielement antenna arrays there are several other types of beam antennas in use. Principal among them are various forms of *long-wire antennas*. These work on much the same idea as the multielement types, but the "elements" are the half-wave sections of continuous wires operated on multiples of a fundamental wavelength.

The study of antennas is a whole field in itself.[1] It will suffice for our present purposes to become a little acquainted with a type of beam that is widely used on the amateur bands from 14 MHz up — the Yagi antenna.

### Yagi Type Beams

The Yagi antenna takes its name from the inventor of the directive system using parasitic elements. In its usual form, the antenna has a driven dipole, usually resonant, and one or more parasitic elements. The simplest arrangement

[1] There are many books on the subject, among them *The ARRL Antenna Book*.

is the *two-element beam* shown in Fig. 14. There is only one parasitic element. Usually it is a *reflector*, so-called because energy it receives from the driven element bounces back to concentrate the radiation in the same direction that a reflector behind a flashlight lamp would concentrate it. This direction is shown in Fig. 14.

The power that a parasitic element picks up from the field of a driven element is practically all *reradiated*. Only a small fraction is lost in heating the resistance of the element itself — no more than in any dipole having the same ohmic resistance and carrying the same current. Thus from a practical standpoint, all the power a parasitic element gets is used in enhancing the radiation of the system in one direction and

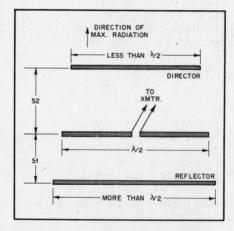

Fig. 15 — The three-element parasitic beam. More parasitic elements — nearly always directors — can be added. The power gain in the favored direction is approximately proportional to the overall length of the antenna measured in the direction of the arrow (S1 + S2 etc.) provided the elements are properly spaced and tuned.

tending to suppress it in others. What it does in this respect depends on how the parasitic element is tuned and on the spacing (in terms of wavelength) between elements.

A parasitic element acts as a reflector, at the spacings normally used, when it is tuned somewhat *lower* than the operating frequency. That is, it is made somewhat *longer* than an electrical half wavelength — about 5 percent longer, ordinarily. The spacing S is usually about 0.15 wavelength. There are no magic figures here. Many values of S and reflector length will give good results. The two quantities are not independent; changing one will require changing the other for optimum results.

More than two elements can be used. When a third one is added it is usually a *director*, as shown in Fig. 15. This element helps the radiation along when it is placed in *front* of the driven

element. To do this it has to be tuned *higher* than the operating frequency, at ordinary spacings. That is, it is made about 5 percent *shorter* than an electrical half wavelength. The spacing S2, between the driven element and the director is from 0.1 to 0.2 wavelength in most antennas. S1 is about the same as in the two-element beam.

We don't need to stop with three elements. The fourth and subsequently added elements are practically always additional directors. Additional directors are usually a little shorter than the first one, and when a large number is used, the spacing for optimum results tends to level off at about 0.2 wavelength. Antennas with many elements are practical only at very short wavelengths, because of the size of the structure required for a large number of elements. Three elements are commonly used at 14 MHz, three or four at 21 and 28 MHz, and four or more at 50 MHz and above.

### The Quad Antenna

Thus far we have assumed that the various antenna arrays have been assemblies of linear half-wave (or approximately half-wave) dipole elements. However, other element forms may be used according to the same basic principles. For example, loops of various types may be combined into directive arrays. A popular type of parasitic array using loops is the quad antenna, in which loops having a perimeter of one wavelength are used in much the same way as dipole elements in the Yagi antenna.

### One-Wavelength Loops

Three forms of one-wavelength loops are shown in Fig. 16. At A and B the

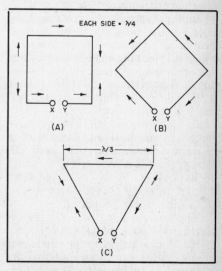

Fig. 16 — At A and B, loops having sides 1/4 wavelength long, and at C having sides 1/3 wavelength long (total conductor length one wavelength). The polarization depends on the orientation of the loop and the point at which the terminals *X-Y* are located.

sides of the squares are equal to 1/4 wavelength, the difference being in the point at which the terminals are inserted. At C the sides of the triangle are equal to 1/3 wavelength. The relative direction of current flow is as shown in the drawings. This direction reverses halfway around the perimeter of the loop, since such reversals always occur at the junction of each half-wave section of wire.

Radiation is maximum perpendicular to the plane of the loop and is minimum in any direction in the plane containing the loop. If the three loops shown in Fig. 16 are mounted in a vertical plane with the terminals at the bottom, the radiation is horizontally polarized. When the terminals are moved to the center of one vertical side in A, or to a side corner in B, the radiation is vertically polarized. If the terminals are moved to a side corner in C, the polarization will be diagonal, containing both vertical and horizontal components.

In contrast to straight-wire antennas, the electrical length of the circumference of a one-wavelength loop is *shorter* than the actual length. For loops made of wire and operating at frequencies below 30 MHz or so, where the ratio of conductor length to wire diameter is large, the loop will be close to resonance when

$$\text{Length in feet} = \frac{1005}{\text{frequency in MHz}}$$

The radiation resistance of a resonant one-wavelength loop is approximately 100 ohms, when the ratio of conductor length to diameter is large. As the loop dimensions are comparable with those of a half-wave dipole, the radiation efficiency is high.

In the direction of maximum radiation (that is, broadside to the plane of the loop, regardless of the point at which it is fed) the one-wavelength loop will show a small gain over a half-wave dipole. Theoretically, this gain is about 2 dB, and measurements have confirmed that it is of this order.

The one-wavelength loop is more frequently used as an element of a directive antenna array than singly, although there is no reason why it cannot be used alone. In the quad and delta loop, it is nearly always driven so that the polarization is horizontal.

The quad antenna was orginally designed by Moore, W9LZX, in the late 1940s. Since its inception there has been extensive controversy whether the quad is a better performer than a Yagi. This argument continues, but over the years several facts have become apparent. Data shows that the quad has a gain of approximately 2 decibels over a

Yagi for the same array length. Also, for a given array height, the quad has a lower angle of radiation than a Yagi.

Two full-wave loops, one as a driven element and one as a reflector, are shown in Fig. 17. This is the original version of the quad; in subsequent development, loops tuned as directors have been added in front of the driven element. The square loops may be mounted either with the corners lying on horizontal and vertical lines, as shown at the left, or with two sides horizontal and two vertical (right). The feed points shown for these two cases will result in horizontal polarization, which is commonly used.

The parasitic element is tuned in much the same way as the parasitic element in a Yagi antenna. That is, the parasitic loop is tuned to a lower frequency than the operating frequency when the element is to act as a reflector, and to a higher frequency when it acts as a director. Fig. 17 shows the parasitic element with an adjustable tuning stub, a convenient method of tuning since the resonant frequency can be changed simply by changing the position of the shorting bar on the stub. In practice, it has been found that the length around the loop should be approximately three percent greater than the self-resonant length if the element is a reflector, and about three percent shorter than the self-resonant length if the parasitic element is a director. Approximate formulas for the loop lengths in feet are

$$\text{Driven element} = \frac{1005}{\text{frequency in MHz}}$$

$$\text{Reflector} = \frac{1030}{\text{frequency in MHz}}$$

$$\text{Director} = \frac{975}{\text{frequency in MHz}}$$

for quad antennas intended for operation below 30 MHz. At vhf, where the ratio of loop circumference to conductor diameter is usually relatively small, the circumference must be increased in comparison to the wavelength. For example, a one-wavelength loop constructed of quarter-inch tubing for 144 MHz should have a circumference about 4.5 percent greater than the wavelength in free space, as compared to the approximately two percent increase in the formula above for the driven element.

In any case, on-the-ground adjustment is required if optimum results are to be secured, especially with respect to front-to-back ratio.

Element spacings of the order of 0.14 to 0.2 wavelength are generally

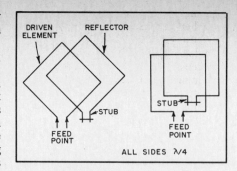

Fig. 17 — The basic quad antenna, with driven loop and reflector loop. The loops are electrically one wavelength in circumference (1/4 wavelength on a side). Both configurations shown give horizontal polarization; for vertical polarization, the driven element should be fed at one of the side corners in the arrangement at the left, or at the center of a vertical side in the "square" quad at the right.

used, the smaller spacings being employed in antennas having more than two elements, where the structural support for elements with larger spacings tends to become difficult. The feed-point impedances of antennas having element spacings of this order have been found to be in the 40- to 60-ohm range, so the driven element can be fed through coaxial cable with only a small mismatch. For spacings of the order of 0.25 wavelength (physically feasible for two elements, or for several elements at 28 MHz), the impedance more closely approximates the impedance of a driven loop alone — that is, 80 or 90 ohms.

### Beam-Antenna Gain

The *gain* of a beam antenna is the ratio of the power radiated in the desired direction to the power radiated by some *reference antenna*, assuming the same power input to both. In amateur work it is understood that the reference antenna is a half-wave dipole. Such a dipole doesn't radiate equally well in all directions; its maximum radiation is along a line at right-angles to the direction of the antenna itself, as shown earlier in this chapter. So the reference dipole must aim, radiation-wise, in the same direction as the beam, in figuring the gain of the beam. Also, it must be at the same height above ground, and otherwise be installed under the same operating conditions as those of the beam.

Since gain is a power ratio, it is usually measured in decibels. Gains of up to 4 or 5 dB can be achieved in the two-element antenna, and up to 7 dB or so in the three-element. As a fraction of a decibel represents a power change that is not observable audibly (remember that one decibel is about the *least* detectable change) it doesn't pay to take too seriously attempts to squeeze out the last one-tenth of a decibel. Also, bear in mind that the same lengths and spacings will lead to the same results whether you make the antenna yourself or buy one ready-made. Once you've decided how many elements you'll use, it's sensible to forget about minor gain differences and concentrate on constructional features that will keep the antenna up in the air and operating throughout all kinds of weather.

## Rotatable Beams

Of course, the gain of a beam antenna is useful only in the direction toward which the beam points. To be able to use the antenna all around the horizon you have to be able to rotate it. Yagi beams are practically always mounted so they can be rotated. The more solidly constructed TV rotators can be used with good results for the smaller amateur antennas. Large ones, though, such as would be used on 14 MHz, usually require much heavier machinery for rotation.

# Transmission Lines

To radiate effectively, an antenna ought to be up in the air as high as it can be put. Also, it should not be close to houses, power lines and the like. You may not have an ideal spot, but even so you probably won't have to bring the antenna right into your operating room.[2] So in most cases the situation is this: The antenna is "out there" and the transmitter is "in here"; how is the rf power to get from the transmitter to the antenna?

The answer, of course, is a transmission line. Your 60-hertz power comes to you through a transmission line, too. However, there is a difference in the way rf lines and 60-hertz lines operate. The reason is the difference in wavelengths. One wavelength at 60 hertz is over 3000 *miles*. If we wanted to build a half-wave antenna for that frequency it would have to extend more than half way across the United States. So even though you may be 20 miles from a power station, you're only a very small fraction of a wavelength away. The time it takes for power to reach you is so short, compared with 1/60 second (one cycle), that the standing-wave effects discussed earlier in this chapter are negligible.

But in transmitting power at a frequency of, say, 7 MHz, the time taken for the power to travel 50 feet isn't at all negligible compared with the duration of one cycle. This means that we can't look upon a transmission line as a simple electrical circuit, which we *can* do at 60 hertz. What is happening at the "far" or "output" end of the line may be quite different from what is happening at the "near" or "input" end at the same instant.

## The "Infinite" Line

A useful concept to explain transmission-line operation is the *infinite line*. This is an imaginary line consisting of two conductors, side by side and close together, extending so far that we can never reach the end.

If an rf voltage is applied to the input end of such a line, one terminal will be negative whenever the other is positive, and vice versa. This causes the current to flow in one direction in one wire and in the other direction in the second, as in Fig. 18. Because the currents flow in opposite directions, the electromagnetic fields set up by them are also opposite. The fields, therefore, cancel each other's effects or nearly do so (there is always a *little* uncancelled field, because the two wires can't actually occupy the same spot). Since the fields cancel, there is no radiation from the line.

Thus, all the energy put into the line travels away from the generator, following the line at almost the speed of light. And since the line is infinitely long, none of the energy ever comes back.

## Characteristic Resistance

Probably the first question you'd ask at this point is this: If the generator voltage is known, how much current will flow in the line? From the discussion of the meaning of resistance in chapter 1, you would be right to infer that such a line must act like a resistance, since energy is being taken continuously from the generator. But how many ohms?

This resistance, called the *characteristic resistance* of the line, has nothing to do with the actual resistance of the conductors. While it may seem odd, the fact is that it is a function of the inductance and capacitance per unit length of line. The resistance actually is determined by the *L/C* ratio of the line. This ratio depends on the diameters of the conductors and the spacing between them. The smaller the conductor diameter and the wider the spacing, the higher the characteristic resistance. Practical values of resistance lie between about 150 and 800 ohms for a "two-wire" or *parallel-conductor* line as shown in Fig. 18.

It is important to realize that this characteristic resistance does not itself consume any power. The power is merely *following* the line on its way to infinity. The characteristic resistance is simply the ratio of voltage to current all along the line. Since the line is imaginary anyway, we can imagine further that the conductors have no actual resistance and there is no other energy loss along the line. Thus, all the power put into the line is delivered to infinity, wherever that may be. This means that the characteristic resistance is "pure" resistance — no reactive effects at all.

## Characteristic Impedance

But what if the conductors do have resistance of their own? Practically, of course, they must have. Also, the practical insulation between the two conductors is not perfect; there is some leakage between the two wires. This leakage is equivalent to a resistance (a high value) shunted across the two conductors. In the topsy-turvy world of transmission lines the presence of these two components of resistance gives rise to *reactance*. So if the line is a practical one having losses, the generator doesn't see a pure resistance and reactance. This is called the *characteristic impedance* of the line.

Because things get complicated at this stage, we like to ignore the reactive part of the characteristic impedance, and do so by assuming that the line has no losses. As long as the losses per unit length are small we can get away with it. Fortunately, this is the case with lines used by amateurs at frequencies below

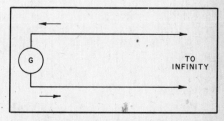

Fig. 18 — An imaginary two-conductor line extending to infinity. Arrows show that the current in one wire flows in the opposite direction to current in the other; this *relationship* is true throughout the entire length of the line, although the actual currents periodically reverse direction as the polarity of the generator's voltage reverses each half cycle.

[2] This has been done; moreover, it is quite possible to "work out" with an indoor antenna. However, it's better to put it outdoors if you can.

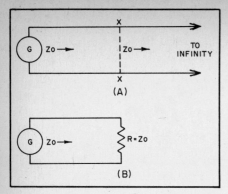

Fig. 19 — An infinitely long line can be simulated by terminating an actual line in its characteristic impedance.

Fig. 20 — A line with no termination — simply an open circuit.

30 MHz. It is even a good-enough assumption in the lower vhf range. When the losses are small the characteristic impedance is *very nearly* a pure resistance equal to the characteristic resistance. The term characteristic impedance is widely used to mean the characteristic resistance of a lossless line. We'll use it that way here, too.

### The Terminated Line

An infinite line, even if we could have one, wouldn't be of any practical use. It happens, though, that a line can be tricked into *acting* as though it's infinitely long.

In Fig. 19A, suppose that the line is cut at *XX*. If the generator is moved up to this point, it will still see the same characteristic impedance (which is commonly designated $Z_O$), since what is left of the line to the right of *XX* is still infinitely long. In the same way, the section of line to the left of *XX* "sees" the section to the right of *XX* as a resistance equal to the characteristic impedance. This is true anywhere along the line. It suggests the idea that the line section to the left of *XX* wouldn't know the difference if a resistor having the same value as the characteristic impedance were substituted for all the line to the right of *XX*.

This is actually so. If a line of any length is *terminated* in a resistance equal to its characteristic impedance, the voltages and currents are just the same in that section as they would be if the line were infinitely long. If the line has no losses, all the power put into it at the generator end is delivered to the terminating resistance.

### Matching

The terminated resistance doesn't have to be a resistor. It can be any device, such as an antenna, that uses up power and thus has no equivalent resistance. If the power-consuming device doesn't inherently have the right value of resistance to match the line, its resistance can be transformed by means

of circuits (such as those described in chapter 1) that will make it "look like" the proper value. Matching of this sort is done more often than not; only occasionally does the load have the right value of resistance, in itself, to match a practical line impedance.

One final point about a *matched line*: If the line has negligible losses, an ammeter inserted anywhere along its length will give the same reading. Also, a voltmeter connected across it at any point will give the same reading. There are no standing waves of current or voltage such as we find along an antenna, even though the line may be many times longer than the antenna. But this is true *only* when the line is terminated in its characteristic impedance.

### Standing Waves on Lines

Now let's look at a line that *doesn't* simulate one that is infinitely long. The length of a matched line didn't matter, because all the power kept going in the same direction — to the load. If the line is not matched, its length becomes quite important.

To take an extreme case, suppose the line just stops, as in Fig. 20. The power goes out from the generator to the open end, at which point it has no path to follow except to turn back and head toward the generator. This it does, just as in the case of the antenna discussed earlier. In coming back it sets up standing waves of voltage and current, just as it did along the antenna.

Here, too, the current and voltage distribute themselves along the line according to the wavelength. If the line length *L* is just one-quarter wavelength, the current and votage distribution are as shown in Fig. 21A. If you will imagine the line to be unfolded so that the wires extend in opposite directions from the generator, you can see that this is the same voltage and current distribution as we found along a half-wave antenna, Fig. 33. The line, too, is resonant to the generator frequency. The total length, for both wires, is still a half wavelength, although the line as a whole is only a quarter wave long.

### Odd Lengths

If the line is less than a quarter wave, as in Fig. 21B, there is room only for the outer sections of the standing waves. The line is not resonant in this case. The generator sees it as a reactance, and in order to put maximum current into the line the reactance must be tuned out by adding reactance of the opposite kind. Inductive reactance is needed here for *loading* the line.

In Fig. 21C the line is more than a quarter wave long. Here we have not only the standing waves we had along the quarter wave line but the beginning of another set, too. This line is not

resonant, either, and again it looks like a reactance to the generator. However, in this case, its reactance must be tuned out by using capacitance for loading.

Finally, Fig. 21D shows a line a half wavelength long. Each wire is like a half-wave antenna. Since one terminal of the generator is always positive when the other is negative, and vice versa, the voltages and currents are always opposite in polarity along the wires, just as in the other cases. The half-wave line is

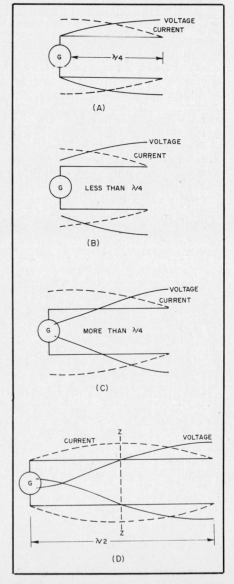

Fig. 21 — Standing waves along open-circuited lines.

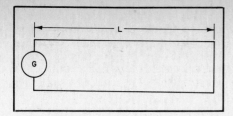

Fig. 22 — Short-circuited line.

also resonant at the applied frequency, since each wire will accommodate exactly a complete standing wave, no more and no less.

This could be continued on for still longer lines. In doing so we should find that the line is always resonant when its length is exactly a multiple of one-quarter wavelength. It is *not* resonant at any other lengths.

### Quarter- and Half-Wave Resonance

Comparing A and D in Fig. 21, you can see that there is a difference even though both can be considered to be resonant. In A the voltage is zero at the generator, but the current has its highest value. In D the current is zero and the voltage has its highest value. Since the impedance seen by the generator is equal to voltage divided by current, the impedance at the input end of the line must be extremely low in A and extremely high in D. If there were no power lost in the line, the impedance values would be zero and infinity, respectively. However, no line can be completely free from loss, so we don't have to worry about what might be meant by zero and infinity. Practically, the impedance is a very low resistance in A and a very high resistance in D.

As you may remember from chapter 1, the same descriptions were applied to series- and parallel-resonant *LC* circuits.

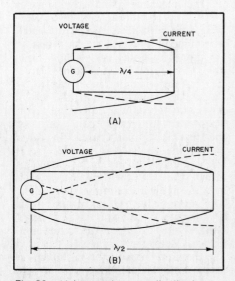

Fig. 23 — Voltage and current distribution along resonant short-circuited lines.

A quarter-wave line open-circuited at the far end acts like a series-resonant circuit. A half-wave line open at the far end acts like a parallel-resonant circuit.

### The Short-Circuited Line

Instead of being left open at the far end as in Fig. 20, the line could be short-circuited as in Fig. 22. Once again, energy traveling out from the generator must turn back when it reaches the short circuit. However, in this case there can be no voltage across the short circuit, although the current can be large. This is just the reverse of the open-circuited case of Fig. 20.

If you will look at Fig. 21D, you will see that just the same condition exists at the point ZZ, one-quarter wavelength from the end of the open line. The voltage between conductors is zero (if there are no losses) at this point. This means that a short circuit could be placed across the line at ZZ without disturbing the currents or voltages. Since it is a quarter wavelength from ZZ back to the input end of the line, this section of line also is resonant.

It is apparent from this that what the generator sees when looking into a quarter-wave short-circuited line is the same as what it sees when looking into a half-wave open-circuited line. That is, a quarter-wave short-circuited line is equivalent to a parallel-resonant circuit. The voltage and current distribution are as shown in Fig. 23A.

By carrying on this line of thought it is easy to demonstrate that a half-wave short-circuited line is equivalent to a series-resonant circuit. The current and voltage distribution are given in Fig. 23B. Lines having in-between lengths are not resonant, and will act like almost pure reactances. Fig. 24 summarizes this.

### Why Open- and Short-Circuited Lines?

Offhand, you might think that open- and short-circuited lines are about as useless, practically speaking, as an infinitely long line. However, the fact is that they are quite useful.

In the first place, a resonant line can be substituted for a resonant circuit and often is. The resonant line is especially useful at vhf and uhf, where it may offer the only resonant-circuit structure that it is physically possible to use. Here is where the multiple resonance that goes with a series of quarter-wave sections often saves the say. A conventional *LC* circuit does not have this feature, and there is a limit to how large, physically, such a circuit can be made for a given frequency.

Second, nonresonant sections of line can be used in place of coils and capacitors, simply by adjusting the length to give a desired value of in-

ductive or capacitive reactance. This is frequently done in antenna matching systems.

Finally, there are applications where multiple resonance in a line lets us do things like short-circuiting a harmonic of the transmitter while the fundamental frequency goes through unaffected. For example, a short-circuited line having a length of one-quarter wavelength at the fundamental frequency has a very high impedance — nearly an open circuit — and can be connected across another transmission line with little effect on the power flowing through it. But at the second harmonic it is a half wavelength long, and it will act as a short circuit across the other line at that harmonic (and all other even harmonics).

### Mismatched Lines

You have seen that the power put into a matched line nearly all gets to the load at the output end. A small amount is used up by the losses in the line itself; this is converted into heat. We are assuming here, of course, that the line conductors are so close together that there is no radiation because of incomplete cancellation of the fields. If the spacing between the conductors is of the order of 1/100 wavelength this is a good assumption, providing the currents and voltages in the line are *balanced*. Line balance means that the current and voltage in one wire are exactly duplicated in the other, except for reversed polarity.

But what if the load connected to the far end of the line does not exactly match the line's characteristic impedance? A case like this falls somewhere between the perfectly matched condition and the extremes of the open- and short-circuited lines. Some of the power reaching the end is absorbed by the load, but some of it also bounces back toward the input end. A *mismatch* is

Fig. 24
**Characteristics of Various Lengths of Transmission Line**

| Length | Open-Circuited Line | Short-Circuited Line |
|---|---|---|
| Less than 1/4 wavelength | Capacitive reactance | Inductive reactance |
| 1/4 wavelength | Series-resonant circuit | Parallel-resonant circuit |
| Between 1/4 and 1/2 wavelength | Inductive Reactance | Capacitive Reactance |
| 1/2 wavelength | Parallel-resonant circuit | Series-resonant circuit |

The line behavior goes through the same series of changes with each added quarter wavelength.

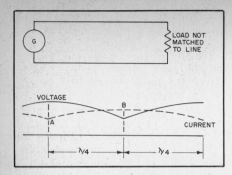

Fig. 25 — The standing-wave ratio is the ratio of the current amplitude at B to that at A, or of the voltage amplitude at A to that at B.

said to exist when the load resistance isn't the same as the characteristic impedance of the line. The worse the mismatch, the greater the proportion of power reflected back.

## Losses

The principal effect here, at least in transmitting, is that the line uses up a little of the power each time the power travels back and forth. But even though some of the power is handed back to the generator (the transmitter) we can still put the same total power *into* the line.

This is simply a matter of the coupling between the transmitter and line. The coupling that would deliver the transmitter output to a matched line won't do it if the line isn't matched. But by changing the coupling as required, the transmitter can be loaded just as well. A little less power will reach the load than would get there if the load matched the line properly, because of the extra line loss. But the difference on this account is too small to cause any worry, if a low-loss line is used. Even with lines which, when matched, have fairly high losses, the *extra* loss caused by mismatching isn't much if you aren't mismatched by a factor of more than three or so.

On a perfectly matched line there are no standing waves because no power is reflected from the load end. On open- or short-circuited lines there are large standing waves. Along such lines the voltage and current go to zero, or very close to it, at the nodes.

When a line is mismatched, but not open- or short-circuited, there are standing waves because some of the power is reflected. But only *some* of it. The reflected voltage and current can't completely balance out the *incident* voltage and current (the voltage and current traveling *to* the load) at the nodal points unless there is just as much coming back as is going out. Since this is not the case, there are no points of zero voltage and current along the line. Instead, there will be points of *minimum*

current and points of *minimum* voltage. Likewise, there will be points where the voltage and current will be maximum.

## Standing Waves on Mismatched Lines

If we went along a mismatched line measuring the amplitudes of the current and voltage, without paying any attention to polarity, we would find that both vary along the line. Fig. 25 is typical of what might be measured. The points of maximum and minimum are still one-quarter wavelength apart, as in the cases discussed before. The ratio of the current at B, a maximum point, to the current at A, a minimum point, is called the *standing-wave ratio*. Measurement of the maximum and minimum voltages would give the same ratio as measurement of current.

If very little power is reflected from the load — i.e., the line is nearly matched — there is relatively little variation in the current and voltage along the line, so the standing-wave ratio — usually abbreviated to *SWR* — is low. The greater the mismatch, the greater the reflected power and the larger the SWR.

## SWR and the Load

It happens that the standing-wave ratio can be measured more readily than the current or voltage, or even the load resistance. So it is customary to measure the SWR in order to find out whether the line is matched. There is a very simple relationship between load resistance, the characteristic impedance of the line and the SWR

$$SWR = \frac{R}{Z_o} \text{ or } \frac{Z_o}{R}$$

Where $R$ stands for the load resistance and $Z_o$ stands for the characteristic impedance of the line. The reason for the choice in this formula is that it is customary to put the larger number on top, so that the SWR is expressed as, for example, 5 to 1, rather than 1 to 5.

Actually, you don't need to know $R$ at all in making most adjustments of load resistance. If you're shooting for no reflected power — that is, an SWR of 1 to 1, meaning that the maximum and minimum values are the same — you adjust for the smallest possible SWR. When you have it, you know you're right.

Fig. 25 shows the voltage high and the current low at the load. It could be the opposite. The drawing is for the case where the load resistance is larger than $Z_o$. The reverse would be true for a load resistance smaller than $Z_o$. The first case approaches the open-circuited line as $R$ is made larger, and the second approaches the short-circuited line as $R$ is made smaller.

With a mismatched pure-resistance load, as in the cases discussed earlier, the generator sees a pure resistance when the line is some multiple of a quarter wave in length. Thus this same length indicates resonance. At all other lengths the generator will see reactance along with resistance. Fig. 24 can be used to find the *kind* of reactance, if the short-circuit column is used for loads loads less than $Z_o$ and the open-circuit column is used for loads greater than $Z_o$.

## Resistance Only!

Finally, a warning: To avoid confusing you with a lot of qualifications, in what was said above, we have omitted one very important point. *The load has to be a pure resistance if any of this is to be true.*

Mostly, you will be working with loads that are "pure," or nearly so. You can't get an SWR of 1 to 1 unless the load *is* a pure resistance; any reactance in it throws the whole thing off. So if you've been able to get the SWR to 1 to 1 or close to it, you can take it for granted that the line behavior will be as described. If not, you can't find out where you stand without a much more detailed knowledge of transmission lines than we can give you in this book.

## Practical Lines

Quite a few varieties of manufactured transmission lines are available. The ones that are of interest to amateurs are usually in stock at radio supply stores, since they are also used for television receivers. There are two general types. One is the *parallel-conductor* type we used for purposes of discussion in the foregoing part of this chapter. The other is the *coaxial line*. This also has two conductors, but one of them is a tube and the other is a wire centered in it.

The coaxial line, familiarly known as "coax" (pronounced with two syllables), obeys the same laws as the parallel-conductor line. All we have said so far applies to both types of line. However, the coaxial line has some distinctive features. The current is carried by the inner conductor and the *inside surface* of the tubular outer conductor. The *outside* surface is "cold" for rf, if the line is properly used. In other words, the active part of the line is shielded from outside influences. This means, too, that there can be no radiation from the inside of the line.

Substantially, all coaxial line in use by amateurs is the flexible type having a braided-wire tube for the outer conductor. Multistrand wire is often used for the inner conductor, although in some small-diameter lines a solid wire can be used without affecting the flexing. The insulation between the two

**Fig. 26**
**Characteristics of Commonly Used Transmission Lines**

| Type of Line | $Z_O$ Ohms | Vel. % | pF Per Ft. | OD | Attenuation in dB Per 100 Feet | | | | | | | |
|---|---|---|---|---|---|---|---|---|---|---|---|---|
| | | | | | 3.5 | 7 | 14 | 21 | 28 | 50 | 144 | 420 |
| RG58/A-AU | 53 | 66 | 28.5 | 0.195 | 0.68 | 1.0 | 1.5 | 1.9 | 2.2 | 3.1 | 5.7 | 10.4 |
| RG58 Foam Diel. | 50 | 79 | 25.4 | 0.195 | 0.52 | 0.8 | 1.1 | 1.4 | 1.7 | 2.2 | 4.1 | 7.1 |
| RG59/A-AU | 73 | 66 | 21.0 | 0.242 | 0.64 | 0.90 | 1.3 | 1.6 | 1.8 | 2.4 | 4.2 | 7.2 |
| RG59 Foam Diel. | 75 | 79 | 16.9 | 0.242 | 0.48 | 0.70 | 1.0 | 1.2 | 1.4 | 2.0 | 3.4 | 6.1 |
| RG8/A-AU | 52 | 66 | 29.5 | 0.405 | 0.30 | 0.45 | 0.66 | 0.83 | 0.98 | 1.35 | 2.5 | 4.8 |
| RG8 Foam Diel. | 50 | 80 | 25.4 | 0.405 | 0.27 | 0.44 | 0.62 | 0.76 | 0.90 | 1.2 | 2.2 | 3.9 |
| RG11/A-AU | 75 | 66 | 20.5 | 0.405 | 0.38 | 0.55 | 0.80 | 0.98 | 1.15 | 1.55 | 2.8 | 4.9 |
| Aluminum Jacket, Foam Diel.[1] | | | | | | | | | | | | |
| 3/8 inch | 50 | 81 | 25.0 | — | — | — | 0.36 | 0.48 | 0.54 | 0.75 | 1.3 | 2.5 |
| 1/2 inch | 50 | 81 | 25.0 | — | — | — | 0.27 | 0.35 | 0.40 | 0.55 | 1.0 | 1.8 |
| 3/8 inch | 75 | 81 | 16.7 | — | — | — | 0.43 | 0.51 | 0.60 | 0.80 | 1.4 | 2.6 |
| 1/2 inch | 75 | 81 | 16.7 | — | — | — | 0.34 | 0.40 | 0.48 | 0.60 | 1.2 | 1.9 |
| Open-wire[2] | — | 97 | — | | 0.03 | 0.05 | 0.07 | 0.08 | 0.10 | 0.13 | 0.25 | — |
| 300-ohm Twin-lead | 300 | 82 | 5.8 | | 0.18 | 0.28 | 0.41 | 0.52 | 0.60 | 0.85 | 1.55 | 2.8 |
| 300-ohm tubular | 300 | 80 | 4.6 | | 0.07 | 0.25 | 0.39 | 0.48 | 0.53 | 0.75 | 1.3 | 1.9 |
| Open-wire, TV type | | | | | | | | | | | | |
| 1/2 inch | 400 | 95 | | | 0.028 | 0.05 | 0.09 | 0.13 | 0.17 | 0.30 | 0.75 | — |
| 1 inch | 450 | 95 | | | 0.028 | 0.05 | 0.09 | 0.13 | 0.17 | 0.30 | 0.75 | — |

[1] Polyfoam dielectric type line information courtesy of Times Wire and Cable Co.
[2] Attenuation of open-wire line based on no. 12 conductors, neglecting radiation.

conductors is a flexible solid plastic — polyethylene.

### Velocity Factor

The presence of this solid insulation does two things: It increases the power loss, as compared with air insulation, and it reduces the speed at which power can go through the line. This means that the wavelength in coaxial cable is shorter, for the same frequency, than in air. The formula for wavelength given earlier has to be modified by a correction factor, called *velocity factor*, on this account. For polyethylene-insulated solid-dielectric coaxial cable the velocity factor is 0.66 and 0.81 for the foam type dielectric. A line one-half wavelength long at 7.1 MHz, for example, would be 0.66 times 69.4 feet (a half wavelength in space), or 45.8 feet long if the solid-dielectric line is used.

### Line Losses

If we should divide a line into sections of equal length and measure the power going in and coming out of each, we should find that there is the same *percentage* loss in each section. Suppose that 100 watts goes into the first section and 10 percent of it is dissipated in heat in the line. Then 90 watts comes out to go into the second section. In the second section 10 percent represents 9 watts, so now we have 81 watts going into the third section. This section loses 8.1 watts, and so on. This sort of power change is exactly what the decibel represents so nicely, so we can express line loss as so many decibels per unit length. The custom is to give the loss in decibels per 100 feet of line.

The loss becomes greater as we go higher in frequency. Losses in dB per 100 feet for the lines most used by amateurs are given in Fig. 26. These losses are for lines that are properly matched by the load. If there is a mismatch the loss will be higher. However, as we said earlier, the additional loss isn't usually serious unless the mismatch is 3 to 1 — that is, an SWR of 3 to 1 — or more. Even then it is not considerable unless the line has high loss when matched.

### Parallel-Conductor Line

The most common type of line is the parallel-wire TV lead-in, consisting of two wires separated by a web of polyethylene approximately 3/8-inch wide. It is sold under several trade names and has a characteristic impedance of about 300 ohms. As shown by Fig. 26, its losses are lower than the losses in coax. This is true of good-quality line, which you can be sure of getting only when you buy a well-known brand. Some of the "bargain" unbranded line is very poor, so it is best to steer clear of it.

The lowest-loss line available is the ladder type, consisting of parallel wires separated about an inch. The wires are held apart by small rods of polyethylene at intervals of a few inches. Thus most of the insulation is air, which has negligible loss.

There are many other types of line, both coaxial and parallel-wire, than those listed. Some have different characteristic impedances, and a few varieties have lower losses or greater power-handling ability. However, the types mentioned are easy to get, and are satisfactory for the majority of amateur installations of medium power.

# Putting the Antenna and Line Together

The half-wave dipole is the basis for most amateur antenna designs. Different types of lines can be used to feed power to it. The line should just carry power to the antenna and not get into the radiating act itself. When this is so, and the dipole does all the radiating, one dipole is the same as another no matter how power may be fed to it. This obvious fact is too often overlooked. Amateurs frequently let themselves be dazzled by some trick name tacked on a dipole-plus-feeder combination, but names don't do the radiating.

The best place to feed a half-wave dipole is at the center. The dipole is a balanced antenna — that is, it is symmetrical about its center. To maintain

**Antennas and Feeders** 97

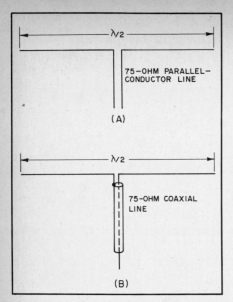

Fig. 27 — Using 75-ohm line to match the center impedance of a half-wave antenna. The antenna length in feet is equal to 468 divided by the frequency in megahertz.

and 28 MHz. Here it is best to cut the antenna for the section of the band that interests you most.

## Matched Antenna Systems

Since the dipole has a center impedance of about 70 ohms, it will match a line having a characteristic inpedance of 70 ohms, or something close to it. (A small — i.e., 20 percent or so — discrepancy doesn't cause any difficulty. When 70-ohm or 75-ohm line is mentioned, it is to be understood that any impedance in that immediate vicinity is meant.) There is a polyethylene-insulated two-conductor 75-ohm line available for this purpose. The antenna is simply cut in the center and a connection made to each line conductor as in Fig. 27.

In spite of the fact that it is desirable to keep the system balanced, a good many amateurs use 75-ohm coaxial line for the same purpose, as in Fig. 27B.

Very often, 52-ohm (a nominal value) line is used instead of 75 ohm. It is not matched as well by the antenna, but the mismatch is not serious.

## The Folded Dipole

The advantages of matched operation also are realized with the *folded dipole* shown in Fig. 28. The folded dipole has two half-wave conductors side by side. One is continuous, but the other is cut at the center for making connection to 300-ohm twin line. The two conductors are joined at their ends.

The wires radiate in parallel. In this respect, the pair is equivalent to a single half-wave dipole. But splitting the conductor into two parts has the effect of making the antenna impedance, as seen by the line, four times the impedance of a single-wire dipole. Thus at the point where the transmission line is connected the antenna impedance is approximately 300 ohms — just right for matching 300-ohm line.

Twin line can be used for the folded dipole itself, but ordinary TV line won't stand the mechanical stresses too well if the antenna is long. There is a special heavy-duty line available which is better. TV ladder line also can be used for the dipole. The spacing between the dipole wires can be anything up to a few inches, so practically any construction that will keep the wires parallel can be used.

## "Open-Wire" Feeders

Fig. 29 shows a half-wave dipole fed at the center through *open-wire* parallel-conductor line. This is line having mostly air insulation, such as the TV ladder line mentioned earlier. Here, there is no attempt at matching the antenna to the line. Consequently, there are fairly pronounced standing waves on the line. However, the high SWR doesn't

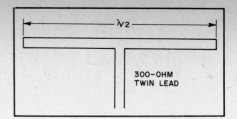

Fig. 28 — The folded dipole. The antenna length is calculated in the same way as for a single-wire dipole.

cause an undue power loss in open-wire line. The principal penalty is that more attention has to be paid to the coupling between the line and transmitter. The advantage is that the antenna can be made to take power at practically *any* frequency.

A transmission line operating with a high standing-wave ratio is often called a *tuned line* or *tuned feeder*. Actually, the only tuning necessary is that required for coupling the transmitter to the line. The line can be any length. However, it does help simplify the transmitter coupling a bit if a resonant length is used. Such a length, as you have seen, will be some multiple of one-quarter wavelength. The line will "look like" a resistance at its input end in such a case, provided the antenna itself is resonant.

On the other hand, in this system the dipole doesn't have to be exactly resonant. Since there is no attempt at matching the characteristic impedance of the transmission line, the antenna doesn't *have* to look like a pure resistance, of just the right value, to the line. The overall length of wire in the system, including both the dipole and the transmission line, is of more interest. It is this overall length that determines whether or not the system as a whole is resonant. One line wire plus one side of the dipole (the length $L$ in Fig. 29) should be a whole-number multiple of a quarter wavelength if you want the system to be resonant. The formula

$$\text{Length in feet} = \frac{234}{\text{frequency in MHz}}$$

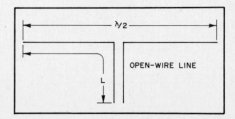

Fig. 29 — Half-wave dipole fed with open-wire line.

this symmetry a balanced line — i.e., a parallel-conductor line — should be used. The dipole *can* be fed at one end, but this also upsets the symmetry of the system.[3]

If the impedance at the center of the antenna matches the characteristic impedance of the transmission line the two can simply be connected together and the line will operate without standing waves. One advantage of this matched operation is that the line length has very little effect on the coupling required between the line and the transmitter. Another is that the losses in the line are least, for a given length, when the line is properly matched. The line losses can either be very important or completely unimportant. They are quite important at vhf even when the best possible job of matching is done. They are unimportant at the lower frequencies, even with a considerable mismatch. The only exception here is when a major error is made in selecting the proper type of line for the use to which it is to be put.

A matched antenna system is actually matched only for one frequency. At best, the system will stay matched over only a small band. As the 7-, 14- and 21-MHz bands are narrow, in terms of percentage, an antenna that is matched at the center of one of these bands should work over the entire band without having the SWR get too large at the band edges. But you can't do quite as well with antennas of this type on 3.5

[3] An exception to this occurs when *two* dipoles are fed from a parallel-conductor transmission line. An example is described shortly.

will give the length of a quarter wave as accurately as is necessary.

## Multiband Operation

As explained earlier, a matched antenna system is essentially a one-band system. There are ways of getting around this, but not with a simple dipole. One such scheme is shown in chapter 14.

The simplest multiband antenna, and the most versatile, is the one shown in Fig. 30, using open-wire feeder. Since the amateur bands are harmonically related in frequency, we can take advantage of the fact that wires have harmonically related resonances. The fundamental frequency of a center-fed wire is the one for which its length is a half wavelength. At twice the frequency

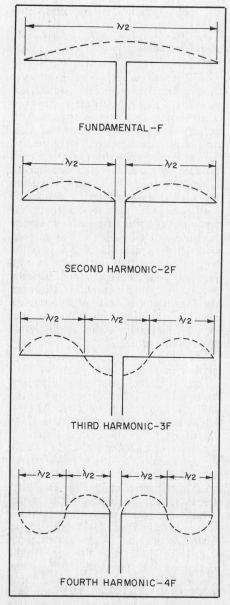

Fig. 30 — Harmonic operation of a center-fed antenna. If the antenna is a half wavelength long at 7 MHz, for example, it will also be resonant in the 14-, 21- and 28-MHz bands.

each *side* of the antenna is a half wavelength long, so at this frequency the transmission line is feeding a pair of half-wave dipoles end-to-end. The current distribution is shown in Fig. 30, which also shows the other resonances up to the fourth multiple.

You should note a few especially interesting things in these drawings. In the second-harmonic case the polarity of the current is the same in both sides of the antenna. There is no reversal such as there was in a continuous wire of the same overall length (Fig. 4). This difference comes about because we have, in effect, two half-wave antennas driven in push-pull, rather than a single antenna a full wavelength long.

There is a somewhat similar situation at the fourth harmonic. Here, too, the currents in the half-wave sections connected to the line have the same polarity. However, when we go out along either wire we find that the normal reversal occurs in the next half-wave section.

This type of current distribution occurs at all *even* multiples of the fundamental frequency. Note also that at the second harmonic the current is minimum where the feeder is connected. Although the voltage distribution isn't shown, the voltage is highest at these same points, just as in the cases discussed earlier. This means that the impedance is high at the connection point. If the antenna is resonant, it is a resistance rather than an impedance, and is of the order of several thousands of ohms. This same condition exists at all even multiples of the fundamental frequency.

## Odd Harmonics

Now look at the drawing for the third harmonic. Here we have the normal current distribution for a wire three half-waves long (Fig. 4). The antenna current has its largest value right where the transmission line is connected. The voltage must be lowest at this point, so the impedance (or resonant resistance) of the antenna is low — more like the impedance at the fundamental.

Thus for all *odd* multiples of the fundamental, the current distribution is the same as in a simple continuous wire of the same overall length, and the impedance at the feed point is low. The impedance goes up a little with each odd harmonic — to a little over 100 ohms at the third harmonic and to about 120 ohms at the fifth harmonic.

Because these figures do not differ too greatly from 70 ohms, it is possible to operate an antenna on its *odd* harmonic when it has been matched on its fundamental. The match is not as good as at the fundamental, but it is not so poor as to result in excessive line loss. Such operation does not really qualify

the antenna for multiband work, because only a few bands — not a consecutive series — can be covered.

If the antenna is fed with 50- or 75-ohm line, you should not try to operate it at *even* harmonics of the frequency for which it is matched. The line losses would be excessive because of the high SWR.

## Transmitter-to-Line Coupling

Nowadays, nearly all transmitter final tank circuits are designed for coupling into resistive loads of 50 to 75 ohms. A properly matched coaxial line will "look like" such a resistance, and when a matched coax line is used there is no difficulty in making the final amplifier load up to the rated input. But if the load isn't properly matched, or some other type of line is used, you may have problems. The loading and tuning adjustments offered by the transmitter usually will give you some leeway — even if the matching at the antenna isn't perfect you may still be able to get the power input you want. Again, you may not.

You can get around troubles of this sort by using a special coupling circuit — a *transmatch* — between the output of the transmitter and the input end of the line. As we saw earlier, the input impedance of the line is not the same as the characteristic impedance of the line unless the line is perfectly matched by the antenna. If the SWR is greater than 1 to 1, the input impedance may differ widely from $Z_o$. If the line is connected directly to the transmitter, the latter may see a load that it can't handle. The transmatch takes the line input impedance and transforms it to what the transmitter wants.

It also does two other things. Practically all transmitter output circuits are single-ended — one side is grounded to the chassis, which is the right way to do it for coaxial line. What to do when a balanced line is used, as in Fig. 27A, 28 and 29? The transmatch easily handles this one; it provides the means for going from a balanced line to coax. In addition, it adds selectivity between the transmitter and the line — selectivity that often is badly needed. It is an unfortunate fact that most transmitters "put out" not only the frequency you want, but also harmonics of that frequency — and, in some cases, lower frequencies too, when lower frequencies are present in the stages leading up to the final amplifier. The transmatch is a circuit that, among other things, is tuned to your desired output frequency and so helps in keeping the unwanted frequencies from reaching the antenna.

## Using the Transmatch

Fig. 31 shows how it is connected, and Fig. 32 is a typical circuit. It isn't

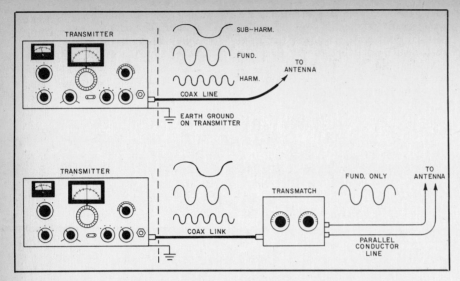

Fig. 31 — The transmatch provides means for matching your transmitter output impedance requirements for going from a balanced transmission line to coax and for filtering out frequencies that shouldn't be allowed to reach the antenna.

the only circuit that can be used, but is probably as versatile as any. The circuit formed by L1 and C1 is tuned to your operating frequency. If the line is the parallel-conductor — balanced — type, the wires are tapped on L1 at equal numbers of turns from the center. The loading is adjusted by changing the positions of these taps. L2 couples the power to L1, and C2 gives you a means for tuning this link circuit. A coaxial line goes from here to your transmitter output terminal. Between these two adjustments you can transform a wide range of line input impedances into 50 or 70 ohms (whichever is the $Z_o$ of the coax line from the transmatch to the transmitter).

The method used for coupling to a coaxial line feeding the antenna is shown at B. It is very similar, the only difference being that the outer conductor of the line is connected to the center of the coil and only one tap is used. The coaxial link circuit to the transmitter remains the same. So does the method of adjustment.

The construction of a transmatch is described in a later chapter. The benefits of the circuit do have their price:

You have to fix things so L1C1 can be tuned to each band you want to use. This usually means that L1 is a plug-in coil. L2 is generally made part of the same coil assembly, since it is advantageous to change it, too, for various bands. The same capacitors can be used for all bands, though, over at least the 3.5 to 30-MHz range.

The adjustment of a transmatch is easy if you have a bridge such as the Monimatch described in a later chapter. Such a bridge is inexpensive and is an almost indispensable station accessory. However, you can arrive at a reasonably satisfactory adjustment simply by varying the tap positions, along with the settings of the two capacitors, while performing the normal tuning and loading operations on your transmitter. After a little cut-and-try, you'll find the transmatch settings that let you load up the final amplifier to the input you want.

### The Grounded Antenna

The antennas described earlier are usually hung more or less horizontally at a height of 25 feet or more above the earth. You may not have the room to put up a horizontal antenna a half wave long at 80 meters; a length of some 130 feet is needed. If you can't, it's always possible to use a center-fed dipole having whatever length your location permits. Open-wire feeder should be used. Except for the antenna length, the system is like that of Fig. 29. It can be tuned up to take all the power your transmitter is capable of giving, if the length L in Fig. 29 is somewhere near 60 feet and you use a transmatch between the line and your transmitter. However, the length of one side of the antenna itself shouldn't be less than about an eighth wavelength — that is, 30 feet or so for 80-meter work.

Possibly the simplest scheme for getting on the air, when your antenna space is limited, is a wire "worked against ground." In this system you put out as long a wire as you can, making it as high as you can, and tune it to resonance at your operating frequency by means of a *loading coil* L1 in Fig. 33. If the transmitter has a coax output fitting, the A terminal in the drawing goes in the inner conductor. The outer sleeve should be connected to earth. Usually there is some piping in the house that you can hook onto for an earth connection. Cold water pipes usually are good, since they tie into the underground water distribution system. Or you can drive a regular ground rod (such as those made for TV grounding) into the earth. In either case you should keep the lead short, since it will want to act as part of the antenna.

The length X in Fig. 33 can be up to

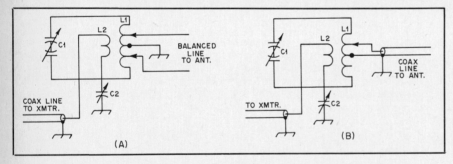

Fig. 32 — A representative transmatch circuit, as applied to balanced lines (A) and coaxial lines (B). Matching adjustment procedure is the same for both cases.

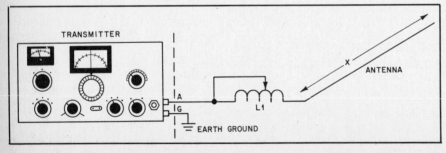

Fig. 33 — A simple antenna for limited space.

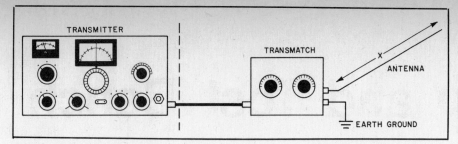

Fig. 34 — Alternative to Fig. 33, using a transmatch for transmitter matching and filtering. The transmatch circuit can be the one shown in Fig. 32B, with the antenna tapped on L1 for the figure in place of the coaxial line.

one-quarter wavelength (60-odd feet at 80 meters) if the ground lead is only a few feet long. For longer ground leads, the lengths of the antenna and ground wires should be added together. The nearer this length to a quarter wavelength, the less inductance you need at L1. If the length is *over* a quarter wavelength, you'll have to substitute a variable capacitor for L1 in order to tune the system to resonance.

The antenna doesn't have to run in a straight line, although it is best to try to make it do so. Put the far end as high in the air as you can. Another scheme is to use metal tubing that you can stand vertically, either self-supporting or with the help of insulated guys. This will radiate better than a slanting wire at lower height.

Antennas such as these aren't the best in the world. However, you may not have any other choice. And they *do* work — often better than you might expect.

### The Receiving Antenna

In most of your amateur communication, the best antenna for receiving is the one you use for transmitting. All antennas work better in some directions than in others. These directions are the same whether the antenna is radiating a signal or picking it up from a distance. If you use your transmitting antenna for receiving, the stations you hear best also will be the ones that hear you best. With a different receiving antenna you might get strong signals from directions that your transmitting antenna covers only poorly. This can be frustrating, because you may spend a lot of time calling stations that don't hear you well enough to make a good contact — and vice versa.

Using the same antenna for both purposes does make it necessary to use some form of switching, since the antenna (or transmission line) has to be connected to the transmitter at one time and to the receiver at another. Manual switching is quite feasible, but a nuisance. Most amateurs use some form of automatic changeover. An antenna relay is probably the most common. Electronic switching also can be used, as described in chapter 11. The electronic system is especially advantageous in break-in code work because it will follow keying. The regular type of relay does not do so well in this respect.

Because of these changeover problems, a great many amateurs do use separate receiving and transmitting antennas. Then no switching is needed. Each antenna is permanently connected, one to the transmitter and one to the receiver. This system is useful for cw work on 80 and 40 meters. To send, you simply press the transmitter key. When the key is open your receiver operates. The method works best at the lower frequencies because the amount of energy picked up by an antenna of given size increases with the *square* of the wavelength, so a receiving antenna just a few feet long will pick up over 60 times as much energy from an incoming 80-meter signal as it would from one on 10 meters. A word of caution is in order before we terminate this part of our chapter. It is possible to induce enough rf energy into the separate receiving antenna during the transmit period to damage the receiver input circuitry. Solid-state receivers are especially prone to this kind of damage. The degree of danger will depend on the proximity of the transmit and receive antennas (the closer they are, the worse the problem) and the amount of transmitter power being used. If a tuner is used to resonate and match the receiving antenna, the rf voltage reaching the receiver input will be considerably greater than if no tuner is used. If a two-antenna system is used, it is suggested that the operator replace the receiver with a 50-ohm resistor, turn on the transmitter, then measure the rms rf voltage across the resistor by means of a VTVM and rf probe. If the developed voltage exceeds one volt, there is a good chance that receiver damage may result. In such a case the receiver input should be shorted out during the transmit period. A solid-state switch can be used for receiver protection. Fig. 35 illustrates the principle under discussion.

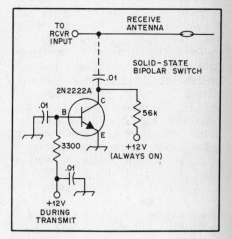

Fig. 35 — Illustration of a bipolar npn transistor used as a receiver-protection switch during transmit periods.

# Chapter 7

# Workshop and Test Bench

Buy something ready-made and you take it for granted that it will perform. Put it together yourself and you savor that unforgettable moment when you first turn on the power, when the big question — will it or won't it work? — is about to be resolved. There's no satisfaction like that which comes from having produced a working piece of equipment with your own hands. And if it doesn't work at first try, you're a wiser amateur after you've found out why. You owe it to yourself to build as much as you can.

Doing a good job of building calls for certain mechanical facilities. Sometimes, it takes ingenuity to provide them. Apartment-house dwellers rarely have space for workshops, but any available table space can be commandeered — temporarily, of course, and with suitable protection against damage from tools and hot soldering irons! It's better, though, to have a spot you can call your own, equipped with a bench or table large enough to let you work in some comfort.

A small shop type bench, around 24 by 48 inches, has enough room for practically all the jobs you'll want to undertake, and even a 2 by 3-foot kitchen table will do. If you have the space, a real luxury is a bench about 3 by 8 feet, or even longer. It isn't hard to make one to fit your own needs if you have just a little aptitude for carpentry. If the bench can be wired with ac outlets, so much the better; you'll need them for soldering and testing. And you'll want plenty of light.

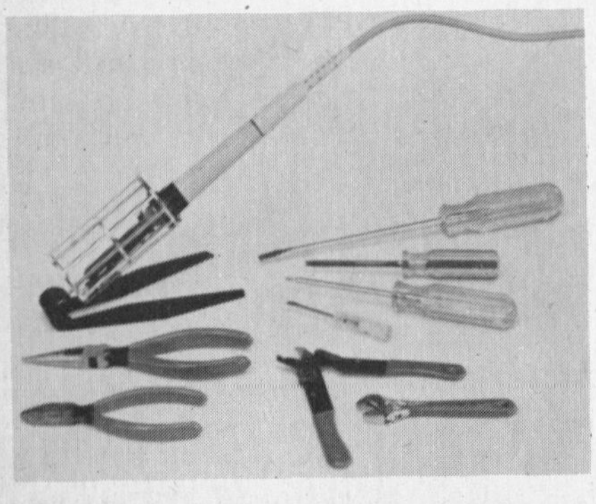

Given a working space that meets these general requirements, the next consideration is tools. It takes only a few to start out, but if you continue to do building you'll accumulate more as you progress.

## Minimum Tools — Kit Building

Building from kits doesn't take many tools — probably no more than you'd need for general station use even if you did no construction work at all. The essential ones are listed below.

A) Small, medium and large screwdriver (flat-blade and Phillips type)
B) Long-nose pliers
C) Diagonal cutters
D) Wire stripper
E) Adjustable wrench
F) Soldering iron, 25- to 60-watt

The wire stripper can be the inexpensive kind but should be adjustable for the size of wire from which the insulation is to be stripped. Properly adjusted, it will strip the insulation off cleanly and will not nick the wire and weaken it.

In addition to the tools listed, a couple of socket wrenches will be handy. Two sizes — for 1/4-inch and 5/16-inch nuts — are most useful. You can find sets with a single handle and interchangeable wrenches in hardware stores. They are inexpensive but quite adequate. In fact, you can get similar screwdriver sets, and this is probably the cheapest way to get an assortment of both wrenches and screwdrivers.

A 25-watt soldering iron is large enough for ordinary wiring. As compared with higher power irons, it is light in weight and easier to poke into tight spots. Also, it lessens the danger of overheating a connection. If you prefer a soldering gun, use one. However, for doing any considerable amount of wiring at one sitting most builders prefer the light iron; it stands up better and is less awkward to handle than the gun.

This is a pretty small list of tools, but it is actually sufficient for any assembly and wiring job, kit or not. In assembling a kit there is no layout work or metal cutting and drilling to do, and that simplifies things mightily.

## Tools and Materials for Metal Fabrication

Most amateur equipment is built on or assembled in a metal chassis. Since ready-made chassis are relatively inexpensive and available in almost any size that the amateur would need, there is seldom a need to build your own. This isn't true of front, rear, side and top panels. In earlier days of radio a large

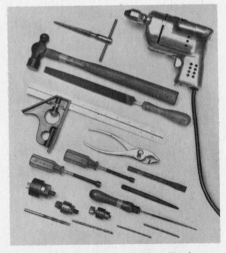

Fig. 2 — Doing your own metal work takes a fair assortment of tools. A hand drill can be substituted for the electric drill shown, with some savings in cost. Chassis punches, lower left, solve the problem of getting smooth-edged round holes for sockets and various types of connectors.

Fig. 1 — This selection of tools will suffice for kit building and ordinary servicing.

amount of equipment was "rack mounted." Various height panels of standard widths were readily available. The trend today is toward all "desk-top" type equipment which is usually much smaller than a rack-mounted counterpart.

There are several different types of materials that are well suited for panels. First is sheet aluminum. It is available in various thicknesses with 0.065 inch common for this application. If a more rigid cabinet is desired, 0.125-inch stock can be used. Thicknesses greater than this would seldom be used for panels on a piece of desk-top equipment. Aluminum sheet is available in several different degrees of hardness of which 6061T6 is standard and easiest to obtain. The only problem associated with using sheet aluminum is being able to purchase it in small quantities. Depending on you local supplier, it may be necessary to purchase an entire 3 X 8-foot piece or pay an exorbitant cutting charge for a smaller piece. Also, some distributors have high minimum order amounts — contact your local supplier about this. If you are planning on building several projects, it would be worth your while to buy a whole sheet. Shop around for the best buy. Not all suppliers' prices are in the same ball park!

An alternative to sheet aluminum of the type just described is an ordinary thick aluminum cookie sheet. Most large discount stores that have a housewares department should carry them. The better sheets are a bit expensive. If you have no other projects requiring aluminum sheet planned, or in the works, this method will be considerably cheaper than purchasing a sheet of aluminum.

Another idea would be to use aluminum chassis bottom plates. They can be obtained from the manufacturers of chassis, but are generally rather expensive and thinner than 0.065 inch. They are suitable for smaller pieces of equipment.

Still another idea for panel material is copper-clad circuit board. If the piece of equipment is not large this represents one of the least expensive methods. Circuit-board material, either single- or double-sided copper, is available on the surplus market at reasonable prices. One of the nice things about using circuit board for panels is that it can be soldered to directly. This is not true of aluminum — at least not easily.

Now we have the panel material, but how do we cut it to size? One way is to use a pair of tin snips. Unfortunately, snips do not function very well in this application, especially on long cuts. Also, the thicker the material is, the harder it will be to cut. Ordinary snips have a tendency to shatter circuit-board material during the cutting process.

Perhaps the easiest and best way for the amateur to cut a panel to size is with the aid of a sabre saw. Straight, smooth cuts can be realized using a piece of wood as a "fence" for the edge of the saw base. Of course, the quality of the cut is dependent on how straight a piece of wood is used. Power saws of this type are not very expensive, some models costing less than $10 at the larger discount houses. A variety of blades is available for these saws, each

Fig. 3 — A straight piece of wood is used as a guide for the sabre saw. Clamps (not visible in this photograph) should be used to secure the wood to the aluminum at each end.

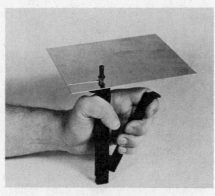

Fig. 4 — A hand nibbler can be used to cut a panel to size. This tool is especially useful for cutting square or rectangular holes in chassis and panels.

with an intended application. The particular application is determined primarily by the number of teeth per inch, their angle and set. Set is the amount that the tips of the teeth are out of line with the flat plane of the blade. Blades designed for cutting aluminum have a large number of teeth per inch with only a small amount of set.

One other device that can be used for cutting the panels to size is a hand nibbler. It is apt to be a long and

tedious process, however, the results are certainly acceptable. After the panel has been cut to the correct size, make sure to file the edges to remove any burrs. A nibbling tool is especially useful for cutting square or rectangular holes in a chassis or panel.

Once you have the chassis and panels, ninety-nine percent of the remaining metal work can be summed up in two words — cutting holes. Most of them are round, varying in size from 1/8 inch to two inches or so. It takes a variety of tools to handle all the situations that may come up. there are two main categories — holes for component mounting screws and holes for sockets. For the former you need a drill, preferably electric, capable of handling metal-cutting bits up to 1/4 inch in size. The drill bits for this purpose come in numbered sizes, and the ones needed most are no. 33 (to pass 4-40 screws), no. 28 (to pass 6-32 screws), and no. 18 (to pass 8-32 screws). A 1/4-inch drill bit is also useful, both on its own account and because a 1/4-inch hole can be reamed out to 3/8 inch, which is the size hole required for the shafts of such items as volume controls, small variable capacitors and phone jacks. A hand reamer, half-inch size (for metal, not wood) or a round file can be used for this job.

The best tool for cutting holes for tube sockets and similar components is a hand-operated (Greenlee) socket punch. Three sizes will take care of practically all tube sockets: 5/8-inch punch (for 7-prong miniature sockets), 3/4-inch punch (for 9-prong miniature sockets), and 1-1/8-inch punch (for octal sockets). The 5/8-inch size also is just right for coaxial fittings of the uhf series, such as the SO-239.

The same tools can be used for working either steel or aluminum. The principal difference is that steel is much harder.

Holes larger than 1-1/8 inch are almost always for special components such as meters. Punches for the large holes are expensive, and for just occasional use probably won't earn their keep. It's more economical (although more work) to cut such holes by drilling a series of small holes around the inside of a circle of the right diameter, breaking or chiseling out the remaining metal, and then filing to smooth out the hole.

Every hole-cutting operation should be started by marking the right spot so the drill will go through where you want it. This takes a center punch. The kind you hit with a hammer is quite inexpensive. More costly, but convenient, is the "automatic" center punch, which has an internal spring-operated mechanism.

You'll also find a flat file or two

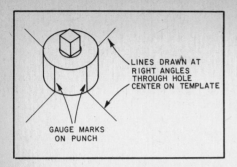

Fig. 5 — How to use gauge marks on a socket punch for centering the punching where you want it.

they will be installed, where those requiring grounding will connect to the chassis, and so on.

Watch out for "interferences" between top, side and bottom-mounted components — but by the same token, don't forget that you can take advantage of the fact that a component mounted wholly on one side of the chassis will leave clear space on the other, except for mounting-screw holes. If you're building something from a printed description, there usually will be photographs of the equipment to guide you.

Once you're satisfied with your layout, mark the exact spots where holes are to be drilled. These will correspond to the mounting holes in each component, of course, and the component can be used as a template for spotting the hole centers accurately. Components whose edges should be aligned with an edge of the chassis should have their mounting holes squared up. This means that you have to be able to draw lines parallel with the chassis edges. A combination square is handy for this, but is not a necessity. An ordinary ruler can be used; simply measure the proper distance from the edge along both adjoining sides of the chassis, mark the points, and draw a line between them. Or you can use a sheet of letter paper as a square, lining one side up along an edge of the chassis.

Mark the *exact* spot for each hole with a pencil dot. Alongside it, jot down the size hole required. When this is done, put all the components on the template, setting their mounting holes over your marked points. This gives you a final check on the accuracy of your work, and if you've inadvertently mislocated some parts so they interfere with each other, you'll discover it before any damage is done.

### Using Chassis Punches

When laying out socket holes on the template, draw a pair of lines at right angles to each other through the center mark. These will let you use the gauge marks on the side of the socket punch for lining up the punch properly. Align both pairs of gauge marks with your pencil lines and the punch will be centered where you want it. See Fig. 5. Be sure to drill a large enough hole so the bolt in the punch can move freely; don't try to use the drilled hole for centering the punch. The punching from the chassis is distorted when you pull the cutter through the metal and will jam on the bolt unless you allow enough clearance. Keep the bolt lubricated with grease and be sure to clean off the small metal chips after each use.

Punchings of this type come out with clean edges and the holes usually need no smoothing. Not so with the

drilled holes. These have to be deburred. An easy way is to use a larger size drill or counter sink.

### Mounting the Components

Most small parts are mounted with either no. 4 or no. 6 machine screws; the size of mounting hole will indicate which to use. Miniature sockets usually have holes for no. 3 screws, but the metal is soft and can easily be reamed out to take a no. 4. Larger components such as small power transformers usually mount with no. 8 screws. If you want your equipment to stay together solidly it's good practice to use star or lock washers under each nut.

In tightening screws use the right size of screwdriver. If the screwdriver bit doesn't fit snugly, it will tend to gouge the edges of the screw slot.

Leave the heavy parts such as transformers and chokes off the chassis until you have the wiring completed to the point where these components have to be mounted. It's much easier to handle the chassis if it doesn't have heavy or

### Laying Out the Chassis

Whether the job before you is large or small, the first step in construction should be making a chassis drilling template. Take plenty of time here. Collect the components to be used, including "mechanical" items that don't appear on the circuit diagram such as tie-point strips and insulators that require mounting holes.

Don't forget to allow room for small items and also make provision — at least mentally — for wiring them in place. These small parts tend to get crowded around such focal points as tube sockets, so you should have a fairly clear picture in advance of just how

useful, especially if you form small mechanical parts, such as brackets, from sheet metal.

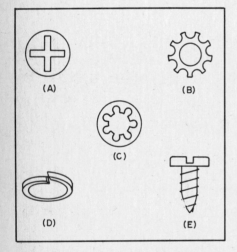

Fig. 6 — The Phillips head (A) may be found on any type of screw; it requires a special screwdriver instead of the common flatblade type used with slotted screw heads. Three types of lock washers are shown at B, C and D; the two former are most commonly used in radio equipment for holding screws up to no. 8 in diameter. E shows a sheet-metal screw for assembling pieces of metal that are too thin for regular screw threads.

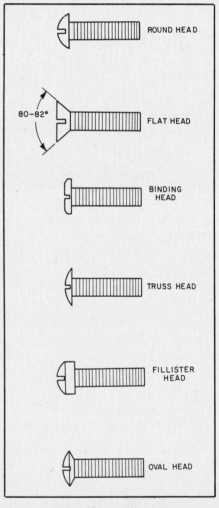

Fig. 7 — Machine screws are known by their heads. The flathead and oval-head types require countersunk holes, but the others shown are intended for use on flat surfaces.

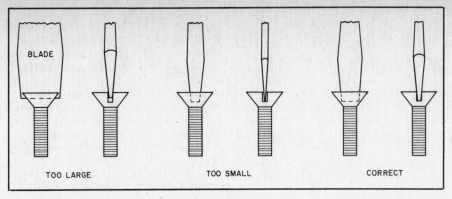

Fig. 8 — The wrong size of screwdriver blade won't turn the screw properly and probably will ruin the slot to boot.

bulky parts on it. Put on the sockets, tie points, and other small parts first, wire as much as you can, and then add the bigger ones as you come to them.

## Wiring

Leads in rf circuits should generally take the shortest route from point to point. However, keep them away from the chassis and other wiring, to reduce unwanted stray capacitance. Leads carrying only dc and 60-Hz ac can be run in any way that happens to be convenient. They can often be bunched together into a cable and laced together into a "harness"; this gives a neat job, especially if the cabled wires are run along the chassis edges.

In audio circuits the leads that are above ground potential should not be allowed to come too close to supply wires, especially those carrying ac. The signal-input lead of a first audio stage often is a particularly touchy one for picking up hum. If you have any trouble on this score, use a piece of shielded wire, grounding the shield to the same point at which the ground return for the stage is connected to the chassis.

Plastic-covered hook-up wire — solid, not stranded — is the easiest kind to strip, as it leaves a clean end. No. 22 is large enough for receiver wiring, including heaters, and for transmitters in stages of comparable power.

## Soldering

Everybody knows how to solder — so they think. But poor soldering is responsible for more trouble with radio equipment than any other single cause that can be named. Learn the *right* way to solder and you'll avoid much unnecessary grief.

The iron must be big enough for the job. As stated earlier, a 25- to 60-watt iron is just about optimum for practically all chassis wiring. It doesn't pay to use one too powerful because some components, such as small composition resistors, will be permanently damaged

by excess heat. A heavier iron — 100 watts or larger — will be needed for bigger jobs such as soldering no. 12 or no. 14 antenna wires.

## Tinning the Iron

The tip of the iron must be clean and well tinned. A dirty tip with poor tinning simply won't make a good soldered joint. One of the first things you need to learn, therefore, is to tin the tip. Start by filing or sandpapering the tip until the metal all over the working end is bright. The end should be pyramid-shaped, pointed rather than stubby. Make sure that the entire tip is clean; in the type of iron having a setscrew, loosen it and take the tip out. Clean out the inside of the heater, too. Then replace the tip and make sure that the setscrew is tight. Let the iron heat up to working temperature.

With the iron hot, file it bright again and run on a little solder. Use the rosin-core type, preferably the 60-40 variety, although 50-50 can also be used. The metal will oxidize rapidly after you file, so you have to work fast at this point, or even do just a part of the tip at a time. With care, you will finish with a tip having a good coating of solder all over the point and extending a half inch or so down the cylinder. The tinning process can be helped along by using a little soldering paste. This will delay oxidation until you can get the solder to run on easily. But *don't* use soldering paste in actual wiring. If you use it in tinning, wipe the tip clean on a rag after the tinning job is done.

## Making a Joint

Cleanliness is absolutely essential in soldering. The parts to be soldered *must* be clean and bright or you won't get a good joint. You may get something that looks like a good joint, occasionally, but looks are deceiving. Scrape the wire clean!

To make the joint, see that the parts

to be soldered are firmly in contact, then hold the hot iron on both parts (or on all, if there are two or more wires in a single lug or prong) until they are hot enough to make the solder flow freely when the solder is touched to the *parts*, not to the iron. Don't try to solder by touching the solder to the iron so it melts and runs over the parts. The iron is there primarily to heat the metal to be soldered so *that* metal will melt the solder.

After the solder has run into and all around the joint, take away the iron and let the joint cool. Don't let the wire or any part of the joint move while this cooling is going on. Especially, don't allow any movement when the solder cools to the mushy stage, which it passes through before becoming firm.

A good joint doesn't need a great deal of solder. Although you shouldn't try to be skimpy with solder, don't pile it up unnecessarily. The soldered joint should have a fairly bright surface, and the solder should taper off along the metal instead of drawing up into a bead.

Soldering paste should never be used in circuit wiring. It is almost impossible to remove it from the vicinity of the soldered joint, and it will collect dust and moisture with time. This can lead to noisy circuits. Rosin-core solder will leave a thin coating or drops of rosin on or around the joint, but these do no harm either electrically or mechanically.

## Some Special Pointers

You have to have *enough* heat to make a good joint, but don't *over*heat.

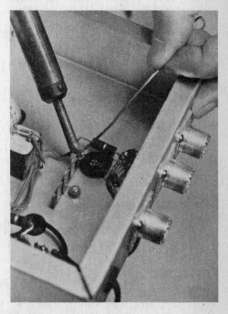

Fig. 9 — Apply the soldering tip to the joint, not to the solder. Let the joint get hot enough to cause the solder to run freely without actually having the solder touch the tip. You can't make a good soldered connection by using the tip to melt solder and letting it run over a cool joint.

As soon as the solder flows the way it should, take the iron away. Small parts aren't helped by being overheated. Some, like semiconductor diodes and transistors, can be damaged even by normal soldering. In soldering the leads from these devices, hold the wire with pliers on the side away from the iron. This will conduct heat away from the device itself and prevent overheating it. Do the soldering just as quickly as you can, and don't take away the pliers until the joint has cooled to nearly room temperature.

Solder "takes" easily on bright copper and brass, or on leads and lugs that have been pretinned. Nickel-plated parts are a little harder to solder. The prongs on coil forms, plug bars, and many plug-in connectors are nickel-plated. It is a good idea to file the plating off the ends of such prongs and tin them by using the iron to apply a little solder before pushing the wires through the prongs. You can keep the hole from filling up with solder by giving the form a quick flick to throw the excess solder off while it is still molten. A good joint can be made between the pretinned prong and wire, with little or no fuss. After wiring a form or connector, always scrape the rosin off the prongs and wipe them with a rag wet with alcohol. You won't get good contact when the form is plugged into a socket unless the prongs are really clean.

Pretinning often is advantageous on the wire leads to small components such as capacitors and resistors. These leads are already tinned, but in time get dirty or an oxide coating forms. This sometimes makes soldering difficult. Fresh tinning will let you make your final joints faster and with more certainty.

Care must be used in soldering prongs or lugs on polystyrene parts such as coil forms. "Poly" softens at relatively low temperatures, and you may ruin a form in soldering to the prongs unless you keep the form itself cool. One way to do this is to make a "heat sink" from a scrap piece of aluminum. Drill holes in it at the same positions as the prongs, making them large enough

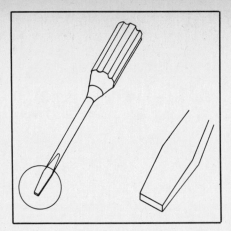

Fig. 10 — A screwdriver should have a blunt end. Touch it up with a file when the edges get rounded with use.

for the prongs to pass through. Slip the metal sink over the prongs and hold it against the bottom of the form while soldering. It will absorb enough heat to prevent the form from softening. Bakelite and similar materials do not need this precaution since they cannot melt.

When several wires are to be soldered to one lug, use special care to ensure that *all* of them get soldered. The one on the bottom may not get hot enough to make a joint. Faults like this are hard to find when the equipment won't work. It isn't a bad idea to solder each wire separately, leaving enough room for succeeding wires to go through the hole in the lug or prong. Use just a little solder each time. Then when the last wire goes in place you can be confident that all of them are in good contact.

### Taking Care of Tools

Good work can't be done with poorly cared-for tools. The first rule of tool care is to use a tool only for the job it was designed to do. A screwdriver, for example, makes a poor chisel, and attempting to use it as one makes it a poor screwdriver in short order.

The preceding section has described how to tin a soldering iron. Keep the tip

clean and brightly tinned. You'll save time in the end by stopping work to re-tin whenever it's necessary. In using the iron, don't let solder pile up on the tip. Keep a clean rag handy and wipe off the excess solder regularly. Also keep the entire tip clean. The part inside the heater usually gets a covering of scale after a time, and the tip should be periodically removed and cleaned. The scale acts as a heat insulator and prevents the tip from heating properly.

The tip of the screwdriver may occasionally require dressing. When you get a new screwdriver, inspect the tip. Observe that the end is *not* sharp, but is made flat so it fits snugly into the slot on the screw it is designed to drive, as in Fig. 10. If the tip gets nicked or worn with use, file or grind it back to the original shape and test it by fitting it into a screw slot. It should not fit loosely, and the blade should go right down to the bottom of the slot so it will turn the screw firmly.

Knives, chisels and the like can be kept in good condition by periodically touching up the edges on a carborundum stone. A small stone can also be used for touching up chassis punches that become dull, but use care in this operation. Never use the stone on the outside circumference of the punch. Look the punch over carefully and use the stone on the flattened part that angles up from the inside to the cutting edge. Keep the angle the same, by grinding parallel with the flat. And go easy, or you may wind up with the punch in worse shape than when you started.

Drills lose their cutting edges with time. Sharpening a drill is an art. We recommend getting a new drill bit in preference to trying to sharpen an old one. Buy only good drills. The "bargain" sets usually lose their edges on the first hole you drill, if the drill doesn't break off before it gets through the metal.

Files should be kept free from accumulations of filings in the grooves. An inexpensive file brush is the best gadget for cleaning.

# Etched Circuit Boards

Until recently, most amateur equipment made use of vacuum tubes. This equipment, for the most part, was built using point-to-point wiring inside an aluminum or steel chassis. Practically all present-day, solid-state equipment is built using etched circuit boards.

An etched circuit is one which is formed by chemically etching away part of a copper foil that is cemented to a

piece of phenolic or epoxy-base sheet material. What is left after etching is the actual wiring between components.

In most such circuits the components are placed on the noncopper side of the "board", and their leads go through small holes drilled through the board and the copper wiring. After mounting, the leads are soldered to the foil.

Etched circuits are especially useful with solid-state circuitry, the advantages being compact construction (no special gimmicks are necessary for mounting components) and ease of assembly once the etching is finished. The materials are readily available from radio supply houses.

There are several commonly used techniques for etching a circuit board.

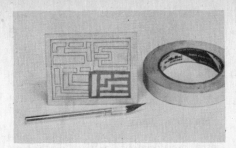

Fig. 11 — Masking-tape method of protecting the copper surface from the etchant. This is perhaps the simplest and quickest way of layout out a circuit-board pattern.

The method that you use will probably depend on the complexity of the pattern, the materials at hand and how neat you want the board to look. No matter which method you choose the idea is still the same — protect those foil areas that you want to remain from the etchant bath. Let's take a look at three different methods which we could use. We'll call them the *masking-tape method, etch-resist pen method* and the *photoetch method.*

## Masking-Tape Method

The masking-tape method is perhaps the simplest and quickest of all. Results with this method are not usually as neat looking as with the other two, but are perfectly acceptable for most circuit patterns. This method would be unsuitable for a complicated digital-circuit pattern. Many thin lines to and from the different ICs are required in this type of circuitry. For layouts of this type the photoetch method is best. However, for relatively simple patterns the masking tape scheme is fine and perferred by many builders.

Basically, the tape method consists of covering the entire copper surface of the board with strips of masking tape. The foil pattern, whether it is taken from a magazine or designed by the builder, is drawn on the masking tape using a pencil or ball-point pen. With the aid of a sharp knife (X-acto or similar) the tape should be cut along the pattern lines, and those pieces of tape covering copper areas that are to be etched away should be removed. The drawing of a typical layout for use with this method is shown in Fig. 11. Large areas of copper between and around the component pads are not completely removed. This provides low impedance ground connections and can aid stability.

Once the tape has been removed from those areas to be etched, it is a good idea to firmly press the remaining tape down on the circuit board. This is especially important along the edges where the tape was cut. If the tape is not stuck tightly to the board, the etchant will have a tendency to work its way under the tape. This results in lines that are not straight and sharp and the finished product will look rather shabby. It's better to take a few extra minutes and ensure that the tape is stuck to the board.

The ferric-chloride etching solution should be placed in a shallow glass or plastic tray to a depth of approximately 1/2 inch. There are two trains of thought regarding the actual etching procedure. The board can either be floated face down on top of the etchant or allowed to sink, face up. It's hard to say if one method is actually better than the other. An automatic agitating and heating system is shown in Fig. 12. It's a handy device and, if you are planning on building many projects, it might be worth your while to construct a similar unit. Heating of the solution is not a requirement; however it does speed up the etching process. Etching the board quickly lowers the chances of undercutting the tape.

The amount of time required for complete etching of the unwanted copper depends on the age and number of times the etchant has been used. With new etchant in an agitated and heated bath, the board should etch completely in approximately 15 to 20 minutes. As the etchant is used over and over again, the amount of time will increase. If it takes more than 45 minutes or so, the old etchant should be discarded and replaced with fresh material. Old etchant can be poured down the sink. It's a good idea to let the tap water run for a minute or two afterwards so the etchant will be adequately dissolved and not etch the copper pipes!

Wear rubber gloves when working with the ferric-chloride etchant or any chemical powder or solution. If some of the solution comes in contact with your skin, rinse the area with clean water. Also, contact with clothing should be avoided since the etchant will permanently stain most types of material.

A board placed in fresh etchant that is not heated, but is agitated, will take on the order of 30 to 45 minutes. Even if the bath isn't heated it should be agitated, if not mechanically then by hand. If it isn't, the board is apt to require several hours in the etchant tank. Once the etching of the board has been completed, wash it off in ordinary tap water. Remove the remaining masking tape and drill the board. A number 60 drill will work fine for most circuit components. Drills this small are rather brittle and should be placed well up into the drill chuck with the minimum amount necessary exposed.

## The Etch-Resist Pen Method

Perhaps the most popular method

Fig. 12 — A homemade stand for processing etched-circuit boards. The heat lamp maintains the etchant-bath temperature between 90 and 115 degrees F and is mounted on an adjustable arm. The tray for the bath is raised and lowered at one end of the action of a motor-driven eccentric disk, providing the necessary agitation of the chemical solution. A darkroom thermometer monitors the temperature of the bath.

for laying out a circuit board involves the use of an etch-resist pen. Paint-like material is contained inside the pen and is deposited directly on the copper surface. Most pens look, and are used, like ordinary felt-tip markers. The desired circuit-board pattern is simply drawn on the board and those areas that are left unprotected are etched away. This method allows more flexibility in laying out a pattern than the tape method since it is easy to draw circles, thin straight lines and curved lines. Results with this method can be almost as good looking as the somewhat more professional photoetch system. Etch-resist pens are available from most of the larger electronic supply houses.

Once the pattern has been drawn on the board, let it dry for the amount of

Fig. 13 — Photo-resist pen and circuit board ready for etching. If you misplace a line or circle, it can be easily removed with the aid of fine steel wool or an ordinary pencil eraser.

time indicated on the instruction sheet. The actual etching procedure is the same as that for the tape method. Again, the board should be etched as quickly as possible for best results. After the etching process is finished wash the board off with tap water. A piece of fine steel wool dipped in lacquer thinner can be used to remove the resist. It shouldn't be necessary to rub very hard; let the thinner do the work. After you have finished this step, wash the board with soap and water to remove any oil that may have been left on the board by the steel wool. Now the board can be drilled and the components mounted.

### Photoetch Process

The photoetch method is by far the most complex way of making a circuit-board pattern; however, it yields the most professional looking results. Many of the commercial circuit-board supply houses use a similar process. It's quite a detailed operation and therefore deserves more than just a cursory look. Once you get the hang of the method, there's really no trick to it. In the photo process, the metal surface is completely covered with a photosensitive resist. This lacquer-like substance can be removed with certain solvents, usually trichlorethylene, until it is exposed to ultraviolet light (UV), after which the resist becomes relatively insoluble.

The pattern of the circuit is transferred by exposing the sensitized board to UV through a photographic negative of the circuit pattern. On this negative image, areas corresponding to those from which the copper is to be removed are opaque. The photoresist receives no light on these areas, so it can be washed away with solvent after exposure for the proper time, leaving a pattern of resist on the copper surface. The unwanted copper can then be etched away in the normal manner.

The negative of the circuit pattern can be produced in several ways. The simplest is probably the *mechanical negative*, a transparent sheet with a coating that is opaque to UV. Portions of the coating are removed with a sharp tool to produce lines and connector pads.

In another method the pattern is drawn in dark ink on semitranslucent paper, and the negative produced by the contact-print process. This is useful in duplicating a project for which a full-size circuit-etch layout is provided. Trace the pattern from the article, or make a Xerox type of copy (if the foil pattern alone is shown), and make a contact negative of it.

A more versatile method involves making tape-artwork transparencies in three steps: the layout, pattern transparencies with graphic-art aids, and con-

tact negatives of these transparencies. Advantages include precise control of line width and path, ease of making corrections and design changes, uniform size and shape of conductor terminals, and ease and precision in fabrication of two-sided boards. This method is covered in detail here.

Following is a list of minimal supplies, in addition to the recommended tool and supply list given earlier.
1) Drawing board. A kitchen cutting board at least 10 by 14 inches will do
2) Sharp, fine-pointed knife for use with drafting aids
3) Pressure-sensitive drafting aids
4) Transparent plastic sheets of proper size
5) Drafting or masking tape
6) Darkroom tongs (the wood variety is desirable for use during the etch-resist development stage — the developer is an

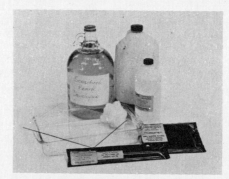

Fig. 14 — Here are the basic materials required for a photoetch circuit board. Sensitized board developer, etchant, reversing film developer, a piece of glass, cotton, an etching and developing tray and reversing film are all required in this process. Not shown in the picture are the drafting aids used for the tape pattern of the circuit board. They can be obtained from most drafting supply houses. While this method is rather complicated, it yields the most professional looking results.

excellent solvent for many plastics)
7) One or two glass trays at least 20 percent larger than circuit boards to be fabricated
8) Sheet of glass approximately 20 percent larger than circuit board; may be clear Plexiglas
9) No. 2 photoflood bulb with suitable (heat resistant!) fixture
10) Reversing film*
11) Reversing film developer*
12) Circuit board developer (trichlorethylene)
13) Presensitized copper-clad circuit boards of proper size*
14) Ferric-chloride etchant solution*

*Available from Kepro Circuit Systems, 3630 Scarlet Oak Blvd., St. Louis, MO 63122.

The work area used for the photochemical processes should be near a source of running water, if possible, and should have a work surface at least 2 feet by 2 feet.

Sensitized circuit boards and reversing film are relatively insensitive to visible light, and may be handled in semidark conditions. The work area must be well ventilated during etch-resist development, as trichlorethylene fumes are toxic.

Begin by taping a piece of paper to the surface of the drawing board. Lightly draw in a full-sized outline of the circuit board as seen from the top side, i.e., the side on which the components will be mounted. The placement of parts can now in large measure by determined by arranging the actual parts on the paper. Keep in mind the location of off-board power and signal connections while arranging the parts. Try to minimize the length of the circuit paths, but avoid crowding the components.

The finished layout is now duplicated on sheets of acetate, using pressure-sensitive drafting aids. Acetate sheets can be cut from transparent three-ring document protectors which should be available from a local stationery store. The pressure-sensitive drafting aids, manufactured by Chartpak Rotex, 2620 S. Susan St., Santa Ana, CA 92704, can be obtained through local drafting supply stores. They are die-cut crepe in the shape of component "doughnut" pads, which are placed at terminal connection points, and uniform-width tape, which is used to form the conductor traces. Also useful are dry transfer letters, which serve neatly to identify components, signal points, and so on. The pads are available, in a wide variety of sizes, in rolls of 250, at about one dollar per roll. Use the 0.065-inch pads for IC and transistor connections, and other sizes up to 0.1 inch for larger components and off-board terminals.

The minimum recommended tape width for conductor traces is 1/32 inch. Maximum recommended current through a conductor of this size is one ampere. Kepro literature recommends no more than five amperes per 1/16-inch width. The advantage of using the widest possible line is very apparent at high radio frequencies, where conductor inductance begins to be critical.

Wherever practical, the use of a ground plane on the component side of the board is recommended. Advantages of this practice include higher noise immunity and lower ground impedance. Chartpak has available rolls of tape in widths from 0.015 inch to 2 inches. The larger widths are useful in blacking out ground-plane areas on the transparency. The minimum recommended spacing between conductors is 1/32 inch.

To begin making the transparencies, tape a piece of plastic sheet over the layout drawing. Ensure that it is firmly in place, as it may have a tendency to move while pressure-sensitive materials are being laid down and trimmed. Place pads over each mark on the layout drawing to which a component connection will be made. The proper technique for laying down pads is something best learned by experience. Practice on a scrap piece of plastic sheet before attempting it on a layout transparency. Absolute precision in laying the pads down from the roll is not vital, as they are easily nudged into the proper place with a pencil point or knife blade.

At this point, tape may be laid down over the lines on the layout drawing, forming the conductor pattern which is to appear on the surface of the board. The tape is flexible and is easily laid down in straight and curved paths. For sharp bends with the wider tape sizes, it may be necessary to cut the tape and make an angular intersection. Precut elbow bends are available on rolls, but it is unlikely that the average builder would use enough of them to make the cost justifiable. If identifying letters or numbers are desired, dry transfer sheets may be used to provide uniform, sharp characters.

Once the transparency is completed, it's time to make the negative. The package of reversing film should be opened in subdued lighting. Remove the contents of the package and cut a piece of film slightly larger than that of the transparency from the roll. Place this piece of film, emulsion side (nonshiny side) down, on a clean surface. Next, lay the transparency on top of the film — right side up. Place the piece of glass or Plexiglas on top of the transparency. You're now ready to expose the film. The no. 2 photoflood bulb should be placed 10 inches away from the glass and turned on for a period of three minutes.

When time is up, turn off the light and remove the film. Place the film on a clean surface, emulsion side up, and pour a liberal amount of reversing film developer on the film. A small amount of developer should be poured onto one or two cotton balls. These balls are then used to rub off the unexposed emulsion from the film. Rub lightly at first moving the developer around on the film. After 30 seconds or so the unwanted emulsion will begin to lift off the film. Continue wiping until all of the unwanted emulsion is removed and then wash the negative off with clean water.

Once the negative is dry we're ready to expose the presensitized circuit board. Again, in subdued lighting, place the presensitized circuit board on a flat surface, copper side up. Lay the negative on top of the board oriented so that the pattern is right side up. With the photoflood light 10 inches away, expose the board for a period of six minutes.

When the exposure is completed, pour resist developer into a glass (not plastic!) tray, to a depth of 3/4 inch or more. Place the exposed board in the solution and slosh the solution back and forth over it for about two minutes. Then, handling the board by the edges, remove it from the developer, and hold it vertically and allow it to dry. *Do not shake, wipe or blow upon the board to speed drying!* The image is very fragile at this time. As the developer evaporates from the board, a faint but clearly defined image of the circuit patterns should be visible. It may be necessary to examine the board at various angles to the light in order for the patterns to be seen. If patterns are not visible, or portions are not well defined, return the board to the developer for another minute. Be sure to agitate constantly, as this prevents suspended resist from being redeposited on the surface of the board. After development, the board may be allowed to dry, standing on one edge, for several hours, or may be post-baked in a 140°F (60°C) oven for five minutes.

After drying, the board may be etched in a tray of ferric-chloride solution. It is at this point that mistakes in the exposure/development process will become immediately evident; for when the board is placed in the ferric chloride, all areas not protected by resist will turn reddish brown, and the pattern of the resist will be clearly visible as shiny copper lines on a reddish brown field. Wash the board thoroughly after etching.

### Soldering

Soldering should be done with some care, because the foil is thin. Use a small iron — 20 or 25 watts — and keep it well tinned. The foil should be polished to a bright finish with fine steel wool. When the component leads are pushed through, bend them over the foil slightly so they stay in place. Touch the tip of the iron to *both* the lead and foil for a second or two, and then touch rosin-flux solder to both, allowing the solder to flow on to make a joint. Don't use any more solder than necessary, and remove the iron as soon as the solder runs. A good joint will form a snug-fitting little mound around the lead, not a small ball. You don't need to worry about solder flowing from one lead to another, because it won't cross the nonmetallic surface between leads.

When the soldering is finished, clip off the excess lead lengths with a small pair of diagonal cutters and your board is ready for use.

### Prepared Templates

Ready-made templates are sometimes offered for particular equipment designs. These will save you the trouble of planning the layout. Use them like the carbon template described above, first drilling the holes to serve as guide points for your painted copy of the template drawing.

### About Components

"Bread and butter" items — sockets, fixed resistors and capacitors, adjustable and variable resistors, and the like — make up the majority of parts used in any radio equipment. These are the components that you can find at most radio supply stores. All of them are made by more than one manufacturer, and components with identical ratings usually are mechanically interchangeable. You can freely substitute one make of part for another if you observe the required electrical ratings and values.

Small fixed resistors up to two-watt ratings are invariably color-coded to indicate the resistance value. The standard method uses three (sometimes four) colored bands starting from one end of the resistor. The band nearest the end gives the first figure of the resistance, the next is the second figure, and the third gives the number of zeros to be added after the first two figures. (A black third band indicates that no zeros are to be added.) See Fig. 15. For example, a resistor having a red (2) first

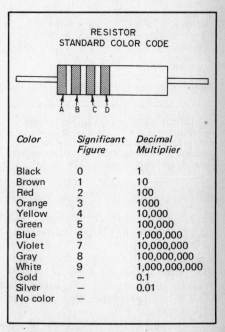

RESISTOR STANDARD COLOR CODE

| Color | Significant Figure | Decimal Multiplier |
|---|---|---|
| Black | 0 | 1 |
| Brown | 1 | 10 |
| Red | 2 | 100 |
| Orange | 3 | 1000 |
| Yellow | 4 | 10,000 |
| Green | 5 | 100,000 |
| Blue | 6 | 1,000,000 |
| Violet | 7 | 10,000,000 |
| Gray | 8 | 100,000,000 |
| White | 9 | 1,000,000,000 |
| Gold | — | 0.1 |
| Silver | — | 0.01 |
| No color | — | |

Fig. 15 — Color coding of fixed resistors (1/2- to 2-watt size). A — first band; B — second band; C — third band; D — tolerance band. Band D may not be present, indicating the widest tolerance (20 percent) available.

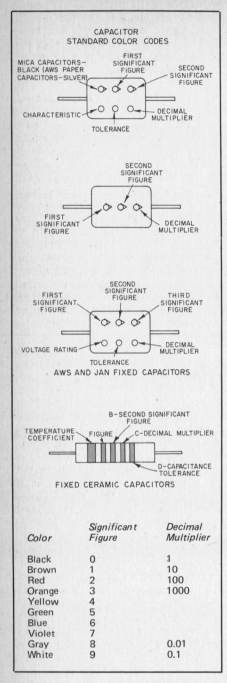

CAPACITOR
STANDARD COLOR CODES

MICA CAPACITORS—
BLACK (AWS PAPER
CAPACITORS—SILVER)

FIRST
SIGNIFICANT
FIGURE

SECOND
SIGNIFICANT
FIGURE

CHARACTERISTIC

DECIMAL
MULTIPLIER

TOLERANCE

SECOND
SIGNIFICANT
FIGURE

FIRST
SIGNIFICANT
FIGURE

DECIMAL
MULTIPLIER

FIRST
SIGNIFICANT
FIGURE

SECOND
SIGNIFICANT
FIGURE

THIRD
SIGNIFICANT
FIGURE

VOLTAGE RATING

DECIMAL
MULTIPLIER

TOLERANCE

AWS AND JAN FIXED CAPACITORS

B—SECOND SIGNIFICANT
FIGURE

TEMPERATURE
COEFFICIENT

FIGURE

C—DECIMAL MULTIPLIER

D—CAPACITANCE
TOLERANCE

FIXED CERAMIC CAPACITORS

| Color | Significant Figure | Decimal Multiplier |
|-------|-----|-----|
| Black | 0 | 1 |
| Brown | 1 | 10 |
| Red | 2 | 100 |
| Orange | 3 | 1000 |
| Yellow | 4 | |
| Green | 5 | |
| Blue | 6 | |
| Violet | 7 | |
| Gray | 8 | 0.01 |
| White | 9 | 0.1 |

Fig. 16 — There are many variations of the capacitor color code but the one shown here is most common on currently produced components. More complete information can be found in *The Radio Amateur's Handbook*.

band, yellow (4) second band, and orange (3) third band has a resistance of 24,000 ohms. The fourth band, when present, gives the rated resistance tolerance. Silver indicates a tolerance of ± 10 percent; gold indicates ± 5 percent. If there is no fourth band, the tolerance is ± 20 percent.

Capacitors come in many different types and it is wise to use those types specified in the plans for a particular piece of equipment. Some of the more common types include disk ceramic,

paper, mica, silver mica, tantalum, electrolytic, computer grade electrolytic and polystyrene. A detailed discussion of these and other types of capacitors is beyond the scope of this book. If you are interested in gathering more information on capacitors, read, "Some Capacitor Basics," by DeMaw in *QST* for January, 1976. Most capacitors come marked with their capacitance and voltage rating. Fig. 16 has been prepared for those types that do not come labelled, but rather are color coded.

Tube and transistor socket prongs are numbered clockwise around the socket *looking at the bottom*. The standard numbering for the commonly used types is given in Fig. 17. Note that on the miniature sockets, there is a wider gap between two of the pins than between the others. You start counting off in the clockwise direction from this wider gap. The octal socket has the pins evenly spaced, but there is a "key" in the socket. The no. 1 pin is just on the clockwise side of this key slot. Many sockets have the pin numbers stamped on the base, but since space is limited it is possible to confuse the pins and numbers. However, if you know the system, you'll not have any trouble.

Transistor bases come in such a variety of shapes and sizes that it is difficult to find sockets for many of them. The smaller transistor types have wire leads which can be bent to fit into a socket in almost any pattern you wish. Besides, in most cases the leads are soldered directly to etched circuit boards and sockets are dispensed with entirely. A socket is advantageous, though, if the circuit is experimental, or if you anticipate having to service the equipment later on. The larger transistors typically have "top-hat" cases in which the metal "hat brim" is mounted directly on a metal chassis or a special heat sink, sometimes with a mica washer for electrical insulation.

Volume controls and similar variable resistors, rotary switches, and phone jacks of various types all mount in the same size panel hole — 3/8 inch, just slightly under 1/2 inch.

### Coaxial Fittings

In most transmitters the rf output is taken from a standard coaxial chassis connector — the "UHF"-series type SO-239. The mating plug is the PL-259. These are military numbers; in some cases manufacturers have their own type numbers for the same components, but regardless of manufacture the numbers given above are sufficient for identification. There is a rather bewildering variety of rf connectors, each having its particular advantages, but the UHF series is used on most amateur equipment.

The plugs in this series are designed

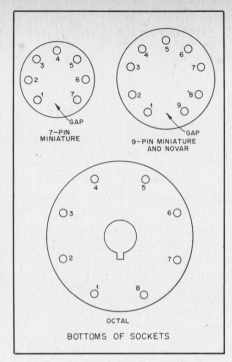

7—PIN MINIATURE

GAP

9—PIN MINIATURE AND NOVAR

GAP

OCTAL

BOTTOMS OF SOCKETS

Fig. 17 — Standard pin numbering of common tube sockets.

primarily for use with cable approximately 1/2 inch in diameter, such as RG-8/U and RG-11/U. An adapter is needed for RG-58/U and RG-59/U cables, as shown in Fig. 14. To use the adapter and PL-259 plug, cut off the insulation as shown, leaving about 1/8 inch of polythylene dielectric protruding, then fold back about 3/8 inch of the braid. Screw the adapter into the body of the plug, solder at the spots indicated, and the job is done. But don't forget to put the outer part of the plug on the cable before doing the rest of the assembly!

With the larger cables, simply cut back the jacket so the braid will be exposed under the solder holes, trim off the insulation from the inner conductor

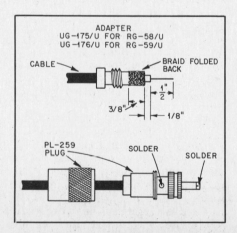

ADAPTER
UG—175/U FOR RG—58/U
UG—176/U FOR RG—59/U

CABLE

BRAID FOLDED BACK

1/2"

3/8"

1/8"

PL-259 PLUG

SOLDER

SOLDER

Fig. 18 — Assembling PL-259 plug and adapter to small coaxial cable.

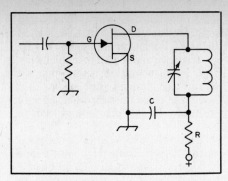

Fig. 19 — Bypass capacitor and decoupling resistor. See text for discussion of range of values.

just as shown in the upper drawing, assemble and solder.

## Component Values and Substitutions

One of the rewarding things about building your own is that you can often save money by using parts salvaged from old equipment acquired in trades with other amateurs, or obtained from any of those sources that traditionally help fill the "junk box." Too often, though, the component you have is not exactly what is called for in the circuit you want to assemble. Will or won't it work?

You can go a long way toward answering that question correctly if you know what purpose the component serves in the circuit, and whether that purpose is one that requires an exact electrical value or whether any of a wide range of values could be used without making any difference in the circuit's performance. This is where it pays off to know something about the "theory" discussed in earlier chapters.

## Bypasses

Take bypass capacitors, for example. The value of bypass capacitance is rarely "critical," in the sense that the exact value specified in the circuit has to be used. As you saw earlier in this book, a good bypass is one having low reactance compared with the impedance of the part of the circuit across which it is connected. "Low" usually can be taken to mean 10 percent or less. Fig. 19 shows a sample rf circuit such as might be used in a receiver or transmitter low-power stage. The drain circuit, including the tuned tank, will usually have a total impedance of a few thousand ohms. A bypass reactance of 100 ohms would be sufficient, in most cases, so far as the plate circuit *alone* is concerned. The important thing here is what is on the *supply* side of the bypass. Perhaps the circuit designer didn't use the decoupling resistor, R. The rf impedance of the power-supply circuit is generally a very much unknown quantity, so the safe thing to do in such a case is to use the largest bypass available in a suitable

physical type. A ceramic capacitor of 0.01 $\mu$F would be a logical choice, then, since it would offer the lowest reactance — a little under 5 ohms at 3.5 MHz — conveniently available.

However, if the decoupling resistor R is included in the circuit, it is possible to proceed with less guesswork. Suppose R is 500 ohms. Then a reactance of 50 ohms or less would suffice, since this is 10 percent or less of the lower of the two impedances to be bypassed. At 3.5 MHz a capacitance of 0.001 $\mu$F would do just as well, and possibly even better, than the 0.01 that isn't backed up by the decoupling resistor. You would have to consider whether the current flowing through R would have an appreciable effect on the voltage reaching the drain of the FET, of course, and possibly it would be better to replace R by a small rf choke. A choke inductance of a few microhenries would do as well as the 500-ohm resistor.

## Capacitor Types

The same principles apply in audio circuits. Whether it is rf or audio, you'll rarely go wrong simply by substituting a *larger* value of bypass capacitance, provided you use a capacitor of the same type — ceramic, paper, electrolytic and so on.

Aside from capacitance, these various types do differ in other important characteristics, some of which are not suitable in certain applications. Electrolytic capacitors, for instance, are not useful at radio frequencies, nor are they useful in purely ac circuits. Paper capacitors become inductive at radio frequencies, particularly in the larger sizes (over 0.01 $\mu$F) and at the higher frequencies (14 MHz and above), so they should not be substituted for disk ceramics. Mica and ceramic capacitors are generally interchangeable for by-passing, at least at frequencies below 30 MHz.

At vhf you may not be able to get away with substituting a different type of capacitor for the one specified in the circuit, because at these frequencies the internal inductance of the capacitor, along with the inductance of the leads, becomes increasingly important. In vhf equipment, better stick to the circuit designer's recommendations until you've gained enough experience to know what you can and can't do.

## Resistance

Resistance values usually should be followed fairly closely, although there is often room for substitution here, too. A volume control in the grid circuit of a tube, for example, usually can be anything from 0.25 to 2 megohms without any very marked effect on the operation of an audio circuit. In most cases it is more important to use a control with an "audio taper," since this gives smoother

control of volume than the "linear" type. Less liberty can be taken with cathode bias resistances, as a general rule, because these determine how the tube operates. However, you can go up or down in cathode resistance by 25 percent or so without doing anything serious to the circuit operation, in most cases.

In transistor circuits you also have reasonably leeway in resistance values, generally speaking. The base-emitter resistance of a bipolar transistor is low, however, so you have to be more careful about audio gain controls than you do with FETs or tubes, which have extremely high input resistance. Also, the bias network values usually want to be duplicated fairly closely, because the resistances connected to the base are in parallel with the base-emitter circuit for signal frequencies. They don't want to be too much on the low side for this reason, and also because the current drain on the power supply is greater, a consideration if the set is battery-powered. On the other hand, too-high values may limit the bias current to an undesirably low figure.

## Tuned Circuits

In rf tuned circuits it pays to stick fairly closely to the inductance and capacitance specified, even though you know that there is a wide range of *LC* combinations that will tune to the required frequency. But you don't always have to use the exact components mentioned. Variable capacitors of the same capacitance range, but of different manufacture, can be substituted. Sometimes this necessitates a minor change in the physical layout, because of different size, shape or terminal arrangement, but this need not keep you from making the substitution.

The principal point about coils is that they should have the right inductance. The diameter, length and number of turns can be varied to suit the form you have, just so long as you come out with the right value of inductance. Of course, you shouldn't use a physically large coil where the layout calls for a compact one, nor should you use a tiny coil to handle rf power when a big one is needed. However, if you can't get a slug-tuned form of exactly the diameter and length specified, one you do have or can get can be substituted if you change the winding so the coil can be tuned to the desired frequency. A smaller diameter form will need more turns, and vice versa. If necessary, the wire size can be changed to the next nearest one that will let you get the turns on the form.

Transmitting coils often are cut to size from commercial coil material which is space-wound on plastic strips and comes in various diameters and

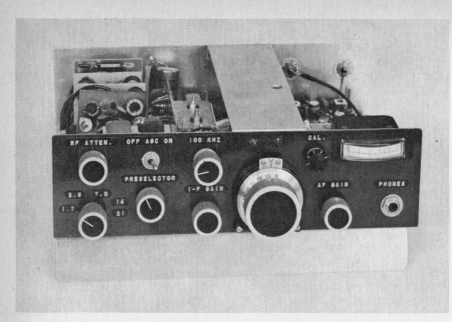

Fig. 20 — Dymo labels are used to indicate the function of each control on the front panel. Decals or dry transfer lettering can also be used.

turns-per-inch. If this, or regular forms, are not to be found in your catalogs or stores, there is a substitute form you can find in practically any drug store — the plastic pill bottle. It comes in several diameters from 5/16 to 1-3/4 inch and lengths from 1-3/4 to 2-5/8. If you have to have a plug-in form, you can even make your own from the size pill bottle that can be cemented inside an octal base taken from an old tube.

Much transistor equipment makes the use of coils wound on ring-shaped ferrite cores, which require very few turns to make up a given inductance. These have the advantage that the coil has high Q and has very little external magnetic field; practically all the field stays in the core. Less care is required in mounting them to prevent unwanted coupling to another circuit, which, in addition to their small size, means that equipment using them can be quite compact.

Don't be afraid to try substituting, but use your knowledge of circuit operation when doing it. If there is anything *really* critical in the circuit you're working on, the designer will have pointed it out, if the article describing the circuit was properly written.

## Some General Remarks

There always have been, and always will be, "haywire artists" whose objective in building is get something working no matter how it looks. How-

ever, most constructors are happier when their creations not only work but are presentable, too. Appearance and performance are not incompatible. Achieving both does take forethought, though. For example, a pleasing layout for panel controls doesn't follow automatically from a good rf-circuit layout. You may have to spend some time moving parts around on the chassis, or making pencil sketches, before arriving at a plan that is desirable both electrically and mechanically. It's worth the effort.

There are a few basic rules that should be kept in mind. While they apply primarily to chassis construction, the same principles should be observed in laying out etched circuits:

Make your rf wiring as short and direct as the placement of components will permit. Give wires that carry rf all the room you can. Don't bunch rf wiring with power or audio wiring.

In laying out and wiring rf amplifiers, keep the rf input wiring well separated from output wiring, with as little wiring exposed as possible. Treat the input and output circuits as though they were deadly enemies, neither to be allowed to know that the other is in the neighborhood. Coupling between these two circuits, whether inductive or capacitive, can lead to all kinds of difficulty with instability.

Run rf ground (chassis ground, that is) leads directly to chassis, with the

shortest possible lead length. The chassis itself, if made of material having good conductivity such as aluminum, has far less resistance and inductance than wire. If the layout permits, it is good practice to keep the grounds associated with a single stage close to each other, but not if you have to run long ground leads to do so.

Don't put components in layers if you can help it. There may come a time when you have to do some trouble shooting. You don't want to have to dismantle half of the circuit just to get at a suspected component at the bottom of the pile.

Don't put controls so close together that you haven't finger room or can't turn one knob without bumping into another and changing its setting.

When you've finished a piece of gear, make a diagram of it *exactly* the way it's wired. A written record is a time saver later. Your memory of what was done, and why, will be hazy after a few months.

Measure the dc voltages, and others if possible, at socket terminals and power distribution points. Jot them on the circuit diagram. If anything goes wrong later these voltages can be checked before you start taking things apart. Knowing what the voltages should be everywhere in the circuit gives you a head start in finding out what has gone wrong.

Label the controls and terminals on your equipment. Unless the unit is in use every day, you'll soon forget which terminals are which. Decals and dry transfer lettering sold by most radio stores are easy to apply, permanent, and give equipment a professional look.

One final tip, if you have an ohmmeter, test every resistor and capacitor before using it. Occasionally a defective or mislabeled one will be found, and it is easier to weed out the unsatisfactory ones before than after the set is ready for testing. Capacitors should be checked to make sure that they test "open" — extremely high resistance — although you may not be able to check the capacitance. In testing electrolytics, remember that the positive battery lead from the ohmmeter must go to the "plus" side of the capacitor. An ohmmeter will show an initial reading on capacitors of high value, but this is simply a charging current and will drop to zero or a very low value in a short time. Wait until the needle stops moving before deciding that the capacitor is good or bad.

# Where to Buy Components

Listening on the air you'll probably hear many hams talking about parts-procurement problems and how that's the reason they no longer build any of their own equipment. This is a rather lame excuse since the parts are available; it just takes a little time and knowledge of where to look. Chances are that those people who are doing all the complaining have actually lost touch with modern solid-state techniques and don't understand present-day circuitry. They're using this as an excuse not to build their own equipment.

The first rule in shopping for parts is to stay away from your local television repair shop. While they might have some of the resistors and capacitors that you need, the prices are apt to be ridiculously high. It's not uncommon for them to double or triple the price that they pay for components. You will simply be padding their pockets! Components such as resistors and fixed-value capacitors are best obtained from stores such as Radio Shack, Lafayette, Allied or a similarly stocked parts emporium.

**Fig. 21**

| Codes | Supplier |
|---|---|
| A, E, I, L, M<br>*35¢ stamp<br>**$10 | Adva Electronics<br>Box 4181<br>Woodside, CA 94062 |
| A, C, D, E, F | Alaska Microwave Labs<br>4335 E. 5th St.<br>Anchorage, AK 99504 |
| B, C | Amidon Associates<br>12033 Otsego Street<br>N. Hollywood, CA 91607 |
| N, O | Atlantic Surplus Sales<br>(facsimile equipment)<br>3730 Nautilus Ave.<br>Brooklyn, NY 11224 |
| A, E, I, T, U | ATV Research<br>13th & Broadway<br>Dakota City, NE 68731 |
| A, C, D, E, H, I, L | Azotic Industries<br>2293 N. Clybourn<br>Chicago, IL 60614 |
| A, B, D, F, G, H | Barker and Williamson, Inc.<br>10 Canal St.<br>Bristol, PA 19007 |
| U | Byte-Me Computer Shop<br>327 Captain's Walk<br>New London, CT 06320 |
| B | Caddell Coil Corp.<br>(coils for ARRL projects)<br>35 Main St.<br>Poultney, VT 05764 |
| A, H, L<br>*free<br>**$10 | Cambridge Thermionic Corp.<br>445 Concord Ave.<br>Cambridge, MA 02138 |
| H | Caywood Electronics<br>(Millen Capacitors)<br>67 Maplewood St., P.O. Box U<br>Malden, MA 02148 |
| A, C, W | Circuit Board Specialists<br>(circuit boards for ARRL<br>projects, kits)<br>P.O. Box 969<br>Pueblo, CO 81002 |
| A, B, D, H, L<br>*stamp | D and V Radio Parts<br>12805 W. Sarle<br>Freeland, MI 48623 |
| D, I, M | Peter W. Dahl<br>4007 Fort Blvd.<br>El Paso, TX 79930 |
| D, E, F, H, I, L, M,<br>N, U<br>**$7 | Diamondback Electronics Co.<br>P.O. Box 12095<br>Sarasota, FL 33578 |
| W | Dynaclad Industries<br>P.O. Box 296<br>Meadowlands, PA 15347 |
| L<br>*$10 | Electro Sonic, Inc.<br>1100 Gordon Baker Rd.<br>Willowdale, ON M2H 3B3 |
| C, D, E, G, H, I, M | Etco Electronics<br>North Country Shopping Center<br>Rte. 9 North<br>Plattsburgh, NY 12901 |
| J | Fox-Tango Corp.<br>(modification kits for amateur<br>equipment)<br>Box 15944<br>W. Palm Beach, FL 33406 |
| D, F, L | Gregory Electronics Corp.<br>249 Route 46<br>Saddle Brook, NJ 07662 |
| A, E, H, U, W | Hamilton Avnet<br>2111 W. Walnut Hill Lane<br>Irving, TX 75062 |
| I, K | Hammond Mfg., Ltd.<br>394 Edinburg Rd. N.<br>Guelph, ON N1H 1E5 Canada<br><br>Hammond Mfg. Co., Inc. (U.S.)<br>1690 Walden Ave.<br>Buffalo, NY 14225 |
| L | Harrison Radio<br>20 Smith St.<br>Farmingdale, NY 11713 |
| A, B, I, K, M, N, T | Herbach and Rademan, Inc.<br>401 E. Erie Ave.<br>Philadelphia, PA 19134 |
| L<br>*25¢<br>**$1 | HI, Inc.<br>(25¢ in coin for manual list)<br>Box 864<br>Council Bluffs, IA 51502 |
| C, E, H, I, L, M,<br>N, U<br>**$10 | Hobbyworld<br>19511 Business Center Dr.<br>Northridge, CA 91324 |
| A, B, C, D, E, F, G,<br>H, I, J, K, L, M, N,<br>O, P, T, U, V | Integrated Circuits Unlimited, Inc.<br>7895 Clairemont Mesa Blvd.<br>San Diego, CA 92111 |
| A, B, C, E, H, I, K,<br>L, M, T, U, W<br>**$10 | Jameco Electronics<br>1355 Shoreway Rd.<br>Belmont, CA 92111 |
| D | JAN Crystals<br>2400 Crystal Dr. P.O. Box 06017<br>Ft. Meyers, FL 33906 |
| F | Jug Wire Co. (Surplus Dept.)<br>2234 36th St.<br>Woolsey, NY 11105 |
| A, E, F, H, M, N | Marlin P. Jones and Assoc.<br>P.O. Box 12685<br>Lake Park, FL 33403 |
| C | Kepro Circuit Systems, Inc.<br>630 Axminister Dr.<br>Fenton, MO 63026 |
| A, E, M, U | Key Electronics<br>P.O. Box 3506<br>Schenectady, NY 12303 |
| F<br>**$10 | Kirk Electronics<br>73 Ferry Rd.<br>Chester, CT 06412 |
| D, H, G, L, N | Leeds Radio<br>57 Warren St.<br>New York, NY 10007 |
| K, L | MFJ Enterprises<br>P.O. Box 494<br>Mississippi State, MS 39762 |
| A, B, D, E, H, M,<br>N, U | MHZ Electronics<br>2111 W. Camelback Rd.<br>Phoenix, AZ 85015 |
| A, G, L | Millen Components<br>Div. of E.I. & S. Corp.<br>42 Pleasant St.<br>Stoneham, MA 02180 |
| A, B, H, J | J. W. Miller Div., Bell Industries<br>19070 Reyes Ave.<br>Compton, CA 90224 |
| A, B, D, E, F, G, H,<br>K, M<br>*s.a.s.e.<br>**$15 | Milo Associates<br>Box 2323<br>Indianapolis, IN 46206 |
| E, F, G, H, L<br>*50¢ | Modern Radio Laboratories<br>P.O. Box 1477-Q<br>Garden Grove, CA 92642 |
| A, C, E, F, G, H, I,<br>K, M, N | Olson Electronics<br>260 S. Forge St.<br>Akron, OH 44327 |
| B | Palomar Engineers<br>Box 455<br>Escondido, CA 92025 |
| T, U, W | P. C. Electronics<br>2522 Paxson<br>Arcadia, CA 91006 |
| L | C. M. Peterson Co., Ltd.<br>220 Adelaide St. N.<br>London, ON N6E 3H4 |
| J | Piezo Technology, Inc.<br>P.O. Box 7859<br>Orlando, FL 32854 |
| E, M, N, P<br>*free | Poly Paks<br>Box 942<br>Lynnfield, MA 01940 |
| A, B, D, E, F, G, H,<br>J, K, L<br>*25¢ | Radiokit<br>P.O. Box 411<br>Greenville, NH 03048 |
| E | Semiconductors Surplus<br>2822 N. 32nd St. Unit 1<br>Phoenix, AZ 85008 |
| D, J | Sentry Mfg. Co.<br>Crystal Park<br>Chickasha, OK 73108 |

Fig. 21 (Cont.)

| | | | |
|---|---|---|---|
| D, J | Sherwood Engineering, Inc.<br>1268 S. Ogden St.<br>Denver, CO 80210 | K | Ten-Tec, Inc.<br>Highway 411, E.<br>Sevierville, TN 37862 |
| F, V<br>*30¢ stamp | Skylane Products<br>406 Bon Air Ave.<br>Temple Terrace, FL 33617 | F, V | Texas Towers<br>1108 Summit Ave.<br>Plano, TX 75074 |
| **$5 | Small Parts, Inc.<br>(mechanical components and<br>metal stock)<br>P.O. Box 381736<br>Miami, FL 33138 | B, O<br>*s.a.s.e. | Typetronics<br>Box 8873<br>Ft. Lauderdale, FL 33310 |
| A, D, J | Spectrum International<br>P.O. Box 1084<br>Concord, MA 01742 | R | Wester Nebraska Electronics<br>Rte. 1 — Box 1<br>Potter, NE 69156 |
| M, N<br>*$4 | Star Tronics<br>P.O. Box 683<br>McMinnville, OR 97128 | E, G, D | Workman Electronic Products, Inc<br>(will refer customer to nearest<br>dealer)<br>Box 3828<br>Sarasota, FL 33578 |
| B, M, O, U<br>**$10 | Teleprinter Corp. of America<br>550G Springfield Ave.<br>Berkeley Heights, NJ 07922 | | |

To the best of our knowledge the suppliers shown are willing to sell components to amateurs in small quantities by mail. This listing does not necessarily indicate that these firms have the approval of ARRL.

### Chart Coding

A — New Components
B — Toroids and Ferrites
C — Etched Circuit Board Materials
D — Transmitting and Receiving Materials
E — Solid State Devices
F — Antenna Hardware
G — Dials and Knobs
H — Variable Capacitors
I — Transformers
J — I-f Filters
K — Cabinets and Boxes
L — General Supplier
M — Surplus Parts
N — Surplus Assemblies
O — RTTY Equipment & Parts
P — Surplus FM Gear and Parts
R — Service of Collins Equipment
T — Amateur TV Cameras & Components
U — Microcomputer Peripheral Equipment
V — Towers
W — Ready-made Printed Circuit Boards
*Catalog price
**Minimum Order

---

The same is true for components such as sockets, plugs, jacks, switches, controls, hook-up wire, small chassis and enclosures, relays and similar items.

It's a good idea to stick with the particular active devices specified in an article rather than substitute some other manufacturers unit. For example, a Motorola MPF102 FET should be used when specified. Certain so-called substitutes do not perform well in many circuits. Don't overlook the possibility that a cross reference sheet might be wrong! The exception to this rule would be for a very common device, say, a 2N2222A transistor.

The larger electronic supply houses carry most major brands of semiconductor devices. Their prices are a bit higher than some of the discount houses but you can be sure that you are buying a good component. If you've ever built a piece of equipment, using all discount house devices you know what we mean. Chances are that it won't work the first time and in most cases a defective component is the cause.

Suppliers listed in Fig. 21 sell amateur equipment-related parts in small quantities. You're best bet would be to arm yourself with catalogs from as many different suppliers as possible. You will, in most cases, have to mail-order components other than the standard ones we listed earlier. Among the more difficult components to obtain are variable capacitors and slug-tuned coils. At least one distributor on the list, G. R. Whitehouse, sells most major brands of these components. Become familiar with each of the distributors catalogs. Know who carriers what and at the best prices.

Don't overlook old television sets and radios as sources of components. Along with a multitude of resistors and capacitors one can extract power transformers, chokes, switches, controls, plugs and a variety of hardware. Also keep a check on hamfests in your area. Flea markets are common at these gatherings and many of the parts that you may need might be available for peanuts.

There are several companies that manufacture etched and drilled printed-circuit boards for some of the ARRL projects. Their names and addresses are listed in Fig. 22. If you do not wish to fabricate your own board, check with these manufacturers to see if they offer a board for the particular project that interests you.

---

### Fig. 22

A number of companies and individuals have established their reputation with us for supplying high-quality ready-made circuit boards. These are listed below. Each supplier is free to offer whatever boards he chooses from ARRL publications, so we suggest you check with one or more to see if they have the boards you want. Since most of these suppliers operate with little or no clerical staff, a stamped return envelope will likely speed along your reply from them.

D. L. McClaren, W8URX
19721 Maplewood Avenue
Cleveland, OH 44135

MFJ Enterprises
P. O. Box 494
Mississippi State, MS 39762

Circuit Board Specialists
P. O. Box 969
Pueblo, CO 81002

PBI Electronics Company
P. O. Box S
Azusa, CA 91702

Charles R. Sempirek, K8WDC
Rte. 3, Box 1
Bellaire, OH 43906

# Trouble–Shooting

Radio equipment, like other machinery, occasionally will develop faults. Getting it back into good operating condition may take some doing. No discussion of trouble-shooting could anticipate *all* the things that might go wrong. The most anyone can do is to outline a few principles. The important factors in locating faults are adequate test equipment, knowledge of the circuit operation, and common sense. Locating the fault is the real problem, because once you've found it the remedy usually is obvious.

We have two different kinds of trouble-shooting to consider. One is the case where you finish building a piece of gear and can't make it work. The other is when a set has been performing properly right along until, more or less suddenly, trouble develops. In the second case the probable cause is a component that has failed, since you know the equipment *did* work. Almost anything could be wrong in the first instance.

### Equipment

First, as to test equipment. The most useful item, all around, is the combination voltmeter, milliammeter and ohmmeter (VOM). The instrument itself is discussed in chapter 13. You need it to spot defects in resistors and capacitors, for measuring operating voltages, and for checking circuit continuity. An electronic voltmeter is even better for many tests, because its use has less effect on the circuit (see chapter 13). However, it won't measure current directly. This is not a serious handicap, since current can be measured in terms of the voltage drop across a resistance.

The dip meter is also useful, especially in testing newly built equipment. It can also serve as a signal source for receiver alignment. With the dip meter and the VOM (or electronic voltmeter), you can handle most of the problems you'll run into. For testing of a more advanced nature, the oscilloscope is in a class by itself, although it doesn't supersede the other instruments. But to use a scope to good effect you have to know it well. We'll confine ourselves here to the simpler testing.

### New Equipment

If you put together a circuit from a book or magazine article and it doesn't do what the author claimed, what to do? First, check your wiring. *Really* check it. It isn't unusual to pass over a wrong connection time and again in checking; you simply have a blind spot for that error. If you can do so, get an amateur friend with some circuit experience to look it over,

too; he may see right away the point you've missed.

Once you're sure the wiring is correct, check voltages. Measure the heater voltage on the tubes, and look at the heaters; with a little experience you'll be able to judge pretty well whether the cathode is showing the right color. If the heater voltage at the socket prongs is right but the cathode isn't up to temperature, something is wrong at the socket. The tube may not be making good contact, or you may have a "cold-soldered" joint on the prong. Measure the voltage on the prongs, not on the soldered connections.

Incidentally, measuring voltages in this way is good practice in *all* cases. If different voltages are measured on the conductors on either side of a soldered joint, something is wrong with that joint and it had better be resoldered. Cases like this crop up more often that you might think.

Having established that the tube heaters are operating properly, check the dc supply voltage and measure the voltages on plates, screens and cathodes where cathode bias is used. The circuit from which you've worked often will have information to guide you here. If not, you must use your good judgment, based on knowledge of what the circuit is supposed to do. For example, screen voltage taken from the plate supply through a dropping resistor obviously will be lower than the supply voltage. (However, you have to be careful here — read the section on "Instrument Effects" in chapter 13 before assuming that the measured voltage is too low. Usually, measurements made with a 20,000-ohms-per-volt meter or an electronic voltmeter can be taken at face value, but beware of the readings of a 1,000-ohms-per-volt meter in high-resistance circuits.) If no voltages have been specified with the circuit, your best plan is to assume that the values should be the normal ones for the type of tube and kind of service. The circuit discussions in earlier chapters can be used as a guide.

In transistor circuits, similar measurements should be made of the voltages (to ground) on the base, emitter and collector (or source and drain, with FETs). With bipolar transistors the base and emitter voltages will differ only a little; the base voltage for a silicon npn is only approximately 0.6 volt more positive than the emitter. Here, though, you have to watch out for the differences between npn and pnp (polarity) and silicon and germanium (the base and emitter are at approximately 0.3-volt difference).

Oscillators can be checked by using

your receiver to listen for the signal from them at the frequencies at which they should be working. Another method, useful with tube oscillators, is to use a voltmeter to measure the dc voltage across the grid-leak resistor. If there isn't any, the oscillator isn't working. This measurement has to be made through an rf choke, as shown in Fig. 23A, to avoid short-circuiting the oscillator grid to chassis. Keep the lead marked A just as short as it can be made. If the oscillator already has a choke in its grid circuit and the grid leak is bypassed as in 23B, the extra choke isn't necessary. Alternatively, a low-range milliammeter can be temporarily connected in series with the low end of

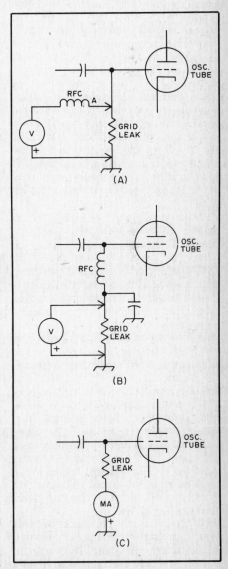

Fig. 23 — Checking oscillator operation by measuring rectified grid voltage with a dc voltmeter, or grid current with a low-range dc milliammeter. The voltmeter resistance should be at least ten times the grid-leak resistance in making such measurements.

the grid leak to measure the grid current. A 0-1 milliammeter will do for low-power oscillators, but a 0-10 instrument may be needed for more powerful circuits. If you get no grid voltage or grid current by this method, try tuning the oscillator circuit through its range; the circuits may simply be off tune. If there is still none, the circuit should be looked over carefully once more, for wiring mistakes or poor connections. If this too fails, use a dip meter to check the circuit tuning, and adjust the tuned-circuit constants to bring the tuning into the right range.

Grid current in any tube stage of a transmitter can be checked by one of the methods shown in Fig. 23.

In a transmitter, if the plate or collector current of an amplifier doesn't behave the way the circuit information said it should, the answer may be self-oscillation in the amplifier. If a tube amplifier has grid current with the excitation shut off (by removing the crystal or disconnecting the VFO), *something* is certainly oscillating. This should be checked with the key closed, of course. The oscillation may be in the amplifier itself or in any preceding stage. Pull out the tube in the stage immediately preceding; if the oscillation continues, it's in the stage you're working on. In final amplifiers, don't hold the key down any longer than is necessary to see if you have grid current. The tube usually will be badly overloaded when it isn't getting its normal excitation.

When an amplifier self-oscillates, it's usually either at a frequency near the intended operating frequency or at some vhf frequency in the 100- to 150-MHz region. In the former case, you may be able to hear the signal in your receiver by checking just as you would check your operating frequency. The vhf parasitic oscillation is harder to spot, but if you can't find a signal near the right operating frequency it's safe to assume that a vhf oscillation is responsible for the poor behavior. Practically all tubes and transistors in hf circuits need vhf parasitic suppressors to be stable, and sometimes the suppressor that worked in the original circuit has to be modified in a copy. Here, the only thing you can do is try various sizes of small coils and resistors, along the lines of the suppressors in the circuits of chapter 10, until you find a combination that makes the amplifier stable.

If you discover an oscillation near your operating frequency, the remedy is to neutralize the stage. If the circuit already has neutralizing provisions, it's a matter of adjustment. The right setting of the neutralizing capacitor is the one that results in the least change in the amplifier grid current when you tune its *plate* circuit through resonance. If there

is no neutralizing circuit, you'll have to put one in, in most cases. However, it is sometimes possible to stop self-oscillation by using resistance loading in the grid circuit. A resistor of a few thousand ohms (a carbon type, not wire-wound) across the tuned circuit connected to the grid may do it. Such loading cuts down the grid drive, though, and if you make the resistance low enough to stop the oscillation there may not be enough drive left to make the amplifier work properly. In such cases neutralization is the *only* answer. Circuits are given in chapters 3 and 10. Transistor power amplifiers can't be neutralized, for the reasons explained in chapter 3. With these, you have to keep the amplifier loaded. Any decent published design will take this necessity into account, and will explain what you should avoid in operating the amplifier if you're likely to run into trouble.

Oscillators in receivers can be checked by the methods described above. In building converters, your principle problem will be getting the circuits to tune to the right frequencies, once you're sure the oscillator is working and the voltages on the converter are right. The dip meter can be invaluable here.

**Forethought**

As a precaution in building any kind of equipment, test every component before you use it. A mismarked resistor or a faulty capacitor can cause lots of your time to be wasted. The best rule is "don't trust — measure!"

And when you finish construction and have the gear working to your satisfaction, measure all dc voltages from socket prongs to chassis. Mark them on your diagram, or list them in notes that you will keep in a safe place. Record voltages out of the power supply, too — in fact, the more such measurements the better. If anything

Fig. 24 — Here is a listing of symbols that are commonly used in electronic diagrams.

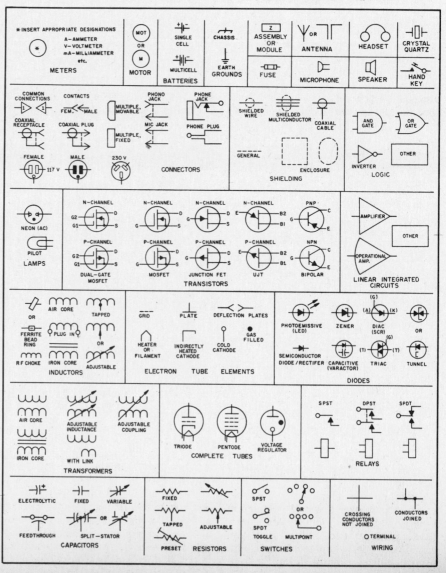

## Fig. 25
## Transformer Lead Color Coding

### Audio Transformers

Blue — plate (finish) lead of primary.
Red — "B" + lead (this applies whether the primary is plain or center-tapped).
Brown — plate (start) lead on center-tapped primaries. (Blue may be used for this lead if polarity is not important.)
Green — grid (finish) lead to secondary.
Black — grid return (this applies whether the secondary is plain or center-tapped).
Yellow — grid (start) lead on center-tapped secondaries. (Green may be used for this lead if polarity is not important.)

Note: These markings apply also to line-to-grid and tube-to-line transformers.

### Power Transformers

1) Primary leads — black
   If tapped:
   Common — black
   Tap — black and yellow striped
   Finish — black and red striped
2) High-voltage place winding — Red
   center-tap — red and yellow striped
3) Rectifier filament winding — yellow
   center-tap — yellow and blue striped
4) Filament winding no. 1 — green
   center-tap — green and yellow striped
5) Filament winding no. 2 — brown
   center-tap — brown and yellow striped
6) Filament winding no. 3 — slate
   center-tap — slate and yellow striped

---

goes wrong later, you'll save time and effort in spotting the cause of the trouble.

### Equipment Failures

As we said earlier, you have one thing going for you when a piece of equipment ceases to operate: You know that it once did work. When it quits, the job is one of finding out what component went bad.

If you buy a receiver, transmitter or what-not, or put one together from a kit, it's good practice to record all voltages and power-supply outputs. The instruction book may have these figures in it, but they are simply representative of what you can expect. They aren't the voltages in *your* set, necessarily. Very often the equipment will work as it should with voltages differing by quite a percentage from those given. If you know what your voltages are at the start, you'll have specific values to check against if something goes wrong later.

No servicing instructions could possibly cover everything that could go wrong. New quirks are discovered every day. Again, your best asset is thorough understanding of the circuit and what each component is supposed to do.

Check the obvious things first. Don't take the set apart and spend fruitless hours on it because the power plug accidentally was pulled from the socket or because an antenna connection fell off.

Your eyes and nose are good test equipment, too, and should be used to best advantage. Components that have "blown," such as resistors and capacitors, often will give themselves away by a burned or blistered appearance. A transformer or filter choke that has been badly overheated will have an unforgettable odor, as do other components in which insulation such as oiled paper or Bakelite is an ingredient. Burned-out rf coils and chokes, too, usually will show external evidence of overheating.

When you discover which component failed, don't replace it until you're certain that you know *why* it failed. Components such as transformers and resistors rarely go bad on their own account, if the set has been designed with a reasonable safety factor. They fail because they have been asked to carry a current much beyond their safe rating, and the current was there because *something else* went wrong. So check for short circuits before replacing the component and turning on the power: Otherwise, you may have to do the same job all over again.

Success in servicing is pretty largely a matter of experience and knowing your circuit. Although it has been prepared in terms of vacuum-tube equipment, the same *general* procedures are used in trouble-shooting transistor circuits. There is one type of circuit to watch out for, though — the direct-coupled type that is frequently used in transistor amplifiers. There are no coupling capacitors or transformers to isolate one stage from another for direct current. The result is that the voltages and currents in one stage depend directly on the voltages and currents in the coupled stage, so if one stage goes bad the measurements become meaningless in *all* stages so coupled. All you can do in such cases is remove all of the transistors and test them, as well as the circuit components, separately. This can be nasty, with etched circuits, because care must be used in unsoldering a transistor to avoid damaging both the transistor and circuit board by too much heat from the soldering iron. Unfortunately, too, the failure of one component in the chain may ruin all the directly coupled transistors; failure in one causes an overload in the next, causing it to fail, and so on. Be prepared to replace all the transistors when something goes wrong in such a setup.

There is no magic road to all the answers in servicing. This is just as true of trouble shooting a piece of ham gear as it is true of repairing an oil burner, an automobile engine or a television receiver.

# Chapter 8

# Building Receivers

No amateur expects that every QSO will be "100 percent." Distant signals may fade out. Local man-made electrical noises may pop up at any time to drown out at least the weaker stations. There may be interference from a stronger signal on, or close to, the frequency of the station you're trying to receive. Some of these things can't be helped even with the best equipment so far invented. But there's a lot your receiver — and *you* — can do about some of them.

What features should a receiver have?

If you ask ten experienced hams that question you'll no doubt get ten different answers. The things each thinks vital will depend on the kind of operating he does — cw, ssb, DX chasing, traffic work and so on. Receivers can be good in one department and not so good in others. But all good receivers do have one thing in common — they are easy to tune. Unless you can operate the controls comfortably and without strain, you can't get the most there is to be had from your receiver. The more advanced its design, the more important it is that the set should be easy to tune.

The two main factors in ease of handling are the receiver tuning rate and stability.

## Tuning Rate

The *tuning rate* of the receiver is the number of kilohertz it covers for each complete turn of the knob. Imagine for the moment that you have a receiver that can separate stations on channels 10 kHz apart. If the tuning rate is 20 kHz per turn of the knob, one turn will move you through two stations, but if the tuning rate is 300 kHz per turn, one turn will move you through 30 stations. It's harder to set the knob on one of those 30, by far, than to set it on one of the two you'd cover with the 20-kHz

tuning rate. Fig. 1 should make this clear.

Most modern amateur and general-coverage receivers use a "one-knob" tuning system. The position of the band switch determines the portion of the radio spectrum in which you are going to listen, and the main-tuning knob allows you to pick out the exact frequency. Many receivers indicate the received frequency on a dial located above the main-tuning knob. This dial, in most cases, is calibrated in 1-, 25-, 50-, or 100- kHz increments. For those receivers with rough calibration marks on this dial (25, 50 or 100 kHz), a more exact frequency readout is usually stamped on the skirt of the main-tuning knob. Calibration in 1-kHz steps is common. Some of the more sophisticated receivers make use of a digital

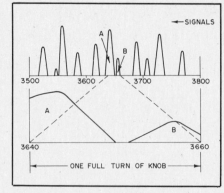

Fig. 1 — How tuning rate affects ease of tuning. With fast tuning (top), you tune through many stations with one turn of the tuning knob, so setting exactly on the one you want is a rather critical operation. A slow tuning rate (bottom) gives a vernier effect and setting on the desired station is much easier. Although with the slow rate each signal seems broader, each comes in and goes out in the same number of kilohertz in both cases. That is, the *selectivity* is not affected by the tuning rate.

display system for frequency readout. Instead of moving dials, this system lights up number displays, similar to the types used in electronic calculators.

Older, general-coverage receivers often used a "two-knob" tuning system. The two controls were called *main tuning* and *bandspread*. As with the system outlined previously, the band switch is used to select the portion of the radio spectrum to be tuned. The main-tuning control adjusts the exact frequency being tuned, but in a coarse manner much like that illustrated at the top of Fig. 1. Bandspread, as its name suggests, spreads a portion of the band over at least several revolutions of that dial. The tuning rate is slower — like that shown at the bottom of Fig. 1.

*Electrical bandspread* and *mechanical bandspread* are names in common use. While either or both can have the spread-out dial scale associated with actual bandspread, the fact that there is a comparatively slow tuning rate is what is actually meant. In the electrical type the slow rate is attained by the design of the tuned circuits. In the mechanical type the tuning is slowed down by a high dial-drive ratio, with pulleys, gears or the pinch-drive equivalent of gears.

## Stability

Good stability in a receiver means, primarily, that once you've set the tuning dial to the station, you want the station to "stay put." If the receiver isn't electrically stable, the signal will gradually drift off tune. Actually, it's the receiver that's doing the drifting, and you have to keep touching up the tuning to keep from losing the signal entirely.

This assumes, of course, that the signal itself is stable. This isn't always the case, and sometimes receivers are accused of frequency drift when the blame rightly goes to the incoming

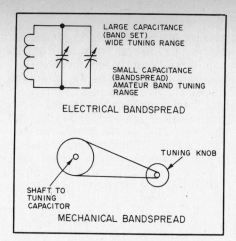

Fig. 2 — Electrical and mechanical bandspread. These are really means of obtaining a slow tuning rate on a circuit that covers a wide frequency range. The band may or may not be spread over a large dial scale; in fact, it isn't likely to be spread out with mechanical bandspread. Other mechanical schemes than the pulley arrangement shown can be used.

signal. So before you condemn a receiver on this score, be sure you do your checking on a really stable signal. A simple crystal-controlled frequency standard such as the one shown in chapter 13 is handy for this.

There are other types of electrical instability, too. When your ac line voltage changes, the voltages in the set will also change. Receiver tuning can be quite sensitive to voltage. If a sudden load on the line, such as a refrigerator going on, detunes the signal you're listening to, your receiver is definitely a candidate for improvement in this respect.

The mechanical construction of the receiver is likewise important. Receiver tuning can be affected by mechanical shock and vibration. Try pounding the operating table or rapping the receiver cabinet. If the beat note on an incoming cw signal remains unchanged, you've got a receiver that is excellent mechanically. This is a rather rough test, but you certainly don't want to lose a signal because you accidentally bump the operating table when you move an arm or leg.

### Not-So-Small Points

There are innumerable "little" things that make operating a receiver pleasurable. For example, there is the matter of knob size. A large tuning knob in effect slows down the tuning rate, so a big knob is definitely an advantage.

There should be plenty of room for your hand, too; you don't want to be bumping into other controls when you tune. And the height of the knob above the table surface makes a big difference in comfort and fatigue.

You want a tuning system that has no *backlash*. There is nothing more annoying than to have the tuning apparently start off in the opposite direction to what you intend, then reverse itself and try to catch up. This is an extreme case of backlash, admittedly, but it does occur. The lesser case, where just nothing happens at first when you start turning the knob, is not enjoyable either.

Good design and construction will overcome these faults. Unfortunately, most of the cheaper receivers suffer from them in some degree, because it costs money to cure them — money that can't be put into a set to sell at a low price. There isn't much you can do to improve a ready-made set, ordinarily, especially in mechanical features. When you build your own it's different. Then you can keep matters fairly well under control, by following the principles set out in this chapter.

### Sensitivity and Selectivity

Probably most amateurs think first of sensitivity and selectivity when "rating" a receiver. But all receiver features are pretty intimately related to each other. *Sensitivity* — the ability to bring in weak signals is the way most hams would define it — is rarely useful unless it is accompanied by good selectivity. If weak signals are always drowned out by strong ones on nearby frequencies, it doesn't do much good to have a sensitive receiver. But as you make the receiver more selective, you find that the tuning becomes more critical; you no longer have wide tolerances in setting the dial.

Thus high *selectivity* puts a premium on stability and tuning rate, the very features we emphasized at the beginning. An unstable, hard-to-tune receiver with high selectivity can quickly drive you to some less nerve-wracking hobby.

In this day it is possible to get almost any desired degree of selectivity. As we have seen in chapter 5, the amount that can be used depends on the kind of signal being received — that is, on the bandwidth of the signal.

A bandwidth of about six kilohertz is needed to receive amplitude-modulated phone signals, and about three kHz is sufficient for ssb. No phone signal *needs* to take up more bandwidth than this, and code signals can get along with far less.

You will want to be able to receive ssb, so it's a good idea in building or assembling your first receiver to base your selectivity on that kind of reception. Construction is somewhat easier than when you try for higher selectivity. The cost is generally less, too. Also, in getting experience with reception of other types of signals, such as cw, you'll develop an appreciation of what higher

selectivity can mean — probably more vividly than if you started out with the most advanced receiver.

### Building Your Own

Building a complete receiver, even a fairly unpretentious one, is quite an undertaking — that is, if the receiver is to meet certain minimum standards of performance that present-day conditions make necessary. One way to get the adjacent-channel selectivity needed is to use the superhet principle. But as we saw in chapter 5, the superhet will bring in all sorts of signals that aren't even in amateur bands, if you give it the chance. Something has to be done about this.

If you remember what you read in chapter 5, you will appreciate that there are several paths that can be taken to solve the image problem. One is to use an intermediate frequency that is fairly high up in the spectrum — above two MHz, say. Another is to use the double superhet idea, with a relatively high first i-f followed by a lower one (usually about 455 kHz) which gives better adjacent-channel selectivity than can be obtained with a high i-f. Still a third is to discard the superhet entirely and use "direct conversion," which is simply a matter of using an oscillating detector (or a mixer and beat oscillator) right at the signal frequency. The adjacent-channel selectivity here is what your own ears provide, so long as the detector is oscillating; the instant it stops, though, you have no selectivity to speak of. This type of detection is best, therefore, for cw and ssb; on a-m it's difficult to hold the detector oscillator right on zero beat so you can understand what is being said.

The second and third of the three methods cited above are the most prac-

Fig. 3 — Complete receiver, as shown, is rather compact. The antenna trimmer capacitor, C1, is the control to the lower left. The vernier dial is mounted directly on the front panel.

tical for home constructors, particularly those who are interested in building in order to learn something about receivers. While the double superhet sounds like an elaborate job, it isn't really so bad if you already have a receiver capable of giving satisfactory results for 80-meter band reception. In that case it boils down simply to the construction of a *converter*, which in essence is just a circuit for changing the signal frequency to some other one; in this case, the 80-meter band.

## The Converter/Receiver Combination

The best type of converter, especially for such bands as 21 and 28 MHz, is one using a fixed-frequency oscillator, preferably crystal controlled. A crystal is of course very stable, so you will have no problem in the converter itself with wobbly signals. With a converter having a fixed oscillator frequency, whether or not it is crystal controlled, the actual tuning of an amateur band has to be done on the receiver with which the converter is

used. That is, the receiver becomes a tunable intermediate-frequency amplifier. Even a low-cost "all-wave" receiver is likely to be satisfactory for this. The necessary stability and tuning rate aren't too hard to get at 80 meters, in inexpensive manufactured sets, although such receivers often are woefully deficient at the high end of the range. So for reception at the higher frequencies, a converter can make an inexpensive receiver look pretty good, if it isn't too bad on 80 in the first place.

# Receiver Circuits

In the pages to follow you'll see four different receiver circuits. The first two designs shown are direct-conversion, single-band affairs which are simple and easy to duplicate. If you're a newcomer to the world of equipment construction, it might be best to try your hand at

building one of these circuits before attempting to build a more complex unit.

A different approach is used in the third circuit. Integrated circuits replace many of the discrete components that would ordinarily be needed in a receiver

this complicated. Single conversion is used with 3300 kHz as the intermediate frequency.

If the builder is looking for an 80- through 10-meter receiver, the fourth circuit shown along with its associated converters, will perhaps be best. The

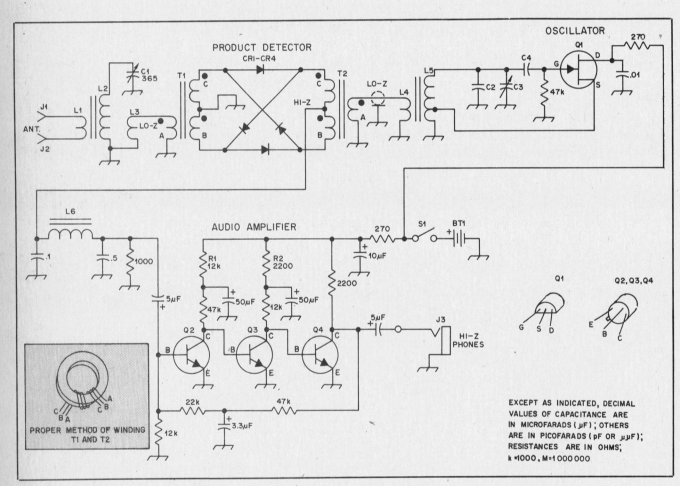

Fig. 4 — Schematic diagram of direct conversion receiver. The 0.01-μF capacitor is disk ceramic. The 0.1- and 0.5-μF capacitors are paper or mylar. Polarized capacitors are 15-volt electrolytic. Fixed resistors are 1/2-watt carbon.

BT1 — 9-volt transistor radio battery.
C1 — 365-pF variable.
C2 — 470-pF silver mica.
C3 — 140-pF variable.
C4 — 680-pF silver mica.
CR1-CR4 — See text footnote.
J1, J2 — Insulated banana jacks.
J3 — Phone jack.

L1, L3 — 3-turn link, no. 28 enameled wire, wound on L2.
L2 — 40-turns, no. 28 enameled wire, wound on 0.68-inch diameter toroid.
L4 — 5-turn link, no. 22 enameled wire, wound on L5.
L5 — 22-turns, no. 22 enameled wire, wound on 0.68-inch diameter toroid; tapped 5

turns from ground end (T-68-2).
L6 — 88-mH toroid.
Q1 — Motorola MPF-102.
Q2, Q3, Q4 — Npn, RCA 40233 or equiv.
R1, R2 — See text.
S1 — Spst toggle.
T1, T2 — See text.

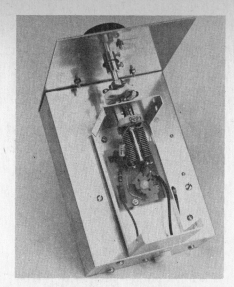

Fig. 5 — The oscillator components are mounted on a single circuit board. The FET is hidden below the tuning capacitor, C3. Note that the output from L1 is taken through a shielded cable. The insulated shaft coupling shown is a Johnson type 250.

basic receiver covers 3.5 to 3.8 MHz and is used as a tunable i-f for each of the higher-frequency converters.

## A Direct-Conversion Receiver for 3.5 MHz

One approach to simple receiver design is the direct-conversion technique. Basically, the direct-conversion method involves applying the desired rf signal and a local oscillator signal to a product detector. The beating of the two signals produces an audio-frequency signal which needs only further amplification in order to be heard.

Examination of the detection process reveals that the true product detector is a linear device. Its output amplitude is nearly proportional to the input signal for all signals of small amplitude as compared to the BFO signal. In any linear system selectivity may be obtained at either af or rf. In this case the receiver selectivity was obtained at audio frequencies by a low-pass filter which is used to eliminate all frequency components above a specified cutoff (about two kHz). A simple, high-gain audio amplifier following the audio filter completes the receiver.

The receiver is shown schematically in Fig. 4. It operates in the 3.5-MHz band. This receiver was designed for simplicity and ease of duplication rather than for ultimate performance. Nonetheless, this unit in many ways outperforms many of the less-expensive commercial receivers on the market.

The antenna is coupled directly to the product detector through a single tuned circuit. Following the input tuned circuit is the heart of the receiver, a product detector. It consists of four diodes operating in a ring configuration as a double balanced mixer. While typical junction diodes can be used in this circuit, hot-carrier diodes are strongly recommended. The local oscillator consists of a simple Hartley circuit with link coupled output. For simplicity, no voltage regulation is used. The product detector provides a constant load to the oscillator, making a buffer stage unnecessary.

The output of the mixer is applied to a single-section low-pass filter using one of the common 88-mH toroidal inductors. This filter is definitely needed in that it prevents mixer output signals beyond the audible audio-frequency range from overloading the audio amplifier. It also defines the bandwidth of the receiver. The audio amplifier, although quite simple, provides over 100 dB gain. Indeed, it provides the gain for the entire receiver. It is quite important that high-beta, low-noise transistors be used. One will note that no audio-gain control is included in the receiver. A strong cw signal will easily saturate the audio amplifier. However, the clipping is symmetrical and minimal distortion is introduced. With stronger ssb signals, the gain may be reduced by slightly detuning the antenna trimmer capacitor.

### Construction

The method of construction of the receiver is not critical with the exception that the local oscillator should be isolated from the rest of the circuitry and the high gain of the audio amplifier should be respected.

The receiver is built on a 5 × 7 × 2 inch aluminum chassis. A 6 × 5 inch piece of aluminum is used for the front panel. A 2-7/8 inch diameter imported vernier dial was used although any suitable dial may be employed. The component layout used in the version shown in the photographs is conservative and should be generally followed.

The local oscillator should be isolated from the rest of the circuitry and for this reason it is housed in a 5 × 2-1/4 × 2-1/4 inch aluminum box mounted on top of the chassis.

The audio amplifier may be constructed on a perforated phenolic board or on a printed-circuit board. The input and output should be physically separated to prevent undesired oscillation. High-impedance headphones (2000 ohms or more) should be used with the amplifier.

It would be wise to test the audio amplifier before mounting it in the chassis. A nine-volt battery and earphones should be connected to the finished circuit board. You should then hear a quiet hissing sound because of the noise generated in Q2. If an audible oscillation occurs, it may be eliminated by increasing the value of the decoupling resistors, R1 and R2. If no noise output is heard, the amplifier may be oscillating at a frequency beyond the audio range (e.g., 100 kHz). This oscillation is usually eliminated by placing a 0.01-μF disk capacitor across the ampli-

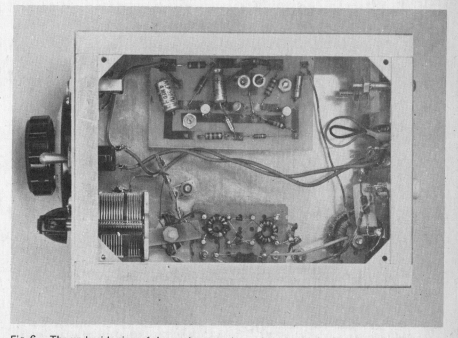

Fig. 6 — The underside view of the receiver reveals a rather uncluttered appearance. The product detector and associated transformers, T1 and T2, are mounted on a small piece of prepunched terminal board which is located in the right center of the chassis. L6 is mounted in the right rear of the chassis. The audio amplifier is mounted on a printed-circuit board to the left. The battery is fastened to the rear wall of the chassis using two machine screws and a plastic plate.

fier output or by again increasing R1 and R2. When mounting the amplifier in the chassis, the low-pass filter elements should be located away from the amplifier output.

The transformers T1 and T2 are easily fabricated on small toroidal coil forms with reference to the inset drawing. Three pieces of no. 28 enameled wire are held together and wound trifilarly on each toroid. Fifteen turns are adequate. After winding, the leads are trimmed to about an inch in length and the enamel is removed. Then, using an ohmmeter, the beginning and end of each of the three windings are identified (A, B, C). Winding A is used as the low-impedance winding. The beginning of winding B is connected to the end of winding C, providing the center tap for the bifilar high-impedance winding.

Fig. 7 — Exterior view of the 7-MHz direct-conversion receiver. The volume control is located at the left, main-tuning dial at the center and the headphone jack at the right of the front panel.

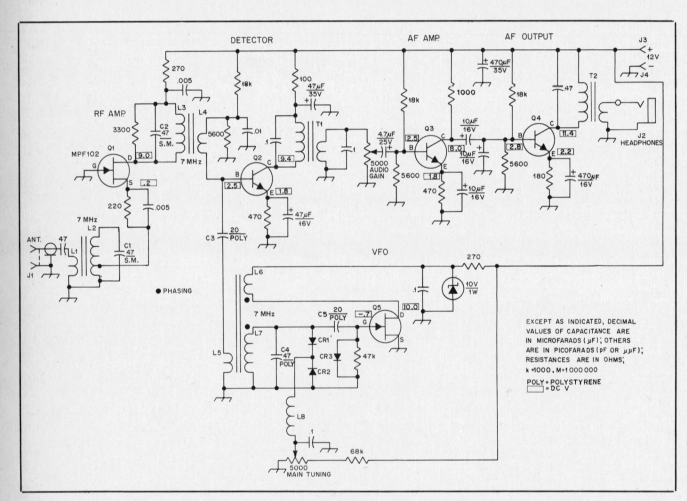

Fig. 8 — Schematic diagram of the Herring-Aid Five. Fixed-value capacitors are disk-ceramic unless specified otherwise. Fixed-value resistors are 1/2-watt composition. The audio-gain control is an audio-taper type potentiometer and the main-tuning control is a linear type potentiometer.

CR1 - CR3, incl. — High-speed switching diode (Radio Shack type 276-1620).
J1 — RCA type phono jack.
J2 — 1/4-inch phone jack.
J3, J4 — Binding post.
L1 — 3 turns insulated hookup wire wound over (ground) end of L2.
L2 — Radio Shack type 273-101 rf choke.

Tap at 4 turns above ground end.
L3 — Radio Shack type 273-101 rf choke.
L4 — 4 turns insulated hookup wire wound over cold end of L3.
L5 — 5 turns insulated hookup wire wound over ground end of L7.
L6 — 3 turns insulated wire wound adjacent to high end of L7.
L7 — Radio Shack type 273-101 rf choke with

six of the original turns removed.
L8 — Radio Shack type 273-102 rf choke.
Q1, Q5 — JFET (Radio Shack type RS-2035).
Q2-Q4, incl. — Transistor (Radio Shack type 276-1617).
T1 — Audio transformer (Calectro D1-722.)
T2 — Audio transformer (Calectro D1-724.)

## A Direct-Conversion Receiver for 7 MHz

Many years back, when it was difficult or impossible to obtain commercial steel or aluminum chassis, builders made use of readily available containers. Tin cans of various sizes were ever present and served as the chassis for many pieces of equipment. While this receiver is constructed in a herring can, there is no reason the builder must use this technique. Any chassis or cabinet that is available can be used.

Most of the components used in the construction of this receiver were obtained from a local Radio Shack store. Total cost of the project, exclusive of the herring can and the vernier dial (using new components) will be slightly more than $20. Of course, it can be built for considerably less if the builder is able and willing to scrounge parts from defunct radios, tape recorders and the like. Armed with a moderately stocked junk box, the builder should be able to duplicate this receiver for around $10. Several evenings at the workbench should yield a perfectly working model. Alignment of the receiver is quite simple and requires the use of a calibrated transmitter, receiver, signal generator or dip meter.

### The Circuit

The receiver design is shown in Fig. 8. Signals in the 40-meter band arriving at the antenna terminal are coupled to the source of Q1 through L1-L2. Q1, a grounded-gate JFET rf amplifier, has its source tapped down on L2 to preserve the Q of the input-tuned circuit. Output from this stage is applied to the product detector, Q2, through L3 and L4. Energy from the VFO is coupled to the detector through C3. Bias for this stage is fed through the turns of the coil to the base of Q2. The emitter resistor is bypassed for audio frequencies with a 47-µF electrolytic capacitor connected from emitter to ground. An interstage transformer, T1, couples the audio signal from the product detector to the af-gain control.

Q3 functions as an audio preamplifier, boosting the output of the detector to a level which is suitable to drive the audio-output stage. Output from Q4 is transformed to a low-impedance level by the output-matching transformer, T2. The circuit was designed for low-impedance headphones. However, there is sufficient output to drive a small speaker. Shaping of the audio channel provides a peak response at approximately 600 to 700 Hz. Many cw enthusiasts consider this the most comfortable frequency range to listen to. The receiver is also usable for ssb as the audio shaping is not prohibitively sharp.

The VFO is of the Armstrong or "tickler feedback" variety. Operating voltage, along with feedback information, is fed to the drain of Q5 through L6. For the circuit to oscillate, L6 and L7 must be phased properly. Tuning of the VFO is accomplished through the use of CR1 and CR2 connected as a voltage-variable capacitor diode (Varactor). With this type of circuit no mechanical capacitor is needed. As the amount of reverse bias applied to the diodes is changed, the capacitance that they present to the tuned circuit changes. In the unit shown the change was quite linear and the calibration of the vernier dial was very close to the actual frequency being tuned. A Zener-diode regulator is used to power the VFO circuit, as this is essential if good frequency stability is to be achieved. L8 prevents rf energy from reaching the arm of the main-tuning potentiometer.

### Construction

The herring can used for the receiver

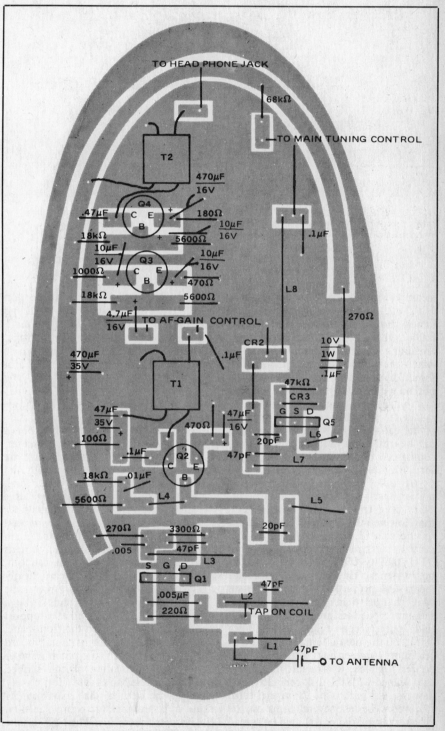

Fig. 9 — Shown here is the full-scale template and parts-placement guide as viewed from the foil side of the board. Gray areas are the foil pattern that remains after etching.

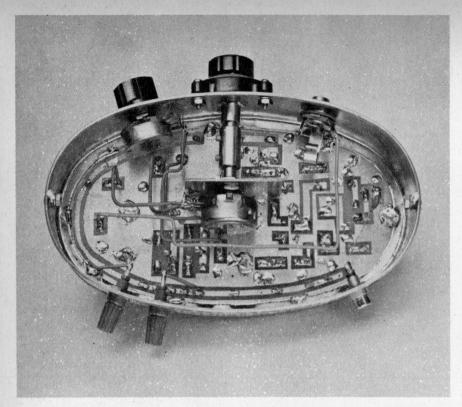

Fig. 10 — Here is the photograph of the inside of the Herring-Aid Five. Note how the main-tuning potentiometer is mounted on a small piece of circuit board, which is mounted, in turn, to the main circuit board.

measures approximately 7 × 3-3/4 × 1-1/2 inches. The bottom of the container must be removed in such a fashion that there is an 1/8-inch ridge remaining around the edge of the can to which the foil side of the circuit board should be soldered. This can be accomplished with the aid of a nibbling tool or saw blade. The circuit-board measurements are the same as the top opening of the can, 7 × 3-3/4 inches. The board can be cut to an oval shape by using a coping saw or nibbling tool. (See Fig. 9 for the circuit-board layout pattern.)

C1 and C2 should be silver-mica or polystyrene capacitors. Disk-ceramic types were tried in these positions but they lowered the $Q$ of the tuned circuits to the extent that out-of-band signals caused interference problems. For best VFO stability C3, C4 and C5 should be polystyrene. This type of capacitor seems less prone to capacitance versus heat changes than silver-mica or disk-ceramic capacitors are. If you can not find polystyrene types, silver mica would be the next alternative, with disk ceramics representing the last (and poorest) choice. Reasonable results can be obtained with the disk-ceramic types, however. L7 has six of its original turns removed. The last several turns on the ground end of the coil should be spread out on the coil form. These turns will serve as an adjustment to set the VFO

on the proper frequency for the portion of the band to be tuned. L6 is wound on the "hi" end of L7 (C5 end), adjacent to the L7 winding. Proper phase of the coils must be observed so that the circuit will oscillate. L5 is wound on the "low" or "cold" end (ground end) of L7.

The inside photograph of the receiver shows how the main-tuning potentiometer and the piece of circuit board are used to support the potentiometer. Care must be taken to ensure that the hole on this board lines up with the front-panel hole for the vernier dial. One simple way of accomplishing this is to drill the hole in the front panel first. Mount the piece of circuit board that holds the potentiometer to the main circuit board. Place the main circuit board in position on top of the can. While holding the circuit board firmly against the can, slip a pencil through the hole in the front panel and scribe a circuit on the potentiometer-support board that lines up with the front-panel hole. Remove the main circuit board and drill the hole for the potentiometer within the boundaries of the scribed mark. If these holes are not closely aligned, the vernier dial may slip because of lateral pressure being placed on the vernier assembly. When all of the parts are soldered to the board and the tuning-potentiometer assembly is in

place, the circuit board may be soldered to the can at several points along the 1/8-inch ridge.

*Adjustment*

The receiver, as shown in the diagram, will tune any 100-kHz segment of the 40-meter band. For example, if the receiver is to tune 7.0 to 7.1 MHz, zero on the vernier dial will correspond to 7.0 MHz and 10 on the dial will correspond to approximately 7.1 MHz. The tuning range can be extended a bit by removing the high end stop inside the vernier-dial assembly. This will allow the potentiometer to move through its full rotation instead of only a portion of it. An additional 40 kHz or so of tuning range can be obtained in this fashion. Of course, there are no calibration markings past the number 10 on the dial.

Suppose it is desired to have the receiver tune the range from 7.0 to 7.1 MHz. Set the vernier dial to zero and loosen the set screw on the vernier output coupling. Rotate the tuning-potentiometer shaft to the end stop that corresponds to the end stop that the vernier is up against. This should be the position with the arm of the potentiometer connected to ground. Rotate the pot approximately 1/16 to 1/8 turn away from the stop, and tighten the set screw securely. This will allow for the "dead" portion near the end of the control. To set the VFO on frequency, one of several pieces of equipment will be needed. If a calibrated transmitter is available, set it to 7.0 MHz, operating with several watts into a dummy load. Place the latter near the receiver. Spread or compress the bottom few turns of L7 until the transmitted signal can be heard in the receiver. Only a small amount of movement of the turns should be necessary. If a transmitter is not available, a calibrated receiver may be used. Again, set the vernier to zero, and while listening to the calibrated receiver set to 7.0 MHz, adjust the bottom few turns of L7 until the VFO is heard in the receiver. If a signal generator or dip meter is available, it may be used for the calibration. Set the dip meter or signal generator to 7.0 MHz and adjust the turns of L7 until the signal is heard in the receiver.

Fig. 11 — Photograph of the Mini-Miser's Dream Receiver and 20-meter converter.

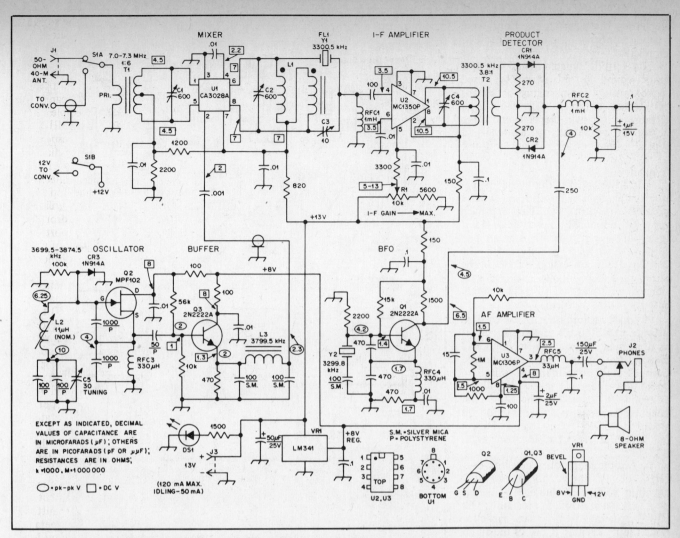

Fig. 12 — Schematic diagram of the 40-meter receiver. Fixed-value capacitors are chip or disk ceramic unless noted otherwise. Capacitors with polarity marked are electrolytic. S.M. indicated silver mica, and P is for polystyrene. Fixed-value resistors are 1/4- or 1/2-W composition.

C1, C2, C4 — 170 to 600-pF mica trimmer (Arco 4213).
C3 — 10-pF subminiature trimmer. Ceramic or pc-mount air variable suitable.
C5 — Miniature air variable, 30-pF maximum (Millen 25030E or similar).
CR1-CR3, incl. — High-speed silicon switching diode
J1, J3 — Single-hole-mount phono jack.
J2 — Closed-circuit phone jack.
L1 — Toroidal bifilar-wound inductor, $Q_u$ = 100 at 3.3 MHz, $Q_L$ = 33, BWL = 0.1 MHz, $L$ = 5.8 µH. 8 turns no. 28 enam., bifilar wound on Amidon FT37-61 ferrite core. Note polarity marks.
L2 — Slug-tuned inductor (see text), 11 µH

nominal. J. W. Miller 42A105CBI or equiv. $Q_u$ = 125.
L3 — Toroidal inductor, 17 µH. 19 turns no. 26 enam. wire on Amidon FT50-61 ferrite core.
R1 — 10,000-ohm miniature composition control, linear taper.
RFC1, RFC2 — Miniature 1-mH choke (Millen J302-1000 or equiv.).
RFC3, RFC4 — Miniature 330-µH rf choke (Millen J302-330 or equiv.).
S1 — Miniature dpdt toggle.
T1 — Toroidal transformer. Primary has 2 turns no. 24 enam. wire. Secondary has 14 turns no. 24 enam. wire on Amidon

T-50-2 core. Turns ratio — 6:1, $Q_L$ of 23, BWL = 0.3 MHz, $L$ = 1 µH.
T2 — Toroidal transformer. Primary has 9 turns no. 26 enam. wire on Amidon FT37-61 core. $Q_L$ = 33, BWL = 0.1 MHz, $L$ = 5.8 µH, turns ratio = 3.8:1. Secondary has 3 turns no. 26 enam. wire. Primary winding has center tap.
U1 — RCA IC. Bend pins to fit 8-pin dual-in-line IC socket.
U2, U3 — Motorola IC.
VR1 — Three-terminal 8-volt regulator IC (National Semiconductor).
Y1, Y2 — Surplus crystal in HC-6/U case or International Crystal Co. type GP with 32-pF load capacitance.

That completes the alignment procedure.

### The Mini-Miser's Dream Receiver

Described here is a slightly more complex receiver than the two previously presented. This receiver is of the single-conversion variety and makes use of a single crystal filter in the i-f. The filter provides approximately 30 dB rejection of the unwanted response (other side of zero beat). At least one supplier[1] markets a complete kit of parts for this project. For those who

don't have the time to scrounge parts this represents a good way to obtain the parts and still "roll your own."

### Circuit Description

In order to keep the circuit as simple as possible, several design tradeoffs were made. The major compromise was the elimination of agc and multiband cover-

[1] Circuit boards, negatives and parts kits for this project are available from WA0UZO. Check other ARRL pc suppliers for board availability.

age. However, there is ample room inside the cabinet of this receiver to accommodate one or two small converters for reception of bands other than 40 meters. This main frame is designed for 7- to 7.175-MHz coverage. Fig. 11 shows an IC being used as the receiver front end — a CA3028A which is configured as a balanced mixer. The input tuned circuit, T1, is designed to match a 50-ohm antenna to the 2000-ohm base-to-base impedance of the mixer IC. The transformer is broadband in nature (300 kHz at the 3-dB points) and has a loaded $Q$ of 23. This eliminates the need for a front-panel peaking control — a cost-cutting aid to simplicity.

The output tuned circuit, L1, is a bifilar-wound toroid which is tuned approximately to resonance by means of a mica trimmer, C2. The actual setting of C2 will depend upon the degree of i-f selectivity desired, and typically the point of resonance will not be exactly at 3300.5, the i-f center frequency.

For i-f selectivity this circuit makes use of a single crystal filter with a phasing capacitor, C3. This approach provides reasonably good single-signal reception and assures much better performance than is possible with the simpler direct-conversion receivers. The latter have equal signal response each side of zero beat, which often complicates the QRM problem.

A single i-f amplifier, U2, is used to provide up to 40 dB of gain. R1 serves as a manual i-f gain control, and will completely cut off the signal output when set for minimum i-f gain. No audio-gain control is used. T2 is designed to transform the 8000-ohm collector-to-collector impedance of U2 down to 500 ohms, and has a bandwidth of 100 kHz. The loaded $Q$ is 33.

A two-diode product detector converts the i-f energy to audio. BFO injection voltage is obtained by means of a crystal-controlled oscillator, Q2. RFC2 and the 1-$\mu$F bypass capacitor filter the rf, keeping it out of the audio line of U3.

Audio-output IC U3 contains a preamplifier and power-output system. It will deliver approximately 300 mW of af energy into an 8-ohm load. RFC5 is used to prevent rf oscillations from occurring and being radiated to the front end and i-f system of the receiver. The 0.1-$\mu$F bypass at RFC5 also helps prevent oscillations.

A three-terminal voltage regulator, VR1, supplies the required operating voltage to U3. It also provides regulated voltage for the VFO and buffer stages of the local oscillator (Q2 and Q3). The latter consists of a stable series-tuned Clapp VFO and an emitter-follower buffer stage. A single-section pi network is placed between the emitter of Q3 and the injection terminal of U1. It has a loaded $Q$ of 1, and serves as a filter for the VFO output energy. The recommended injection-voltage level for a CA3028A mixer is 1.5 rms. Good performance will result with as little as 0.5 volt rms. A 1-volt level is available with the circuit shown in Fig. 12.

A red LED is used at DS1 as an on-off indicator. Since it serves mainly as "window dressing," it need not be included in the circuit.

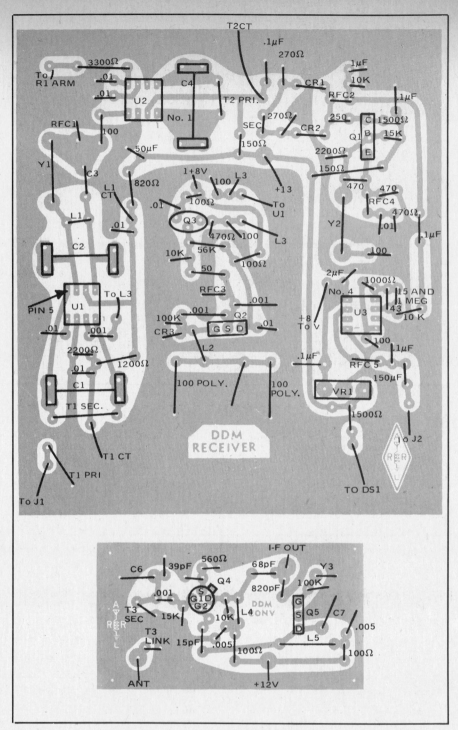

Fig. 13 — Foil-side scale pattern of the pc board. Circuit board is double-sided glass-epoxy material. Ground-plane copper should be removed directly opposite Q2 and related components (oscillator) for area of 1-1/2 X 1-1/2 inches. Remove copper in similar manner on ground-plane side of board opposite L1, C3 and Y1 (1 X 1-1/4 inch area). Removal of foil will prevent unwanted capacitive effects in those critical parts of the circuit. Ground-plane side of board should be electrically common to ground foils on opposite side of board at several points.

## Construction Notes

The front panel, rear panel, side brackets and chassis are made from double-sided circuit-board material. The chassis is an etched circuit board, the pattern for which is given in Fig. 13.

There is no reason why the top and bottom covers for the receiver can not be made of the same material by soldering six pieces of pc board together to form two U-shaped covers.

The local oscillator is housed in a

Fig. 14 — Interior view of the receiver. The front end is at the lower right. The leads of U1 are bent to align with an 8-pin dual-in-line IC socket. The rim of the speaker is tack-soldered to the pc-board side wall at two points. The 20-meter converter mounts on the rear wall inside the receiver (upper left corner).

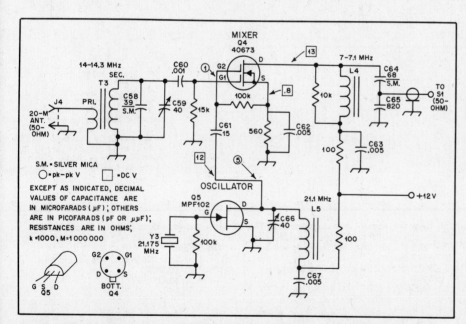

Fig. 15 — Schematic diagram of the 20-meter converter. Fixed-value capacitors are disk ceramic unless noted otherwise. Resistors are 1/4- or 1/2-W composition.

C6, C7 — 40-pF subminiature ceramic trimmer.
J4 — Single-hole-mount phono jack on rear panel of main receiver.
L4 — Toroidal inductor, 12 turns no. 26 enam. wire on Amidon FT37-61 core. $Q_L$ = 14, BWL = 0.5 MHz, $L$ = 8 $\mu$H.
L5 — Toroidal inductor, 24 turns no. 26 enam. wire on Amidon T-50-6 core. $Q_u$ = 200 at 7.9 MHz. $L$ = 2.4 $\mu$H.
Q4 — RCA transistor.

Q5 — Motorola transistor, MPF102, 2N4416 or HEP802.
T3 — Toroidal transformer, 10:1 turns ratio. $Q_L$ = 46, BWL = 0.3 MHz, $L$ = 1.85 $\mu$H. Pri. has 2 turns no. 26 enam. wire. Sec. contains 21 turns no. 26 enam. wire on Amidon T-50-6 core.
Y3 — 21.175-MHz fundamental crystal in HC-18/U case (International Crystal Co. type GP with 32-pF load capacitance).

compartment made from pc-board sections. It measures (HWD) 1-3/8 × 1-5/8 × 2-3/4 inches. A 1/4-inch high pc-board fence of the same width and depth is soldered to the bottom side of the pc board (opposite the top partition) to discourage rf energy from entering or leaving the local oscillator section of the receiver. Employment of the top and bottom shields stiffens the main pc board, and that helps prevent mechanical instability of the oscillator, which can result from stress on the main assembly.

Silver plating has been applied to the main pc board and to the front and rear panels. This was done to enhance the appearance and discourage tarnishing of the copper. It is not a necessary step in building the receiver. The front panel has been sprayed with green paint, then baked for 30 minutes by means of a heat lamp. A coarse grade of sandpaper was used to abrade the front panel before application of the paint. The technique will prevent the paint from coming off easily when the panel is bumped or scratched. Green Dymo tape-labels are used to identify the panel controls.

There is ample room inside the cabinet, along the rear inner-panel surface, to install a small crystal-controlled converter for some other hf band. A switch, S1, is located on the front panel to accommodate a 20-meter converter. A suitable circuit is given in Fig. 15.

All of the toroidal inductors are coated several times with $Q$ dope after they are installed in the circuit. The VFO coil is treated in a like manner. The polystyrene VFO capacitors should be cemented to the pc board after the circuit is tested and approved. This will help prevent mechanical instability. Hobby cement or epoxy glue is okay for the job. Use only a drop or two of cement at each capacitor — just enough to affix it to the pc board.

### Alignment and Operation

The VFO should be aligned first. This can be done by attaching a frequency counter or calibrated general-coverage receiver to pin 2 of U1. Coverage should be from 3699.5 to 3874.5 kHz for reception from 7.0 to 7.175 MHz. Actual coverage may be more or less than the spread indicated, depending on the absolute values of the VFO capacitors and stray circuit inductance and capacitance. Greater coverage can be had by using a larger capacitance value at C5, the main-tuning control. Those interested in phone-band coverage (only) can align the VFO accordingly and change Y2 to 3302.3 kHz.

Final tweaking is effected by attaching an antenna and peaking C1, C2 and C4 for maximum signal response at 7085 kHz. To obtain the selectivity

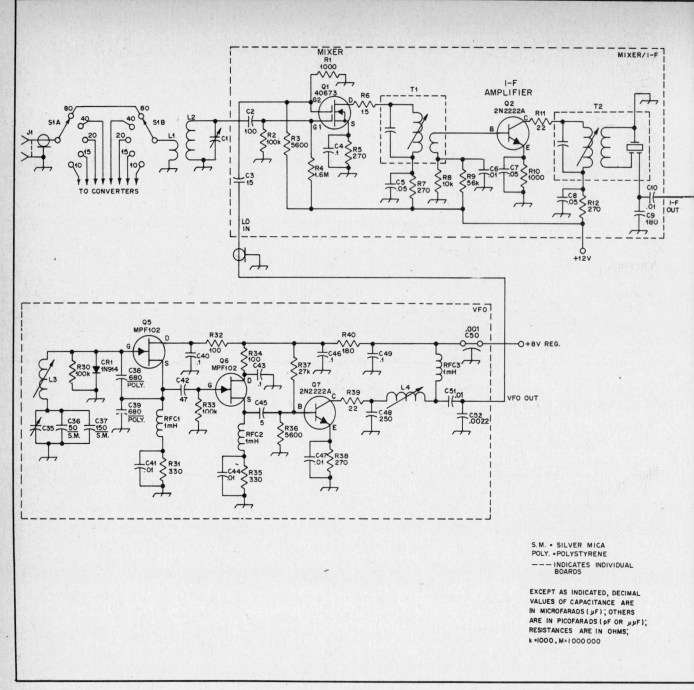

Fig. 16 — Schematic diagram of the basic 80- through 10-meter receiver, minus converters. The circuitry shown in dotted lines are components that are mounted to circuit boards.

C1 — Variable, 365 pF maximum.
CR2 — Varicap diode, Motorola MV-104 or equiv.
L1 — 5 turns no. 28 enam. wire wound over L2.

L2 — 40 turns no. 28 enam. wire wound on a T-68-2 core.
L3 — 40 turns no. 28 enam. wire wound on a Miller.
L4 — Miller.

T-68-2 core.
L3 — 40 turns no. 28 enam. wire wound on a Miller 42A0000CPI.
L4 — Miller 23A155RPC.

characteristics desired (within the capability of the circuit), adjust C2 and C3 experimentally. C2 will provide the major effect. C3 should be set for minimum response on the unwanted side of zero beat. A fairly strong signal will be needed to hear the unwanted response.

For reception of lower sideband it will be necessary to use a different BFO frequency — 3298.7 kHz. Those wishing

to shift the BFO frequency a few hundred Hz can place a trimmer in series with Y2 rather than use the 100-pF capacitor shown.

Because there is no agc in this receiver, the i-f gain should be set low, for comfortable listening. Too much gain will cause the audio circuit to be overdriven, and distortion will result. To prevent ear-splitting signal levels, one can install a pair of 1N34A diodes (back

to back) across the output jack, J2.

## An 80- to 10-Meter Receiver

The basic receiver described here covers the frequency range from 3.5 to 3.8 MHz. It functions as a single-conversion receiver on this band with 455 kHz as the i-f. For the higher frequency bands (7, 14, 21 and 28 MHz) converters are used ahead of the receiver. These converters mix the incoming sig-

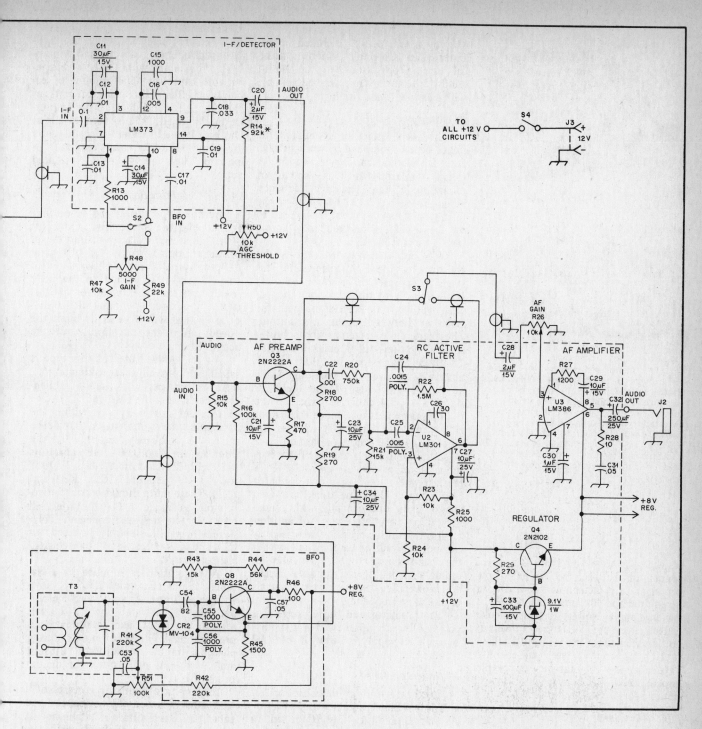

Q1 — RCA 40673 or equiv.
Q2, Q3, Q7 — 2N2222A or equivalent.
Q4 — RCA 2N2102 or equivalent.
Q5, Q6 — Motorola MPF 102 or equivalent.
RFC1, RFC2 — Miniature type, 1 mH.

S1 — Rotary, 2 pole, 5 position.
S2, S3, S4 — Toggle, single pole, double throw.
T1 — I-f transformer, Miller 9-C1.

T2 — Miller 8814 or equivalent.
T3 — I-f transformer, Miller 9-C2.
U1 — National Semiconductor LM-373.
U2 — National Semiconductor LM-301.
U3 — National Semiconductor LM-386.

nals in the desired band with a local-oscillator signal. The output from the converter is in the 3.5 to 3.8 MHz range and can be detected by the basic receiver. On the bands above 3.5 MHz the receiver functions as a double-conversion circuit. For example, if we use a 21.0- to 21.3-MHz converter ahead of the basic receiver, the first conversion is down to 3.5 to 3.8 MHz. The second conversion is to 455 kHz — the i-f of the basic receiver.

For ease of construction, the receiver is built in a modular format. Five modules make up the basic receiver and four additional boards are required for 40- through 10-meter coverage. There is no need to build all of the converters at first, since they can be built one at a time and added to the system. You might want to build the basic receiver and a 7-MHz converter at first. Later on,

if you want to try your hand at the higher bands, you can build the appropriate converters.

### The Circuit

Following the circuitry from left to right, the first item after the antenna connector is S1. Two sections of this switch select any one of four converters, or none at all. For the switch position shown in the schematic (3.5 MHz) no

Fig. 17 — Interior and exterior view of the 80- through 10-meter receiver. In the upper photograph the space at the lower right portion of the cabinet is reserved for the converter boards. These boards should be mounted vertically to save space. The circuit boards in order from left to right are audio, VFO, mixer/i-f, bfo and i-f/detector. L1/L2 is located on a terminal strip between the mixer/i-f and the i-f/detector boards.

converter is used and there is a direct connection between the antenna connector and L1. Remember, no converter is required for 80-meter operation. S1C switches supply voltage to the particular converter in use. All other converters not in use at that time are turned off.

L1, L2 and C1 step up the low impedance of the antenna or output impedance of the converters to a level suitable for driving the mixer, Q1.

## Mixer/I-F Board

Energy from the antenna or one of the converters is applied to gate 1 of a 40673 dual-gate MOSFET. Dual-gate devices make better mixers, in many applications, than do single-gate FETs. Approximately 40 dB of isolation between the rf and local-oscillator signals can be obtained. This can help reduce mixer ill effects (cross modulation and desensitization) when the receiver is operated on a band packed with strong signals. The output of Q1 is tuned to resonance at 455 kHz by means of T1, a miniature transformer.

The secondary of T1 is connected to an i-f amplifier stage, Q2, which uses a 2N2222A transistor. Bias for the base is fed through the secondary winding of

T1. The collector of Q2 is tuned to 455 kHz by means of T2. Included in this transformer is a single-section mechanical filter. The filter narrows the i-f bandwidth more than would be possible with a simple tuned circuit.

## VFO Board

The local oscillator input for the mixer board is supplied by the VFO. Q5 and associated circuitry comprise a Clapp oscillator which is capable of generating a signal on any frequency from 3.045 to 3.345 MHz. C35 is the main-tuning capacitor and L3 is used to set the oscillator on frequency at the low end of the range.

C41 couples energy from the oscillator stage to the first buffer, Q6. This stage is operated in a source-follower configuration so that the input impedance will be very high along with the isolation between input and output. These are desirable traits for a buffer stage as pointed out in chapter 3. Q7, a 2N2222A transistor, functions as an amplifier, as well as providing some additional buffering of the oscillator signal. C47, L4 and C51 make up the the output pi network. Since this circuit is low pass in nature, it reduces the amplitude of the oscillator harmonics. It is desirable to keep the oscillator-harmonic level as low as possible. In a receiver where more than one oscillator is running at the same time, harmonic energy from one can mix with fundamental or harmonic energy of another to form spurious signals. These signals can be received, when they fall within the band being tuned, just like an ordinary signal. If the spurious signals are strong, they can mask weaker signals on the same frequency.

The oscillator and buffer stages are powered by a regulated 8.5-volt supply. A regulated supply is a *must* if the VFO is to be frequency stable.

## I-F/Detector Board

The heart of the i-f/detector board is a National Semiconductor LM-373 subsystem. Built into this IC is an i-f amplifier along with detector circuitry for a-m, fm and ssb use. Only the product-detector portion is used in this receiver since we are mainly interested in receiving cw and ssb signals. The position of S2 determines whether the gain of the LM-373 will be controlled by the manual i-f gain adjust (R48) or whether it will be controlled by an internally derived agc voltage. The agc threshold control, R50, sets the level at which signals will begin to activate the agc circuitry. When the agc circuit is activated, the i-f gain control will have no effect on the circuit operation.

## BFO Board

Q8 and the other components of the

BFO board make up a Colpitts oscillator. The frequency on which the oscillator will operate is determined primarily by T3 along with CR2, a voltage-variable capacitor. The amount of capacitance that this device presents to the circuit is dependent on the amount of bias applied. R51 is used to adjust the bias level. In order to ensure good frequency stability, the oscillator is powered by an 8.5-volt regulated supply.

## Audio/Regulator Board

Audio output from the detector is fed to the af preamplifier, Q3. This stage is biased for Class A operation and provides approximately 20 dB gain. Output from the preamplifier is fed to the *RC* active filter and to the filter in-out switch. The position of this switch determines whether the audio-output stage will have as its input the output from the preamplifier or the active filter.

An *RC* active filter of this type is capable of providing approximately 12 dB of roll-off per octave as the frequency departs from the passband. The stage gain is set for unity (1) within the passband. The components that determine the frequency response of the filter are the two 0.0015-$\mu$F capacitors (C23 and C24) and the 1.5-M$\Omega$, 750-k$\Omega$ and 15-k$\Omega$ resistors (R22, R20 and R21). These parts should be of relatively close tolerance so that the filter will peak at the design frequency. Polystyrene capacitors should be used for C23 and C24 because of their high-$Q$ characteristics.

Audio output is supplied by a National Semiconductor LM-386 low-voltage audio power amplifier. The output stage is powered by the 8.5-volt regulated supply and consumes approximately 27 mW of power during no-signal input conditions. Current drain with full audio output is on the order of 200 mA.

The voltage regulator consists of a transistor, Zener diode, a resistor and capacitor. Base voltage is established at 9.1 volts by means of the Zener diode. This voltage will remain constant for moderate variations in supply voltage. The drop across the base-emitter junction is 0.6 volt so the output from the regulator is 9.1, −0.6 or 8.5 volts. Two regulated supply taps are provided — one for the VFO and the other for the BFO.

## Converter Boards

A single circuit design is used for each of the converters. The circuit is shown in Fig. 18. Only the crystal and tuned circuit components differ for the various bands of operation. Parts values that are different for each converter are also given in Fig. 18.

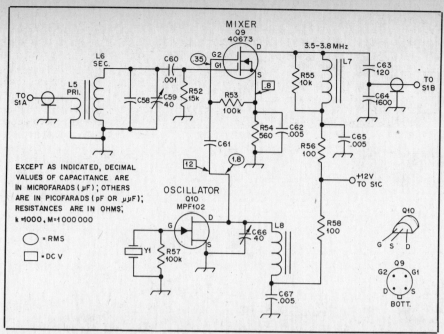

Fig. 18 — Schematic diagram of the 40- through 10-meter converters. See table below for parts values not listed on the schematic.
C59, C56 — Variable, 40 pF maximum.
L7 — 20 turns no. 28 enam. wire on an FT-37-61 core.
L8 — 30 turns no. 30 enam. wire on a T-37-2 core.
Q9 — RCA 40673 or equivalent.
Q10 — Motorola MPF 102 or equivalent.

| BAND | C58 | C61 | L5 | L6 | Y1 |
|---|---|---|---|---|---|
| 40 | 120 pF | 33 pF | 3 turns no. 28 on L6 | 29 turns no. 28 on a T-37-2 core | 10.8 MHz |
| 20 | 39 pF | 33 pF | 2 turns no. 28 on L6 | 25 turns no. 28 on a T-37-6 core | 10.5 MHz |
| 15 | 20 pF | 20 pF | 2 turns no. 28 on L6 | 20 turns no. 28 on a T-37-6 core | 17.5 MHz |
| 10 | Omit | 12 pF | 2 turns no. 28 on L6. | 17 turns no. 28 on a T-37-6 core | 24.5 MHz |

The only operational difference between the converters occurs on 7 MHz. On this band the tuning is backward from each of the other bands. In other words, 7.0 MHz on the dial will be where 3.8 MHz is and 7.3 MHz will correspond to 3.5 MHz. This is because the crystal frequency is above the band that the converter is to cover. This is just the opposite from each of the other converters. If this converter were designed in the same manner as the others, the local-oscillator frequency would be 3.5 MHz. Since this is the lower frequency limit tuned by the basic receiver, the local oscillator would interfere with reception at the bottom portion of the 40-meter band. By using a 10.5-MHz local-oscillator signal, no interference will occur.

Q10 and associated components form a tuned-gate tuned-drain oscillator. C66 and L8 tune the drain to resonance at the crystal frequency. C61 couples energy from the oscillator to the mixer, Q9, a 40673 MOSFET. The drain of the mixer is, for each of the converters, broadly tuned to the first i-f — 3.5 to 3.8 MHz. Although the converters have no rf amplifier, adequate sensitivity (less than 1 μV) was obtainable on all bands.

## Construction

The entire receiver, minus a power supply, is built into a cabinet that measures 10 × 3-1/2 × 6-1/2 inches. Placement of the individual circuit boards is not critical. If the builder wishes, he or she can follow the general layout shown in the accompanying photographs. All wiring that interconnects the circuit boards should be made with miniature coaxial cable. RG-174 should work fine. The exception to this would be those runs carrying only dc. These can be made with ordinary hook-up wire.

The front-panel controls include the main-tuning vernier, volume control, on-off switch, headphone jack, preselector, manual i-f gain adjust, agc on-off switch, audio filter in-out switch and the BFO frequency adjust. Located on the rear apron are the dc power-supply terminals, antenna connector and agc threshold control.

The VFO is enclosed on four sides with double-sided circuit-board mate-rial. The pieces are soldered together along the entire length of adjoining surfaces. This construction technique serves several purposes. First, it provides a solid surface on which to mount the main-tuning capacitor. Second, the assembly is quite rugged and discourages frequency instability caused by flexing of the circuit board. Also, the frequency-determining components in the VFO are shielded from air currents which could cause short-term drift problems. Finally, the shielding helps keep stray rf currents from the VFO circuitry.

All of the circuit boards, with the exception of the VFO board, are constructed from double-sided pc-board material. One side of the board has the foil pattern while the other is left unetched. This provides a complete ground plane on that side of the board. A small amount of copper must be removed from around each of the component holes on the ground-plane side of the board so that the components are not shorted together. This can be done by countersinking the holes a small amount with a large drill bit (3/8 inch is suitable). Drill only deep enough so that the circuit-board insulating material is visible around the component hole. The ground-plane side of the board should be connected to the ground portion of the foil pattern side at several locations. Double-sided board construction of this type can help reduce ground-loop problems and unwanted coupling between stages. Although it isn't necessary, the boards can be silver plated to prevent tarnishing of the copper surface.

### Checkout and Alignment

If the builder has access to an assortment of test equipment, the modules can be checked and aligned individually. Since this is not normally the case, an alternative method is to wire all of the modules together and work from there.

Initial alignment should be done on the basic receiver with no converters placed ahead of it. The converters will be aligned later. Preset the receiver controls as follows: af gain maximum counter clockwise position; audio filter off (wide); agc off; i-f gain maximum clockwise position; agc threshold, main-tuning control and preselector at any position.

After a power supply has been connected and the power switch has been turned on, a check of the dc operating at the various boards should be made. If there is a major wiring error or defective components, chances are that this will be reflected in a reading vastly different from those shown on the diagram. Readings within 10 or 20 percent of those given can, in most cases, be considered normal. After it has been

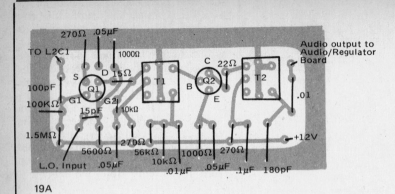

**19A**

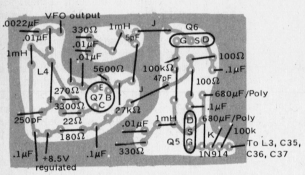

**19B**   J=Jumper   K=Cathode

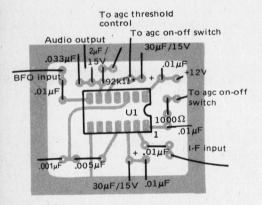

* = 82-kΩ resistor in series with 10-kΩ

**19C**

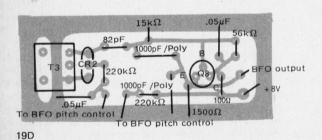

**19D**

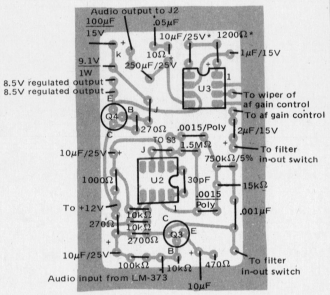

**19E**

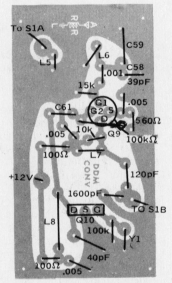

**19F**

determined that the dc voltages are in order, the receiver can be aligned.

The first step in the alignment procedure is to set the VFO on frequency at the low end of its range. To do this you'll need a frequency counter, calibrated general-coverage receiver or dip meter (used in the detector mode). Loosely couple any one of these pieces of equipment to the output of the VFO. With C35 fully meshed, adjust L3 so that the oscillator frequency is 3.045 MHz. Next, fully unmesh the capacitor and read the frequency to which the oscillator is tuned. It should be 3.345 MHz or slightly higher. If none of the pieces of equipment listed above are available, preset L3 so that its slug occupies approximately 3/4 of the total number of turns on the core. An alternate method for aligning the VFO will be described later.

The next step requires that the BFO be placed on frequency. A frequency counter or a-m table radio can be used for this step. With the BFO pitch control set at midrotation, adjust T3 so that the frequency displayed on the counter is 455.0 kHz. If a counter is not available, an a-m radio can be used,

providing it has a 455-kHz i-f. Tune the radio to a clear channel, set it next to the receiver, and adjust T3 for a zero-beat condition as heard in the a-m radio. This method will probably not set the frequency exactly at 455.0 kHz; however, it should be close enough. Reset the BFO pitch control to the 10-o'clock position.

For the next alignment step, connect a pair of headphones at J2 and an antenna at J1. With the controls set as outlined above, advance the af-gain control. A rushing noise should be heard in the headphones and if the main-tuning control is tuned, signals should be received, although they may be weak at this point. Tune in a cw signal and rotate the preselector control slowly, leaving it set at the position which provides the best (loudest) reception. Now, adjust T1 and T2 for maximum audio output as heard in the headphones.

The next adjustment should be made with the receiver tuned in a clear spot in the band. Switch the agc control to the on position and adjust the agc threshold control so that the background noise just begins to drop off in amplitude as

compared to the agc off position. Back the control off a fraction of a turn and leave the control at that setting.

If the VFO was not set on frequency earlier, it should be done next. Set the main-tuning capacitor so that its plates are fully meshed. A signal generator, calibrated transmitter or 100-kHz crystal calibrator can be used. If a transmitter or signal generator is to be used, set the frequency to 3.5 MHz and lightly couple the output to L1L2. Adjust L3 so that the signal is detected by the receiver.

Do the same if a 100-kHz crystal calibrator is used. It will be necessary to check the receiver to make sure the 3.5-MHz marker was actually used and not the 3.4- or 3.6-MHz marker. A quick scan of the lower portion of the band should indicate if the correct marker was used.

Each of the converters is aligned in an identical manner. With the converter wired into the circuit and the band switch placed in the appropriate position, tune in a signal somewhere near the center of the band. Simply adjust C59 and C66 for maximum signal level as heard in the headphones.

# Some General Remarks on Building Receivers

With increasing experience, you may want to build a receiver that will give you exactly what you want in all respects. The construction of advance receivers is beyond the scope of this book, but you can find plenty of information in this field in *The Radio Amateur's Handbook* and in articles of *QST*.

If you build a more elaborate receiver, you'll want to concentrate on stability, along with the ease of tuning discussed earlier. These are the really basic receiver requirements, so a few remarks about them are in order, in case you're tempted to go farther in the receiver-construction field.

### Frequency Drift

Slow *drift* in frequency is usually caused by heating in the receiver. The heat is generated in the tubes and transistors, power transformers, and resistors. It takes a good deal of time — sometimes several hours — before the heat distributes itself throughout the set and all the components settle down to a stable temperature. While the components in the tuned circuits are warming up, the materials of which they are made expand, causing their electrical values to change slightly. In other words, the heating actually tunes the receiver over a small frequency range.

There are several ways of combating this frequency change. An obvious one is to put the critical components as far as possible from the sources of heat — away from the items that get hot. An ideal way would be to take the critical tuned circuits out of the receiver entirely. This can be done, actually, but is a little cumbersome; most people like to have all the receiver controls on one panel. Another scheme is to remove the main source of heat — the power supply components — from the receiver and make a separate unit out of it. This is good practice if you build your own. However, in the interests of convenience most commercially made receivers today are complete with power supply in one cabinet.

Transistors have an inherent advantage over tubes in receiver heating, cause they use so little power and none of it is used in heating a cathode. However, their operating characteristics are much more dependent upon temperature than is the case with tubes. Oscillators, especially, should be operated at the lowest practicable input in order to avoid frequency drift, and considerable care must be used in oscillator circuit design to minimize the effects of heat rise in the tiny transistor elements. Frequency drift with a transistor receiver can be as bad as with

tubes — or even worse — if these precautions aren't followed. The frequency of a transistor oscillator is also more sensitive to voltage changes than is ordinarily true with tubes. This is the reason why you will nearly always find a Zener regulator associated with a transistor oscillator, particularly the tunable type.

### Heat Reduction

If you're using, or planning to buy, a manufactured receiver, there isn't a great deal you can do about the heat problem. But if you're going to build your own, here are some ways of keeping the temperature rise down, especially in tube receivers.

1) Use no more power from the line than you actually need. The biggest power consumer, aside from the power supply itself, usually is the audio amplifier. Don't build in a high-power audio output stage; use an audio transistor that takes only a small amount of total power.

2) Don't skimp on chassis size. Compactness — which means that components are crowded together — may sometimes be necessary, but usually isn't. The same number of input watts spread over twice the chassis area will cut the temperature rise by a large margin.

3) Give the set, especially the high-temperature components, plenty of ventilation. Don't put transformers, tubes and power resistors below chassis. The heat they give off will be trapped there. Put them on top so the heat can rise out of the receiver. You're better off if you don't use a cabinet, since cabinets trap heat too. If you *do* use one, punch holes in the top, and also in the sides just above the top-of-chassis level. This will give you a good air draft so the heat can get out.

4) Make sure that the tuned-circuit components, especially those in oscillators, are not close to the big producers. It may help, too, to use a heat shield between these high-temperature elements and other parts of the circuit. A heat shield is nothing more than a metal plate or baffle big enough so that the circuit element you want to protect can't "see" the source of heat. This cuts off the direct heat radiation in the same way that it cuts off light. The shield should be made of bright metal because that kind of surface is the best reflector of heat as well as light.

## Temperature Compensation

Manufactured receivers often use *temperature-compensating* elements — usually capacitors — in the vulnerable tuned circuits. As the temperature rises, the change in value in these compensators is in the opposite direction to the change that normally accompanies heating. Thus, under ideal conditions the "positive" change in one part of the circuit is just balanced by the "negative" change in another, resulting in a net change of zero. The design of circuits using such compensation is rather tricky, and to do a good job requires a fair amount of equipment and extensive measurements. You can go part way in your own home-built gear using *zero-temperature-coefficient* capacitors in tuned circuits where fixed capacitors are applicable. These do not compensate for changes in other circuit components, but at least show little or no shift in value by themselves, as the temperature changes.

Actually, there are many parts of the receiver that aren't particularly affected by heat. The really critical circuits are the oscillators and those where the selectivity is quite high, as in the i-f amplifier. Even in these circuits it is only the components actually in the tuned circuits that have much effect on the receiver tuning and thus on the observed frequency drift. These components include oscillator coils, tuning capacitors, and i-f transformers. Coupling and bypass capacitors, as well as resistors, usually are not critical as to value. As a result, a small change in the values of such components, such as might result from heating, has little or no effect on frequency drift. This is because any change in the load that the oscillator "sees" will affect the oscillator frequency, and a change in the voltage on a mixer screen will change the load on the oscillator.

## Mechanical Stability

A receiver that "jiggles" the signal when there is a little vibration is a receiver that will get more cussing out than praise. Again, it is the oscillator circuits that require the attention. They *have* to be solidly built — no flimsy construction, no floppy wiring. The higher the frequency, the more important this becomes.

Variable tuning capacitors rate careful selection when the oscillator operates at a high frequency. Pick out one with wide spacing between the plates. Also, it is preferable to use one with rather small, relatively heavy plates. Use a double-bearing capacitor, because bearings at both ends of the shaft will hold the rotor rigidly in line with the stator. Finally, don't handicap a good capacitor; anchor it firmly to the chassis. It should be mounted on the same support that is used for the oscillator coil and other components, so it can't move with respect to any other oscillator components or wiring.

Coils, too, should be solidly built and mounted. Small diameter coils on acetate bars ("Miniductor" type) are good when firmly supported. If you wind your own on slug-tuned forms, "dope" the wire so it can't move. Duco or a similar cement can be used. Pick out a form in which the slug fits tightly.

Crystal-controlled oscillators are less susceptible to drift and vibration than the tuned-circuit kind, since the frequency of a crystal is a pretty stable thing. However, even a crystal isn't *perfectly* stable, and the oscillator frequency *can* be affected by the same things that affect the frequency of tuned-circuit oscillators. So use a reasonable amount of care in constructing crystal oscillators, too.

# Chapter 9

# Accessories for Your Receiver

Receiver circuits intended for construction by beginners are simplified by leaving out features that, although useful, are not actually necessary. This is a good approach, because it lets the builder concentrate on essentials, with no side issues to cause confusion and possible trouble. After the receiver has been finished and the operator has had time to become familiar with how it works, other circuits that will improve reception in one way or another can be added. Many of these additions can be in the form of external accessories, such as the ones shown in this chapter. Often they are useful with the more elaborate receivers, too.

Small outboard gadgets usually have only one or two transistors and need very little dc power for their operation. Provided you don't try to use too many accessories at once, it is usually possible

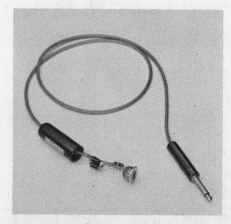

Fig. 1 — Simple diode audio clipper built into a cord-mounting headphone jack. The circuit is given in Fig. 2. R1 and the two diodes are bunched together at the rear end of the jack (left end in this view). R2 is the resistor visible in the center.

to take the power from the receiver accessory socket.

## Audio Clipping

In cw reception it is helpful if strong signals can be prevented from rising above a predetermined level in the headphones. Many receivers, especially the older models, have no provision for using automatic gain control on cw. With such sets an *audio clipper* is a real ear saver. The clipper chops off all of the signal above a selected amplitude so, no matter how strong it may have been before *clipping,* it is brought down to the size you choose in the clipping process.

The simplest such device uses silicon diodes as shown in Fig. 2. The diodes are simply connected back to back across the audio line to the headphones. As pointed out in Chapter 2 the threshold voltage (the voltage at which a diode begins to conduct appreciably) of a silicon diode is about 0.6 volt. Signals below this level are not affected by the presence of the diodes, but once the signal amplitude rises above 0.6 volt the diodes prevent the amplitude at the headphones from rising farther. The loudness in the phones at this voltage level is ample for most operators.

R1 and R2 help improve the clipping action. These resistors cut the headphone volume as compared with the level straight from the receiver, but this is nearly always unimportant because most receivers have far more gain than is needed. R1 should be about 47 ohms to take care of all receiver output impedances. R2 should be several times the headphone impedance if low-impedance (8 or 16 ohms) phones are in use, but with high-impedance phones it may be left out. However, as R2 can be adjusted to set the signal strength in the phones at the level you want when the clipping

point is reached, it may be useful to include it even when it isn't needed for good clipping. The value for this purpose has to be found by trial and will depend on the headphone impedance.

## How to Use It

To use the clipper, simply plug P1 into the receiver phone jack and plug your headphones into J1. The overall signal level has to be fitted to the clipper, for optimum results. The optimum condition usually is one where clipping just begins on the moderately strong signals, leaving the weaker ones and the usual hiss type noise background unaffected. This gives good protection to the ears without making the general run of signals take on the somewhat "thin" sound that accompanies heavy clipping. Generally, it is best to run the audio gain fairly wide open and adjust for the clipping level by means of the rf and i-f gain controls on the receiver.

The clipper differs in several important respects from an automatic gain-control system. The clipping action is instantaneous; there is no thump while the gain is being reduced such as occurs when ordinary agc "takes hold." Neither is there a long recovery time

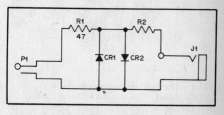

Fig. 2 — Audio limiter or clipper circuit. CR1 and CR2 may be any small silicon diodes. P1 is a phone plug and J1, a single-circuit phone jack. See text for discussion of R1 and R2. Both are 1/2-watt.

before the gain gets back to normal, as happens with agc. You can hear everything that may come along between dots and dashes, which is a real advantage when break-in is being used.

## The CW CRUD-O-Ject

In copying cw signals with the receiver BFO on, the signal you're listening to generates just one audio tone. You can vary the tone by varying the receiver tuning or by adjusting the BFO, of course, but there is always just *one* beat note. It follows that the audio amplifier in the receiver only has to amplify this one audio tone. In fact, it helps a great deal if it *doesn't* amplify other tones, because that means that the signal you want will be amplified more than the signals you don't want. In other words, an audio amplifier that builds up one tone more than others will give you selectivity for code reception — selectivity that isn't built into the receiver itself. This *audio selectivity* not only can be used to help reception with a receiver that isn't very selective, but often will be a welcome addition to a receiver that *does* have a fair amount of selectivity of its own.

Many amateurs, in their search for a good headset, find the comfort and sensitivity of hi-fi "cans" very desirable. Since these phones are available within almost any price range and from many local dealers, they are quite popular. Although the typical headset designed for hi-fi use is comfortable and sensitive, it has certain characteristics which are *undesirable* from an amateur standpoint. The most undesirable feature is the frequency response. Hi-fi enthusiasts are interested in hearing not only very low frequencies, but very high-pitched tones, too. For amateur cw communi-

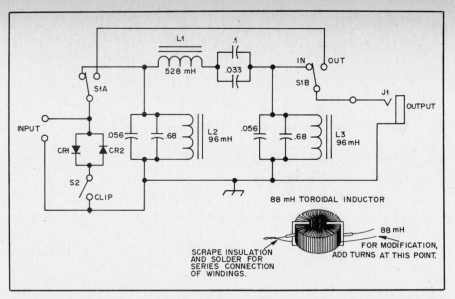

Fig. 4 — Schematic diagram of the CRUD-O-Ject. All capacitances are in microfarads ($\mu$F), and all capacitors should be of high-quality paper or polyester dielectric with 75-V or higher ratings. (Sprague type 225P "orange drop" capacitors were used in the unit photographed.) Parallel capacitor combinations of stock values are shown in the filter section, but other values of individual components may be used to obtain the desired total capacitance.

CR1, CR2 — Silicon rectifier, Mallory M2.5A, 1N4001, or similar. Avoid small-signal diodes.
J1 — Phone jack.
L1 — 528 mH, made by connecting six 88-mH toroids in series.

L2, L3 — Modified 88-mH toroid; add 40 turns no. 30 enam. wire, wound in same direction as original windings.
S1 — Dpdt toggle.
S2 — Spst toggle.

Fig. 3 — Outside and inside view of the CRUD-O-Ject. The inductors are mounted with special retaining hardware, as mentioned in text. This model uses a combination of three capacitors across L2 and L3 to make up the required capacitance. The circuit board is mounted using a two-inch section of angle aluminum bolted to the top of the cover.

cations, the high and low frequencies can be classed as *CRUD* (*C*ontinuous *R*andom *U*nwanted *D*isturbances), because they do not contribute to communications effectiveness. Most hi-fi phones are of low impedance, and it is usually desirable to connect the headset to the receiver speaker terminals. This allows a good match for the headset, but it also provides a higher hum level than is heard with limited-frequency-range earphones.

Many audio-filter circuits have been designed over the years. Most of these filters have a design center frequency of approximately 1 kHz. In this frequency range, a very sharp response can be obtained easily with surplus toroidal inductors. While these filters can (and do) eliminate *CRUD*, they may also have "super" selectivity leading to a monotone and even ringing performance. What is needed is a band-pass filter which will eliminate the *CRUD* but not be ringing sharp. The *CRUD-O-Ject* has these characteristics.

### The Circuit

The schematic diagram of the CRUD-O-Ject is shown in Fig. 4. The heart of the circuit is a 3-pole band-pass filter having what is called a Butterworth response. This response, plotted against frequency, can be seen in Fig. 5. We can see from this graph that 600 Hz is the center frequency. Most ardent cw

operators, when receiving code, prefer to hear a tone around this frequency.

Many receivers suffer from audio hum and annoying high-pitched hiss. This filter will attenuate 120-Hz power-supply hum more than 50 dB, and the same is true for frequencies above 2600 Hz. Hum resulting from 60-Hz pickup in the receiver audio system is attenuated by more than 70 dB.

The filter design makes use of six surplus 88-mH toroidal inductors for L1, rather than a single inductor which would not be readily available on the surplus market and would cost $8 or $9 new. L2 and L3 are also made from surplus 88-mH toroids.

Silicon diodes CR1 and CR2, connected across the input when S2 is closed, limit the amplitude of signals reaching the output of the *CRUD-O-Ject*

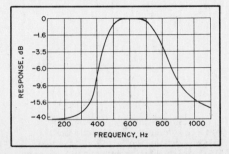

Fig. 5 — Shown here is the theoretical response of the filter section of the CRUD-O-Ject.

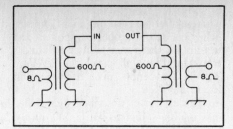

Fig. 6 — This partial diagram shows how to wire the impedance-matching transformers for 8-ohm operation.

to a comfortable listening level for most operators who use sensitive headphones. With S1 and S2, selection of filtering or clipping may be made independently, or both may be used simultaneously. The insertion loss of the filter is approximately 2 dB, so when switching the filter in or out, the change in volume is just barely noticeable in the headset.

### Construction

A circuit board was fabricated to allow convenient mounting of the toroids with commercially available plastic retainers. The homemade box measures 11 × 2 × 3 inches. Unlike some projects, the container was made to fit the circuit board, but almost any packaging arrangement can be used.

There are several techniques which are suitable for mounting a string of toroids. Probably the most popular is to stack them and run a long bolt through the center. Then the various pigtail leads can be attached to terminal strips running beside the stacked coils. If stacked toroids are mounted in a metal box, one end of the long bolt must be insulated from the box or it and the box will act as a shorted turn around all the inductors. There are no special precautions to be taken with the wiring of the *CRUD-O-Ject* except that any long runs of wire (over three inches) should be shielded to prevent leakage around the filter. See

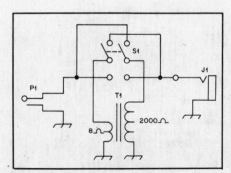

Fig. 7 — Schematic diagram of the headphone impedance matcher. The transformer is of the miniature audio variety and P1 and J1 are 1/4-inch phone plug and jack.

the pictorial drawing in Fig. 4 for details on connections of the 88-mH toroids.

### Operation

Connecting the filter to the station receiver is simple if the receiver has a 600-ohm output terminal. If a 600-ohm source is not available, an audio line transformer may be used to transform the speaker 4- or 8-ohm output to 600 ohms. See Fig. 6. Likewise, the same kind of transformer may be used to match the output of the filter to a low-impedance headset (or the station speaker) if 600-ohm "cans" are not available. The important point here is that the filter *must* be terminated in 600 ohms at both the input and output if proper performance is to be realized.

This filter is one of the few station accessories which does not require "operator technique." On cw it is turned on; on phone it is turned off. The two front-panel switches are used for disabling the clipper and bypassing the filter. There are occasions when the operator may want to listen to a low-frequency beat note, such as when tuning the receiver to zero the calibrator. In order to hear the low-pitched tone near zero beat, it is necessary to switch out the filter. The clipper should be left in; otherwise, the operator takes the chance of getting his ears thumped *severely* by an unusually loud signal.

The clipper is a desirable feature to include in the circuit, as it limits the input signal to a comfortable level. Static crashes, locals and DX stations are all the same volume. The output of the audio clipper is rich in harmonic content, however, and the inherent distortion products give an odd sound to relatively strong signals when the filter is not used. By placing the filter after the clipper, the audio distortion is reduced to a point where it is undetectable. Any apparent thumping, clicks or other noises created in the receiver are virtually eliminated with both the clipper and filter in use. In short, the *CRUD-O-Ject* is a most useful station accessory.

### A Headphone Impedance Matcher

As you have probably realized by now, not all receiver audio systems are designed to operate into the same impedance levels. Some require a 2000-ohm load while others may require 8- or 16-ohm loads. The same is true for headphones. Some are high impedance (600 to 2000 ohms) and others are of the low-impedance variety (4 to 16 ohms). For best results the headphone impedance should closely match that of the receiver. If, for example, 8-ohm headphones are plugged into a 2000-ohm audio channel very little, if anything, will be heard. The same is basically true if 2000-ohm head-

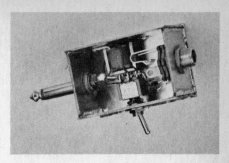

Fig. 8 — This is the interior view of the headphone impedance matcher (top cover removed). After all of the wiring is complete and the unit has been tested, the top cover should be installed.

phones are used with an 8-ohm audio system. An impedance matcher, such as the one described here, will help solve this problem.

### The Circuit

The simple circuit shown in Fig. 7 consists of an audio transformer, a double-pole double-throw switch and one each phone jack and phone plug. Depending on the position of S1, the impedance will be stepped up or stepped down. If S1 is in the position shown in the diagram, J1 is connected to the 8-ohm side of the transformer. Therefore, P1 is connected to the 2000-ohm winding. With a set of headphones connected to J1, and with P1 plugged into the receiver headphone jack, this arrangement would be useful for matching low-impedance headphones to a high-impedance receiver output. Just the opposite is true if S1 is switched to the other position. If you don't foresee the need of impedance switching, you can simply wire the unit for step-up or step-down operation — depending on what is needed for your situation.

The matcher is constructed in an enclosure made from double-sided circuit-board material. All adjoining pieces are soldered along the entire length of the seam to ensure mechanical stability. The ground lead of P1 is cut

Fig. 9 — WWV converter as nested in the chassis. The shield shown in the photograph was found to be unnecessary since stray coupling between the input and output of the rf amplifier proved not to be a problem.

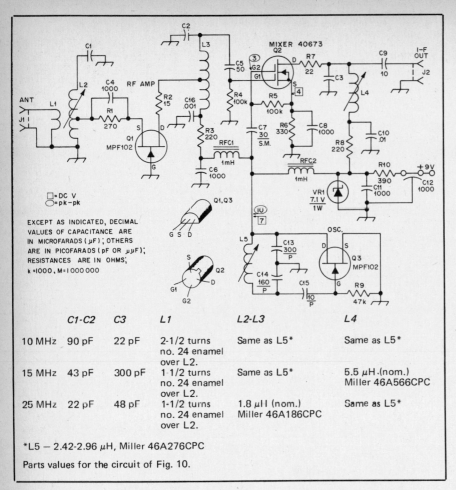

EXCEPT AS INDICATED, DECIMAL VALUES OF CAPACITANCE ARE IN MICROFARADS (μF); OTHERS ARE IN PICOFARADS (pF OR μμF); RESISTANCES ARE IN OHMS; k =1000, M=1000000

□ = DC V
○ = pk–pk

| | C1-C2 | C3 | L1 | L2-L3 | L4 |
|---|---|---|---|---|---|
| 10 MHz | 90 pF | 22 pF | 2-1/2 turns no. 24 enamel over L2. | Same as L5* | Same as L5* |
| 15 MHz | 43 pF | 300 pF | 1-1/2 turns no. 24 enamel over L2. | Same as L5* | 5.5 μH (nom.) Miller 46A566CPC |
| 25 MHz | 22 pF | 48 pF | 1-1/2 turns no. 24 enamel over L2. | 1.8 μH (nom.) Miller 46A186CPC | Same as L5* |

*L5 — 2.42-2.96 μH, Miller 46A276CPC

Parts values for the circuit of Fig. 10.

Fig. 10 — Schematic diagram of the WWV-to-ham-bands converter. The oscillator output frequency of 11 MHz was chosen to provide the reception of the three most commonly used WWV frequencies, (10, 15 and 25 MHz), without the need to change the oscillator frequency.

short, bent over, and soldered to the copper surface. Wiring of the switch may be done with any small size wire. If your impedance-transformation requirements are quite a bit different than the 8/2000-ohm system shown, a different transformer should be substituted for T1. If you need a transformation of 8 ohms to 600 ohms, for example, a transformer with those specifications should be used for T1.

## WWV Converter

Nearly every amateur needs to monitor the standard-frequency transmissions from the National Bureau of Standards (NBS) stations WWV or WWVH. These transmissions can be used for checking the accuracy of a crystal calibrator (see chapter 12), finding out the correct time, obtaining propagation information along with a variety of nonamateur-related items.

Some amateurs may have a problem using this information source because a large portion of amateur gear manufactured in recent years is for ham-bands-only reception. Some receivers do offer an "extra" band, usually 15 MHz, which is useful sometimes, in some areas of the world, but not in others. An inexpensive solution to the problem for those who want to receive the NBS stations' transmissions, but don't want to spend the money for a general-coverage receiver, is a converter which uses one of the amateur frequencies for an i-f output. Selection of the proper component values allows the potential user to build a converter that will cover the WWV or WWVH frequency most usable at his location.

The converter described here, when used with an amateur-bands-only receiver, provides for reception of 10-, 15- or 25-MHz NBS stations WWV or WWVH. The receiver, when tuned to 4, 14 or 21 MHz, serves as the i-f amplifier, detector and audio stages. The low current drain of the converter (15 mA typical) lends itself to operation from a 9-volt transistor-radio battery and to use with QRP equipment.

### The Circuit

The schematic diagram of the converter is given in Fig. 10. With the exception of the Miller coil forms, nearly all of the components used can be purchased from Radio Shack or Lafayette Radio Electronics or similarly stocked parts stores. For coverage of the 10-, 15- and 25-MHz WWV frequencies, component values of the three tuned circuits in the rf-amplifier and mixer stages must be selected from Fig. 10. This approach reduces the complexity of the converter by eliminating band-switching circuitry, but restricts the converter to use on only one NBS frequency at a time.

A common-gate JFET rf amplifier provides 8 dB of gain in this converter and has good overload immunity. A 40673 MOSFET is used as the mixer in the converter. The output circuit of the mixer uses a low value of coupling capacitor as an alternative to an rf voltage divider or other output coupling technique. This was done as a parts-saving step and does not seem to degrade the performance of the converter significantly.

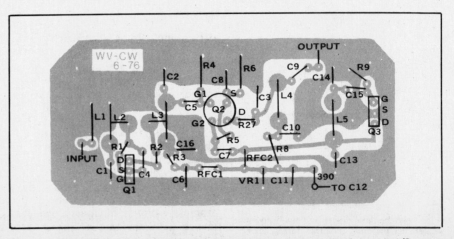

Fig. 11 — Etching pattern and parts-placement guide for the converter circuit board. 1/2-watt resistors were used throughout, but 1/4-watt resistors may also be used if preferred.

Fig. 12 — Outside and inside view of the attenuators. In the upper unit the resistors are mounted directly on the switch, using short pigtails wherever possible. Wide strips of copper are used for the input and output leads. The lower unit has each attenuator section individually shielded. The entire assembly is made up of double-sided circuit-board material, cut to form the necessary sections and soldered on all abutting edges. All resistors should be connected with the shortest possible leads. A U-shaped piece of aluminum forms the base.

VR1 provides adequate regulation of the V+ to the converter pc board. The regulator diode is placed on the V+ line for the entire circuit of the converter; the converter, therefore, is operating at 7.1 volts. Any voltage from 9 to 18 volts will power the converter.

The converter is housed in an aluminum Mini-box; dimensions of the box are 4 × 2-1/8 × 1-5/8 inches. Radio Shack part number 270-239 is suitable. As can be noted from the photograph, the converter pc board was laid out to facilitate 1/2-watt resistors, but 1/4-watt resistors are acceptable since power consumption for the converter is very low. Silver-mica or polystyrene capacitors should be used for C7, C13, C14 and C15 because they aid stability in the oscillator circuit. Disk-ceramic capacitors are suitable for use in the remainder of the converter circuit.

The only alignment required is that of peaking coils L1 through L4 while receiving WWV or WWVH. L5 should be adjusted so that the oscillator operates on 11 MHz. This can be checked while using a general-coverage receiver or dip meter.

## Front-End Overload Protection for the Receiver

It is not uncommon to experience front-end overloading when the station receiver is subjected to an extremely strong signal. Frequently, it becomes necessary to install some type of external attenuator between the antenna and the input of the receiver to minimize the bad effects caused by the strong signal, or signals. Ideally, such an attenuator should be designed to match the impedance of the antenna feed line and the input impedance of the receiver. Also, the attenuator should be variable, enabling the user to have some control over the amount of attenuation used. Manufacturers of some modern receiv-

ing equipment build into the front end of their receivers attenuators offering benefits that are not available from the normal rf gain-control circuit.

Examples of two such attenuators are given in Fig. 14A and 14B. At A a ladder-type attenuator gives a 0- to 40-decibel range of control in five steps. A precision step attenuator is illustrated at B. The latter offers an attenuation range of 3 to 61 decibels in 3-dB steps by closing one or more of five toggle

switches. Both units are designed for use in low-impedance lines. The one shown at B is designed for a midrange impedance of 60 ohms, making it satisfactory for use with receivers having a 50- or 75-ohm input. Although designed for an impedance of 50 ohms, the attenuator at A will work satisfactorily with 75-ohm receiver inputs if accurate attenuation steps are not required.

Standard-value 1/2-watt resistors are used in the simple attenuator, which will give good results from the broadcast band to 30 MHz. Isolation between sections is not good enough to make this unit particularly effective above 30 MHz. The precision step attenuator, if carefully constructed to reduce leakage to a minimum, will be effective to 150 MHz or higher. The smaller 1/4-watt resistors are used as they have less inductance than the 1/2-watt types.

Either attunator can be used ahead of the receiver or can be built into the receiver as an integral part of the circuit. Such a device is particularly useful ahead of receivers that do not have an rf gain control, such as simple regenerative receiving sets.

## The 80-10 FET Preselector

It is often necessary to put new life into tired or inexpensive receivers, especially when operation is marginal on the three higher hf bands — 14, 21 and

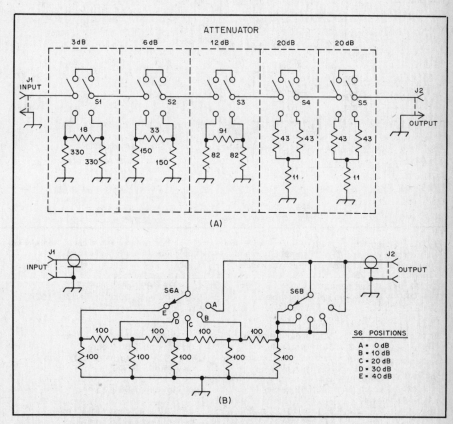

Fig. 13 — Schematic diagrams of the two step attenuators. All resistors are 1/4- or 1/2-watt composition. five-percent tolerance. S1 through S5 are miniature toggle switches and S6 is a phenolic rotary type, one-section, two-pole, five-positions. J1 and J2 can be any type of connector suitable for use with coaxial cable.

Fig. 14 — The 80- to 10-meter preselector is constructed in a cabinet made from two U-shaped pieces of sheet aluminum. Press-on feet are used. Panel decals (obtained from H. H. Smith) lend a "finished" appearance to the unit.

28 MHz. A preselector of the type described here can pep up the front end of such receivers while at the same time offering additional selectivity on all the hf bands. The latter helps to reduce images and generally improves the reception on some of the low-cost receivers. Often, signals heard on the amateur bands actually originate on quite different frequencies. They appear on ham sections of the dial as a result of image reception or overload of a receiver mixer.

### Circuit Details

This preselector is self-contained, except for the power supply, and no modifications are required in the receiver used. The diagram of the unit is shown in Fig. 15. Input and output tuned circuits consist of the preselector tuning capacitor, C1, and high-$Q$ coils wound on small toroid cores. Each coil has a trimmer capacitor for alignment purposes. A secondary winding is added which serves as the input or output 50-ohm link. Band changing is accomplished by S1, a multipole miniature switch. An "off" position is included so that the preselector may be bypassed when it is not required.

Two JFETs are operated in a cas-

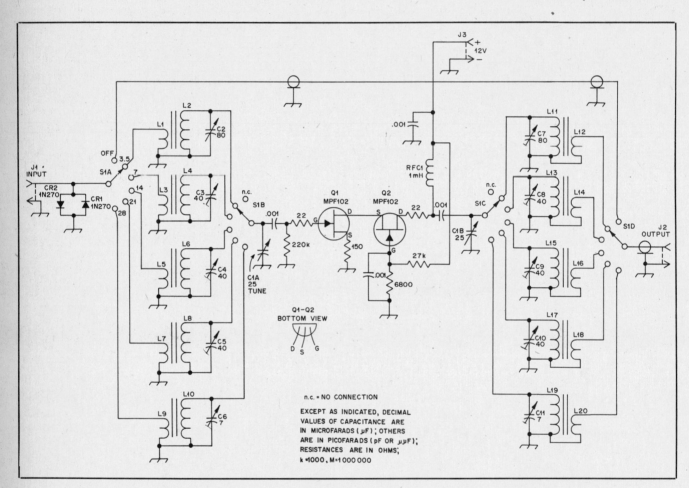

Fig. 15 — Schematic diagram of the selective preselector. Unless otherwise indicated, decimal values of capacitance are in $\mu$F; others are in pF. Resistors are 1/4- or 1/2-watt composition and fixed-value capacitors are disk ceramic.

C1 — Split-stator variable, dual section (Hammarlund HFD-25).
C2-C11, incl. — See table.
CR1, CR2 — High-speed switching diodes.

J1-J3, incl. — Phone jack, panel mount.
L1-L20, incl. — See table.
Q1, Q2 — HEP 802 or 2N5486.
RFC1 — Miniature choke (Miller 70F103A1).

S1 — Ceramic miniature rotary switch, four pole, six position, two section (Centralab PA-2011).

| | | | |
|---|---|---|---|
| 80 | L1, L12 — 5 turns no. 30 enam. over L2, L11, respectively. | L2, L11 — 85 turns no. 30 enam. on Amidon T-50-2 core. | C2, C7 — 7-80-pF compression trimmer, Calectro A1-247 |
| 40 | L3, L14 — 3 turns no. 30 enam. over L4, L13, respectively. | L4, L13 — 40 turns no. 30 enam. on Amidon T-50-2 core. | C3, C8 — 4-40-pF compression trimmer, Calectro A1-246 |
| 20 | L5, L16 — 2-1/2 turns no. 22 enam. over L6, L15, respectively. | L6, L15 — 20 turns no. 22 enam. on Amidon T-50-2 core. | C4, C9 — 4-40-pF compression trimmer, Calectro A1-246 |
| 15 | L7, L18 — 2 turns no. 22 enam. over L8, L17, respectively. | L8, L17 — 13 turns no. 22 enam. on Amidon T-50-6 core. | C5, C10 — 4-40-pF compression trimmer, Calectro A1-246 |
| 10 | L9, L20 — 1-1/2 turns no. 22-enam. over L10, L19, respectively. | L10, L19 — 10 turns no. 22 enam. on Amidon T-50-6 core. | C6, C11 — 0.9-7-pF compression trimmer, Calectro A1-245 |

Note: Amidon Associates, 12033 Ostego, North Hollywood, CA 91607

code circuit. The advantage of this arrangement is that the capacitance between input and output is only a fraction of a picofarad — so low that neutralization is not required in the hf range. Current drain is low, so the preselector may be operated from a 9-volt transistor-radio battery if desired, with only a slight loss of gain and dynamic range. Otherwise, a 12-volt miniature power supply, such as the type sold for battery replacement, should be used. If battery operation is contemplated, it would be well to add a power on/off switch; otherwise, current will be drawn all of the time.

The gain for each band has been set at approximately 20 dB by adjustment of the turns ratio on the rf transformers. Although the cascode circuit can provide up to 30 dB of gain, care must be taken so that the preselector does not overload the succeeding stages in the receiver.

### Construction

The preselector is built on a 4 × 5-inch etched circuit board which is housed in a 7 × 5 × 3-inch homemade cabinet. The enclosure is made from two U-shaped pieces of aluminum stock. Any of the popular commercially made cabinets may be substituted. Also, point-to-point wiring using terminal strips may be employed in place of the etched board. Whatever the assembly technique chosen, good isolation between the input and output tuned circuits is of prime importance. Any stray coupling can cause instability. If trouble develops, a shield between Q1 and Q2 may be of help.

The band switch, S1, is mounted on

Fig. 16 — Inside view of the preselector. The circuit board is held off the chassis with 1/4-inch standoff pillars. The 80- and 40-meter coils are along the rear of the circuit board, with the 20-, 15- and 10-meter input coils to the right of the switch while the output coils for the 14- to 28-MHz bands are to the left. Q1 is on the bottom left of the circuit board, with Q2 just above.

an aluminum bracket, which is, in turn, mounted at the center of the circuit board. The toroid coils are held in place with a drop of epoxy cement. The shield that separates the two sections of C1 must be grounded to the etched board with a short lead. This metal strip provides vital shielding between sections A and B. The PRESELECTOR capacitor is mounted directly to the front panel using hardware supplied with the unit. All of the trimmer capacitors are mounted on the circuit board.

During assembly, whether or not a circuit board is used, a heat sink should always be employed when soldering the transistor leads. If excessive heat reaches

the body of the transistor, the device can be ruined.

The input, output and power jacks are mounted on the rear apron of the chassis. The rf protection diodes, CR1CR2, are connected right across J1. Subminiature coax (RG-174/U) is used to connect the input and output jacks to the circuit board. Sockets for the transistors were included in the original model to facilitate experimentation; they may be omitted if desired.

### Alignment

The completed preselector is best adjusted with a signal generator. However, if no test equipment is available, on-the-air signals may be used. The antenna or generator should be connected to J1 and a short patch cord run from J2 to the receiver. Start with the 10-meter band, and set C2 with the plates fully unmeshed. Then tune in a signal at the uppermost point in the band. Adjust trimmers C6 and C11 for maximum indication on the receiver S meter. Repeat this procedure for the other bands, setting the appropriate trimmers. The lower frequency bands will appear to tune more broadly. However, the selectivity provided by the high-$Q$ rf transformers is about the same on each band.

If this preselector is to be used with a transceiver, the unit will have to be switched *out* of the antenna line when transmitting. Otherwise, severe damage will result to the coils and transistors in the unit. If the transceiver has a separate receiving-antenna input, as some do, the preselector can be connected to this jack, and the feeder switched with an external antenna-changeover relay.

# Chapter 10

# Building Transmitters

Many elements go into the making of a good transmitter, but most amateurs would agree that a most important one is stability. A signal that can't be held in tune by the receiving operator isn't going to get many contacts. Of course, you want to get the maximum possible power from the outfit, consistent with the amount of power put into it; the more rf power radiated, the bigger the signal. But if the signal does not stay put on one frequency, well enough to be copied on a highly selective receiver, all the attention you may put into other details will be wasted.

At this point it would be a good idea to go back to the latter part of chapter 8 and read what is said there about oscillator stability. All the effects described there, and the remedies suggested, apply just as much to the oscillator in a transmitter as to the oscillators in receivers. However, it takes even more care to stabilize a transmitting oscillator, simply because it is associated with higher power amplifier stages than is the case in a receiver. These stages can "kick back" on the oscillator in various ways.

Generally, too, we try to get more power out of a transmitting oscillator than out of a receiver oscillator, especially in the case of the single tube or transistor oscillator/amplifier transmitter. This tends to exaggerate the effects of temperature, of voltage changes, and so on. Therefore, it's good practice to operate the oscillator at very low power level and build up the power by amplifiers, even if it takes more stages. It is well worth the sacrifice of some simplicity.

The crystal-controlled oscillator offers the easiest way to get satisfactory stability. It would be an exaggeration to say that a crystal oscillator is foolproof in this respect. However, it does avoid many of the problems that have to be solved in constructing a good variable-

frequency oscillator. The disadvantage is that you can't move around in the band at will, unless you have a whole selection of crystals. However, this is by no means a fatal defect, especially in the Novice bands.

## Determining "Safe" Crystal Frequencies

Fig. 1 lists the frequencies on which each class licensee is permitted to operate in the hf bands.[1] Bear in mind that *all* of your signal, including key clicks on cw and sidebands on phone, must be inside the limits of these subbands. This has to be kept in mind in all your operating, but it is especially important not to forget it when you're selecting crystal frequencies for a crystal-

[1] As of date of going to press. See the latest edition of the *ARRL License Manual* for current frequencies.

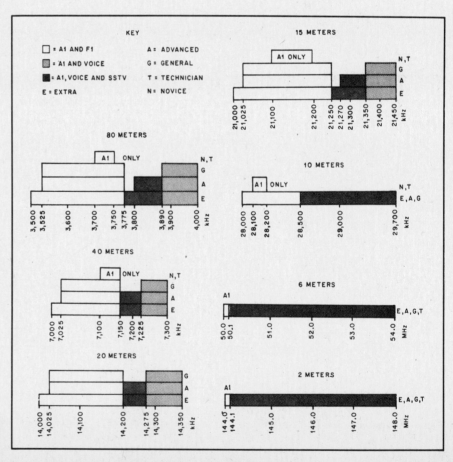

Fig. 1 — Frequency allocations for each class of amateur license.

controlled transmitter. You have to remember that the frequency marked on a crystal is not exact; there are manufacturing tolerances. Also, the frequency is going to depend somewhat on the oscillator circuit in which you use it. It is going to be affected by temperature, too, both the temperature in the transmitter and by the heat generated in the crystal itself when it's operating.

The crystal as it comes from the manufacturer is likely to have a rated tolerance of plus or minus one kilohertz if it is ground for the 3.5-MHz band and two kilohertz if ground for 7 MHz. So if your output is going to be on the fundamental frequency of the crystal, make sure its marked frequency is at least 1 kHz inside the band edge on 80 meters and two kilohertz on 40. If a harmonic of the fundamental frequency is going to be used, multiply these frequencies by the number of the harmonic. For example, suppose a 7-MHz crystal is going to be used for the cw-only part of the 21-MHz band by a General class licensee. If operation is to be close to 21,025 kHz, the low edge, dividing 21,025 by 3 gives 7008.33 as the fundamental *if the frequency is known to be exact*. To allow for the tolerance, though, we have to add two kHz, giving 7010.33 kHz. However, since the crystals come rated at integral one-kHz intervals, the frequency chosen should not be lower than 7011 kHz.

The same sort of calculation has to be made for phone, but here we have to allow for one sideband at the *output* frequency. Thus if the same licensee is going to operate phone near 21,350 kHz, the low edge of the subband, the closest safe frequency is 21,350 plus three kHz, the width of one sideband, making the lowest possible output frequency come to 21,353 kHz. Dividing this by three for the 7-MHz crystal fundamental gives 7117.67, and the safest *marked* frequency would be the nearest round figure at least two kHz higher — in other words, 7120 kHz.

Unless you can measure frequency very accurately, it is best to choose your crystal frequencies a couple of kilohertz, at least, on the safe side. Remember that the responsibility for staying inside the band is entirely yours, in the eyes of the FCC monitors.

## Crystals

Besides the fact that crystals can handle only a small amount of rf power, there are some limitations on the frequencies for which they can be manufactured. Two kinds of crystals are available — *fundamental* and *overtone* types. The former oscillate on a frequency which is determined by the thickness of the quartz plate. This is called the fundamental frequency of the crystal.

Fundamental type crystals are not usually made for frequencies higher than 30 MHz or so. They have to be very thin at much higher frequencies and are mechanically weak. For this reason, the design of simple cw and phone transmitters for the amateur bands up to and including the 28-MHz band commonly is based on using fundamental crystals operating at frequencies no higher than the 7-MHz band. Frequency multiplication is needed if output is to be obtained in the 14-, 21- and 28-MHz bands from such crystals.

Overtone crystals have higher frequencies marked on their holders — frequencies that often are in the vhf part of the spectrum. In suitable circuits, they vibrate in a complex way at a frequency that is a close approximation to an odd-numbered harmonic of the fundamental frequency determined by the thickness of the crystal. The term overtone is used in preference to harmonic because a crystal having a fundamental frequency of, say, 10 MHz will not have its *third overtone* at exactly 30 MHz. The actual frequency will be slightly different. The third and fifth overtones are the ones most used.

Almost any crystal, whether fabricated for overtone operation or not, can be made to operate on its third overtone. Many of them will also oscillate on the fifth overtone. However, for best overtone operation the crystal must be specially processed. Even so such crystals are less *active* than the fundamental types — that is, getting them to oscillate reliably requires more care in adjustment of the circuit.

## Equipment in This Chapter

The transmitting circuits and equipment shown in this chapter were chosen primarily to satisfy the requirements of the Novice regulations. In most cases, though, the circuits look ahead a bit — to the day when the Novice will become a General class licensee. Thus, other bands than those the Novice can use may be provided for. Also, the equipment may be capable of running a higher power input than Novices are permitted. If you are a Novice licensee, you simply stay inside the Novice assignment and keep your power input down to 250 watts. Then on the happy day when the "General" arrives, you branch out into wider fields wherever they attract you.

If you're "up" on the kind of equipment that is being used for single-sideband communication, you'll observe that the transmitters described here use a quite different scheme for getting on various frequency bands. The more-or-less standard ssb setup is a transceiver, which combines both the receiver and transmitter in one circuit with a common frequency control. This has many

advantages for ssb communication, but such transceivers invariably are based on frequency control by a VFO, the output of which is converted to various bands by mixing with another suitable oscillator frequency. The transceiver is much more difficult to build. Our intention here is to show *simple* equipment, so we aren't getting into the realm of transceivers.

The hf transmitters described in this chapter are as simple in design as is consistent with good performance. Every attempt has been made, too, to keep the cost down. Military surplus has been a happy hunting ground for components for a couple of decades, and quite a bit is still available if you look for dealers handling it. Discarded TV receivers are a gold mine for power-supply equipment and miscellaneous small parts such as fixed capacitors and resistors; the tubes and rectifiers from these receivers may not be the latest style, but they do the job at minimal cost.

Components of the types that amateurs want when they build their own often are hard to find. The resourceful builder isn't stopped by this — he makes substitutions, and he uses whatever he can find or can acquire from an amateur friend or two. How to go about substituting is explained in chapter 7. Don't hestitate to do it. It will give you the experience and know-how that are the real reward of building your own.

## A Simple QRP Transmitter for 40 Meters

To go along with the herring-can receiver described in chapter 8, we have here a two-transistor, 40-meter cw transmitter built in a tuna can. Of course, a tunafish can is not essential as

Fig. 2 — View of the assembled Tuna-Tin 2. Dymo tape labels are used to identify the connectors and switch. The chassis is affixed to a base plate by means of no. 6 spade bolts.

a foundation for this rig. Any container that suits the builders' fancy can be used, providing all of the necessary components will fit. The power output of this transmitter is 350 milliwatts, and while that may not sound like much, it's more than sufficient to provide numerous contacts over long distances. This assumes, of course, that a reasonably good antenna system is used (see chapters 6 and 14).

### Circuit Details

A look at Fig. 3 will indicate that there's nobody at home, so to speak, in the two-stage circuit. A Pierce type of crystal oscillator is used at Q1. Its output excites the base of Q2 with a few milliwatts of drive power, causing Q2 to develop approximately 450 milliwatts of dc input power as it is driven into the Class C mode. Power output was measured as 350 milliwatts (1/3 W), indicating an amplifier efficiency of 70 percent.

The collector circuit of Q1 is not tuned to resonance at 40 meters. L1 acts as a rf choke, and the 100-pF capacitor from the collector to ground is for feedback purposes only. Resonance is actually just below the 80-meter band. The choke value is not critical and could be as high in inductance as 1 mH, although the lower values will aid stability.

The collector impedance of Q2 is approximately 250 ohms at the power level specified. Therefore, T1 is used to step the value down to around 60 ohms (4:1 transformation) so that the pi network will contain practical values of *LC*. The pi network is designed for low *Q* (loaded *Q* of 1) to assure ample bandwidth on 40 meters. This will eliminate the need for tuning controls. Since a pi network is a low-pass filter, harmonic energy is low at the transmitter output. The pi network is designed to transform 60 to 50 ohms.

L1 is made by unwinding a 10-$\mu$H Radio Shack choke (no. 273-101) and filling the form with no. 28 or 30 enamel covered wire. This provides an inductor of 24 $\mu$H. In a like manner, unwind another 273-101 so that only 11 turns remain (1.36 $\mu$H). The 11 turns are spaced one wire thickness apart. Final adjustment of this coil (L2) is done with the transmitter operating into a 50-ohm load. The coil turns are moved closer together or farther apart until maximum output is noted. The wire is then cemented in place by means of hobby glue or *Q* dope. Indications are that the core material is the Q1 variety (permeability of 125), which makes it suitable for use up to at least 14 MHz.

T1 is built by removing all but 50 turns from a Radio Shack no. 273-101 rf choke (100 $\mu$H). The ferrite core in this choke seems to be on the order of 950, in terms of permeability. This is good material for making broadband transformers, as very few wire turns are required for a specified amount of inductance, and the *Q* of the winding will be low (desirable). A secondary winding is added to the 50-turn inductor by placing 25 turns over it, using no. 22 or 24 enameled wire. The secondary is wound in the same rotation sense as the primary, then glued into position on the form. Tests with an *RX* meter show this to be a very good transformer at 7 MHz. There was no capacitive or inductive reactance evident. The primary winding has an inductance value of 80 $\mu$H after modification.

Increased power can be had by making the emitter resistor of Q2 smaller in value. However, the collector current will rise if the resistor is decreased in value, and the transistor just might "go out for lunch," permanently, if too much collector current is allowed to flow. The current can be increased to 50 mA without need to worry, and this will elevate the power output to roughly 400 mW.

### Construction Notes

The pc board can be cut to circular form by means of a nibbling tool or coping saw. It should be made so it just clears the inner diameter of the lip which crowns the container. The can is prepared by cutting the closed end so that 1/8 inch of metal remains all the way around the rim. This will provide a shelf for the circuit board to rest on. After checkout is completed, the board can be soldered to the shelf at four points to hold it in place. The opposite end of the can is open. The container

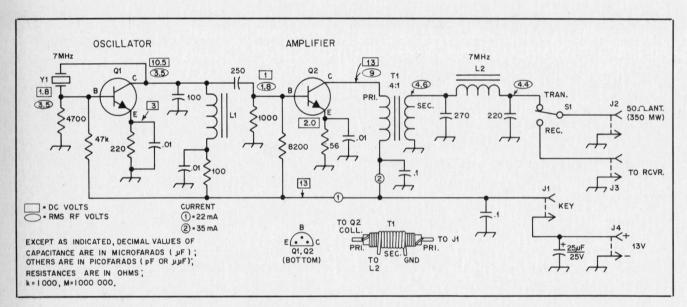

Fig. 3 — Schematic diagram of the two-transistor QRP rig. Capacitors are disk ceramic. Resistors are 1/2-watt composition. The polarized capacitor is electrolytic. See parts list for data on other components.

J1 — Single-hole-mount phone jack. Must be insulated from ground. Mount on tuna tin (Archer 274-346).
J2, J3, J4 — Single-hole-mount phono jack (mount on tuna tin).
L1 — Modified Archer 273-101 rf choke (see text).

L2 — Modified Archer 273-101 rf choke (see text).
Q1, Q2 — Archer 276-1617 npn silicon transistor. Equivalent to 2N2222A type.
S1 — Antenna changeover switch. Miniature spdt toggle (see text).

T1 — 4:1 broadband transformer. Modified Archer 273-102 100-$\mu$H rf choke. Primary has 50 turns, secondary has 25 turns (see text).
Y1 — Fundamental crystal, 7 MHz (International Crystal Co. type GP or equiv.).

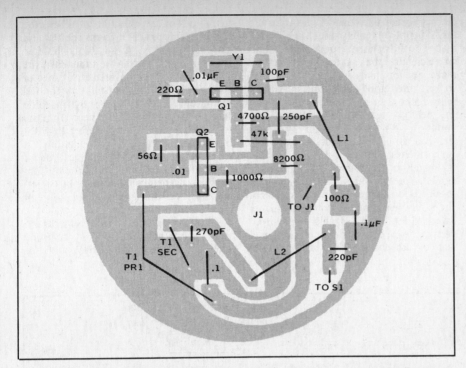

Fig. 4 — Scale layout of the pc board. Copper is etched away where J1 is mounted to prevent shorting the terminals to ground and other parts of the board. Size is for 6-1/2-ounce food can. Square format may be used if different chassis is desired. The 25-$\mu$F capacitor mounts between J4 and the pc-board ground foil.

can be mounted on a metal plate if the builder wishes. A base plate will help keep the transmitter in one spot on the operating table, especially if adhesive-backed plastic feet are used on the bottom of the plate.

Those with art in their souls may choose to paint the tuna can some favorite color. Alternatively, decorative contact paper may be used to hide the ugliness of the bare metal.

### Comments

Keying quality with this rig was

Fig. 5 — Low-power Novice transmitter for 80 and 40 meters. The amplifier tuning capacitor, C1, is operated by the knob at the right through an extension shaft and coupling. Just below the knob is the compression-trimmer loading control, screwdriver-adjusted.

good with several kinds of crystals tried. There was no sign of chirp. Without shaping, the keying is fairly hard (good for weak-signal work), but there were no objectionable clicks heard in the station receiver.

The voltages shown in Fig. 3 will be helpful in troubleshooting this rig. All dc measurements were made with a VTVM. The rf voltages were measured with an rf probe and a VTVM. The values may vary somewhat, depending on the exact characteristics of the transistors chosen. The point marked 1 and 2 (in circles) can be opened to permit insertion of a dc milliammeter. This will be useful in determining the dc input power level for each stage. Power output can be checked by means of an rf probe from J2 to ground. Measurements should be made with a 51- or 56-ohm resistor as a dummy load. For 350 mW of output, there should be 4.4 rms volts across the 56-ohm resistor.

Operating voltage for the transmitter can be obtained from nine Penlite cells connected in series (13.5 volts). For greater power reserve one can use size C or D cells wired in series. A small ac-operated 12- or 13-volt regulated dc supply is suitable also, especially for home-station work.

### A One-Tube Transmitter for the Novice

The 80- and 40-meter bands are good ones for the Novice to start out

on, and the transmitter shown in Figs. 5 to 8, inclusive, is not only simple to build but will provide many satisfying contacts on those two bands — even though the power input is a bit less than 10 watts. It uses a single tube — a 6T9 — which, however, is equivalent to two, as it has a triode and a pentode power amplifier in the same bulb. The triode section is used as a Pierce crystal oscillator, with untuned coupling to the pentode amplifier.

The complete circuit diagram is given in Fig. 7. The Pierce oscillator, as you learned in chapter 3 requires no tuning. The pentode amplifier, since its grid circuit is untuned, does not require neutralizing to be stable. It has a pi-network tank circuit, with C1 the tuning capacitor and C2 the loading capacitor. Plug-in coils are used to shift bands. The screen voltage for the amplifier is obtained through a 15,000-ohm dropping resistor from the plate supply.

A milliammeter is included for reading the amplifier plate current as an aid to tuning and to determine when the amplifier is properly loaded.

Since the value of capacitance needed at C2 for proper loading on 80 meters is greater than can be supplied by C2 alone, an additional capacitor, C6, is connected into the circuit automatically when the 80-meter coil is plugged in. C2 by itself is sufficient on 40 meters.

These circuits will be familiar to you from your study of chapter 3, including Z1, the amplifier vhf-parasitic suppressor, and the 22-ohm resistor in series with the triode grid, which is also a

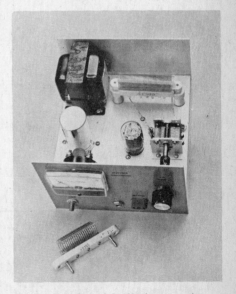

Fig. 6 — Top view of the Novice transmitter. The power transformer and amplifier tank coil are along the rear edge of the chassis. In front of the transformer is the 100-$\mu$F filter capacitor, C3. The 6T9 oscillator-amplifier tube is to its right, with the tank tuning capacitor, C1, alongside.

parasitic suppressor. The cathodes of both tube sections are keyed, and key clicks are reduced by C4 and R1 connected in series across the keying line.

The power supply uses a full-wave center-tap rectifier with silicon diodes. The power-supply filter is simple — just a 100-µF electrolytic capacitor connected across the rectifier output. A 35,000-ohm bleeder resistor discharges the capacitor when power is shut off, and also helps to improve the voltage regulation. The rectifiers are shunted by 0.01-µF capacitors to protect them from transients (see chapter 12).

### Construction

A standard 7 X 7 X 2-inch aluminum chassis forms the base of the transmitter. The panel and cabinet are homemade, both for the purpose of providing an enclosure that is no larger than is really needed, and — more important — to provide good shielding and thus reduce chances of causing interference in nearby television receivers. You should have no trouble with TVI if you make a similar enclosure. The panel, seven inches wide by 5-1/4 inches high, is made of 1/16-inch aluminum. A similar piece 3-3/4 inches high is mounted on the rear edge so it comes to the same height as the top of the panel. The smaller height of this piece allows clearing the connections on the back wall of the chassis while still providing metallic contact at the back to the U-shaped piece which forms the top and sides of the box. A 1-1/2-inch hole in the top, directly over the tube when the cover is in place, is covered by a piece of Reynolds do-it-yourself perforated aluminum held in place by machine screws. This hole lets the heat from the tube escape to the surrounding air without making a gap in the shielding. A rectangular piece of the same type of perforated aluminum covers the bottom of the chassis, held in place by sheet-metal screws, although it is not visible in the photographs.

The parts layout is shown in Figs. 6 and 8, top and bottom. A 12-prong socket is needed for the 6T9, and it is

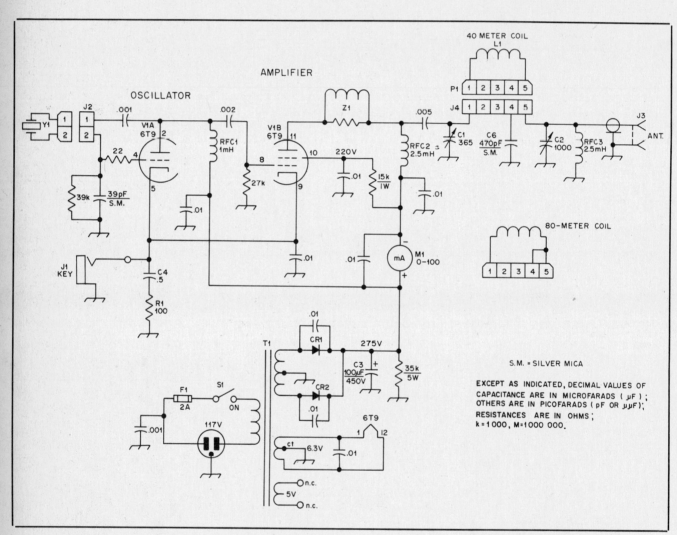

Fig. 7 — Circuit diagram of the 80-40 Novice low-power transmitter. Resistors are 1/2 watt unless otherwise specified. Capacitors with polarity marked are electrolytic; others not specified below are disk ceramic, 1000-volt rating.

C1 — 365-pF air variable.
C2 — 360 to 1000-pF padder.
C3 — 100-µF, 450-volt electrolytic.
C4 — 0.5-µF paper.
C6 — 470-pF silver mica.
CR1, CR2 — 100-volt PRV, 750-mA silicon rectifier.
F1 — 2-amp., 3AG fuse.
J1 — Open-circuit key jack.
J2 — Crystal socket.
J3 — Coaxial chassis fitting, type SO-239 or phono jack.
J4 — Coil jack bar (Millen 41305).
L1 — 80 meters, 43 turns no. 20, 16 turns-per-inch, 3/4 turns dia. (B&W Miniductor 3011). 40 meters, 30 turns no. 20, 16 turns-per-inch, 3/4 turns dia. (B&W Miniductor 3011).
M1 — 100-mA meter.
P1 — Coil plug (Millen 40305).
P2 — Line plug, with cord.
RFC1 — 1-mH rf choke (Miller 4652-E or similar).
RFC2, RFC3 — 2.5-mH rf choke (Miller 4666-E or similar.
R1 — For text reference.
S1 — Spst toggle.
T1 — Power transformer, 470 volts, center-tapped, 40 mA; 6.3 volt, 2A; 5 volt, 2A (not used); Stancor PC8401 or equivalent.
Y1 — 80- or 40-meter crystal, FT243 type, as required; see text.
Z1 — 7 turns no. 16 wire, space-wound on a 100-ohm, 1-watt carbon resistor.

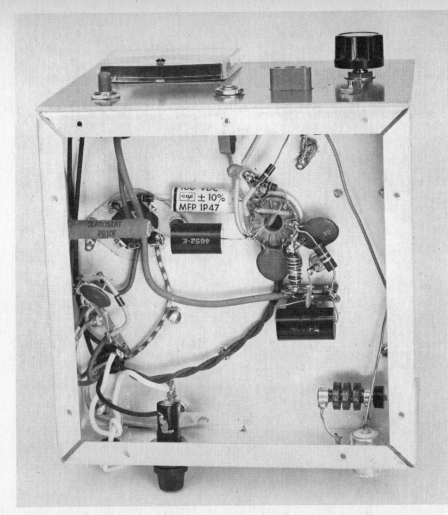

Fig. 8 — Underneath the Novice transmitter chassis. The resistor above the tube socket with its lead extending under the lip of the chassis is the 22-ohm unit in series with the grid of the 6T9 triode; the 39,000-ohm grid leak for the tube connects to it on one of the crystal-socket prongs. The resistor mounted horizontally above the socket is the 27,000-ohm grid leak for the pentode-tube section. The pentode screen resistor and Z1 are below the socket to the right. Black cylinders are encapsulated rf chokes; the one in the lower right-hand corner (RFC3) is not "potted." but an encapsulated type can be used. C4 and R1 extend to the left from the tube socket. Power-supply rectifiers are mounted on a terminal strip near the left-hand edge.

watching the lamp dummy antenna as you do. It should brighten, reach a maximum brightness, and then taper off as you continue to decrease the capacitance. Set C2 for maximum brightness and retune C1 to see if any further improvement can be made. The plate current should be between 30 and 40 mA at this point.

If there is no output the crystal isn't oscillating — assuming, of course, that you've checked all the wiring and found it to be in order. If the crystal won't oscillate the plate current will rise to 50 mA or more on closing the key, but if there is *no* plate current the key isn't closing the cathode circuits. The only thing to do when the crystal won't oscillate is to try another one.

With everything working right, you're ready to go on the air. The transmitter can be used with any antenna system that will show it a 50-ohm load on the band in use. A transmatch may be needed to make the actual antenna/feeder combination look like 50 ohms to the transmitter. Chapter 6 suggests a number of antenna systems that will be suitable.

For best keying, the crystal frequency and the output frequency should be the same. It is possible to use the amplifier as a doubler to get output on 40 from an 80-meter crystal, but since the keying characteristics aren't as good that way, we don't recommend it.

## A 75- to 120-Watt CW Transmitter

The transmitter shown in Fig. 9 is designed to satisfy the cw requirements of either a Novice or higher class licensee. The PA stage will operate at 120-watts dc input. The rig provides

mounted so that the index (open space between pins 12 and 1) faces directly toward the rear of the chassis. J3 and the fuse holder are mounted on the rear chassis wall. The line cord runs through a rubber grommet in the same wall.

The "hot" rf connections between the top and underside of the chassis (from C1 to C2) run through feed-through bushings. Rubber grommets can be substituted; use stiff wire (no. 16 or larger) and keep it spaced from the grommets.

The coils, cut from Miniductor coil material, are mounted on five-prong plug bars, Millen type 40305, which fit into a bar socket, type 41305, mounted on the chassis. The unused pins in the plug bars have been removed from the coils shown; this makes it easier to insert them in the jack bar. They can be cut off with a hacksaw or clipped off with heavy diagonal cutters.

Any inexpensive 0-100 milliammeter

can be used for measuring the plate current.

### Adjustment

The amplifier tank circuit is designed for working into a load of approximately 50 ohms. For a preliminary test, connect a 10-watt, 115-volt lamp to J3, with the shell of the lamp base to ground and the center connection to the center of J3. The lamp can be mounted in a socket as shown in chapter 11.

Turn on the power and allow the tube to warm up thoroughly. Connect a key to J1 and plug a crystal into J2. Install the coil for the same band as the crystal (3.5-MHz coil for 3.5-MHz crystals, 7-MHz coil for 7-MHz crystals). Start out with the capacitance of C2 at maximum (trimmer screwed up tight). Close the key and turn the knob on C1, watching for a sharp dip in the plate current. Tune to the dip and then decrease the capacitance of C2,

Fig. 9 — This 120-watt cw transmitter can be operated at 75-watt dc input for Novice-band use. The slide switch puts the meter in the grid or cathode circuit of the 6146B amplifier. Directly to the right of the slide switch is the FUNCTION switch and crystal socket. Continuing at this level, farther to the right is the GRID TUNING, grid BAND SWITCH, and the DRIVE level control. The controls to the upper right are the final BAND SWITCH, FINAL TUNING, and FINAL LOADING.

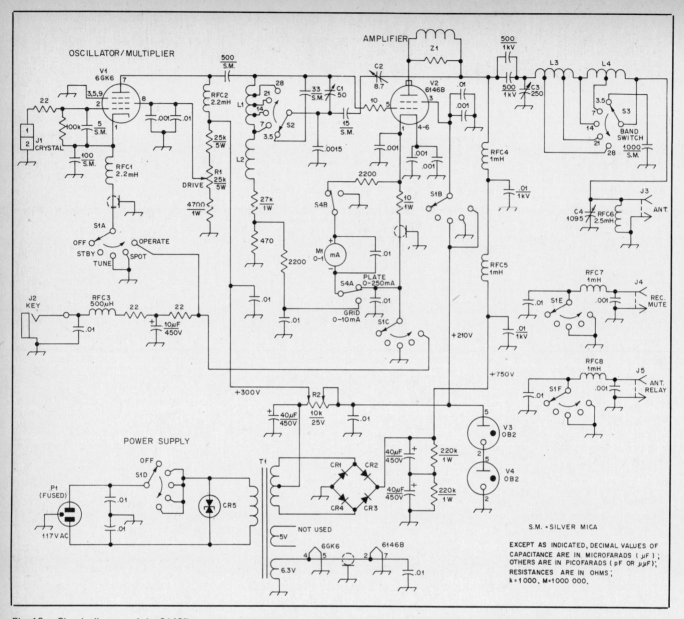

Fig. 10 — Circuit diagram of the 6146B transmitter. Capacitors with polarity marked are electrolytic; others are disk ceramic. Resistors are 1/2-watt composition.

C1 — Air variable 50 pF max.
C2 — Air variable (Johnson 160-104).
C3 — Air variable, 250 pF maximum, transmitting type.
C4 — Three-section broadcast variable, 365 pF per section, all sections connected in parallel.
CR1-CR4, incl. — 1000-PRV, 1-A silicon.
CR5 — Transient suppressor (GE 6RS20SP4B4).
J1 — Crystal socket.
J2 — SO-239-style connector, panel mount.
J3, J4 — Phono connector, panel mount.
L1 — 37 turns, no. 20, 16 tpi, 3/4-inch dia. tapped at 4 turns from the tube end for 28 MHz, 6 turns for 21 MHz, 12 turns for 14 MHz, and using the entire coil for 7 MHz (B&W 3011).

L2 — 28 turns, no. 20 32 tpi, 3/4-inch dia. (B&W 3012).
L3 — 12 turns, no. 18, 8 tpi, 1-inch dia. tapped at 3 turns from the tube end for 28 MHz, 6 turns for 21 MHz, and using the entire coil for 14 MHz (B&W 3014).
L4 — 21 turns, no. 20, 16 tpi, 1-inch dia. tapped at 9 turns in from the junction with L3 for 7 MHz, and using the entire coil for 3.5 MHz (B&W 3015).
M1 — Milliammeter (Calactro D1-912).
P1 — Fused plug (use 3-A, 3AG fuses).
R1 — 25,000-ohm, 5-W wirewound control (Mallory VW25K).
R2 — 10,000-ohm, 25-W wirewound.
RFC1, RFC2 — 2.2 mH (Miller 73F223AF).
RFC3 — 500 μH (Millen 34300-500).

RFC4 — 1 mH (Miller 34107).
RFC5, RFC7, RFC8 — 1 mH (Miller 4527).
RFC6 — 2.5 mH (Miller 4532).
S1 — Ceramic rotary switch, 6 pole, 3 section, 6 position (5 used), nonshorting contacts (Centralab PA-2023).
S2 — Ceramic rotary switch, 2 pole (1 not used), 6 position (1 not used) section, nonshorting contacts (Centralab PA2003).
S3 — Ceramic rotary switch 1 pole, 6 position (1 not used), nonshorting contacts (Centralab 2501).
S4 — Dpdt slide switch.
T1 — Power transformer, 117-volt primary, secondary 540 volts ct at 260 mA, and 6.3 volts at 8.8 A (Stancor P-8356).
Z1 — 7 turns of no. 16 wire on a 100-ohm 1-W composition resistor.

station control and other operating features. A SPOT position is provided on the FUNCTION switch which permits identifying the operating frequency in a band. The transmitter has been designed for ease of assembly, with the beginner in mind.

The circuit diagram of the transmitter (Fig. 10) shows the oscillator tube, V1, to be a 6GK6. This pentode works "straight through" on some bands while multiplying in its plate circuit on others. An 80-meter crystal will develop either 80- or 40-meter

energy in the subsequent stage (6146B) grid circuit, depending on the setting of S2 and C1. Similarly, a 40-meter crystal will permit the oscillator to drive the final tube on 40, 20, 15 and 10 meters. The final amplifier is always operated straight through for maximum power output. Since the amount of excitation will vary with the degree of frequency multiplication, a screen-voltage-adjustment control, R1, is included.

To insure stability, the 6146B amplifier is neutralized. This is done by feeding back a small amount of the output voltage (out of phase), to the 6146B grid through C2. The adjustment of this circuit is described later. Provision is included to measure the grid and cathode current of the amplifier stage. With the 6146B it is important to insure that the grid current is kept below 3 mA at all times; *high grid currents will ruin the tube in short order*. The meter, which has a basic 0-1 mA movement, uses appropriate multiplier and shunt resistors to give a 0-10-mA scale for reading grid current, and 0-250 mA for monitoring plate current.

The plate tank for the final amplifier uses the pi-section configuration for simple band switching. This network is tuned by C3, and C4 provides adjustment of the antenna coupling. The pi network also assures excellent suppression of harmonics when properly terminated, typically 35 to 40 dB. All connection points to the transmitter are filtered to "bottle up" harmonic energy, which, if radiated, could cause television interference.

Silicon rectifiers are used in the "economy" power supply. A center-tapped transformer with a bridge rectifier provides all of the operating voltages for the transmitter. Depending upon the line voltage, the high-voltage supply will deliver about 750 volts, key up, dropping to about 700 volts under load. If the line voltage is above 120, these figures will be increased by about 50 volts. The screen supply to the 6146B is regulated by two OB2 VR tubes.

The FUNCTION switch turns the transmitter on and selects the spot, tune or operate modes. Leads from this switch are brought out to the rear deck of the transmitter to mute the station receiver and key the antenna relay. Thus, S1 provides one-switch transmit-receive operation. In the OPERATE position, the oscillator and amplifier are keyed simultaneously by grounding the common cathode circuit. An *RC* network across the cathode line is included to shape the keying, thus preventing key clicks.

### Construction

An 11 × 7 × 2-inch aluminum chassis (Bud AC-407) is used as the base for the transmitter. A homemade aluminum U shield encloses the final amplifier. The chassis is fitted with an 11 × 7-inch front panel which is cut from sheet aluminum. The panel is held to the chassis by the switches and panel

Fig. 11 — Top view with the perforated metal cover removed. The small capacitor beside the 6146B provides the neutralizing adjustment. L3 and L4 are mounted one above the other. The smaller tube inside the rf compartment is the 6GK6 oscillator.

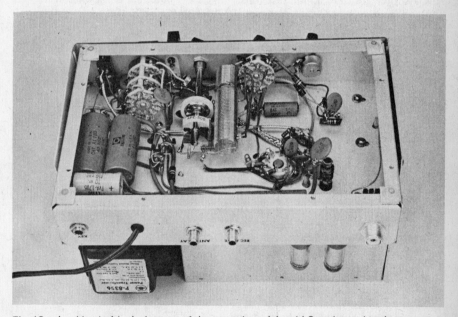

Fig. 12 — Looking inside the bottom of the transmitter, L1 and L2 are located at the center, next to the grid-tuning capacitor. All of the output jacks are spaced along the rear wall of the chassis. The bottom cover has been removed in this photograph. It should be kept in place during operation.

bushings common to both units. Correct placement of the various parts can be determined by viewing the photographs. Only an experienced builder should try to relocate the major components. The rf compartment has 3/4-inch mounting lips bent along the back side and the

ends to give a finished size of 5 × 8-3/4 inches. This rear housing is held to the chassis and front panel with 6-32 hardware, and a perforated metal cover is fastened to it with no. 6 sheet-metal screws.

The lead to RFC4 is routed through

an insulated bushing. A small bracket supports a piece of Lucite which insulates C2, the neutralizing capacitor, from ground. Another bracket supports C1 and S2. C1 is above ground for rf and dc, so an insulated coupling (Millen 39016) is to be used on its shaft. Tie strips are used to support the small capacitors, resistors and rectifier diodes.

The five-volt winding of T1 is not used. Therefore, these leads should be cut and taped to avoid accidental contact with the chassis. The filter capacitors and bleeder resistors are mounted on tie strips. Care should be used in making all high-voltage connections to prevent accidental shorts from occurring. Also, don't omit the "spike prevention" Thyrector diode, CR5, as this unit protects the supply from transient voltage surges.

### Adjustment

After the transmitter has been wired, check it a second time for possible wiring errors. Next, the two voltage-regulator tubes should be plugged in their sockets. With S1 at off, plug the line cord into a 117-volt outlet. When S1 is moved to STANDBY, the VR tubes should glow. The high voltage at RFC4 should measure about 750 volts. The oscillator voltage, checked at pin 7 of the 6GK6, should be close to 300 volts. If it is not, move the tap on R2 accordingly. *Make all measurements with care as these voltages are dangerous.* Then turn S1 to off and make certain the voltage drops to zero at RFC4, and at the 6GK6 socket. Normally, it will take at least a minute for the high voltage to drop to near zero (a fact which should be remembered during subsequent tests).

Remove the line cord from the outlet — *never work on a transmitter unless the ac power is disconnected.* Install the tubes and connect the plate cap to the 6146B. Insert an 80-meter crystal in J1 and set both band switches to the 80-meter position. Set the FUNCTION switch to the tune position, and plug the power cord into the mains. After the tubes warm up, swing C1 through its range. If the oscillator stage is working, grid current will be read on M1. C1 should be used to peak the grid current. The total current drawn should be kept below three mA. Use the DRIVE control, R1, to set the drive level. Change S2 to the 40-meter position and confirm that the second harmonic of the crystal frequency can be tuned. With a 40-meter crystal in J1, it should be possible to obtain grid current with S2 set for 7, 14, 21 and 28 MHz. The maximum grid current obtainable on the higher frequency bands will be somewhat less than on 80 and 40 meters (about 2.5 mA on 21 MHz, and 1.5 mA on 28 MHz). The latter value is not

enough for full drive on the 10-meter band. The dc input power to the 6146B should be limited to 90 watts on 10 meters, and this operating condition will provide approximately 50 watts output. On the other bands 60 to 70 watts output will be possible. If an absorption wavemeter is available, it is a good idea to check the setting of C1 for each band to insure that the tuned circuits are operating on the proper harmonic frequency. It may be possible to tune to an incorrect harmonic frequency, *which can lead to out-of-band operation.* Once

Fig. 13 — Photograph of the completed quarter-kilowatt amplifier.

Fig. 14 — This is an inside view of the amplifier. C1 is located at the lower right. C2 is mounted below the chassis and is connected to L1 using a feedthrough insulator.

the proper setting of C1 has been determined, mark the front panel so that this point can be returned to quickly when tuning up. Lacking a wavemeter, a receiver (with the antenna disconnected) can be used to check output on the various bands.

With S2 and S3 set for 15 meters, tune C1 for maximum grid current. Then, set the indicated value to about two mA with the DRIVE control. Set C4 at half scale, and slowly tune C3 while watching the grid-current meter. At the point which C3 tunes the tank

through resonance, a dip in grid current will be seen, unless by chance the amplifier is already neutralized. A slow rate of tuning is required, as the indication will be quite sharp. When the dip has been found, adjust C2 until no dip can be noted, or, at least, the dip is less than 0.1 mA. All preliminary tests should be made as quickly as possible, as the transmitter is operating without a load, and extended operation can damage the final-amplifier tube.

When neutralization has been completed and all circuits appear to be operating normally, connect a load to the transmitter. Preferably, this should be a 50-ohm dummy load, but a 100-watt light bulb will do. If an output indicator or SWR bridge is available, it should be connected between the transmitter and the load. The lamp is a fair output indicator on its own. Adjust the transmitter as outlined above for two mA of grid current on the desired band. With a key plugged in at J2, set C4 at full mesh, and switch S4 to read plate current. Watching the meter, close the key and adjust C3 for a plate-current dip. This dip-and-load procedure should be repeated until a plate current of 170 mA is reached at resonance.

### A 250-Watt Amplifier

Most Novice class licensees own transmitters that are not capable of running the maximum legal-power input for that class license — 250 watts. This amplifier was designed primarily with this in mind. Approximately 25 watts of power are required to drive the amplifier to 165 watts output on 80 meters. If a 75-watt transmitter is used to drive the amplifier, the transmitter output should be reduced to a level just sufficient to drive the amplifier to its full-power input. This can usually be accomplished by lowering the drive to the transmitter output stage and reloading.

### The Circuit

The main ingredient in this amplifier is a pair of 6KD6 television-sweep tubes (see Fig. 15). Although the tubes are rated at 33 watts of plate dissipation, they can handle temporary overloads of at least 100 watts without sustaining permanent damage. These tubes were chosen over 811s or 572Bs because they can often be "liberated" from old television sets or can be purchased new from most TV service shops.

VR1, an 11-volt Zener diode, provides cathode bias for the tubes and establishes the operation as Class B. That class of amplifier requires less driving power than does a Class C stage for the same power output. It is easier to reduce the output from a transmitter that has more than enough power to drive the amplifier than it is to boost

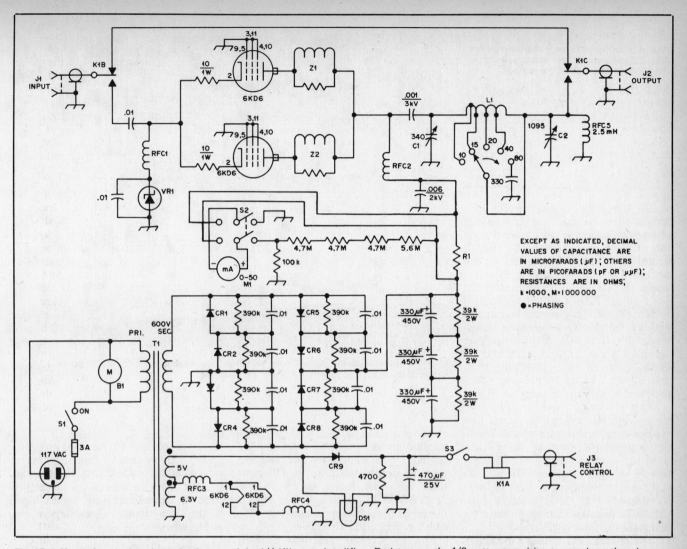

Fig. 15 — Shown here is the schematic diagram of the 1/4-Kilowatt Amplifier. Resistors are the 1/2-watt composition type unless otherwise specified. Fixed-value capacitors are disk ceramic unless otherwise noted. Polarized capacitors are electrolytic.

B1 — 117-V ac blower.
C1 — Variable capacitor, 340 pF maximum (Millen 19335 or equiv.).
C2 — Variable capacitor, 1095 pF maximum (surplus 3-section 365-pF variable).
CR1-CR8, incl. — Silicon diodes, 1000 volt, 2 ampere.
CR9 — Silicon diode, 50 volt, 1 ampere.
DS1 — Pilot lamp assembly, 12 volt.
J1, J2 — Coaxial connector, SO-239.
J3 — Connector, phono type.
K1 — Dpdt relay, 12-volt field, 2-ampere contacts.

L1 — 18 turns B & W 3022 coil. The entire coil is used for 80-meter operation and is tapped for the other bands as follows: 7-1/2 turns for 40 meters; 13-1/2 turns for 20 meters; 14-1/2 turns for 15 meters; 15-1/2 turns for 10 meters. Turns are measured from C2 end of coil.
M1 — Panel meter, 0-50 microamperes (Calectro DI-910 or equiv.).
R1 — Meter shunt, 1 foot no. 24 enam. wire wound of a large ohmic value 2-watt composition resistor.
RFC1 — 20 turns no. 24 enam. wire on an

Amidon FT-82-72 core.
RFC2, RFC5 — Rf choke, 2.5 millihenry, 500 milliampere.
RFC3, RFC4 — 15 turns no. 14 enam. wire on an Amidon FT-82-72 core.
S1 — Spst toggle switch, 4 ampere.
S2 — Dpdt toggle switch, low current type.
S3 — Spst toggle switch, low current type.
T1 — Television transformer (see text).
VR1 — Zener diode, 11 volt, 50 watt.
Z1, Z2 — 5 turns no. 18 enam. wire on a 47-ohm 1-watt resistor.

the output from a transmitter that provides insufficient drive. Class B operation was chosen for that reason.

The power supply uses a TV set transformer that has three secondaries: 600 volts, 6.3 volts and 5.0 volts. The 600-volt winding supplies the full-wave bridge rectifier with ac energy. Dc output from the rectifier assembly is filtered by means of three 330-$\mu$F capacitors. The 47-k$\Omega$ resistors across each of the capacitors equalize the voltages across the capacitors and drain the charge when the power supply is turned off. Equalizing resistors are used across

each of the diodes to ensure that the reverse voltage will divide equally between the two diodes in each leg. The capacitors across each diode offer spike protection. Each 6KD6 draws 2.85 amperes of filament current. Both filaments are connected in parallel across the 6.3-volt transformer winding. The 5-volt winding is connected in series with the 6.3-volt winding; the total (11.3 volts) is rectified, filtered and used to power the relay.

A 0-50 mA meter is used to measure the plate voltage and current. The meter reads 0-1000 in the plate-volts position.

A 0.26-ohm shunt is placed in the high voltage lead to facilitate metering of the plate current. One should be careful if working near the meter with the power on, as full plate potential will be present between each of the meter leads and ground. *Caution: Turn off and unplug the amplifier before making any changes or adjustments.*

### Construction

Perhaps the best way to classify this amplifier would be to call it a "junker type" amplifier. Every attempt was made to keep the amplifier as simple

Fig. 16

Typical input/output power relationships for various input levels. These measurements were performed in the 80-meter band.

| Power Input (Watts) | Power Output (Watts) |
| --- | --- |
| 2 | 10 |
| 5 | 25 |
| 10 | 60 |
| 15 | 90 |
| 20 | 130 |
| 25 | 165 |

Fig. 17 — Underneath the chassis. Parts placement is not especially critical. Tie-point terminals are used to support the point-to-point wiring.

and easy to build as possible. The only critical values are those for the amplifier plate-tank circuitry. Reasonable parts substitutions elsewhere in the circuit should have little or no effect on the performance of the amplifier. For example, if 330-$\mu$F filter capacitors are not available 250- or 300-$\mu$F units could be substituted. They should be rated at 450 volts or greater to provide a margin of safety. If a .001-$\mu$F plate-blocking capacitor is not on hand and a .005-$\mu$F unit is, use it. Often, builders attempt to match parts exactly to the type specified in a schematic or parts list. A few projects are this critical in nature, but the majority, including this one, are not.

The transformer used in this amplifier was garnered from an old TV set. Any hefty transformer with a high-voltage secondary between 550 and 700 volts should be adequate. Most of these transformers will have multiple low-voltage secondaries suitable for the tube filaments and relay requirements.

The chassis used to house the amplifier happened to be on hand and measures 3 × 10 × 14 inches. No doubt the amplifier could be constructed on a smaller chassis. The beginner is cautioned not to attempt to squeeze too much in too small a space.

The front, rear, side and top panels are constructed from sheet aluminum and help to keep the amplifier "rf tight." Any air flow openings are "screened" with perforated aluminum stock. The front-panel meter opening is shielded by means of an aluminum enclosure (a small Minibox would serve quite nicely). The on-off power switch, pilot light, meter switch, band switch, tuning and loading controls and amplifier in-out switch are all located on the front panel. On the rear panel are the amplifier input and output connections, relay control jack and the fuse holder. As can be seen from the photograph, a fan is located near the tube envelopes to keep them cool during operation.

### Setup and Operation

Attach the output of the transmitter to the amplifier input connection. Then, join the output of the amplifier to a 50-ohm noninductive dummy load. Connect the relay control line to the transmitter or external antenna-relay contacts. Then plug in the line cord and turn the power switch to the ON position. With the meter switch in the PLATE VOLTS position, the reading on the meter should be approximately 425, which corresponds to 850 volts. If the power transformer used has a high-voltage secondary other than 600 volts, the reading will vary accordingly. If no plate voltage is indicated by the meter, check your wiring for possible errors or defective components. Next, place the meter in the PLATE CURRENT position, the band switch to the 80-meter band, and apply a small amount of drive to the amplifier — enough to make the meter read 50 mA (5 on the meter scale). With the plate-tank loading control fully meshed, quickly adjust the plate tuning capacitor for a dip in plate current. Apply more drive (enough to make the meter read 100 mA), advance the loading control approximately an eighth turn and readjust the plate tuning control for a dip in plate current. Continue this procedure until the plate-current maximum dip is approximately 300 mA. The final value of plate current at which the amplifier should be run depends on what the plate voltage is under load. In our case this value was 800 volts. Therefore, the amount of current corresponding to 250 watts input is approximately 310 mA. ($I = P/E$, $I = 250/800$, $I = 312.5$ mA.) The same tune-up procedure should be followed for each of the other bands. The amplifier efficiency on 80 through 20 meters is approximately 65 percent, dropping to 60 percent on 15 meters. On 10 meters, efficiency is slightly less than 50 percent. Poor efficiency on the higher bands is caused primarily by the high-output capacitance characteristics of sweep tubes.

### A Two-Band VFO for Tube Type Transmitters

The VFO shown in Fig. 18 and the subsequent photographs and diagrams is intended to replace the 80- and 40-

Fig. 18 — Two-band transistor VFO, designed for use as a crystal substitute with tube type transmitters. It includes a two-watt amplifier for ensuring adequate drive for the transmitter in which it replaces the crystal. The knob at the lower left controls the band switch, S1, and the one at the lower right is for the function switch, S2.

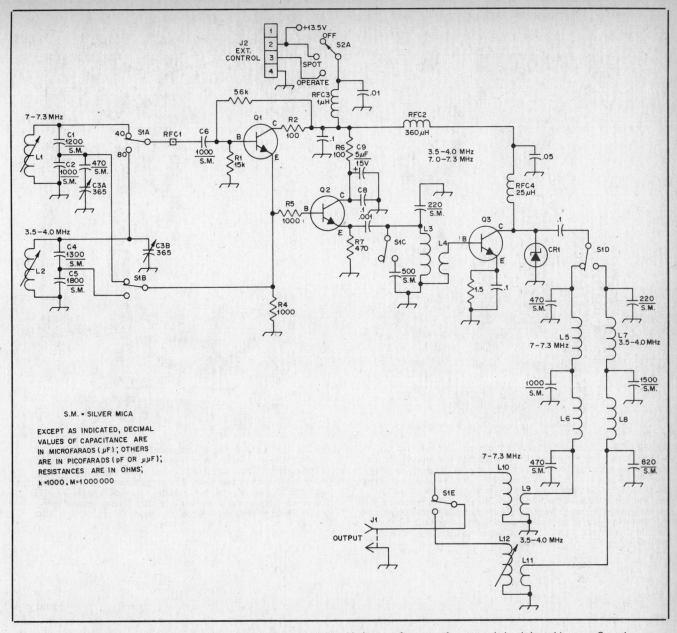

Fig. 19 — Circuit diagram of the VFO. Component designations not listed below are for text reference and circuit-board layout. Capacitors are disk ceramic except those marked S.M. (silver mica). Resistors are 1/2-watt composition.

C3 — Dual-section air variable, 365 pF per section (Miller 2112).
CR1 — Zener, 36 V, 1 W.
J1 — Phono connector, panel mount.
J2 — 4-terminal ceramic strip (Millen E-304).
L1 — 0.68-1.25 $\mu$H, slug tuned (Miller 42A106-CBI).
L2 — 2.2-4.1 $\mu$H, slug tuned (Miller 42A336CBI).
L3 — 2 $\mu$H, 25 turns of no. 24 enam. wire on Amidon T-50-2 toroid core.
L4 — 12 turns no. 22 hook-up wire over L3.

L5, L6 — 13 turns of no. 20 enam. wire on Amidon T-68-2 core.
L7, L8 — 18 turns of no. 20 enam. wire on Amidon T-68-2 core.
L9 — 7 turns of no. 26 enam. wire over L10.
L10 — Approx. 3 $\mu$H, Miller 4405 with the slug and 4 turns removed.
L11 — 7 turns no. 26 enam. wire over L12.
L12 — 23 $\mu$H (Miller 4407).
Q1 — HEP-55.
Q2 — 2N2222.
Q3 — 2N2102.

RFC1 — Three Amidon ferrite beads on a 1/2-inch length of no. 22 wire. A 15-ohm resistor may serve as a substitute.
RFC2 — Miniature choke (Millen J300-360).
RFC3 — Miniature choke (Millen 34300).
RFC4 — 2.5-$\mu$H rf choke (Millen J300-25).
S1 — Home-assembled ceramic rotary switch made from a Centralab PA-272 kit and 3 Centralab RRD sections, 2 poles, 5 positions per section (nonshorting), 2 positions used.
S2 — Rotary switch, 2 pole, 3 position, one section, nonshorting contacts (Mallory 3223J).

meter crystals that the average tube type transmitter uses. It illustrates many of the features we discussed in chapter 3. It also shows what needs to be done in order to get enough output from transistors for driving the tube that formerly was the crystal oscillator in the transmitter.

The circuit is given in Fig. 19. Q1 is the oscillator. Q2 is the buffer amplifier, and Q3 is a power amplifier. The oscillator circuit is a high-*C* Colpitts. Two tuned circuits are provided, one covering 3.5-4 MHz and the other 7-7.3 MHz. The one desired is selected by S1A and S1B. Note that this switching

is done *outside* the tuned circuits; this is good practice, because switch contacts in a tank circuit often cause irregular little frequency changes in an oscillator. The transistor bias is obtained from R1R2, plus R4 in the lead from emitter to ground. R4 also raises the emitter above ground for rf to provide feed-

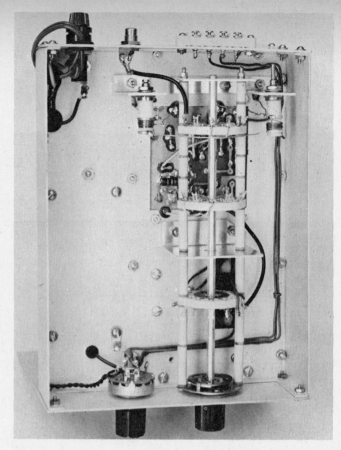

Fig. 20 — Top view of the VFO with the cover removed from the rf compartment. The section to the right is the power supply. At the left, the output amplifier circuit board is toward the rear, mounted over a cut-down section of the chassis. The circuit board containing the oscillator and buffer is mounted vertically near the left wall, with the foil side facing the tuning capacitor. The board is supported by brackets, bent from aluminum, mounted on the chassis and extending toward the tuning capacitor. L2 is toward the front panel in this view. L1 and L2 are adjusted through holes drilled in the left wall of the rf compartment.

Fig. 21 — Underneath the VFO chassis. The A section of S1 is nearest the front, where the control knob is. Other sections follow alphabetically to the rear. The foil side of the amplifier circuit board can be seen in this view. The output transformers, L9L10 and L11L12, are mounted horizontally on brackets alongside S1E. The power-supply fuse, rf output jack, and external-control connector are on the rear wall of the chassis.

back, since the collector is grounded through C7. RFC1 and R3 are for suppressing parasitic oscillations at vhf.

The oscillator is coupled to the buffer, Q2, through R5, which serves both to give the base of Q2 some dc bias (from the voltage developed across R4) and to make the rf coupling fairly loose. Q2 is operated as an emitter-follower amplifier, R7 being the emitter load resistor. R7 is shunted by a tuned circuit consisting of L3 in parallel with either of two capacitors, selected by S1C, depending on the band in use. L4 steps down the rf-output voltage of the buffer to a value suitable for driving the base of Q3, which is a grounded-emitter amplifier.

### The Amplifier

The collector of Q3 is shunt fed through RFC4. The Zener diode, CR1, between the collector and ground is a protective measure, preventing voltage

peaks in the collector circuit from rising above 36 volts and thus keeping them within the safe rating of the transistor. Separate collector-output circuits are provided for 3.5 and 7 MHz. Each is a half-wave filter working into a step-up tuned transformer (L9L10 and L11L12), a combination which reduces harmonic output and raises the output voltage to a value suitable for driving the former crystal-oscillator tube in the transmitter. L10 and L12 are tuned to the band center by the coaxial cable which connects J1 to the transmitter crystal socket. This cable should be a 36-inch length of RG-58/U for tuning the circuits properly.

The function switch, S2, has OFF, SPOT (for giving you a signal that won't overload your receiver when you're setting the VFO frequency) and OPER-ATE positions. In the OPERATE position it is intended that an external spst switch be connected between terminals

2 and 3 to turn on the VFO along with the transmitter. An extra set of switch contacts that can be used for this often can be found on the transmitter function switch.

### Regulated Power Supply

The power supply, the circuit of

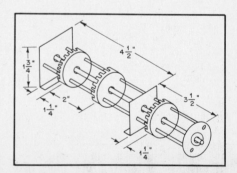

Fig. 22 — Details of the band-switch assembly.

which is given in Fig. 23, uses a 24-volt filament type transformer which has a center-tapped secondary winding. This permits use of a full-wave center-tap rectifier to obtain an output voltage high enough to be applied to the series regulator circuit which consists of Q1, Q2 and CR3. CR3 is used to establish a reference voltage (approximately 15 volts) against which the output voltage can be held.

Q1, the regulator transistor, acts as a variable resistance the value of which is controlled by the current flowing into its base through the collector-to-emitter circuit of the control transistor, Q2. Any change in the voltage output of the rectifier system (as might result from a change in line voltage) tends to change the voltage at the output terminals of the supply correspondingly. However, this in turn causes a change in the emitter-to-base voltage of Q2, since the base-to-ground voltage is held constant by CR3. The change is in such a direction as to vary the resistance of Q1 so that the output voltage returns to its former value. This is between one and two volts less than the Zener voltage of CR3.

A regulated voltage supply, as we have observed earlier, is indispensable with a VFO if the stability is to be maintained in the face of power-supply voltage changes. The regulator circuit assures the necessary constancy of voltage. It also supplements the normal filtering so the output ripple is very low — another desirable feature in a VFO supply.

If you have trouble finding a 24-volt transformer with a center tap, a 12-volt transformer can be substituted if the rectifier is changed to the bridge circuit. This will require two extra rectifiers similar to CR1 and CR2, but in all other respects the circuit will be unchanged. You'll find information on the bridge rectifier in chapter 12.

### Construction

The photographs show the general layout. Three separate etched-circuit boards are used, one for the oscillator/buffer, a second for the rf amplifier, and the third for the power supply. Templates are given in Figs. 24, 25 and 26. (Note that the latter two are half-scale).

The aluminum chassis measures 7 × 9 × 2 inches. The tuning capacitor is mounted along the center line, and an insulated coupling is used between its shaft and the dial drive. The trapezoidal-shaped brackets which support the oscillator/buffer circuit board have lips bent at the bottom for fastening to the chassis, and on the circuit-board side for holding the board. The board should be installed close to the tuning capacitor so short, stiff leads can be used between

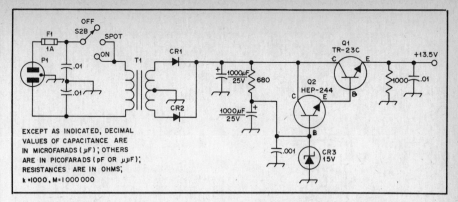

Fig. 23 — Regulated power supply for the two-band VFO. Capacitors with polarity marked are electrolytic, others are disk ceramic. Resistors are 1/2-watt composition.
CR1, CR2 — 1-amp. silicon, 100-PRV.
CR3 — Zener, 15 V, 1 W.
F1 — Fuse, 1 amp.
P1 — Line plug.
Q1 — 40-watt npn power transistor (International Rectifier TR-23C).
Q2 — Motorola HEP-24.
S2 — See Fig. 19.
T1 — Filament transformer, 24 V c.t. at 1 A.

the board and the stator sections of the capacitor.

The rf sections are enclosed by a shield box extending the entire 9-inch depth of the chassis. The box is home fabricated, and the principal point about the dimensions is that enough room should be left on the chassis for the power supply. Good shielding around the rf circuits is essential to protect the VFO from strong transmitter fields which could cause the oscillator to be unstable. A rectangular plate covers the box and completes the shielding.

The amplifier circuit board is mounted over a cutout in the chassis measuring 2-1/2 × 3-1/2 inches. Lock washers should be placed between the ground foil on this board and the chassis to insure good electrical contact.

The band switch, S1, is assembled from a kit, and is mounted on two rectangular brackets in addition to being supported by the front lip of the chassis. The bracket dimensions are not critical, so long as they are large enough for holding the switch. Spacing between brackets and switch sections is shown in Fig. 22, and an overall view is given in Fig. 21.

RFC2, RFC3 and C11 are external to the circuit boards, as are the switches, variable capacitor and terminals.

The power-supply board is supported above the chassis by spacers, as can be seen in Fig. 20. The 24-volt transformer is just behind the board on the chassis. In mounting Q1 (Fig. 26) on the board, make sure that the mounting screws do not touch any grounded copper foil, because the case of the transistor is internally connected to the collector.

### Calibration

The 80- and 40-meter ranges can be centered on the dial by adjustment of the slugs in L2 and L1, respectively. The dial used has spaces on the scale for calibration. The calibration for each band can be made by listening to the VFO signal in the receiver and observing the dial settings at which it comes into zero beat with signals of known frequency, preferably from a marker generator such as that described in chapter 13.

In keeping with the usual design of Novice transmitters, bands higher than 7 MHz are reached by frequency multiplication in the transmitter, starting out with the VFO frequency on 7 MHz. The calibration for these bands is the 7-MHz calibration multiplied by the particular harmonic used for the output frequency — by two for 14 MHz, by three for 21 MHz, and so on.

### Coordinating with the Transmitter

In general, the output of the VFO will be applied between the grid and cathode of the former crystal oscillator tube in the transmitter. This may not be all there is to it, however. In many cases the introduction of a tuned circuit at this point will cause the tube to "take off" — go into oscillation at a frequency close to the operating frequency. The oscillation invariably is too unstable to be useful (if it were stable, there wouldn't be any necessity for going to the trouble of building a relatively elaborate VFO — a simple tuned circuit would suffice). So measures must be taken to prevent self-oscillation in the transmitter ex-crystal-oscillator circuit. Incidentally, oscillation will invariably occur if the VFO output is simply plugged into the crystal socket; this is simply a case of substituting one tuned circuit (LC in the VFO) for another (the crystal). Don't try to get away with it.

What you need to do is to eliminate any feedback from the plate to the grid

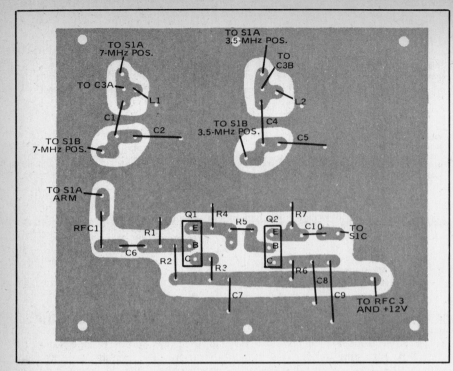

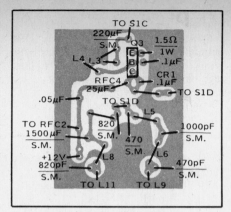

Fig. 24 — Full-scale template for the VFO/buffer circuit board. Clear areas represent copper remaining after etching. Dots mark positions of holes to be drilled for component leads.

Fig. 25 — Half-scale template for the rf amplifier circuit board. Shaded areas represent copper remaining after etching. Dots mark positions of holes for component leads.

circuit that could cause self-oscillation. (Such feedback has to be present for the crystal oscillator.) In the triode Pierce circuit (see chapter 3) the side of the crystal socket connected to the plate can be moved to ground. In this case the remaining feedback is that through the grid-plate capacitance of the triode, but if the plate circuit is untuned, as many of them are, the feedback will be too low to do any damage. With the pentode or tetrode Pierce, where the screen grid is used as the anode, you shouldn't have much trouble if you simply ground the screen for rf through a 0.01-μF bypass. Even though the plate circuit may be tuned, the plate-to-control-grid capacitance should be low enough to keep the circuit stable. But check it to make sure. Turn off the VFO power and vary the plate tuning of the tube. If any setting of the tuning control makes grid current show on the final amplifier, you've got self-oscillation. The tube will require neutralizing in such a case.

With the pentode or tetrode grid-plate oscillator the feedback will practically disappear if the rf choke in the cathode lead is removed. Substitute a resistance of a couple of hundred ohms for the choke (to provide protective bias) and change the capacitance from cathode to ground to 0.01 μF. Again, though, this may not be enough if the tube is one having relatively large plate-to-grid capacitance and its plate circuit is tuned.

As a last resort, the oscillator grid-leak resistance can be reduced in order to load the grid circuit more heavily. This will sometimes stabilize the circuit if the feedback is not too great to begin with. The VFO just described will develop as much as 20 volts across as little as 5000 ohms shunted across its output, and this should be ample for driving the transmitter equally as well as the crystal did.

### Keying

Don't attempt to key the VFO. The transmitter built-in keying method can continue to be used. In fact, it now becomes possible to shape the keying waveform to prevent clicks in a way that wouldn't have been possible in the average Novice transmitter in which the crystal oscillator was keyed along with the other stages — not possible, that is, without running into chirps. With a well isolated VFO, you'll no longer have to compromise between key clicks and chirps.

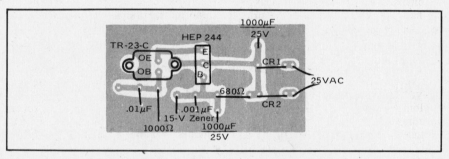

Fig. 26 — Half-scale template for the power-supply circuit board. Shaded areas represent copper remaining after etching. Dots mark positions of holes for component leads.

# Chapter 11

# Transmitting Accessories

Getting a signal out into the air may take something more than a transmitter and an antenna. Obviously, a telegraph key will be needed for code work, and a microphone for phone. But there are other items that will add immensely to the ease with which you can operate, and which sometimes will be essential to success.

## Coupling the Transmitter to the Antenna

With very few exceptions, transmitters have final-amplifier tank circuits designed around loads of 50 to 75 ohms. The load is not restricted to *exactly* these figures, in most cases. A few manufactured sets come with no tuning or loading adjustments built in, and the load has to be just right for these sets to work properly. But whether or not this is the case, it is good practice to make the load — your antenna or transmission line — look like about 50 or 75 ohms as the transmitter sees it.

Some antenna systems do it for you automatically. With these (some of them are described in chapter 6), you simply connect the transmission line to the transmitter output terminals and you're in business. However, there are other systems that can't be handled so simply. One, for example, is the "random-length" antenna that many amateurs are forced to use, for lack of facilities for putting up anything better.

The random-length antenna is simply a wire of whatever length can be used. One end comes in to your operating position and the other is fastened to some support at as great a distance and as great a height as can be managed.

If the station end of such a wire is connected to the "hot" output terminal of the transmitter the chances are good that no adjustment of the loading and tuning controls can be found that will load the final-amplifier to normal input. This is because the fed end of the antenna looks like something quite dif-ferent from 50 to 75 ohms. The problem here is to change whatever load the antenna represents into a load that the transmitter can handle. This job can be done by matching circuit — a *transmatch* (chapter 6).

A transmatch suitable for random-length antennas is shown in Fig. 1. The circuit, Fig. 2, uses only a tapped coil and a variable capacitor. Note that one side of the circuit is connected to an earth ground. This can be a connection to the cold-water system of your house or to a driven ground stake (see chapter 6). The earth is necessarily a part of an end-fed antenna system, so it pays to use as good a ground as you can get. If the connection is omitted, the rf nevertheless will look for a way to get to earth, and the only path is through the transmitter and ac line. The rf characteristics of such a path are usually unknown, and not what could be considered desirable in any case. So use a separate ground connection and keep it as short as you can.

The transmatch is connected to the transmitter through a length of coaxial cable. RG-58/U or RG-59/U will be satisfactory for moderate power. There are two general methods of adjusting the transmatch, one without and one with the aid of a standing-wave-ratio indicator in this coaxial link between the transmitter and transmatch. If you don't have an SWR indicator such as the "Monimatch," first set the transmitter loading control at minimum (maximum capacitance in a pi-network tank) and adjust the tank tuning capacitor to the dip in plate current that indicates resonance. Set the tap on L1 in the transmatch at one end of the coil, and then turn C1 through its complete range. If some setting of C1 causes the plate current to change, leave it there and

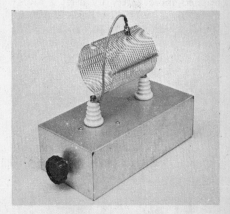

Fig. 1 — A simple transmatch for use with random-length antennas, using the circuit of Fig. 2. The coaxial fitting for the connection to the transmitter can be mounted to any convenient spot on the chassis wall. The chassis in the photograph is 3 by 5 by 10 inches. The knob on the front of the chassis is the control for C1. The clip lead, which is 9 inches long, is connected to the input end of the coil. The clip is an E. F. Johnson type LC8. Feedthrough insulators are used to hold the coil in place. A clip on the antenna lead can be used for connecting the antenna to the output end of the coil.

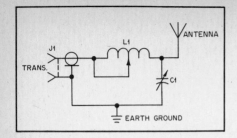

Fig. 2 — Circuit diagram of the transmatch for random-length antennas.
C1 — 140-pF variable (Hammarlund MC-140-S; E. F. Johnson 140R12, or equiv.).
J1 — Coaxial chassis receptacle, SO-239.
L1 — 24 turns no. 12, 6 turns per inch, 3-inch diameter (B&W 3033).

readjust the transmitter tank tuning capacitor for the plate current dip. Then try increasing the loading by means of the transmitter output control, always readjusting the tank tuning for the dip after each change in the loading control. If you can't reach the desired plate current at resonance, move the tap on L1 a turn or two and go through the process again. Eventually you will reach a pair of settings for L1 and C1 that enable you to make the transmitter load up.

This is a cut-and-try process that will result in adequate loading, but it is not necessarily the best adjustment of the transmatch. Also, it will hold good only for the particular length of coaxial cable used between the transmitter and transmatch. If the length of this line has to be changed for some reason, the whole process will have to be gone through again. The optimum adjustment can be reached more surely by using a Monimatch in the coaxial link. The next section describes how to build one. The method of using it is basically the same

Fig. 3 — Universal transmatch. It can be used with any antenna and transmission-line system. The jack bar (Millen 41305) for the plug-in coils is mounted on small ceramic standoff insulators to allow the contacts to clear the chassis. Four coils cover the range 3.5 to 30 MHz; a single coil suffices for both 21 and 28 MHz. All are mounted on Millen 40305 plug bars.

for all transmitters and transmatches, so it will suffice here to say that the transmatch of Fig. 2 is adjusted simply by trying different taps on L1, along with different settings of C1, until the Monimatch shows the null which indicates that the antenna load is matched to the coaxial link.

The transmatch doesn't have to be installed close to the transmitter, although it is convenient to have it within reach if you change bands frequently. For rf reasons, it is better to have it close to the spot where the end of the antenna comes into the station, since this avoids running any appreciable part of the antenna around the room and may also make a shorter ground lead possible. The coaxial link can be any convenient length.

### Universal Transmatch

The transmatch circuit shown in Fig. 4 can be used for matching between the transmitter and any type of line used for feeding the antenna. It can also be used for random length and coax-fed antennas as shown in Fig. 5.

The parallel circuit formed by L2 and C2 is resonant at the operating frequency and the taps on L2 are used for adjusting the impedance ratio between the line and the coaxial input terminal, J1. With correct adjustment the impedance at J1 matches the coaxial line used as a link between the transmatch and the transmitter. Thus the proper load is offered to the transmitter. C2 should be insulated from the chassis and should have an insulated coupling between its shaft and the dial. C1 gives a smooth adjustment of the effective coupling between L1 and L2 as a further aid in the matching adjustment.

Fig. 3 shows a suitable layout for the transmatch. The capacitors used have a plate spacing adequate for transmitter powers up to 150 watts or so. The chassis is of aluminum, 2 × 7 × 9 inches, with a 6 × 7-inch front panel. Dials with at least a 10-division scale should be used so settings for different bands can be recorded and returned to without readjustment. The input connector, J1, is mounted on the rear wall of the chassis, and is connected to L1 by a lead running through a grommet underneath the coil socket.

The L1 coil is mounted inside L2, in each case. It is centered in L2 and held in place with plastic cement. The leads from L1 go between the turns of L2 to the plugs on the mounting bar. Use spaghetti tubing over these leads to prevent accidental short circuits. The L2 coils need no special mounting other than their leads (which go into the end prongs on the bar) if the leads are bent so the coil almost rests on the bar. Soldering the coil leads in the prongs

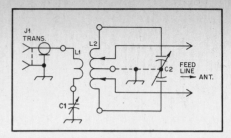

Fig. 4 — Circuit of the universal transmatch.
C1 — 325-pF variable (Hammarlund MC-325-M).
C2 — 140-pF per section dual variable (Hammarlund MCD-140-M).
J1 — Coaxial receptacle, chassis-mounting type SO-239.
L1 — 10 turns per inch, 2-inch diameter, no. 16 wire (B&W 3907-1).
  3.5 MHz: 10 turns
  7 MHz: 6 turns
  14 MHz: 3 turns
  21/28 MHz: 2 turns
L2 — 3.5 MHz: 44 turns no. 16, 2-1/2-inch diameter, 10 turns per inch. (B&W 3031). Coils for 7 through 28 MHz are 2-1/2-inch diameter, no. 12 wire, 6 turns per inch (B&W 3905-1).
  7 MHz: 18 turns
  14 MHz: 10 turns
  21/28 MHz: 6 turns

will be a little easier if the nickel plating is filed off the ends of the prongs first. After soldering the leads in place, be sure to clean off all traces of rosin flux, since a coating of rosin will interfere with good contact between the prong and its jack.

Type 235-860 (E. F. Johnson) clips can be used for making the taps on L2. Once the proper tap positions have been determined for a coil, solder a lug at each point so it projects outwards. The clip can be put on the lug sidewise and will fit snugly if its adjusting screw is tightened. This method makes coil changing easy as compared with using the clips directly on the coil turns. Ordinary alligator clips can be used instead. Get the copper-plated kind if you can, because they will cause less rf loss should they get into the field of the coil.

No terminals are shown in Fig. 3 for connecting the transmission line to L2 as these will depend on the type of line used. Binding posts or a screw type terminal strip can be used for parallel-conductor line, and also for the random-length antenna. A coaxial line should have a separate chassis connector, which can be mounted on the rear wall.

The best way to adjust the transmatch is shown in the setup of Fig. 9, using a Monimatch as an indicator. The procedure is the same as already described. Keep the amplifier tank tuning at resonance throughout the tune-up process, and adjust the loading for a high reading on the Monimatch meter with the switch in the "forward" posi-

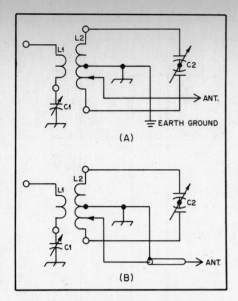

Fig. 5 — Circuits for use with a random-length antenna or single-wire feed (A) and for a coax-fed antenna (B). A coaxial fitting can be installed on the chassis for the latter type of line.

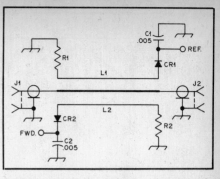

Fig. 6 — The Monimatch circuit. See Fig. 8A for dimensions of L1, L2 and the center-conductor extension of the coaxial transmission line (heavy line in the above drawing). The following values also apply to the layout of Fig. 5A.
C1, C2 — 0.005 µF disk ceramic, 50 volts.
CR1, CR2 — Germanium diode, perferably high back resistance (1N34A satisfactory).
J1, J2 — Coaxial socket (SO-239).
R1, R2 — 56 ohms, 1/2 watt.

tion. With open-wire line, set the taps on L2 at equal distances from the center of the coil, using a few turns each side at the beginning. Switch the Monimatch to the "reflected" side, and try to bring the reading down to zero by varying both C1 and C2. Switch over to "forward" occasionally to make sure that power is going to the transmatch. If the reading won't go to zero, move the taps closer together and go through the process once more. Continue until there is a good zero or null reading with a high forward reading.

Usually, it will be possible to get a good null over a range of tap positions on L2. If so, always put the taps as far apart as you can. This will broaden the tuning of the transmatch. The frequency range, within a band, that can be covered without readjustment will depend a good deal on the type of antenna and transmission line you use. It is a good idea, when first putting the transmatch into operation, to see how much range you can cover before readjustment becomes necessary. The "reflected" reading can be allowed to go up to 20 percent or so of the "forward" reading without retuning. Almost any band can be covered with two or three settings of the capacitors. Log these band-segment settings and you won't have to rematch when changing frequency.

Fig. 4 shows optional connections from chassis to the center of L2 or to the rotor of C2. There will be no difference in the matching either way, or even if neither is used. This optional ground is provided so that harmonic radiation can be reduced. Depending on the feed-line length, better harmonic

suppression may result when C2 is grounded, and vice versa. The best way to determine this is to have a fellow amateur tune his receiver to the frequency of your second harmonic. A quick test or two will show which connection results in the least harmonic output.

For random-length antennas (Fig. 5A) or coaxial line (Fig. 5B), the center of L2 should be grounded to the chassis. Only one tap is used with either of these systems, since they are not balanced to ground. The adjustment procedure is exactly the same as for the parallel-conductor line except that only one tap need be moved.

If you don't have a Monimatch, follow the same general adjustment procedure, but with the object of loading the transmitter to normal input. The use of the Monimatch is strongly recommended, though, because its use leads to the optimum adjustment quickly and easily.

### The Monimatch

The Monimatch is a form of *reflectometer*, an instrument capable of distinguishing between the forward and reflected voltages on a transmission line and indicating them separately. The basic circuit is shown in Fig. 6. It consists of a short section of transmission line with an added conductor — L1, for example — between and parallel to the two line conductors. The circuit is usually built for use with coaxial line, and L1 is ordinarily fairly close to the center conductor of the line, shown heavy in the drawing. (Actually, L1 is coupled to both the inner and outer conductors, but the latter has been omitted in Fig. 6 in order to avoid complicating the drawing.) The coupling between L1 and the line is both inductive and capacitive, and it is on this "hybrid" coupling that the operation of the device depends.

L1 is terminated at one end in a resistor, R1, and at the other in a rectifier circuit, CR1C1, so that the relative rf voltage induced in L1 can be read by a dc meter. The physical dimensions of the Monimatch and the resistance of R1 determine the characteristic impedance of the device, which must match the characteristic impedance of the line with which it is to be used.

If a matched line — that is, one operating with a 1 to 1 standing-wave ratio — is connected to J2 and power from a transmitter is fed into J1, rf voltages induced in L1 (inductive and capacitive) balance out at the diode, so the dc voltage at the REF terminal is zero. However, if the line is *not* matched, there will be reflected as well as forward voltage on it and the reflected voltage will cause the meter to register a reading. The reading will be

proportional to the reflected voltage if the meter circuit is linear.

If the rf connections to the Monimatch are reversed so that the load is connected to J1 and the transmitter to J2, the dc voltage at the REF terminal will be proportional to the *forward* rf voltage on the line. Thus reversing the connections allows us to read the forward and reflected voltages separately. To avoid the nuisance of changing connections, the circuit of Fig. 6 incorporates a second "pick-up" conductor, L2, which has its termination, R1, and rectifier circuit opposite to the arrangement used with L1. Then if the transmitter is connected permanently to J1 and the load to J2, a meter connected to the REF terminal will read reflected voltage and one connected to the FWD terminal will read forward voltage. A single dc meter is generally used for the

Fig. 7 — Inside view of the Monimatch. R1 and R2 are mounted vertically from the board; their upper ends connect to soldering lugs secured by the lower socket-mounting screw on the same side. Keep leads short. See text for discussion of the metal plate at the center. The inside edges of the cover have strips of masking tape to prevent dc shorts.

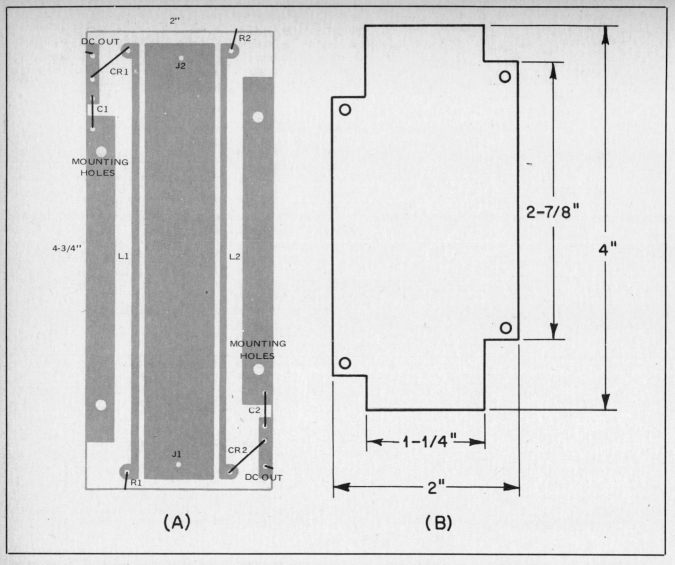

Fig. 8 — (A) Full-size template for the etched Monimatch. Shaded areas represent copper remaining after etching. (B) Full-size template for the metal plate completing the outer conductor of the line sigment. This view looks at the side which faces the etched board after assembly.

sake of economy, with a switch to change from FWD to REF.

### Construction

Monimatch dimensions and resistor values are rather critical, so the practical version shown in Fig. 6 uses an etched circuit which it should be possible to duplicate quite accurately. It is designed for use with 50-ohm line. The etched-board pattern is given in Fig. 8A.

The simplest kind of "resist" to use in making the board is ordinary masking tape having a width of 3/4 inch. Stick a 3/4-inch wide strip in the center as shown. Then add a strip on each side, with exactly 1/16-inch separation between strips. Next, use a metal straight-edge and a razor blade to cut these added strips to exactly 1/16-inch width and remove the excess tape. Use pieces of tape for the side strips in which the mounting holes are placed and also for the small strips to which the capacitors

rectifiers and dc output leads will be connected. The small tabs at the end of L1 and L2 can be dabs of paint.

Before etching, make sure that the tape is stuck securely, especially at the edges. Don't carry the etching process any farther than is necessary to remove all the copper between strips of tape. The drilling layout can be transferred from Fig. 8A by the method described in chapter 7.

All components are mounted on the noncopper side of the board and should be soldered in place before final assembly. For the connections to J1 and J2, solder short pieces of wire (about no. 18) at the points indicated so they extend through the board for connection to the coaxial sockets after assembly. The dc output wires go in the opposite direction, through holes drilled in the box directly under the terminal connections on the circuit board. They run to tie-point strips mounted on the

outside. Shielded wire should be used for the leads from the tie-points to the meter and switching circuit shown in Fig. 9.

The copper side of the board is mounted facing one wall of the 2-1/4 × 2-1/4 × 5-inch Minibox (Bud CU-2104-A). Quarter-inch metal spacers separate the board from the box and also serve to make connection between the side strips (ground) and the box.

The sockets should be mounted with their centers 7/8 inch above the side of the box on which the board is mounted, to provide clearance. These should be mounted *last*; it isn't possible to install the board after the sockets are in place.

The metal plate shown extending across the board in Fig. 7 completes the outer conductor of the Monimatch line segment. Its spacing from the copper underneath offers a small amount of adjustment for the best null on a matched line. The plate rests on the

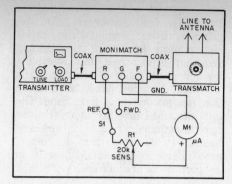

Fig. 9 — Using the Monimatch in adjusting a transmatch. Adjustment procedure depends on the type of transmatch used, but is always aimed at getting the meter to read zero when S1 is in the "reflected" position, while giving the highest possible reading in the "forward" position. See text regarding R1.

nuts (two on each of the four screws) which hold the board in place; these space it 3/16 inch from the top side of the board. If a good 50-ohm dummy antenna is available, the spacing can be varied, using shims, until the best null is secured throughout the 3.5 to 30-MHz frequency range. However, adjustment is not a necessity, since the operation will be entirely satisfactory for practical work if the specifications given are followed exactly.

## Using the Monimatch for Transmatch Adjustment

The indicator part of the Monimatch is not built into the instrument itself, as it is often convenient to make it up separately so it can be placed on the operating table where it can be seen easily. It consists of the meter, sensitivity control resistor and spdt switch shown in Fig. 9. Use 50-ohm line in making the coaxial connections shown in Fig. 9.

To adjust the transmatch, turn on the transmitter and set its tank tuning to resonance. (Throughout the procedure that follows, always keep the tank tuned to resonance.) Set S1 in the "forward" position and adjust the sensitivity control, R1, for a reading near maximum on M1, or as much of a reading as you can obtain by adjustment

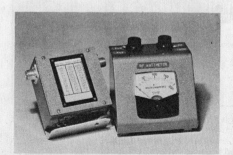

Fig. 10 — Rf power meter.

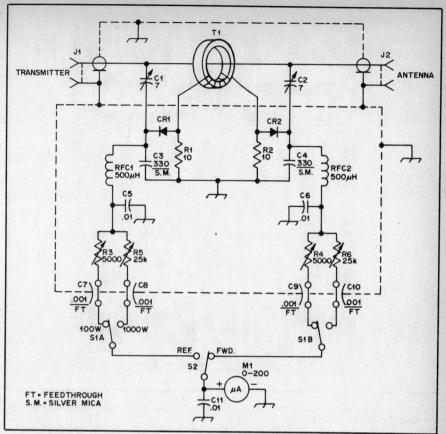

Fig. 11 — Schematic diagram of a practical power wattmeter. A calibration scale for M1 is shown also. Fixed-value resistors are 1/2-watt composition. Fixed-value capacitors are disk ceramic unless otherwise noted. Decimal-value capacitances are in $\mu$F. Others are pF. Resistance is in ohms; k = 1000.

C1, C2 — 1.3 to 6.7-pF miniature trimmer (E. F. Johnson 189-502-4.)
C3-C11 incl. — Numbered for circuit-board identification.
CR1, CR2 — Small-signal germanium diode. IN34A, etc. (See Text.)
J1, J2 — Chassis-mount coaxial connector of builder's choice. Type SO-239 used here.
M1 — 0 to 200-$\mu$A meter (Triplett type 330-M used here).
R1, R2 — Matched 10-ohm resistors (see text).
R3, R4 — 5000-ohm printed-circuit carbon control (IRC R502-B).

R5, R6 — 25,000-ohm printed-circuit carbon control (IRC R252-B).
RFC1, RFC2 — 500-$\mu$H rf choke (Millen 34300-500 or similar).
S1 — Dpdt single-section phenolic wafer switch (Mallory 3222J).
S2 — Spdt phenolic wafer switch (Centralab 1460).
T1 — Toroidal transformer; 35 turns of no. 26 enam. wire to cover entire core of Amidon T-68-2 toroid (Amidon Assoc., 12033 Otsego St., N. Hollywood, CA 91607).

of the transmitter controls. Then set S1 in the "reflected" position and try various adjustments of the transmatch controls with the object of making the meter pointer drop to zero. When a zero or near-zero reading is obtained, put S1 in the "forward" position and readjust the transmitter for maximum reading. Then switch back to "reflected," and check the adjustments again. After one or two trials, the meter reading should be zero or very close to it no matter how high it reads in the "forward" position. This represents the matched condition. Finally, adjust the transmitter controls for maximum output as shown by the highest reading forward. The rated plate current of the transmitter final amplifier should not be exceeded, of course, in adjusting for maximum output.

S1 can be left in the "forward" position to serve as a continuous indicator of output.

The forward-current reading for a given rf power increases with the frequency, in the Monimatch, so greater sensitivy is needed in the dc meter when working at the lower frequencies. The rectified current to be expected depends, of course, on the rf power as well as the frequency. With the instrument shown in Fig. 7, the forward current, with 50 watts of rf in the line, is slightly over one milliampere with R1 in Fig. 9 set for minimum resistance. At 28 MHz it is about 9 mA. The corresponding figures for 10 watts in the line are 100 $\mu$A and 3.5 mA, respectively. These readings were obtained with dc meters having relatively low resistance — a few hundred ohms at most. With some

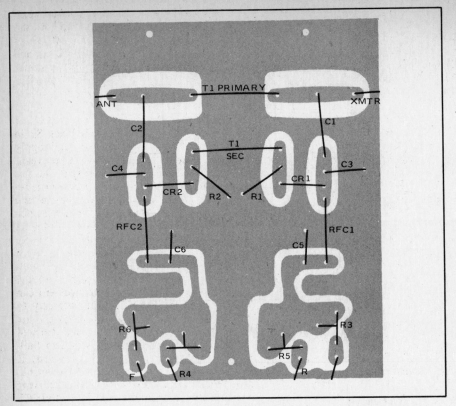

Fig. 12 — Circuit-board template and parts layout for the power meter. Grey areas represent the unetched copper surface.

here over those of Monimatch bridges is that these instruments are not frequency-sensitive. Monimatch indicators become more sensitive as the operating frequency is increased, thus making it impractical to calibrate them in watts for more than one band, or for more than one portion of a given band. The units described here are more sensitive than Monimatches are. This makes it possible to calibrate them for power levels as low as one watt, full scale, in any part of the hf spectrum.

### Construction

The power meter of Fig. 11 is built in two sections. The rf circuit and the calibrating resistors are housed in a 4 × 4 × 2-inch aluminum utility box. All components other the J1, J2, and the feed- through capacitors, are assembled on the etched-circuit board. Switches S1 and S2, and the meter, M1, are installed in a sloping- panel utility box which measures 5 × 4 inches. Four-conductor sheilded cable — the shield serving as the common lead — is used to join the two pieces. There is no reason why the entire instrument cannot be housed in one container, but it is sometimes awkward to have coaxial be housed in one container, but it is sometimes awkward to have coaxial cables attach to a unit that occupies a prominent place in the operating position. Built as shown, the two-piece instrument permits the rf pickup head to be concealed behind the transmitter, while the control head can be mounted where it is accessible to the operator.

"sensitive" instruments such as inexpensive 0-50 microammeters, the readings are considerably smaller since the instrument resistance is of the order of a few thousand ohms. Such meters are quite practical for use with the Monimatch, however, since it is desirable to have a sizable resistance in the meter circuit.

The value of R1 depends on the meter resistance and its full-scale reading. About 10,000 ohms is satisfactory for a 0-1 milliammeter, and 100,000 ohms for a 0-50 microammeter, for adjustment to full-scale over the 3.5- to 30-MHz range.

### A Simple RF Wattmeter

It is neither costly nor difficult to build an rf wattmeter. And, if the instrument is equipped with a few additional components it can be switched to read reflected power as well as forward power. With the foregoing feature the instrument can be used as an SWR meter for antenna matching and trans-match adjustments.

Perhaps the most difficult task faced by the constructor is that of calibrating the power meter for whatever wattage range he desires to have. The least difficult method is to use a commercial wattmeter as a standard. If one is not available, the power output of the test transmitter can be computed by means of an rf ammeter in series with a 50-ohm dummy load, using the standard formula, $P = I^2 R$. Or, if one is not interested in obtaining power readings, the bridge can be used solely as an SWR indicator, as is done with the Monimatch-style SWR bridge.

The advantage of the circuits shown

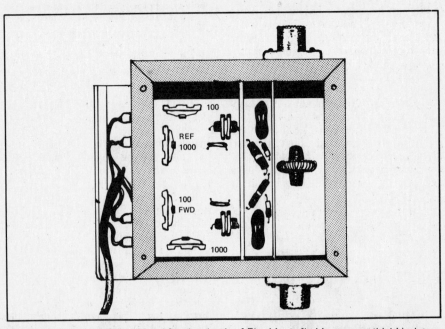

Fig. 13A — Top view of the rf head for the circuit of Fig. 11. A flashing-copper shield isolates the through-line and T1 from the rest of the circuit. The second shield (thicker) is not required and can be eliminated from the circuit. If a 2000-watt scale is desired, fixed-value resistors of approximately 22,000 ohms can be connected in series with high-range printed-circuit controls. Or, the 25,000-ohm controls shown here can be replaced by 50,000-ohm units.

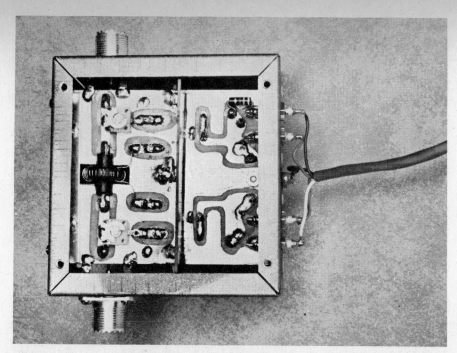

Fig. 13B — Bottom view of the rf head for the circuit of Fig. 11. The fixed-value resistor at the lower left does not belong in the circuit, but was added as a shunt for one of the calibrating controls which was too high in value — a 50,000-ohm unit that was on hand. The shield partition shown here proved unnecessary and can be eliminated.

Toroidal transformer T1 fits into a cutout area on the circuit board. A one-inch long section of RG-8/U cable — vinyl jacket and shield braid removed — provides a snug fit in the center hole of the toroid, and is used to complete the line between J1 and J2. The inner conductor of the RG-8/U section solders to the circuit board, thus holding T1 in place.

A flashing-copper shield divides T1 and its center-conductor line from the remainder of the circuit. This partition is shown in dotted lines in Fig. 13A. It is mounted on the nonfoil side of the circuit board and is secured at each end to solder lugs which are mounted under the retaining screws for J1 and J2.

The circuit board is held in place, at the end near T1, by means of an aluminum L bracket. The circuit-board end nearest the feedthrough capacitors is held in place by a no. 6 spade bolt. A solder lug is mounted under the no. 6 nut (outside the case) which secures the spade bolt. The lug serves as a connection point for the common lead between the rf head and the control box. Two solder lugs are mounted under the bottom two retaining screws of each coaxial connector. The free ends of the lugs are soldered to the copper foil of the circuit board.

A partition is visible in the foil-side view of the rf head. It can be eliminated if desired, since it did not prove necessary when the unit was tested. Similarly,

an extra shield partition is shown on the top side of the board. It too can be eliminated, for it turned out to be unnecessary. The flashing-copper shield discussed earlier is the only one required for the circuit of Fig. 11.

### Check-Out and Tuneup

Once the instrument is wired and ready to test, it should be inspected for unwanted solder bridges between the circuit-board foils. It is usually a good idea to scrape out the rosin buildup between the foils, and this can be done with the blade of a small screwdriver. A continuity check for "opens" and "shorts" should also be made before power is applied to the unit. Make certain that the diodes are installed for the correct polarity — the banded ends (cathodes) toward C1 and C2.

Connect a noninductive 50-ohm dummy load to J2. A Heath Cantenna or similar load will serve nicely for adjustment purposes. Place S2 in the FORWARD position, and set S1 for the 100-watt range. An rf ammeter or calibrated power meter should be connected between J2 and the dummy load during the tests, providing power-calibration points against which to plot the scale of M1. Apply transmitter output power to J1, gradually, until M1 begins to deflect upward. Increase transmitter power and adjust R4 so that a full-scale meter reading occurs when 100 watts is indicated on the rf am-

meter or other standard in use. Next, switch S2 to REFLECTED and turn the transmitter off. Temporarily short across R3, turn the transmitter on, and gradually increase power until a meter reading is noted. With an insulated screwdriver adjust C2 for a null in the meter reading.

The next step is to reverse the coax connections to J1 and J2. Place S2 in the REFLECTED position and apply transmitter power until the meter reads full scale at 100 watts output. In this mode the REFLECTED position actually reads forward power because the bridge is reversed. Calibrating resistance R3 is set to obtain 100 watts full scale during this adjustment. Now, switch S2 to FORWARD and temporarily place a short across R4. Adjust C1 for a null reading on M1. Repeat the foregoing steps until no further improvement can be obtained. It will not be necessary to repeat the nulling adjustments on the 1000-watt range, but R5 and R6 will have to be adjusted to provide a full-scale meter reading at 1000 watts. If insufficient meter deflection is available for nulling adjustments on the 100-watt range, it may be necessary to adjust C1 and C2 at some power level higher than 100 watts. If the capacitors tune through a null, but the meter will not drop all the way to zero, chances are that some rf is leaking into the bridge circuit through stray coupling. If so, it may be necessary to experiment with the shielding of the through-line section of the rf head. If only a small residual

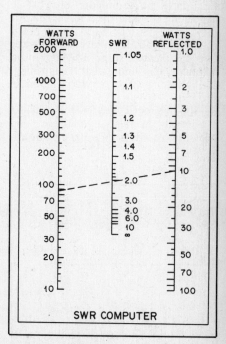

Fig. 14 — Nomograph for computing SWR knowing forward and reflected power levels.

reading is noted, it will be of minor importance and can be ignored. In the circuit of Fig. 10 there remained approximately one half a meter division when the null was reached, and this occurred only on the 1000-watt range. Since this was representative of less than two watts of power, it was deemed inconsequential.

With the component values given in Fig. 11 the meter readings track for both power ranges. That is, the 10-watt level on the 100-watt range, and the 100-watt point on the 1000-watt range fall at the same place on the meter scale, and so on. This no doubt results from the fact that the diodes are conducting in the most linear portion of their curve. Ordinarily, this desirable condition does not exist, making it necessary to plot separate scales for the different power ranges.

Tests indicate that the SWR caused by insertion of the power meter in the transmission line is negligible. It was checked at 28 MHz and no reflected-power could be noted on a Bird watt-meter. Similarly, the insertion loss was so low that it could not be measured with ordinary instruments.

# Radio–Frequency Interference (RFI)

Whether you are a newcomer or an old-time amateur, one bug-a-boo that will probably be faced is RFI. Whenever an amateur operates his transmitter, the immediate area around his antenna and station is surrounded by a field of radio-frequency energy. Although this energy is being radiated on the desired amateur frequency, it can be the source of interference to many types of home-entertainment devices in the neighborhood. Included are TV sets, hi-fi gear, record players, tape recorders, p-a systems, a-m and fm broadcast receivers, and organs.

What is the responsibility of the amateur as far as interference is concerned? Actually, it is rather clear. The amateur is *only* responsible to the extent that the rf energy generated and radiated by his station is on the correct frequency. This does not mean he can ignore the complaints of neighbors. It should be made clear that the majority of owners of home-entertainment devices have no knowledge of what is happening to cause the interference. All they know is that when "that ham" goes on the air, they have interference. It is the amateur's responsibility to be helpful by explaining what is happening, and above all else, to be *diplomatic* about it.

The amateur's interference problem is primarily one relating to hi-fi gear and television receivers. More and more information on curing hi-fi and other interference has been discovered in the last few years, and it is hoped that this section will be of help to amateurs who have the problem. Here is a symposium of ways and means to cure such interference problems.

### Hi-Fi Gear

Hi-fi gear can consist of a simple amplifier, with record or tape inputs, and speakers. The more elaborate installations may have a tape deck, record player, fm and a-m tuners, an amplifier and two or more speakers. These units are usually connected together by means of shielded leads, and in most cases the speakers are positioned some distance from the amplifier via long leads. When such a setup is operated near an amateur station, say within a few hundred feet, there are two important paths through which rf energy can reach the hi-fi installation to cause interference.

### Speaker Leads

The most frequent path for RFI is along speaker leads. Usually, the speaker is coupled to the amplifier by way of two wires, as in Fig. 15. These wires can act like an antenna to pick up the rf energy and feed it into the amplifier.

Most high-fidelity sets use a feedback circuit in the audio amplifier and it is through this part of the circuit some of the unwanted signal may enter. Fig. 16 illustrates this path. With this type of RFI, you'll find that the audio gain control on the hi-fi unit will have no effect on the audible level of the interference. The reason is that the interference is getting into the set *after* the audio control, in the final stages of audio amplification.

A suggested method of effecting a cure is shown in Fig. 17 The first step is to bypass the speaker leads at the chassis with disk-ceramic capacitors from 0.001 to 0.02 μF. The 0.001-μF value would be used for vhf operation and the larger value for low-frequency work. Be sure to bypass *all* speaker leads even though one lead may appear to be

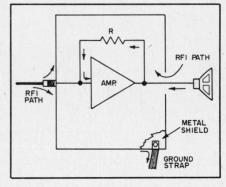

Fig. 16 – Feedback and RFI path in an audio amplifier.

grounded. In many amplifiers there is a feedback tap at the ground side of the output transformer. In stubborn RFI cases it might help to use shielded speaker leads. While Fig. 17 shows the shield grounded at both ends, it might help to leave the shield ungrounded at the speaker end. This is because the equipment at each end of the connecting cable will always have some sort of return to a common ground, and connecting the shield at both ends completes a loop which often will respond to magnetic fields. There is no hard and fast rule however, and it is wise to try various combinations.

If you should find that the inter-

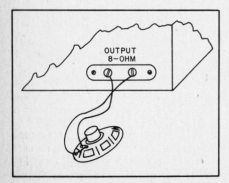

Fig. 15 – Typical speaker connection on a hi-fi set.

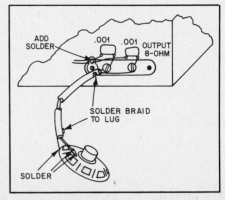

Fig. 17 – Bypassing of speaker leads to prevent RFI.

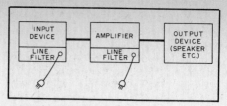

Fig. 18 — Ideal system.

ference exists only on one band, it might help to try different lengths of speaker leads because of probability that the lead is a resonant length on the band in question. Sometimes rerouting the speaker leads will eliminate the interference.

## Grounding

There is no set rule about grounding hi-fi equipment. Connecting the equipment to an earth ground such as a water pipe may not eliminate the interference. In fact, grounding the equipment could make the interference worse. The best procedure is to try grounding. See if it helps.

In one difficult solid-state hi-fi interference case, it was found that there were several etched circuit boards in the unit. One board had not been connected to a chassis ground, and when it was bypassed to ground, all interference vanished.

## AC-Line Pickup

The second major path for RFI is via the ac lines. The lines act as antennas in a strong rf field, so the rf is brought into the hi-fi unit through the lines. There are commercial RFI filters available that can be installed between the ac socket and the hi-fi equipment. A simple filter that some hams have found to be

effective for suppressing this type of interference is an rf choke wound on a ferrite rod. The choke is almost identical to the type used in grounded-grid amplifiers (to keep the filaments above rf ground). The ac line for the hi-fi amplifier is simply wound around the ferrite rod, using enough close-spaced turns to cover the length of the rod. Electrical tape can be used to hold the turns in place. The ferrite rod and windings should be at the plug end of the ac line. This homemade assembly serves as an rf choke to help keep rf from entering the set. In addition to the rf choke, it may be helpful to install 0.001- to 0.01-μF bypass capacitors in the amplifier chassis from each side of the ac line to chassis ground. Be sure the capacitors are the type recommended for use with ac voltages.

## Turntables and Tape Decks

In the more elaborate hi-fi setups, there may be several assemblies connected together by means of patch cords, Fig. 18. It is a good idea when checking for RFI to disconnect the units, one at a time, observing any changes in the interference. Not only disconnect the patch cords connecting the pieces together, but also unplug the ac line cord for each item as you make the test. This will help you determine which section is the culprit.

Patch cords are usually, *but not always,* made of shielded cable. The lines *should* be shielded, which brings up another point. Many commercially available patch cords have poor shields. Some have wire spirally wrapped around the insulation, covering the main lead, rather than braid. This method provides poor shielding and could be the reason for RFI problems.

Record-player tone-arm connections

to the cartridge are usually made with small clips. The existence of a loose clip, particularly if oxidation is present, offers an excellent invitation to RFI. Also, the leads from the cartridge and those to the amplifier are sometimes resonant at vhf, providing an excellent receiving antenna for rf. One cure for unwanted rf pickup is to install ferrite beads, one on each cartridge lead. Check all patch-cord connections for looseness or poor solder joints. Inferior connections can cause rectification and subsequent RFI.

Tape decks should be treated the same as turntables. Loose connections and bad solder joints all can cause trouble. Ferrite beads can be slipped over the leads to the recording and play-back pickup heads. Bypassing of the tone-arm or pickup-head leads is also effective, but sometimes it is difficult to install capacitors in the small area available. Disk capacitors (0.001 μF) should be used as close to the cartridge or pickup head as possible. Keep the capacitor leads as short as possible.

## Preamplifiers

There are usually one or more pre-amplifiers used in a hi-fi amplifier. The inputs to these stages can be very susceptible to RFI. Fig. 19 illustrates a typical preamplifier circuit. In this case the leads to the bases of the transistors are treated for RFI with ferrite beads by the addition of RFC2 and RFC4. This is a very effective method for stopping RFI when vhf energy is the source of the trouble.

Within the circuit of a solid-state audio system, a common offender can be the emitter-base junction of a transistor. This junction operates as a forward-biased diode, with the bias set so that a change of base current with signal will produce a linear but amplified change in collector current. Should rf energy reach the junction, the bias could increase, causing nonlinear amplification and distortion as the result. If the rf level is high, it can completely block (saturate) a transistor, causing a complete loss of any audible symptom. Therefore, it may be necessary to reduce the transmitter power output in order to pinpoint the particular transistor stage that is affected.

In addition to adding ferrite beads it may be necessary to bypass the base of the transistor to chassis ground, C1 and C2, Fig. 19. A suitable value is 100 pF, and keep the leads short! As a general rule, the capacitor value should be as large as possible without degrading the high-frequency response of the amplifier. Values up to 0.001 μF can be used. In severe cases, a series inductor (RFC1 and RFC3) may be required, Ohmite Z-50 or Z-144, or their equivalents (7 and 1.8 μH, respectively). Fig. 19 shows

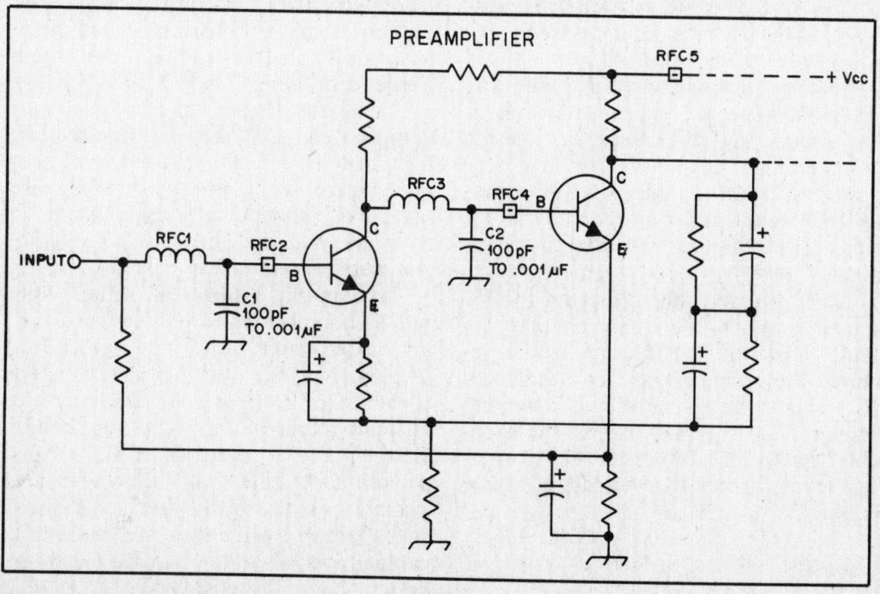

Fig. 19 — Typical circuit of a solid-state preamplifier.

the correct placement for an inductor, bypass capacitor, and ferrite bead. Also, it might help to use a ferrite bead in the plus-B lead to the preamplifier stages (RFC5 in Fig. 19). Keep in mind that Fig. 19 represents only one preamplifier of a stereo set; *both* channels may require treatment.

Similar treatment may be required in tube type amplifiers. Fig. 20 shows an example of such a circuit with a series resistor, R1, and the bypassing recommended for a solid-state unit.

## FM Tuners

There is often an fm tuner used in a hi-fi installation. Much of the interference to tuners is caused by fundamental overloading of the first stage (or stages) of the tuner, effected by the amateur's signal. The cure is the installation of a high-pass filter, the same type used for TVI. The filter should be installed as close as possible to the antenna input of the tuner. The high-pass filter will attenuate the amateur *fundamental* signal, thus preventing overloading of the front end.

## Shielding

Lack of shielding on the various components in a hi-fi installation can permit rf to get into the equipment.

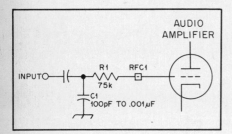

Fig. 20 — Tube type amplifier.

Many units have no bottom plates, or are installed in plastic cases. One easy method of providing shielding is to use aluminum foil. Make sure the foil doesn't short-circuit the components, and connect it to chassis ground.

## Organs

Another RFI problem area is the electronic organ. All of the techniques outlined for hi-fi gear hold true in getting rid of RFI in an organ. Two points should be checked — the speaker leads and the ac line. Many organ manufacturers have special servicemen's guides for taking care of RFI. However, to get this information you or the organ owner must contact the manufacturer, not the dealer or distributor. Don't accept the statement from a dealer or serviceman that there is nothing that can be done about the interference.

## P-A Systems

The cure for RFI in p-a systems is almost the same as that for hi-fi gear. The one thing to watch for is rf on the leads that connect the various stations in a p-a system together. These leads should be treated the same as speaker leads, and bypassing and filtering should be done at *both* ends of the lines. Also, watch for ac-line pickup of rf.

## Telephone Interference

Telephone interference won't be covered in detail here because it was treated in a *QST* article.[1] What is important is that telephone interference, along with the other types of RFI discussed in this article, is *not* the fault of the amateur. The problem is caused by lack of protection against RFI in the manufactured product. It is not suggested that an amateur work on a neighbor's equipment, because if anything goes wrong the amateur must be prepared to assume the blame. However, and this is an important point, this article can be shown to the *set owner* and the *serviceman* to inform them about what must be done.

## Television Interference

If the operation of a transmitter disturbs reception in a nearby television receiver, the reason can be tracked down to one (or both) of two distinct causes. One is that the transmitter may actually be radiating a signal in a television channel. Such a *spurious* signal may be a harmonic of the fundamental frequency, or perhaps a parasitic oscillation. Either way, it has no right to be there. Interference from this cause is something that the operator of the transmitter has to eliminate.

The second is no fault of the transmitter. The TV receiver just "folds up" when its antenna input circuits are hit by the extremely strong signal they will get from a nearby transmitter, even a low-power one. The receiver doesn't have enough selectivity to reject a powerful signal outside the TV channels. Different makes of receivers vary a great deal in their ability to reject non-TV signals.

Unfortunately, the effect on the TV screen is much the same whether the fault lies with the transmitter or receiver. However, experience has shown that, when the transmitter is operating on the 3.5- to 7-MHz bands, the probable cause of TVI (television interference) is receiver overloading rather

[1] Bercovici, "How to Handle Telephone Interference," *QST*, May, 1972.

than harmonics from the transmitter. On 14 MHz and above, transmitter harmonics, especially those that fall in channels 2 to 6 (54 to 88 MHz) become important. Receiver overloading, too, becomes worse, because the transmitting frequency is closer to the TV channels.

It is your responsibility, as the operator of a transmitter, to make sure that no TVI results from harmonics or parasitic oscillations. The transmitter always generates harmonics, so the problem is one of preventing them from reaching the antenna to be radiated. Good shielding around the transmitter circuits is the first essential, because without it harmonics may leak out in spite of all you may do in the way of adding selective circuits between the transmitter and the antenna system. Chapter 10 shows examples of transmitter construction with adequate shielding.

Once the shielding is good enough to prevent "spraying" of harmonics directly from the transmitter, circuits may be added externally to keep harmonics from reaching the antenna. The transmatch is an example of a selective circuit that might help in eliminating TVI.

If your transmitter is well shielded and you still have TVI, you may need a *low-pass filter* for your transmitter. A low-pass filter is one that passes all frequencies below a frequency (set by the filter design) called the *cutoff frequency,* but which won't let frequencies above the cutoff frequency get through. Such filters have to be designed for the same characteristic impedance as that of the transmission line in which they are inserted and should be used only in lines that are operating with a low standing-wave ratio. The cutoff frequency has to be higher than the highest frequency you're going to use for transmitting, so low-pass filters are most useful for reduction of vhf harmonic radiation (not the lower-frequency harmonics) in Novice work.

Low-pass filters tend to become complicated, when they are designed for high attenuation above the cutoff frequency, so we won't go into details here. You can find information on how to build and use them in *The Radio Amateur's Handbook.*

Modern-day, low-pass filters are rather complicated when designed for high attenuation above the cutoff frequency. Not only are they complicated to build (critical parts values), they are difficult to align (often requiring sophisticated test equipment). High-performance filters of this sort are available commercially and are aligned at the factory. While these filters are not inexpensive, they are apt to perform better than those a beginner could build.

Fig. 21 — In this photograph a Kenwood TS-820 transceiver is operated in the TVI reducing enclosure. The hinged door need not be closed.

nate such as Formica could be used for the top and sides. Pieces of aluminum or screening could be attached to the inner faces of the boards and electrically connected to adjoining pieces. Don't forget to include a piece of shielding material for the equipment to sit on. The shielded enclosure must be "rf tight" with only the front open. It might be wise to allow for a small muffin type fan within the enclosure for ventilation purposes. Other pieces of equipment such as keyers, wattmeters, clocks, etc. can be placed on top of the console.

### TV Receiver Overloading

There isn't anything you can do to your transmitter to prevent receiver overloading. The remedy here is to keep your fundamental-frequency signal from getting into the TV front end of the receiver. A *high-pass filter* on the TV receiver is the answer to this. There are low-cost filters on the market for this purpose; a popular and effective one is the Drake TV-300-HP. This filter is made for use with 300-ohm twin line such as is used for TV lead-ins. It allows the TV signals to reach the receiver without attenuation, but discriminates against signals below 54 MHz. It should be installed in the TV receiver as close as possible to the antenna terminals so that the very minimum of exposed lead will be used between the filter and the antenna posts.

You may be able to demonstrate the effectiveness of a high-pass filter to a neighbor, but there is no reason why you should furnish it to him. Receiver shortcomings aren't your fault. The set owner should be able to get a filter through the dealer from whom he purchased the receiver, or from any local TV service organization. If there is a TVI Committee in your locality — check this through your radio club — it is a good idea to let the committee handle questions of this nature.

Unfortunately, a low-pass filter alone may not be the answer to your TVI problem. The reason for this is that most transmitters and transceivers currently manufactured are not shielded adequately. Harmonic energy leaks out of the case through meter holes, open backs and poor electrical connections between the cabinet sides, top and bottom. This energy "hops" on the feed line or, for that matter, any other cable connected to the transmitter. When this occurs, the low-pass filter will do little or nothing toward reducing the interference. Harmonic energy simply flows on the coaxial braid to the low-pass filter, over the metal case of the filter, and onto the coaxial line which runs out

to the antenna. Remember, the low-pass filter attenuates only those harmonic signals flowing on the inner conductors of the coaxial cable.

"Well, what can be done?" you might ask. Considerable work has been done along these lines by Tony Dorbuck, W1YNC, of the ARRL headquarters staff. He has found that by placing the transmitter or transceiver in a metal enclosure somewhat larger than the rig itself, and by running all leads connected to the equipment out of the back of the case, that interference caused by harmonic currents can be eliminated or reduced to a low level. To date this has been the most effective measure he has found. A picture of such an enclosure is shown in Fig. 21.

As we said, all of the leads must be routed through the rear of the enclosure. The output of the transmitter is attached to a low-pass filter which in turn is connected to a feed-through uhf connector of type normally used for connecting cables through windows or walls. A brute-force line filter of the type shown in Fig. 22 is used to keep rf energy from migrating to the ac mains. The key line can also be routed through the rear panel.

The enclosure can be built from aluminum panels that are solidly bonded together. One alternative would be to use brass screening soldered together at the seams. For those who are adept at woodworking, it should be possible to build a TVI reducing console. Wood covered with a plastic lami-

Fig. 22 — "Brute-force" ac-line filter for receivers. The values of C1, C2 and C3 are not generally critical; capacitances from 0.001 to 0.01 μF can be used. L1 and L2 can be a 2-inch winding of no. 18 enameled wire on a half-inch diameter form. In making up such a unit for use external to the receiver, make sure that there are no exposed conductors to offer a shock hazard.

Fig. 23 — The entire keyer is contained in a small Minibox.

# Other Useful Accessories

## An Integrated-Circuit Keyer

As is true with most amateurs, your first keying device was or will be a straight key. While there are a few people who can send excellent code with this type of key, most cannot. After a minute or so of sending your arm is apt to tire with a subsequent rise in sending errors. One alternative to the straight key is a semi-automatic bug. This device automatically forms perfect length and spaced dots. The operator must make his own dashes. A sideways motion is used instead of the up and down action of the straight key, all but eliminating arm fatigue.

Another alternative is the automatic electronic keyer. This unit will automatically form both dots and dashes. The amount of time between each element in a series of dots or dashes is controlled by the keyer.

Described here is an electronic keyer which features variable speed and self-completing action while drawing a minimum of current. When operated from a 12-volt battery, the current required is only 10 mA. The keyer operates properly with a 9-volt battery, also.

### The Circuit

The design, shown in Fig. 24, is based on a pair of inexpensive operational amplifiers, U1 and U2. In this application, however, the op amps are functioning without the usual negative feedback in a differential-comparator configuration. One input of each op amp is based at a fixed voltage (about one-third of the supply voltage) while the other inputs are used to sense the voltage on the appropriate *RC* timing circuits. During key-up periods, the noninverting (+) input of U1 is held positive by R1 which keeps it saturated toward the positive supply. This keeps Q2 saturated. Similarly, the inverting (−) input of U2 is held positive by R2 keeping the output transistors cut off. A dot is initiated by discharging C2 through the collector of Q2. The output of U2 saturates positively which keys the transmitter. Simultaneously, Q1 saturates, and this action discharges C1. This turns off the output of U1 which allows Q2 to cut off. The dot capacitor, C2, is now free to charge through R2. When the voltage on the inverting input of U2 reaches the reference level on the noninverting input, the amplifier changes state with its output going nearly to ground potential. This terminates the dot and allows Q1 to cut off, which in turn allows the space-determining capacitor, C1, to charge. When C1 has charged to the same potential as the inverting input voltage on U1, this op amp changes state and Q2 goes into saturation again. If the paddle is still depressed, another element will be initiated. A dash is formed by discharging C3 in parallel with C2.

The network composed of R3, R4 and C4 introduces a subtle but essential delay into the cycle. This amounts to about 500 microseconds and occurs just after a dot or dash actuation. The timing capacitors, C2 and C3, are completely discharged for each element sent. The emitter follower, Q3, assures that the speed-control voltage remains stable during timing. Q3 could be eliminated if the voltage divider were much stiffer. However, this would increase the keyer current consumption. Two outputs are provided, Q4 being suitable for keying a positive voltage to ground (about 20 mA maximum) while Q5 is available for grid-block keying tube transmitters.

### Construction and Operation

The construction of this unit is about as noncritical as any project can be. The unit shown was built on a small piece of Vectorbord. Building and testing can be completed in one evening. Ten-percent-tolerance tantalum capacitors were used at C1, C2 and C3. The op amps are common types available from many sources. While intended for operation with a 12-volt supply, this keyer may be used with voltages up to 30. The speed is independent of the voltage used.

Although this device does not offer the precise timing of digital circuitry, the accuracy is more than adequate. The

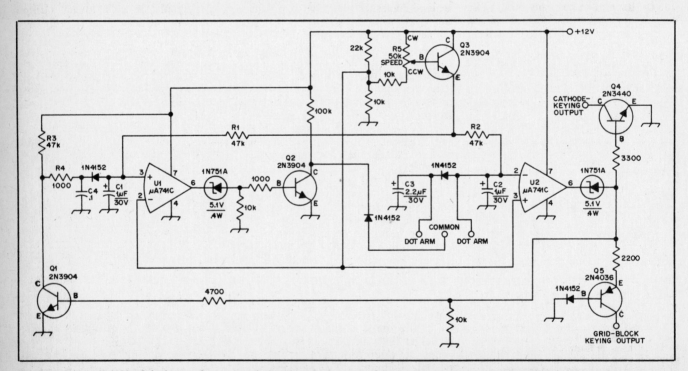

Fig. 24 — Circuit diagram of the keyer. Component designations are for text reference. Fixed-value resistors are 10 percent composition; fixed-value capacitors are disk ceramic unless otherwise noted. R5 is a 50,000-ohm, linear-taper, composition control.

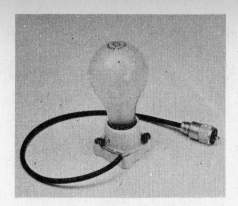

Fig. 25 — An incandescent lamp as a dummy antenna. Lamp rating should be selected to be approximately equal to the expected power output of the transmitter.

excellent performance, along with extreme simplicity and low power requirements, makes the unit an ideal addition to the modern portable station.

## Dummy Antennas

A *dummy antenna* is a device for absorbing the power output of a transmitter. Using one lets you test the transmitter without putting a signal on the air, as you would if you used a regular antenna for this purpose. (Using a real antenna for transmitter testing is not permitted by the regulations, except very briefly, and is inconsiderate of others besides.) The basic ingredient of a dummy antenna is resistance, since resistance absorbs power.

An ideal dummy would be a pure resistance matching the characteristic impedance of coaxial cable, 50 or 75 ohms, approximately. Small composition resistors are fine at frequencies up to 150 MHz or even higher, but they can't handle much power. Two watts is the maximum for the largest commonly available resistor of this type. Several resistors can be combined in series, parallel or a combination of both series and parallel, for handling more power. However, it takes a great many of them to dissipate, say, 100 watts safely. Also, when a large number of them are wired together some of the good characteristics are lost — the wiring adds inductance and capacitance and the resistance is no longer pure.

Actually, most transmitter testing doesn't require a dummy of known resistance. Anything that will let you load up the final amplifier to normal input will do. The cheapest and most satisfactory resistor, in many respects, is an ordinary incandescent lamp. It will light up on rf just as well as on 60 hertz ac at frequencies below 30 MHz. Its brightness will give you a fair indication of your power output. Simply choose a lamp that will light up to about normal brightness on the output of your transmitter, and compare it with one of the same rating in a regular 115-volt socket. Beware of estimating power output when the lamp isn't close to being normally bright, though. Just a couple of watts will make a 50- or 100-watt lamp show color!

The lamp can be put in a dime-store socket, for convenience in changing sizes. See Fig. 25. Use a foot or so of coax, with a fitting on one end, to connect the socket to your transmitter. The coaxial braid should go to the shell connection and the inner conductor should connect to the center stud of the lamp.

One disadvantage of the lamp is that its resistance changes with the temperature of the filament. This represents a changing load as you tune up, so you have to be careful in adjusting your loading and tuning controls. One thing you can be sure of — when the lamp is as bright as you can get it with any possible tuning adjustment, your transmitter is delivering all the power you can expect to get from it.

## An RF-Sensed Antenna Changeover Relay

Some amateurs who build their own equipment or purchase transmitters and receivers of different manufacture, sometimes resort to using a manually operated switch for transfering from receive to transmit. The circuit described here and shown in simplified form in Fig. 26 was designed with this in mind. Basically, this system detects the presence of rf at the output of the transmitter and immediately breaks the antenna connection to the receiver. At the same time the antenna connection to the transmitter is made. One of the features of this system is that no modifications to either the transmitter or receiver are required.

### Circuit Description

R1 of Fig. 27 serves as an rf-voltage divider to permit the circuit to be used with transmitters of various power-output amounts. Rf energy is routed

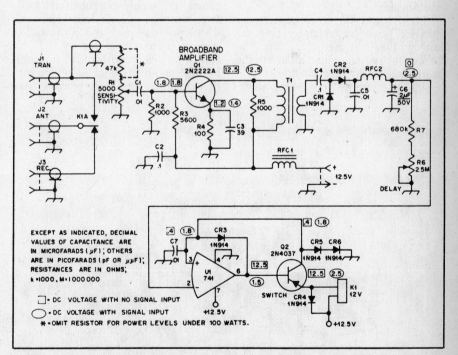

Fig. 27 — Schematic diagram of the rf-sensed antenna-changeover relay. All resistors are half-watt composition type. Capacitors are disk-ceramic unless noted otherwise. Component numbers not appearing in the parts list are for identification purposes only.

J1, J2 — Connector, SO-239.
J3 — Connector, phono-type.
K1 — Dpdt relay, 5-ampere contacts, 12-volt field.
R1 — Linear potentiometer, 5000 ohms.
R2 — Linear potentiometer, 2.5 megohms.
RFC1, RFC2 — Rf choke, 42 turns no. 28

enam. wire on an Amidon FT-50-43 core.
T1 — Broadband transformer. Primary: 25 turns no. 28 enam. wire on an Amidon FT-50-43 core; secondary: 5 turns no. 28 enam. wire wound over primary winding.
U1 — Op amp, 741.

Fig. 26 — Simplified drawing of the antenna changeover relay.

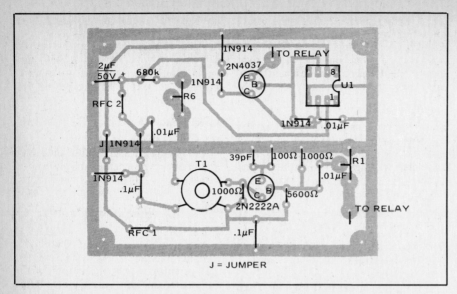

Fig. 30 — The solid-state T-R switch constructed on an etched circuit board of the pattern shown in Fig. 32.

Fig. 28 — Circuit-board etching pattern for the changeover relay. The pattern is shown at actual size from the foil side of the board with gray areas representing copper. Decimal-value numbers alone represent capacitance in microfarads. Whole-number values with no units represent resistances in ohms; k = 1000. J = wire jumper. All components are mounted on the nonfoil side of the board. K indicates the cathode of a diode.

through C1 to the base of broadband amplifier Q1. The amplified hf-band energy is supplied to a voltage-doubler (CR1 and CR2) through a broadband toroidal step-down transformer, T1. The rectified rf voltage at the output of CR1 and CR2 is filtered by means of RFC2, C5 and C6. This prevents unwanted rf from reaching U1 and affecting its performance.

C6, R7 and R6 comprise a timing network (variable) which governs the hold-in time of the relay, K1. The smaller the resistance amount at R6, the shorter will be the time delay.

U1 functions as an inverting ampli-fier. When the input dc voltage at pin 2 increases, the output dc voltage at pin 6 decreases. The output voltage causes the base of relay driver Q2 to be forward biased negatively when it drops below approximately 1.4 volts. Diodes CR5 and CR6, by virtue of their combined barrier voltages (0.7 V each), establish the 1.4-V fixed bias level. Without the diodes, Q2 would conduct sufficiently to prevent the relay from dropping out during no-signal periods. CR4 is used to suppress transients caused by the field coil of K1. When no rectified rf reaches U1, Q2 is cut off because of the high positive base voltage it receives from

U1, and the relay contacts to the transmitter are open.

### Construction

In Fig. 28 is a suggested printed-circuit board layout showing the foil pattern and parts placement. R1 and R6 may be circuit-board-mounted potentiometers if the builder desires, as the board layout was designed to accommodate such units. Potentiometers of this type are entirely suitable if the builder does not anticipate frequent changes in power levels and length of delay, as these controls must be readjusted for such changes. If the builder is interested in having access to these controls, panel-mounted potentiometers can be used at the front apron, in which case wires will have to be run from the circuit board to the controls.

Our finished model was housed in a 5 × 3 × 2-inch aluminum Minibox. R1 and R6 were mounted on the front panel and Kurz-Kasch knobs were placed on the control shafts to dress up the appearance of the finished product. CR4 is attached directly to the relay terminals. The rear panel supports the terminals for the transmitter, antenna, receiver antenna and power supply. SO-239 connectors were used for the transmitter and antenna connections, and a phono connector was employed for the receiver antenna. Any type of connectors may be substituted to match those used in the builder's station. The power-supply lead is brought out through a feedthrough capacitor. This type of feedthrough is not necessary: A simple feedthrough insulator or wire could be used instead. In our case, the capacitor lead served as a convenient tie point during preliminary testing of the unit.

### Operation

Connect the antenna, transmitter, receiver antenna lead and the power-supply connections to the appropriate terminals. Set R6, the time-delay control, to its minimum delay position (ccw) and the sensitivity control to its

Fig. 29 — This photograph shows the inner layout of the antenna-changeover relay. Wiring or placement of circuit board and other components is not critical.

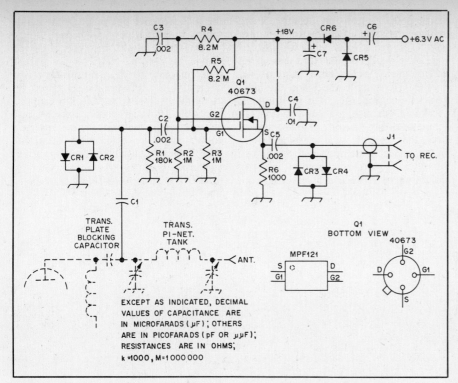

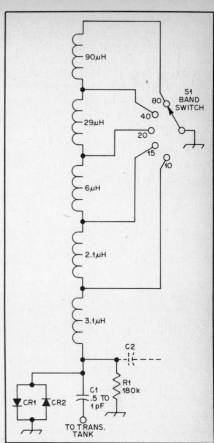

Fig. 31 — Circuit diagram of the T-R switch. All resistors are 1/2-watt composition.

C1 — 5- to 10-pF mica.
C2, C3, C5, — 0.002-µF disk.
C4 — 0.01 µF disk.
C6, C7 — 100-µF, 25-volt electrolytic.
CR1, CR2, CR3, CR4 — 1N914 or equiv.
CR5, CR6 — 100 PRV, 100-mA silicon diode.
J1 — Coaxial chassis fitting.

Q1 — RCA 40673 or Motorola MPF121.
R1 — 180,000 ohms.
R2, R3 — 1 megohm.
R3, R4 — 8.2 megohms.
R6 — 1000 ohms.

Fig. 33 — Circuit diagram of the T-R switch additions for high-power operation.

midrotation position. While keying the transmitter, decrease the setting of the sensitivity control to a point just above that where the transmitter no longer makes the relay energize. Once this has been set, it may be left in that position until a moderate change in power level has been made. The delay control should then be adjusted for the length of delay desired.

## Electronic Transmit-Receive Switching

While it is always good practice to use the same antenna for both receiving and transmitting, to do so you have to shift the antenna or feeder connections back and forth. This can be done by manual switching or with an antenna relay. However, neither of these can be operated rapidly enough to follow keying, so in either case break-in operation becomes impracticable. But if the switching is done electronically, it can be practically instantaneous. A device which does this is called an *electronic T-R (transmit-receive) switch*.

One of the simplest approaches to T-R switch construction is illustrated in Figs. 30 and 31. A gate-protected dual-gate MOSFET couples an incoming signal to the receiver. When the transmitter is keyed, a sample of the signal is used to turn Q1 off. The dc voltage required to operate Q1 is obtained by rectifying 6.3 volts ac from the transmitter filament line. Connection to the line should be made to the ungrounded side of the heater supply.

### Installation

Mount the T-R switch close to the transmitter PA tank. The coupling capacitor, C1, which should have a voltage rating of at least twice the plate voltage of the transmitter PA stage, should be connected with one end to the input side of the pi-network coil, as shown in Fig. 31. Mount a coaxial chassis fitting on the back of the transmitter chassis, and run a connecting line of coaxial cable from the fitting to the T-R switch. (This length of coaxial cable is shown in Fig. 31, extending out the right-hand side of the photograph.) Make sure the coaxial braid is grounded at the fitting and at the T-R switch. The receiver antenna terminals can then be connected, using coaxial cable, to the T-R terminal on the transmitter.

With high-power transmitters, near

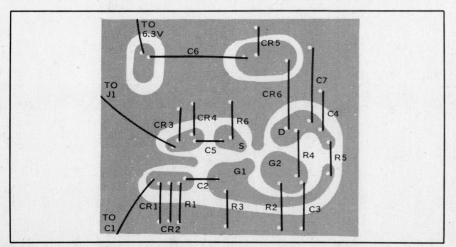

Fig. 32 — Template for the etched circuit board. The foil side is shown and the dark areas are the etched portion of the board.

the kilowatt level, the value of C1 should be changed to no more than 1 pF. Because of this light coupling, a broadly resonant input circuit may be required on the T-R switch in order to have adequate gain during reception. This may be obtained by connecting an inductor from the junction of C1 and R1 to ground. The following values are suitable; 10 meters — 3 $\mu$H; 15 meters — 4 $\mu$H; 20 meters — 11 $\mu$H; 40 meters — 40 $\mu$H; and 80 meters — 130 $\mu$H. For operation on more than a single band, a single-pole, 5-position rotary band switch may be used, with inductor values of 3.1 $\mu$H, 2.1 $\mu$H, 6.0 $\mu$H, 29 $\mu$H, and 90 $\mu$H connected in series. One end of the 3.1-$\mu$H inductor is connected to the T-R switch input, and the junction of this and the 2.1-$\mu$H inductor is grounded through the band switch for 10-meter operation. For 15-meter operation, the junction of the 2.1- and 6-$\mu$H inductors is grounded, and so on, so that for 80-meter operation, all five inductors in series are connected from the T-R switch input through the band-switch to ground.

One thing about this type of device should be pointed out. The T-R switch is connected to the transmitter tank circuit via C1, a low-value capacitor. If as in the case of Class AB linear amplifiers, the amplifier plate current is not cut off when receiving, there may be enough noise generated in the amplifier tube to be objectionable during receive. Such noise should not be noticeable with Class C or with cathode-keyed amplifiers.

# Chapter 12

# The Power Supply

Except for a few measuring instruments, practically all radio equipment needs some form of power supply before it can function. This power is usually taken from the ac lines when the equipment is operated at a fixed location. For mobile operation the prime source of power is normally the car storage battery. For the moment let's concentrate on power supplies operating from the ac mains.

In vacuum-tube equipment one necessity is power for heating the cathodes. This is easy because most tube heaters will work from "raw" ac. A simple transformer can step the voltage down to the appropriate value — generally 6.3 volts for receiving and small transmitting tubes.

But heaters, while certainly essential, usually take no direct part in circuit operation. The tube electrodes that do have such a part require dc power. Furthermore, it must be *good* dc — that is, unvarying in amplitude. The same is true for solid-state circuitry. While the voltage requirements are considerably lower in most cases, the dc must also be pure.

Changing the 115-volt ac to an appropriate level of dc calls for a diode rectifier and filter in addition to a transformer. The transformer changes the 115 volt ac line to a more usable value; the rectifier changes the ac to dc; and the filter takes the rather rough dc from the rectifier and smooths out the unwanted fluctuations.

## AC Terminology

Before we take a look at the actual workings of a power supply we should study the different methods of rating a sine wave. Two of these ways are shown in Fig. 1. As we can see, the sine wave starts at zero, goes through a positive extreme, down through zero to a negative extreme and back again to zero. The absolute top and bottom of the waveform are called *peaks.* Voltage or current values corresponding to these positive or negative extremes are called *peak voltage* or *peak current.* The total swing from one extreme to the other is called the *peak-to-peak* value, often abbreviated *pk-pk.* If an ac signal is connected to the vertical plates of an oscilloscope, the waveform shown in Fig. 1 would be displayed.

Peak or peak-to-peak measurements are fine for some applications but not for all. For example, it is impossible for most ac meters to measure a peak or peak-to-peak voltage or current. Most ac mains operate at 50 or 60 cycles per second — much too fast for a meter to follow faithfully. The value that most meters are designed to read is the *rms* (root-mean-square) value. Rms or the effective value is defined as 0.707 of the peak. This is shown in Fig. 2. The importance of an rms value of ac voltage or current stems from electric-power relations in ac circuits. A detailed discussion of the 0.707 factor involves calculus and is beyond the scope of this book.

An alternating current is effectively the same as a direct current when it produces the same heating effect under the same conditions. We have already learned that power in a dc circuit is equal to the product of the voltage and current

$$P_{dc} = E_{dc} \times I_{dc}$$

The power that is developed in an ac resistive load is equal to the product of the rms voltage and the rms current

$$P_{ac} = E_{rms} \times I_{rms}$$

As we mentioned, the rms value is 0.707 of the peak. Simple computation shows us that the peak is 1.414 times the rms value. These two formulas are worth remembering, since we will be using them extensively during our study of electronics. In equation form

$$E_{rms} = .707 \times E_{peak}$$

$$E_{peak} = 1.414 \times E_{rms} \qquad \text{(Eq. 4)}$$

It is worth mentioning at this point that power transformers are rated in terms of rms voltage. For example, a power transformer with a 6.3-volt secondary delivers 6.3 volts rms. The peak voltage from the transformer (using Eq. 4) is 8.91 volts. We know that the peak-to-

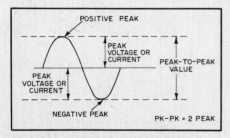

Fig. 1 — Ac waveform showing peak and peak-to-peak values.

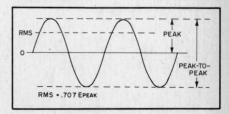

Fig. 2 — Ac waveform illustrating rms relation.

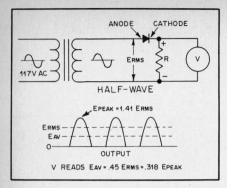

Fig. 3 — Half-wave rectifier circuit.

peak voltage is simply twice the peak value or, in this case, 17.82 volts.

Another method of measurement, used mainly for dc circuits, is called *average*. We won't be using this method for defining a sine wave; however, we should be aware of its existence. The average value of a sine wave is zero. This is because the wave spends the same amount of time above the zero axis as it does below. In order to have some value of average voltage other than zero, we must modify the sine wave in one way or another. More on this in a minute.

### Half-Wave Rectifier

A half-wave rectifier, as its name implies, rectifies one half of the sine wave. This can be seen in Fig. 3. As shown in the drawing, an ac signal is present at both the input and output connections of the transformer. We have already learned that a diode will pass current in only one direction. The waveform after rectification is shown to the right of the circuit. We can see that the bottom half of the waveform has been removed and all that remains is that portion of the wave above the zero axis.

The dc voltmeter connected across the load resistance would read the average dc voltage level. An ac waveform, as we know, has an average level of zero. Output from the half-wave rectifier is no longer ac and, therefore, has an

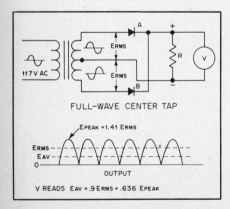

Fig. 4 — Full-wave center-tap rectifier circuit.

average value. This value is equal to 0.318 times the peak or 0.45 times the rms voltage.

### Full-Wave Center Tap

The circuit shown in Fig. 4 is called a full-wave center-tap rectifier circuit. As you might have guessed, the full-wave circuit operates over the entire ac waveform. During one half of the ac cycle, diode A will conduct and the load resistor will have the voltage polarity shown. On the other half cycle, diode B will conduct and the load resistor will have the same polarity as it did during the period of time diode A conducted. Comparing the dc output from this circuit to the one in Fig. 3, we notice that there are twice as many half cycles above the zero axis. The average dc level is twice that of the previous circuit, which is what we would expect. Average voltage in this case is equal to 0.636 times the peak or 0.9 times the rms voltage. In the center tap circuit each side of the center-tapped secondary must provide the rms voltage that is to appear at the output of the circuit.

### Bridge Rectifier

A third type of rectifier circuit, frequently used in amateur transmitters, is the *full-wave bridge* shown in Fig. 5. The output current or voltage waveshape is the same as for the full-wave center-tap circuit. The *amplitude* of the output voltage, as compared with the voltage at the transformer secondary, is different. In the center-tap circuit *each side* of the center-tapped secondary must develop enough voltage to supply the dc output voltage desired. In the bridge circuit no center tap is needed. Dispensing with the center tap has a price, though — two additional diodes must be used.

In the bridge circuit diodes A and B are connected to the transformer secondary in the same way as the two rectifiers in the center-tap circuit. The second pair, C and D, is also connected in series between the ends of the transformer winding, but in reverse. When the upper end of the transformer winding is positive, the current path is through A, the load R and D back to the lower end of the winding. When the lower end is positive the path is through B, R and C.

### The Voltage Doubler

A circuit that is frequently used in transmitter power supplies is the *voltage-doubler* shown in Fig. 6. This works by charging the capacitors through separate half-wave rectifiers on alternate halves of the supply cycle, and then discharging them in series through the load, R. When voltage at the upper end of the transformer secondary is positive, C1 is charged to the peak value of the ac

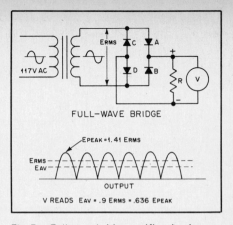

Fig. 5 — Full-wave bridge-rectifier circuit.

voltage through diode A. When the lower end of the winding is positive, C2 is similarly charged through B. The stored voltages on the two capacitors add together to give a total output voltage twice what one would expect to get from the half-wave rectifier of Fig. 7A. Both halves of the supply cycle are used, so this is a full-wave rectifier circuit. However, *each* capacitor has to be as large as the single capacitor used in the half-wave circuit, for the same smoothing. It is a particularly useful circuit when a moderately high dc voltage is wanted, because the transformer voltage need be only half as great as in the half-wave circuit, and only one-fourth as large as the total secondary voltage required by the full-wave center-tap circuit. The voltage doubler is used in a number of manufactured transmitters and kits.

### Filters

Although the output of a rectifier is direct current, its amplitude fluctuates all the way from zero to the peak output voltage from the transformer. In the full-wave circuit the rate at which this happens is twice the supply frequency. That is, the *ripple* in the output

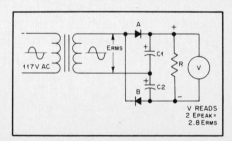

Fig. 6 — The voltage doubler circuit. Two half-wave rectifiers, working alternately, charge capacitors connected in series.

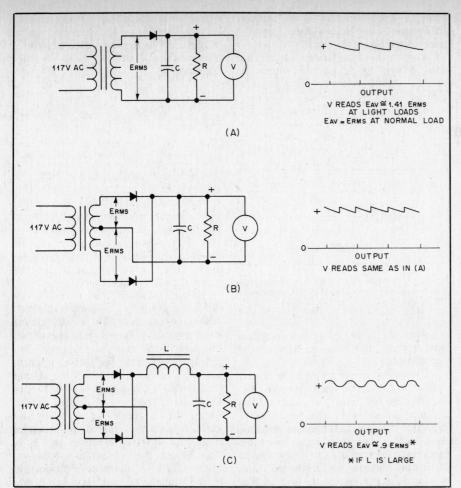

Fig. 7 — Capacitor- and choke-input filters. The approximate shape of the ripple voltage remaining after filtering is shown by the drawings at the right. Divisions along the horizontal axis represent one cycle of the line frequency. Output voltage shown at C neglects drops in the transformer, rectifiers and filter choke.

voltage has a frequency of 120 hertz when the supply frequency is 60 hertz. The ripple frequency in a half-wave rectifier is equal to the supply frequency.[1]

If an attempt is made to use the rectifier output as is with, for example, a receiver, there will be nothing but a roaring hum from the loudspeaker. The fluctuations must be smoothed out so the ripple is substantially eliminated. This is where the filter comes in.

### Capacitor and Choke Input

Filters having a capacitor next to the rectifier are called *capacitor-input* filters. Those having an inductance between the rectifier and capacitor are called *choke-input* filters. *All* power-supply filters use capacitors, although not all use chokes.

Both types of filters, with half-wave

[1] More accurately, these are the *fundamental* frequencies of the ripple. Actually, the ripple waveform is highly distorted, and there are many harmonic frequencies in it along with the fundamental.

and full-wave rectifiers, are shown in Fig. 7. The drawings at the right give an idea of the form of the ripple on the dc output. The approximate output voltages also are indicated. In the case of the choke-input filter, C, the output voltage will have the value shown only when a large inductance is used. "Large" here means an inductance, in henrys, greater than the load resistance, $R$, divided by 1000. For example, if the load is 100 mA, at 300 volts, the value of $R$ is 300/0.1 amp, or 3000 ohms. Thus $L$ should be at least 3 henrys.

### Ripple and Filter Sections

Notice that there are twice as many "bumps" in the dc output voltage per cycle of line frequency (the length of a cycle is indicated by the short vertical lines along the horizontal axis of the output drawing) when a full-wave rectifier is used. This is just another way of saying that the ripple frequency is doubled with full-wave rectification. Values of $L$ and $C$ in the filter need be only half as large with full-wave rectifi-

cation as with half-wave rectification, for the same smoothing of the dc output.

The inductance and capacitance can smooth out the dc because they store energy while the voltage from the rectifier is rising, and release it when the rectified voltage is falling. Less energy has to be stored, for the same overall effect, if the charge-discharge periods are quick instead of drawn out over a longer period of time.

An *LC* combination such as is shown in Fig. 7 at C is called a *filter section*. Sections can be added either to the simple input capacitor (A) or to a choke-input section (B). As many sections as may be necessary to get the desired smoothing can be used.

How much inductance and capacitance are needed for good filtering? There is no definite answer. Your standard for "good" may differ considerably from the next fellow's. The intended use of the power supply has a lot to do with it. If you wear headphones for listening to weak signals, a hum that you find highly objectionable may not even be audible when a small speaker is used. As a general rule, receivers require more elaborate filters than transmitters.

Practical power-supply circuits you'll find later in this chapter are representative. So are those given in other chapters in association with receiving and transmitting equipment. It does no harm to use the largest economical value of capacitance. The difference in cost between 40-$\mu$F and 20-$\mu$F electrolytic capacitors, for example, is rather small; it pays to use the larger value. This is less true of chokes, which tend to be expensive in the higher values of inductance. But the effectiveness of a filter section is proportional to both $L$ and $C$, so if you have to use a small inductance, or even none at all, a larger capacitance will compensate for it.

### RC Filters

Another type of filter is shown in Fig. 8. This is called a *resistance-capacitance* or *RC* filter. The resistor serves the same purpose as the decoupling

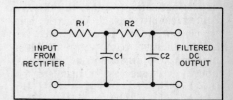

Fig. 8 — Resistance-capacitance filter. It is principally useful where the load current is small, since the dc voltage drop in R1 and R2 precludes using a large resistance value for heavy currents. The *RC* filter makes a good "back-up" for an *LC* section in many circuits.

resistors discussed in earlier chapters. There is an ac (ripple) voltage drop in the resistor, so less ripple reaches the capacitor. This makes the smoothing job of the capacitor easier. However, there is also a *dc* voltage drop in the resistor. In contrast, the dc voltage drop in a choke would be quite small.

Resistance-capacitance filters are used principally in circuits where the current is small enough to make the dc voltage drop in the resistor unimportant. An example of such a circuit is a resistance-coupled audio voltage amplifier.

# Rectifiers and Ratings

You're already familiar with the way a diode rectifies. A power-supply rectifier is just a diode (or several of them) big enough to handle the current and voltage needed in a power supply. Many sizes are available.

In choosing and using power-supply diodes there are some important factors that must never be overlooked. One is the *peak reverse voltage,* often abbreviated *PRV.* This is the maximum voltage applied to the rectifier in the *nonconducting* direction. For example, in Fig. 4 when diode A is conducting and B is not, the full transformer voltage is applied in the reverse direction to B, because there is very little voltage drop in A when it is conducting. Since the peak value of the voltage is 1.41 times the rms value, you can see readily that in Fig. 4 the PRV is 1.41 times the *total* secondary voltage. Values for the various rectifier circuits are given below

| Circuit in Fig.: | PRV |
|---|---|
| 3 | 1.41 $E_{rms}$ |
| 4, 7B, 7C | 2.82 " |
| 6 | 1.41 " |
| 7A, | 2.82 " |

In Figs. 6 and 7 the PRV is the sum of the peak transformer voltage and the dc voltage stored in one filter capacitor. The maximum value shown is for light loads — that is, with little or no output current. For safety, the diode rating always should be chosen on the basis of no-load PRV.

The current rating of the diode also must be considered. Diodes usually are rated for two current values, the *average dc output current* and the *maximum peak current*. The former is the direct current flowing to the load, so if your load needs a current of 100 mA, you would choose a rectifier having at least that output-current rating. In full-wave rectifier circuits each diode carries half the current, so each can be rated for half the desired output current. When there are two diodes in one assembly, though, as in the case of many of the

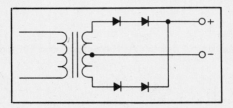

Fig. 9 — Using two semiconductor diodes in series doubles the peak-inverse voltage rating.

full-wave rectifier tubes used in receivers, the rating is based on what the *pair* can do.

The peak-current rating is the largest current that can be allowed to flow through the rectifier at any time during the rectified cycle. It is important with capacitor-input filters because most of the charging current into the first filter capacitor flows in a short burst, reaching a peak value several times the value of the dc output current. In a choke-input filter the peak current is very little larger than the dc output current, so with this type of filter the peak-current rating can be neglected.

## Tube Rectifiers

Many amateur transmitter power supplies use vacuum-tube rectifiers of the type found in broadcast and television receivers. The 5Y3G, 5U4G, 6X4 and several others are typical. These contain two rectifiers in one envelope for full-wave rectification. The full-wave rectifiers usually have directly heated cathodes rated at five volts and two or three amperes, depending on the tube type. The PRV rating is around 1400-1500 volts.

## Semiconductor Rectifiers

Although there are several types of solid-state rectifiers (among them selenium and copper oxide), the silicon junction diode has superseded all others in newer equipment. It has also superseded tube rectifiers in most applications where low or moderate dc voltages are required. The forward voltage drop in the silicon diode is low — only 1 to 1.5 volts in the sizes that will deliver up to 750 mA — and it has the further advantage of very small size. Because of the low voltage drop the efficiency is very high. Also, there is a considerable power saving because a semiconductor diode doesn't need cathode heating the way a tube diode does.

Silicon rectifiers come with various PRV ratings up to a maximum of about 1000 volts per diode. These ratings *must* be observed if failure is to be prevented. The safe rms voltage that can be applied can be found from the factors given in the table on this page for the several rectifier-filter circuits. It is well, too, to allow an ample safety factor. If the voltage to be applied exceeds the safe value, two (or even more) diodes can be connected in series, as shown in Fig. 9. This divides the PRV across the diodes, so the safe PRV increases in proportion to the number of rectifiers. For example, if each of the rectifiers in Fig. 9 has a rating of 400 volts PRV the total rating is 800 volts. From what was said earlier (Fig. 4), the total transformer voltage that could be applied safely to this combination is 800/1.41, or approximately 560 volts, or 280 volts each side of the center tap.

Small silicon rectifiers are made in a number of case shapes and sizes, mostly with axial wire leads. Sometimes the cathode end is indicated and sometimes not. If it isn't, the only safe thing to do in the absence of definite information is to check the diode with an ohmmeter, using a moderate-resistance scale (100 ohms or more). Measure the resistance and then reverse the ohmmeter connections and measure again. One way the resistance will be low, and the other way it will be very high. The actual values are of relatively little significance; the important thing is that there will be a *big* difference in the readings if the diode is good. The cathode is the diode terminal to which the *positive* lead from the ohmmeter is connected when the resistance reads *high.*

# Filter Components

Filter capacitors in amateur transmitting equipment in the power range we're considering in this book are nearly always the electrolytic type. They are far less expensive than paper-dielectric capacitors, but are not made to stand voltages higher than 450 or, in a few cases, 500 or 600 volts.

However, two or more units can be connected in series to raise the safe voltage. It is seldom necessary to use more than two in series in transmitters up to 150 watts or so. Of course, the total capacitance of the combination is less than that of either unit alone, as you learned earlier. Fig. 10 is a typical example. When connecting such capacitors in series it is advisable to make them identical. If the capacitances are different, the voltages do not divide equally, and one capacitor may operate considerably over its rating while the other is well under. To make certain that the voltages do divide equally, identical resistors often are connected across each capacitor in a series string, as shown in the figure. These need not take much current, so values of the order of 100,000 ohms are common for these *equalizing resistors*.

## Polarization

Electrolytic capacitors are *polarized*. This means that they must be connected in a dc circuit in only one way. The terminals are always marked to show which one goes to the positive side of the circuit and which to the negative. When the container is a metal can, the can is usually the negative terminal. However, this should be checked before using an electrolytic. If the capacitor is connected the wrong way, it will be ruined in short order.

All electrolytic capacitors have a small *leakage current* – a few milliamperes flowing through the capacitor itself. This is not serious in a power-supply filter, but prohibits using the capacitor in many other circuits. Also, the capacitor must always be used in a circuit in which the dc voltage is larger than the peak value of any ac voltage that may be superimposed. Electrolytics cannot be used on "raw" ac.

## Paper Capacitors

Paper-dielectric capacitors do not have these limitations. The leakage current is practically unmeasurable if the unit is not defective. Also, since these capacitors are not polarized, they will work on either dc or ac. These two factors make them well suited to such uses as interstage coupling in audio-frequency amplifiers. However, the larger values of capacitance, at the higher voltage ratings, are very much more costly than equivalent capacitance in electrolytics.

## Filter Chokes

Filter chokes resemble transformers in appearance and general construction. However, there is only one winding. Also, the core laminations are not interleaved to provide the best possible magnetic path, as is the practice in transformer construction. In fact, a small *air gap* is made in the core, as shown in Fig. 11. (The gap in the drawing is much exaggerated; actually it would be only a small fraction of an inch, almost invisible, in an ordinary choke such as you would use in your equipment.) The reason for this is that the direct current flowing through the choke would tend to *saturate* the core to the point where a change in current would no longer cause a corresponding change in the magnetic field in the core. Saturation reduces the effective inductance of the choke for alternating currents, so the choke no longer can smooth out the ripple in the rectified ac.

Even with the air gap there is always some tendency toward saturation, with the result that the inductance of a choke steadily decreases as the direct current through it is increased. It is customary to rate chokes in so many henrys of inductance at such-and-such direct current. The inductance will be larger at smaller currents, and smaller at higher currents. Just how much larger and smaller is a matter of the choke design. Chokes in which these changes are small are rather expensive, for a given inductance rating. However, in power-supply filter design the principal thing is to have enough of everything that contributes to smoothing. So if the components have adequate ratings in the output current you want, there's no necessity for worrying about what may happen at smaller currents. The filtering just gets better when you reduce the load.

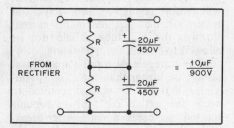

Fig. 10 — Electrolytic capacitors connected in series to increase the voltage rating. Equalizing resistors, *R*, help divide the dc voltage properly.

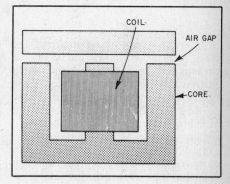

Fig. 11 — Power-supply choke construction.

# Voltage Regulation

The amount of direct current that a receiver or transmitter demands from the power supply is not always constant. A cw transmitter may take very little current with the key open, but with the key down it may load the supply up to the maximum current it is designed to give. The total current taken by a receiver circuit will vary depending on the setting of the rf gain control.

These changes in current affect the output voltage of the supply.

The change in output voltage with current is called the *voltage regulation* of the supply. It is usually expressed as a percentage of the output voltage at the rated load current. For example, the supply may be designed to deliver a current of 200 mA at 600 volts. If the voltage rises to 800 when the output current is zero, the change is 200 volts and the regulation is 200/600. This is 1/3, or 33-1/3 percent.

Several things contribute to the voltage drop in the supply. One is the resistance and reactance of the transformer windings. Another is the voltage drop between the anode and cathode of the rectifier. (The rectifier drop amounts only to a volt or so with silicon

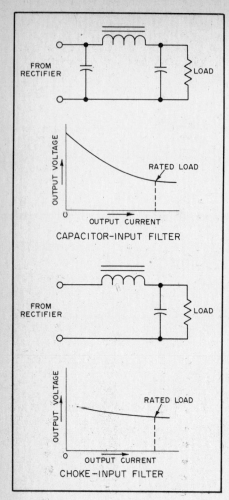

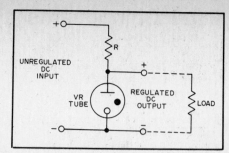

Fig. 13 — Voltage-regulator tube circuit for maintaining constant output voltage.

Fig. 12 — The curves are typical of the way the output voltage varies with load current for the two types of filters shown.

CAPACITOR-INPUT FILTER

CHOKE-INPUT FILTER

rectifiers, but can be significant if the tube rectifier is used, amounting to perhaps 40 or 50 volts at full rated current.) A third is the resistance of the filter choke and any resistors that may be used for filtering. The voltage drops in all of these increase with current. Finally, in a capacitor-input filter the output voltage depends on the amount of energy stored in the input capacitor and the rate at which the energy is released to the load. This rate increases with an increase in load current, causing the voltage to decrease accordingly. With no output current the voltage in a capacitor-input filter builds up to the peak value of the rectified voltage, or 1.41 times the rms voltage applied to the rectifier (Fig. 3).

A choke-input filter with a large value of inductance will prevent this voltage buildup at small output currents and will tend to hold the output voltage at the *average* amplitude of the rectified waveform. (Fig. 7C). The voltage drops mentioned above still cause the output voltage to drop off with increased current, of course.

The comparison between choke- and

capacitor-input filters in their effect on voltage regulation is shown in Fig. 12.

## Bleeders

In discussing choke-input filters we said that the input choke must have an inductance equal to or larger than $R/1000$ when a full-wave rectifier is used. If there is no $R$ — i.e., no load on the supply and no output current — the output voltage is not held down to 0.9 $E_{rms}$ but rises to 1.41 $E_{rms}$. The regulation would be just as poor in this case as with a capacitor-input filter. The remedy is to *bleed* some current from the supply all the time, even when there is no current to the actual load.

This can be done by connecting a resistor across the output terminals of the supply. Obviously, we don't want to waste any more power in this resistance than is absolutely necessary. The proper value of *bleeder resistance* is equal to the inductance in henrys multiplied by 1000. Thus the larger the choke inductance, the higher the permissible resistance, therefore the less wasted power.

The bleeder serves another useful purpose: It discharges the filter capacitors when the supply is turned off. A bleeder should always be used, even with capacitor-input filters. It will prevent many an accidental shock — and the shock you can get from a filter capacitor is nothing to trifle with. Resistance values of 25,000 to 50,000 ohms are common. However, anything that will discharge the capacitors will do, and larger values are often used.

Bleeder resistors have to dissipate a fair amount of power, as a rule. Having decided on the resistance you want to use, calculate the power by Ohm's Law: $P = E^2 R$. For instance, if the bleeder is 25,000 ohms and the voltage is to be 400, the power the resistor must handle is $(400)^2/25,000$, or a little over 6 watts. A 10-watt resistor should be used, to give a safety factor.

## Voltage Regulators

Circuits or devices which hold the output voltage at a constant value regardless of changes in current are called *voltage regulators*. One type, useful in the 90-150 volt range, is the gas-tube regulator, or *VR tube*. The voltage drop in an ionized gas tends to be independent of the current flowing through the gas. This property can be used to advantage in maintaining constant output voltage from a power supply.

How the tube operates can best be illustrated by seeing how the circuit, Fig. 13, is designed. Suppose the load wants 150 volts, regulated, at a current of 25 mA, and that the unregulated dc input voltage is 250. Allowing 5 mA (the minimum current for stable opera-

tion) for the current through the 150-volt VR tube, the total current through R is $5 + 25 = 30$ mA. The resistor R thus must drop 250 volts to 150 volts; that is, the drop in R must be 100 volts. By Ohm's Law, its resistance is $100/0.03 = 3300$ ohms.

Now if the input voltage rises to, say, 300 volts, the drop in R must increase to $300 - 150 = 150$ volts, to keep the output voltage constant at 150. The current through R therefore must be $150/3300 = 45$ mA. The load is still taking 25 mA, since the voltage across it has not changed, so the additional current, $45 - 25$ or 20 mA, must flow through the VR tube. In other words, the tube regulates the voltage by taking more current when the input voltage tends to rise, and by taking less when it tends to decrease.

A little thought will show that a design such as this should be based on the *lowest* input voltage likely to exist, if a minimum VR current of 5 mA is used. Increasing the minimum current will permit regulation both ways, but remember that the *maximum* current through the VR tube should not be allowed to exceed the tube rating.

The unregulated input voltage must always be higher than the *striking voltage* — that is, the voltage required to cause the gas in the tube to become ionized or "break down." After breakdown the *maintaining voltage* (the voltage at which the tube regulates) keeps the gas ionized. The striking voltage is usually about 25 percent higher than the working voltage.

## Zener-Diode Regulator

If a reverse voltage applied to a semiconductor diode is gradually increased from zero, it will be found that at first the current (leakage current) is very small and changes very little with increasing reverse voltage. A point will be reached, however, at which the current suddenly rises; beyond this point it increases very rapidly for a very small increase in reverse voltage. The diode is said to *avalanche* at this point which is also called the *Zener voltage*.

Since the current in the avalanche region can change over a wide range

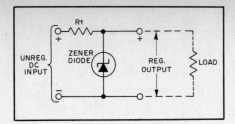

Fig. 14 — Voltage-regulator circuit using a Zener diode. Principle of operation is similar to that of the VR-tube circuit of Fig. 10.

while the voltage stays practically constant, the Zener diode can be used as a voltage regulator, Fig. 14, in just the same way as the VR tube described above. The design procedure is a little more complicated, however, because the amount of current that a Zener diode can handle depends on its power rating, and is not conveniently fixed at either 30 or 40 mA as with the VR tubes. Also, Zener diodes come in a wide assortment of power ratings — 150 mW to 50 W, typically — and voltage ratings — from about 3 to 200 volts. The lower voltage ratings, up to 20 or 30 volts, are highly useful for regulating the voltages in transistor circuits.

To calculate the current that the Zener can pass safely, divide the power rating by the Zener voltage. If a diode is rated at 1 watt, 15 volts, for example, the maximum current is 1/15 amp (67 mA). The minimum current for maintaining constant voltage should be a couple of milliamperes.

The regulated voltage will vary somewhat from the rating, and tolerances of 5 and 10 percent are frequently available. Also, the voltage varies with temperature, so there will be a small drift in regulated voltage as the diode warms up to a stable operating temperature. This temperature in turn depends on the current through the diode, so there will be a small change in regulated voltage each time the current changes. These variations are small enough to be neglected, though, except when very "tight" voltage regulation is required.

### Electronic Voltage Regulation

Several circuits have been developed for regulating the voltage output of a power supply electronically. While more complicated than the VR-tube and Zener-diode circuits, they will handle higher voltage and current variations, and the output voltage may be varied continuously over a wide range.

Voltage regulators fall into two basic types. In the type most commonly used by us amateurs, the dc supply delivers a voltage higher than that which is available at the output of the regulator, and the regulated voltage is obtained by dropping the voltage down to a lower value through a dropping "resistor." Regulation is accomplished by varying either the current through a fixed dropping resistance as changes in input voltage or load currents occur (as in the VR-tube and Zener-diode regulator circuits), or by varying the equivalent resistive value of the dropping element with such changes. This latter technique

is used in electronic regulators where the voltage-dropping element is a vacuum tube or a transistor, rather than an actual resistor. By varying the dc voltage at the grid or current at the base of these elements, the conductivity of the device may be varied as necessary to hold the output voltage constant. In solid-state regulators the series-dropping element is called a pass transistor. Power transistors are available which will handle several amperes of current at several hundred volts, but solid-state regulators of this type are usually operated at potentials below 100 volts.

The second type of regulator is a switching type, where the voltage from the dc source is rapidly switched on and off (electronically). The average dc voltage available from the regulator is proportional to the duty cycle of the switching wave form, or the ratio of the ON time to the total period of the switching cycle. Switching frequencies of several kilohertz are normally used to avoid the need for extensive filtering to smooth the switching frequency from the dc output.

The above information pertains essentially to voltage regulators. A circuit can also be constructed to provide current regulation. Such regulation is usually obtained in the form of current limitation — to a maximum value which is either preset or adjustable, depending on the circuit. Relatively simple circuits, such as described later, can be used to provide current limiting only. Current-limiting circuitry may also be used in conjunction with voltage regulators.

# Practical Circuits

The various rectifier and filter circuits can be combined in just about any way you please, in order to arrive at some desired set of operating characteristics — output voltage, output current, filtering and voltage regulation — provided the principles discussed are observed. However, experience has evolved several more-or-less standard arrangements.

### Supplies for Transistor Circuits

One of the simplest forms of solid-state regulation is shown at Fig. 15. A bridge rectifier supplies 25 volts dc to a series regulator transistor, Q1, whose base bias is established by means of a Zener diode, VR1, providing a voltage reference of a fixed level. C1 is the input capacitor for the filter. R1 is chosen to establish a safe Zener-diode current, which is dependent upon the wattage rating of the diode. A 1-watt Zener diode is adequate for the circuit

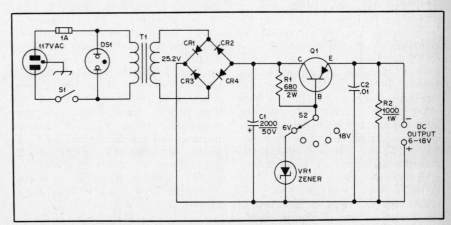

Fig. 15 — Schematic diagram of the power supply. Capacitances are in µF; capacitors marked with a polarity are electrolytic. Resistances are in ohms; R1 and R2 are composition.

C1 — 2000-µF 50 volts dc electrolytic (Mallory CG23U50C1).
C2 — .01-µF disk ceramic.
CR1-CR4, incl. — 50 PRV 3-A silicon diode (Motorola 1N4719).
DS1 — Neon lamp assembly with resistor (Leecraft 32-2111).

Q1 — 2N1970.
S1 — Spst toggle switch.
S2 — Phenolic rotary, 1-section, 2-pole (1 used), 6-position, shorting (Mallory 3126J).
T1 — Filament transformer, 25.2 V, 2 A (Knight 54 D 4140 or similar).
VR1 — Voltage-regulator diode.

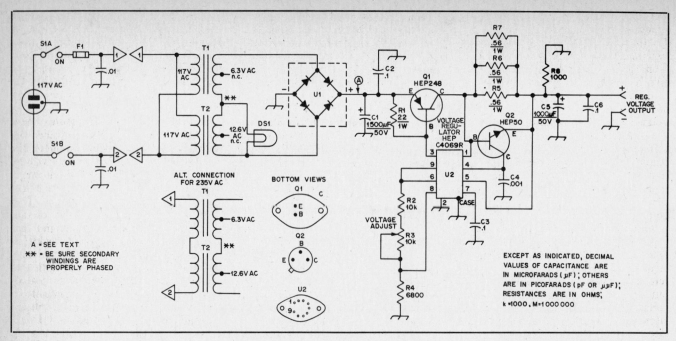

Fig. 16 — Circuit diagram for the power supply. Unless otherwise noted, all resistors are 1/2-watt composition. Component designators not listed below are for text reference and circuit-board layout purposes. Capacitors are disk ceramic except those with polarity marked, which are electrolytic.

C1 — 1500 µF electrolytic, 50 volts dc (Sprague TVA 1318).
C5 — 1000 µF electrolytic, 50 volts dc (Sprague TVA 1316).
DS1 — 12-volt pilot lamp.
F1 — 1.5 A, type 3AG fuse.
Q1 — Motorola HEP248 or equiv.

Q2 — Motorola HEP50, 2N706A or equiv.
R3 — 10-kΩ printed-circuit-mounting pot (Radio Shack 271-218).
R5, R6, R7 — 0.56 Ω 1-watt wirewound resistor (Radio Shack 271-072).
S1 — Miniature dpst toggle.
T1 — 117-volt pri., 6.3-volt ct sec. (ct unused),

3 amperes (Radio Shack 273-1510).
T2 — 117-volt pri., 12.6-volt at sec. (ct unused), 3 amperes (Radio Shack 273-1511).
U1 — Full-wave bridge rectifier assembly, 50 volts, 10 amperes (Radio Shack 276-1156).
U2 — Motorola HEP C6049R, MC1469R or MC1569R.

of Fig. 15. R2 is a bleeder resistor and C2 is an rf bypass. If several output voltages are desired, say from 6 to 18 volts, Zener diodes from 6 to 18 volts can be wired to S2 as shown. When a 2N1970 is used at Q1, the value of R1 will be 680 ohms. This value offers a compromise for the five reference diodes used (6, 9, 12, 15 and 18 volts).

The output of the supply is equal to the Zener voltage minus the emitter-to-base bias voltage of Q1. Both the Zener voltage and bias voltage will be approximately zero with only R2 as a load, but will rise to roughly 0.3 volt with a 1-A load connected to the output. An increase in load current lowers the unregulated dc input voltage which appears across VR1 and R1. Zener current is reduced, decreasing the voltage at which the diode regulates. How much the voltage drops depends upon the characteristics of the particular Zener employed.

This power supply has very low output ripple. The main limitation of the circuit is the possibility of destroying Q1, the series-regulator transistor, when a dead short or heavy overload is connected across the output of the supply. To protect Q1 during normal operation, it should be mounted on a fairly large heat sink which is thermally coupled to the main chassis of the supply. The transistor should be insulated from the sink by means of a mica spacer and a thin layer of silicone grease. The sink can then be bolted directly to the chassis.

## IC Regulators

The solid-state regulator described above provides only fixed voltages. Regulator circuits with the output voltage continuously variable over a wide range and with a very high degree of regulation can be built, but the number of circuit components is comparatively large when discrete components are used. Integrated-circuit devices can be used in a solid-state regulator circuit to replace many or all of the discrete components, depending on the output requirements. The voltage reference, control, shut-down (for current limiting) and pass-transistor driver elements are contained on a single silicon chip. The construction of a regulated power supply is simplified to a few interconnections if an IC regulator is used.

## An Adjustable Voltage Supply

This regulated power supply is suitable for use as a "battery eliminator" for transceivers of the 10-watt output variety, or for general purpose workbench duty. This supply is designed to provide up to 2 amperes continuously at 12 volts, although the output voltage may be adjusted with the externally mounted control within the range of 5 to 20 volts.

## Circuit Description

The use of two transformers, rather than one, allows a certain degree of flexibility of operation, in that the supply may be used on either 117 or 235 volts ac with only minor differences in wiring. The dc voltage at point A is approximately 30. Q1 is used as a series-pass transistor. Its function is to drop the voltage at point A of Fig. 16 to the desired output value, and maintain that voltage over wide variations in the output load current. U2 is an integrated-circuit voltage regulator which, with the aid of a few external components, is capable of handling up to 600 mA of output current. Since an output current of 2 A is desired, however, U2 is used here to properly bias Q1, which has a much higher current rating. The inner circuitry of U2 can be divided into four basic elements: a fixed voltage reference, a variable voltage reference derived from the fixed reference, an error amplifier and an output regulator. An internal Zener diode is used as the fixed reference. This reference voltage is applied to one input of a differential amplifier (a differential amplifier responds to the difference between two applied voltage levels), while the other input is connected to the junction of R3 and R4 (pin 8 of U2). R3 (in series with R2) and R4 form an externally adjustable voltage divider, from the differential amplifier output (pin 9 of U2) to ground. Thus, the output of the differential amplifier will swing to the level that results in the voltage at pin 8 of U2 being identical to the fixed reference voltage. A second differential amplifier serves as the error amplifier. One input (pin 6 of U2) is tied directly to pin 9, while the other input (pin 5 of U2) is connected to the power-supply output bus. The error-amplifier output controls the internal output-regulator bias of the IC, which in turn controls the bias applied to Q1. When connected in this manner, the error amplifier responds to any difference between the power-supply output level and the (previously adjusted) voltage-reference level. The output regulator acts on Q1 to correct the discrepancy. C3 and C4 are used in the interest of maintaining amplifier stability. R5, R6, R7 and Q2 are included in the circuit to protect the power supply and regulator in the event of an inadvertent short circuit between the output terminals or if the current demanded by the load is too heavy for safe operation. The operation of the current-limiting feature is as follows: When the current flowing through the parallel combination of R5, R6 and R7 (equivalent parallel resistance of about 0.18 ohm) is large enough to produce a 0.6-volt drop across the resistors, Q2 is biased into conduction. The action of Q2 on the IC internal output regulator results in the reduction of the current through Q1. The short-circuit output current in this case will be limited to 3.3 amperes (0.6/0.18 = 3.3), which is within the safe regulator/pass-transistor limits. The value of the current-sensing resistance required for short-circuit currents of other than 3.3 amperes is calculated as follows by Ohm's Law: $R_{SC} = 0.6/I_{SC}$ where $R_{SC}$ is the current-sensing resistance and $I_{SC}$ is the maximum allowable short-circuit current. If a long run of cable is used between the power supply and the load, the voltage drop in the cable may be large enough to be of concern. If this is the case, a separate remote voltage-sensing wire may be run from the load to pin 5 of U2, rather than connecting pin 5 to the output at the power supply. The regulator will compensate for the voltage drop in the cable. This wire may be of a small gauge, as little current will be drawn through it.

## Construction Details

Most of the components were mounted on an etched circuit board (see Fig. 17), although point-to-point wiring on a perf board would have sufficed. As the transistors inside the IC are capable of operation at vhf, it is good practice to use short leads for interconnecting the regulator components to prevent unwanted oscillations from occurring. The manufacturer recommends a low-inductance connection between the case of the HEP C6049R and ground. No evidence of instability was noted with this circuit.

All parts are housed in an 8 X 6 X 3-1/2-inch aluminum enclosure. Two standoff insulators support the pc board, while the power transformers, T1 and T2, are bolted directly to the Minibox. As Q1 dissipates several watts when maximum load current is being drawn, a heat sink is required. The Motorola HEP500, consisting of an MS-10 predrilled heat sink and an MK-15 power-transistor mounting kit, is ideal for this application. In accordance with the instructions supplied with the HEP500, the MK-15 should be coated on both sides with a thin layer of silicon thermal compound (Radio Shack 276-1372), with the bottom of Q1 and the center area of the heat sink treated similarly. After the Q1 emitter and base pins are inserted through the proper holes in the washer, the transistor is mounted in the socket. The mica washer insulates the case of Q1 (which is connected internally to the oscillator) electrically from the heat sink and chassis, while the silicone compound increases the thermal conductivity between Q1 and the heat sink. Care should be taken to prevent contact between the case of Q1 and any grounded object, as the full supply voltage appears on the transistor case, the current-limiting feature will not protect the device from destruction in event of an accidental short from Q1 to ground, since the current-sensing resistors (R5, R6 and R7) are connected between Q1 and the power-supply output terminals. The heat-sink assembly is bolted to the rear panel of the Minibox with no. 6 hardware. The MS-10 is 3 inches high and 4-1/2 inches wide, so it must be located off center in order to accommodate the fuse holder and the line cord on the rear panel. A 1-inch-diameter hole was punched in the rear panel prior to the heat-sink installation to allow access to the transistor-socket pins. Short lengths of hookup wire are used between the pc board and the transistor socket. U1 is coated with silicone compound and then bolted to one of the inside walls of the Minibox, which serves as a heat sink for the diodes. Ventilation of the Minibox is desirable. Large holes punched or cut in the sides and bottom of the box and covered with perforated metal stock can be used, or ventilation holes can be drilled individually in the metal enclosure. The regulator IC is mounted directly on the pc board, and it does not require a heat sink.

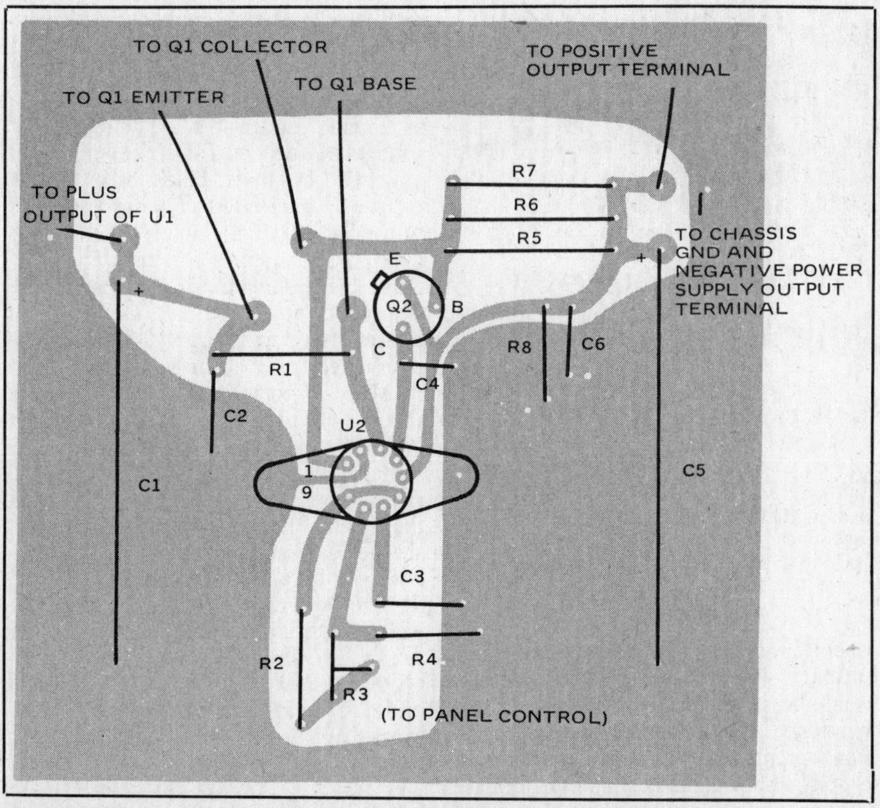

After the pilot lamp, the power switch, and the binding posts are in-

Fig. 17 — Foil pattern and parts layout for the regulated power supply.

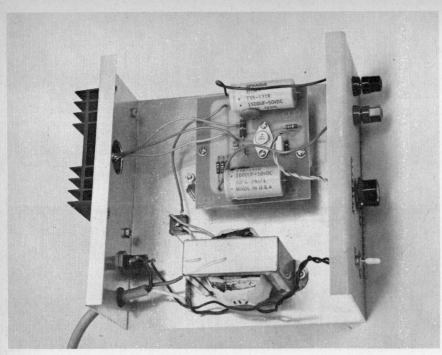

Fig. 18 — Inside view of the regulated power supply. The use of the 4-inch square pc board (visible at upper right) simplifies the interconnection of most of the parts. The full-wave bridge-rectifier assembly (U1) and the heat sink for Q1 are bolted to the chassis floor. A single transformer has been used here in place of T1 and T2 as described in *QST* for January, 1975.

Fig. 19 — The Universal Power Supply is constructed on a standard-size aluminum chassis. Back-to-back plugs with appropriate jumper wires make changing from 117-V to 220-V input operation or from 6.3-V to 12.6-V filament operation a simple matter of reversing a plug.

stalled on the front panel, T1 and T2 can be bolted in place near the front of the box. The transformer primaries can be tied in parallel for operation from 117 volts ac, or in series for 235-volt ac operation. The T1 and T2 secondaries must be connected in series and in proper phase for the power supply to operate correctly. If the unloaded ac output voltage as measured with a VOM is in the neighborhood of 20 volts, the windings are connected properly. If, however, the VOM reads approximately 6 volts, the secondaries are out of phase and the leads from one of the transformers must be reversed.

If the primary leads are brought out to four separate terminal posts, changing from 117-volt to 235-volt operation will be a simple matter of changing appropriate jumpers. Alternatively, a 117/235 switch may be installed easily on the rear panel if frequent line voltage changes are anticipated. In either case attention should be paid to the matter of proper phasing of the windings. The use of a 3-wire ac cord installed in a properly grounded outlet is intelligent practice for this and any line-operated power supply. If a transformer with a secondary rating of approximately 18 volts at 3 amperes is available, it may be used in place of T1 and T2. Details for the modification of a 24-volt secondary transformer are given in *QST* for January, 1975.

## A Universal Power Supply for the Amateur Station

Presented here is a general-purpose unit with provisions for 117-220-volt operation, and it is adapted easily for use with most commercially available gear by constructing appropriate power cords. The supply delivers 800 V at 300 mA dc, 300 V at 175 mA dc, and 0- to 130-V at 25 mA. In addition, the supply provides ac filament potentials of 6.3 V at 11 A or 12.6 V at 5.5 A.

Often the station power supply is a heavy black box that is tucked away in a corner and just sits there. A large cable interconnects this device with the station transmitter or transceiver and the amateur never comes directly in contact with it; all of the supply functions are remotely controlled from the panel of the station transmitting gear. But what happens if an instance arises where a particular voltage (or combination of voltages) is needed for an experimental project? Can that "black box' in the corner be pressed readily into service? And what about the amateur who buys two power supplies for his station because his mobile transceiver cannot be plugged directly into his home-station transmitter power supply? This supply is designed to fill all these needs.

Many of today's commercially available ac supplies are not equipped for 220-volt operation. If the station includes a two-kilowatt amplifier, a separate 220-volt line should be available in the shack. Blinking house lights are not always a result of running a high-powered amplifier. It could be caused by the intermittent 400- or 500-watt load presented by an exciter power supply to the 117-volt source. Connecting the exciter supply to a 220-volt outlet (providing a dual-primary transformer is used) can be helpful in this regard.

### Circuit Details

The supply is shown in Figs. 19

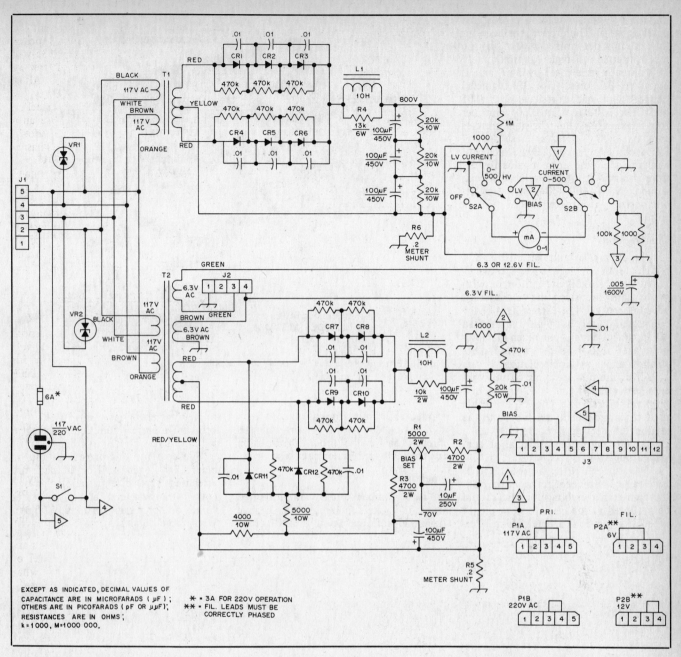

Fig. 20 — Circuit diagram for the Universal Power Supply. Component designations not listed below are for text reference.

CR1-CR12, incl. — 1000-PRV, 2.5-A silicon diode (Mallory M2.5A or equiv.).

J1, J2 — 5-pin tube-type socket (Amphenol 78RS5 or equiv.).

J3 — 12-lug terminal block (Cinch 12-140 or equiv.), and 12-lug fanning strip (Cinch 12-160L or equiv.).

L1 — 10 H, 200 mA (Hammond 193J).

L2 — 10 H, 300 mA (Hammond 193M).

P1, P2 — 5-pin plugs to mate J1 and J2, 4 req'd (Amphenol 86-PM5 or equiv.).

R1 — 5-watt linear-taper control.

R2, R3 — For text reference.

R4 — Three 39,000-ohm 2-watt resistors connected in parallel.

R5, R6 — See text.

S1 — Spst toggle rated at 6A or greater.

S2 — 2-pole, 6-position rotary, nonshorting (Centralab 1411 or equiv.).

T1 — Dual primary, 117 or 220 V ac; secondary 890 volts each side of center tap at 300 mA (Hammond type 101059).

T2 — Dual primary, 117 or 220 V ac; secondary 350 volts each side of center tap at 175 mA, 6.3 volts ac at 6 A, 6.3 volts ac at 5 A (Hammond special 273BX).

VR1, VR2 — Thyrector assembly (G. E. 6RS20SP4B4).

through 21. Primary power may be applied to the supply in two ways. First, terminals 6 and 8 of J3 may be shorted together; this is normally the function of the station transmitting equipment on-off switch. On the other hand, S1 may be actuated when the supply is used independently. Transient voltages on the ac line are eliminated by Thyrector assemblies VR1 and VR2.

Full-wave rectification is employed in the secondary circuit of each power transformer to develop the three dc operating voltages. Choke-input filtering provides adequate regulation of both the 300- and 800-volt outputs. Both L1 and L2 are shunted with suitable resistors to reduce the possibility of diode damage when primary power to the supply is removed.

The bias voltage is adjustable and may be set to any value between −40 and −80. Should a range between −80 and −130 volts be required, R1 may be interchanged with R3. Likewise, if a range from 0 to −40 volts is needed, R1 may be swapped with R2.

## Metering

A six-position switch and a 0-1-mA meter allows monitoring of high and low voltages, the current for each of these, and the bias voltage. The sixth position permits the meter to be disabled. The meter shunts for both current positions of S2 are homemade and provide a full-scale reading of 500 mA on each range. The proper resistance for the shunts is determined by dividing the meter internal resistance (approximately 100 ohms in this case) by 500, and is equal to 0.2 ohm. No. 30 enameled copper wire has a resistance of 105 ohms per 1000 feet, or 0.105 ohm per foot. Extending the division another step, one inch of wire has a resistance of 0.008 ohm. Approximately 23 inches of wire provided the correct value for the shunts. Each 23-inch length of wire is wound on a 100,000-ohm, two-watt composition resistor which serves as a form.

## Construction

The supply is built on a 10 × 8 × 3-inch aluminum chassis. The spot welds at the four corners are reinforced with no. 6 hardware since the transformers are quite heavy. The total weight of the completed supply is slightly more than 40 pounds. Several one-inch-diameter holes are cut in the chassis bottom plate to allow adequate air circulation.

All of the power-supply output voltages are present on a 12-connection terminal block. The end of the cable used to interconnect the supply to the station transceiver is equipped with a 12-lug fanning strip, providing a convenient means to disconnect it.

One special wiring precaution is necessary; the bleeder resistors for both the high and low-voltage circuits should be mounted in the clear to allow plenty of air circulation around them. Per-

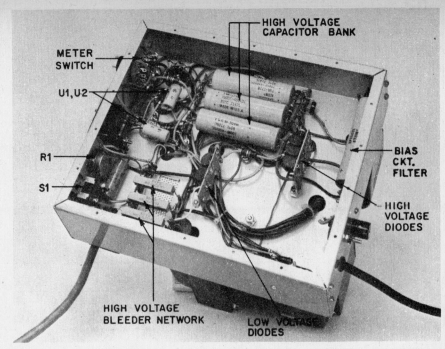

Fig. 21 — Bottom view of the Universal Power Supply.

forated aluminum stock is placed over a 1 × 3-inch cut in the chassis which is directly above the mounting position for the 800-volt bleeder network.

## Operation

Two jumper plugs are mounted "back-to-back," making the change from 117-volt operation to 220 volts a simple matter of reversing P1. P2 performs an identical function to select 6 or 12 volts for the filament line.

The cost for this project should be under $100, even if all of the parts are purchased new. The price of the two power transformers and two filter chokes comprises approximately 60 percent of the total cost.

# Chapter 13

# Making Measurements

Whole books could be (and have been) written on electrical measurements. The subject has a fascination all of its own. However, in this chapter we'll not attempt to do more than touch on a few measurements aimed at helping you adjust your equipment for optimum results.

## What Accuracy Means

At the outset, it may be useful to give you a little perspective. There is no such thing as an "absolute" measurement. No matter how good the measuring equipment and the care with which it is used and read, the best that one can do is to say that the true value of a measurement lies between a pair of limits. Inside those limits the value is uncertain. An accurate measurement is one in which the limits are close together. The farther apart the limits are, the more "fuzzy" the measured value.

The limits, for a piece of measuring equipment, usually are specified in terms of *percentage accuracy,* but sometimes other methods are used.

One example should suffice. You have a 0 to 100-dc milliammeter. If it is a good-quality instrument, it will probably have the scale divided into 50 parts, each representing a 2-milliampere change in current. Suppose in measuring the plate current of a tube, the pointer comes to rest between the divisions representing 54 and 56 mA.

## What is the Current?

If the pointer seems to be about half-way between the two divisions, you would naturally say that the current is 55 mA. But on looking up the specifications on the instrument, you find that it is rated to be accurate to "within plus or minus 2 percent of full scale." The full-scale reading is 100 mA, and 2 percent of that is 2 mA. So you have a built-in uncertainty of plus or minus 2

mA — one whole division on the scale. The best you can say is that the *actual* current should be between 55 − 2 and 55 + 2, that is, between 53 and 57 mA.

That isn't bad accuracy, for many measurements. An error of 10 percent or even 25 percent or more won't make any practical difference in many cases. For example, the capacitance used in a power-supply filter can have any value within a wide range, just so long as it is large enough. But there are other cases where the accuracy of measurement has to be exceedingly good. The frequency limits of the band in which your transmitter operates is such a case. If you're going to work near the edge, you have to *know* just where that edge is. Here an error of just a few cycles in several million per second can get you into trouble with the FCC.

The instruments described in this chapter will be accurate enough for their intended purposes. This does not mean that you can expect your measurements to agree absolutely with those made by highly specialized and often highly expensive equipment. It *does* mean, though, that the results you get, in terms of adjustment of the equipment with which these instruments are used, will be just as good as they would be with measuring gear of higher accuracy.

## DC Measurements

The same basic instrument is used for measuring direct current and voltage. No doubt you already own a *milliammeter* or *voltmeter*. They come in various shapes and sizes. All of them use electromagnetism to make the pointer move across the scale. Some — the inexpensive kind — simply have a coil through which the current flows, exerting a magnetic pull on a soft-iron vane to which the pointer or "needle" is attached. The larger the current, the

greater the magnetic attraction and the greater the pointer movement. The scales on these instruments are *non-linear.* That is, the divisions are spread out more at one end of the scale than the other.

Better-quality (and higher priced) instruments have the coil pivoted between faces of a permanent magnet. This is called a *D'Arsonval movement*. It is capable of higher accuracy — although this depends on the care in construction — and the scale is linear.

Milliammeters should be selected with an eye to the range of currents to be measured. The accuracy is greatest in the upper half of the scale. Thus, if you want to measure currents in the neighborhood of 150 mA, an instrument having a full-scale range of 200 or 250 mA would be optimum. But measuring a current of, say, 10 mA with such a meter would be considerably less accurate — remember the example above! — and a 25-mA meter would be much better.

## Multirange Instruments

Very often you do need to measure currents of widely different values. The plate current of a tube may be around 50 times as great as the grid current; nevertheless, it is advantageous to measure both with the same instrument, rather than having to purchase two separate meters with appropriate ranges. This can easily be done, because a low-range meter can always be made to measure currents *greater* than its own full-scale reading. The range can be increased by adding *shunts* across the meter terminals.

A shunt is simply a resistance placed in parallel with the meter so the current has two paths to follow. By diverting some of the current through the shunt, there is less to go through the meter. If you know how much more goes through

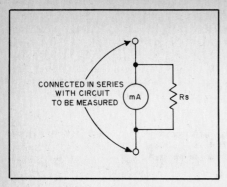

Fig. 1 — How a shunt, $R_S$, is connected for extending the full-scale range of a milliammeter.

the shunt than through the meter, you simply read what the meter says and then multiply by the shunting factor to find the actual current. For example, in Fig. 1 if four times as much current goes through the shunt, $R_S$ as through the meter, the meter is getting only one-fifth of the total current, so the current in the circuit is five times the meter reading.

### Values for Shunts

To know what resistance to use in the shunt for a desired scale multiplication, you first have to know the resistance of the meter itself. This is probably given in the manufacturer's data on the meter. It is often of the order of 50 ohms for a 0-1 milli-ammeter, decreasing as the full-scale current range increases. The shunt resistance $R_S$ is then equal to the meter resistance divided by the desired current multiplication minus one. For instance, if you have a 10-mA meter having a resistance of 5 ohms and want to increase its range to 100 mA (10X multiplication) you divide 5 by (10 − 1) or 9, so the shunt resistance required is 0.55 ohm.

The resistance of a shunt is usually rather low, as this example shows. You can easily make your own from small-gauge copper wire. No. 30 is suitable for most shunts. It has a resistance of 0.105 ohms per foot, so to make a 0.55-ohm shunt you would need 0.55/0.105 = 5.3 feet of wire. It can be scramble-wound on a wooden matchstick to make a small coil.

If you don't know the resistance of the meter, start out with a *short* piece of wire as a shunt. Measure a current near full scale without the shunt, then put on the shunt and observe the new reading. If you want a 10X shunt, change the wire length until the reading drops to one-tenth its value without the shunt. The same method can be used for other multipliers. However it is best not to go more than 10 times in one jump. The first 10X multiplier can be used to

find the right shunt for the next, and so on.

### Voltmeters

A voltmeter is simply a milliammeter with a high resistance in series, Fig. 2. The current through the resistor is measured and then, by Ohm's Law, the voltage drop across it can be found. The combination is connected across the circuit in which the voltage is to be measured.

In most cases we don't want the voltmeter to load the circuit it is measuring. That is, we want the current the meter takes to be very small compared with the current flowing in the circuit. For this to be so the meter itself usually has to be quite sensitive. A full-scale range of 1 milliampere is about the largest that is commonly used. Meters that give a full-scale deflection with as little as 50 microamperes are used in many test instruments.

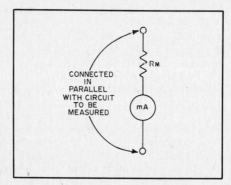

Fig. 2 — A voltmeter is a milliammeter (or microammeter) with a high resistance, $R_M$, in series.

The resistance needed for the voltmeter (resistor $R_M$ in Fig. 2 is called the *multiplier*) is easily calculated. It is equal to the full-scale voltage to be read divided by the full-scale meter current in amperes. One volt divided by 1 milliampere (0.001 ampere) is 1000 ohms, so a voltmeter using a 0-1 milliammeter is called a "1000-ohms-per-volt" meter. With such a meter you simply multiply the desired full-scale voltage by 1000, to find $R_M$. Thus a 500-volt voltmeter would require 500 × 1000 = 500,000 ohms, or 0.5 megohm, for $R_M$.

In making a voltmeter multiplier keep in mind that the power that has to be dissipated in the resistor may not be negligible. The power is equal to the voltage multiplied by the current, and in the example above would be 1/2 watt. However, small resistors sometimes have a maximum voltage rating as well as a maximum power rating, so look up both ratings before selecting a resistor. Actually, it costs only a few cents to be

conservative and use two resistors in series where you might get by with only one.

### Measuring Resistance

Ohm's Law points the way to measuring resistance with a milliammeter. All we need to do is apply a known voltage to the resistor and milliammeter in series, measure the current, and the resistance is equal to the voltage divided by the current. The known voltage can be taken from one or two small dry cells. These give 1.5 volts each.

A 0-1 milliammeter can be used this way for measuring resistances ranging from about 100 to 50,000 ohms, with useful accuracy. This covers a great many of the resistance values you need to use in transmitting and receiving equipment. For higher values of resistance, it is necessary to use a meter with more sensitivity — 50 or 100 microamperes full scale — and for lower values a more complicated circuit arrangement is required.

The circuit used for resistance measurement is given in Fig. 3. If the unknown is a very low resistance, connecting it across the terminals AB practically amounts to short-circuiting them. The safe meter current would be greatly exceeded in that case if it were not for the series resistor R1, which is selected so that the meter just reads full scale when terminals AB are shorted. R1 can be an adjustable resistor, if you wish, so the current can be adjusted to make the meter read *exactly* full scale with AB shorted. This adjustment helps compensate for the change in battery voltage as the dry cells run down with age and use.

### Combination Instruments —
### the Volt-Ohm-Milliammeter

You can't be in ham radio very long without feeling a need for a test instrument — completely independent of your transmitter, receiver, and other communication equipment — that will let

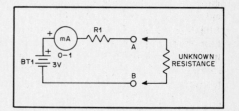

Fig. 3 — Simple ohmmeter circuit. The resistance of R1 should be equal to the battery voltage divided by the full-scale reading of the milliammeter. For a 3-volt battery and 0-1 milliammeter, R1 is 3/0.001, or 3000 ohms. If a variable resistor is used, it should have somewhat larger resistance (5000 ohms would be suitable in this case) to allow leeway for adjustment. A composition control can be used but an equivalent wire-wound control will be more stable.

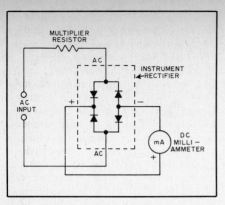

Fig. 4 — One type of ac voltmeter using a dc meter movement with a rectifier.

you measure voltage (both dc and ac), resistance, and, with lesser urgency, current. Although you can get separate instruments for each of these measurements, it is far more convenient to have everything in one compact multirange unit.

The same basic meter movement can be used, its range being extended by supplementary circuits such as the shunts and multipliers described earlier. This suggests that the assembly can be built up from scratch by buying the necessary parts. However, we don't recommend it, unless you get one of the special kits made just for the purpose. Much of the value of an instrument is in its calibration and the convenience with which its scales can be read. In this field, you're badly handicapped by not having the facilities available to manufacturers. Furthermore, if you buy the parts separately and assemble them, you wind up by spending more than you would for a kit — or even, in many cases, more than for a completely assembled instrument.

The *volt-ohm-milliammeter* — or *VOM*, as it is usually called — is available in a variety of sizes, sensitivities and ranges. The simplest generally has several dc-voltage ranges up to 500 or 1000 volts, with a resistance of 1000 ohms per volt. The useful "ohms" range will be of the order of 50,000 ohms in these instruments. Direct-current ranges, if included (they may not be) may go up to 250 mA or so. There are usually ac-voltage scales corresponding to the dc-voltage scales. As you go up the price ladder, the number of ranges increases and so does the sensitivity; the better instruments of this type have 20,000- to 100,000-ohms-per-volt dc-voltage scales, higher voltage ac scales, and more elaborate ohmmeter circuits that not only can measure low values of resistance but also extend the high range up to a megohm or more. In the end, it pays to buy the most versatile instrument you can afford. However, a low-cost "handy

tester" will take care of a lot of jobs for you.

## AC Measurements

Meters for measuring 60-hertz ac voltage and current are similar in principle to those used for dc. There is rarely a need for measuring current at the supply-line frequency, so you will seldom if ever see an ac ammeter or milliammeter in an amateur station. Ac voltmeters frequently are used in transmitters having high-power tubes, because good tube life requires that the filament voltage be kept at the rated value. Instruments of this type usually are accurate only at the frequency for which they are designed — 60 hertz, generally.

A different type of voltmeter is incorporated in the multipurpose test instruments mentioned earlier. The basic meter in these instruments must measure dc, and to make the meter useful on ac an ac voltage must first be converted to dc. A semiconductor (copper oxide) full-wave bridge rectifier is often used for this (Fig. 4). The copper-oxide rectifier ac voltmeter will work well over the audio-frequency range from 50 to 5000 hertz.

The readings of all types of ac meters must be taken with reservations. The scales on such instruments are always calibrated in terms of the rms value of a sine wave. But rectifier-type instruments do not actually respond to the rms value, so the readings are within the rated accuracy of the instrument only when the voltage is sinusoidal. Generally, it is safe to assume that the voltage will be sinusoidal if it is coming from the ac line directly or through a transformer. Thus you should get a reasonably accurate reading on, say, the 6.3-volt heater winding of a transformer. Measurements on audio circuit, particularly voice waveforms, are useful only in a relative sense — i.e., stronger or weaker; in general, the scale reading means little without supplementary information about the waveform.

## RF Voltage

The rectifier scheme is a particularly good one for measuring radio-frequency voltages. Ordinary instruments will not do for frequencies in the rf range. Rf circuits, particularly tuned ones having relatively high impedance — as is the case in most receiving and transmitting equipment — are acutely sensitive about having things connected to them. Test leads have too much inductance and capacitance; they detune the circuit so much that measurements are worthless.

On the other hand, a germanium point-contact diode (the 1N34A is typical) has a capacitance of only about one picofarad and physically is so small that it can be installed right in the rf

circuit where the voltage is to be measured. Then only dc leads need be brought out to go to an ordinary milliammeter. Fig. 5 is a typical circuit. The part to the right of the dashed line is the voltmeter; the part to the left is merely one type of connection that could be made. The leads from the rf circuit through CR1 and C1 would be made as short as possible by installing these components right at the circuit being measured — usually installing them permanently. Sometimes the voltmeter components are made up in the form of an *rf probe* which can be touched directly on the circuit to be measured, with negligible lead length in the rf part. The dc leads can be any length desired.

In amateur equipment the rf voltmeter is used principally for *relative* voltage indications. An example is the rf output indicator used as a tuning aid in many transmitters. For this purpose it isn't necessary to know the actual voltage, since the practical purpose of the instrument is fully realized when you make the meter pointer go as far toward maximum as possible.

In some rf measurements — in measuring SWR for example — it is necessary that the meter indications be linear, if the measurements are to mean anything. Even here, though, you don't have to know the *actual* value of the voltage — it is sufficient to know that the voltage will be directly proportional to the scale reading. The principal purpose of R1 in Fig. 5 is to make the meter linear. With little or no added resistance in the circuit, the meter indications tend to be proportional to the

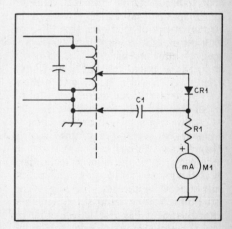

Fig. 5 — An rf voltmeter circuit. CR1 usually is a 1N34A or a similar type diode. The value of C1 is usually 0.001 or 0.01 μF; a ceramic capacitor is recommended. M1 can be a 0-1 milliammeter. R1 (see text) can be variable if the sensitivity of the system is to be adjusted (the larger the resistance value the lower the current); a 10,000-ohm composition control is typical.

In the circuit above, the coil in the rf circuit provides a dc return to ground for the rectifier. If the circuit does not offer a dc return, an rf choke should be connected from the upper end of the rectifier to ground.

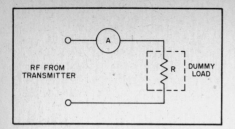

Fig. 6 — Using an rf ammeter to measure current in a dummy antenna of known resistance, for power measurement. The power is equal to $I^2 R$. A current of 1.5 amp. flowing in a 50-ohm resistance is, therefore, $2.25 \times 50 = 112$ watts.

square of the rf voltage applied to the rectifier. It takes about 10,000 ohms at R1 to make a reasonably linear voltmeter when M1 is a 0-1 milliammeter.

### RF Current

The instrument used to measure rf current is a *thermocouple rf ammeter.* A *thermocouple* is a junction of two dissimilar metals which has the property of generating a small direct current when heated. In the rf ammeter the radio-frequency current flows through a short length of resistance wire which heats up in proportion to the rf power it dissipates. This heat is applied to the thermocouple, and the current generated by the junction flows through a dc milliammeter. The face of the instrument is calibrated in rf amperes.

An rf ammeter is expensive when purchased new, but a variety of these instruments have been available at low prices through military surplus. It is rarely necessary to use one in an amateur transmitter; the principal value of an rf ammeter in amateur work is in measurement of rf power (Fig. 6). For this purpose it is necessary to have a load of known resistance, and to know that it is a "pure" resistance. By Ohm's Law, the rf power in such a load is equal to the square of the current multiplied by the resistance of the load.

Aside from such measurements, it usually suffices to know the *relative* change in current when you're adjusting a transmatch or the transmitter tuning. A flashlight or dial lamp is a cheap, but satisfactory, indicator for this. The brightness of the lamp shows whether an adjustment has resulted in more or less rf output. Ways of using the lamps for this purpose are described in chapter 11. The circuit given in Fig. 7 is typical for checking feeder current.

### Instrument Effects

You can have an instrument of excellent quality, capable of a high degree of accuracy, and still make measurements that are wide of the mark.

Why? Because every instrument becomes a part of the circuit in which the measurements are being made. To the extent that the presence of the instrument *changes* the circuit conditions, as compared with those existing when it isn't present, the indications will be in error. Of course, if you leave the instrument in the circuit permanently this doesn't matter. But it *does* matter when a test instrument is used temporarily for checking.

Errors of this nature are more likely to be appreciable in measuring voltage than in measuring current. Fig. 8 is an illustration. By Ohm's Law, the voltage across each 100,000-ohm resistor in A must be 50 volts when 100 volts is applied to the two in series. If we try to measure the voltage across the lower resistor, R2, with a 1000-ohms-per-volt meter, its resistance, also 100,000 ohms for a 100-volt scale, is in parallel with R2. The resistance of this combination

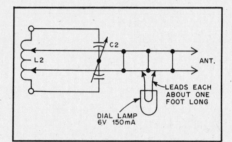

Fig. 7 — Using a dial lamp as a substitute for an rf ammeter to show relative rf current. In measurements of this type the actual value of current need not be known; in fact, the current in amperes will be different at different frequencies in tuned feeder systems, for the same power. The important thing is to get as much current as possible into the feeder at the frequency in use.

is only 50,000 ohms, so now there is only 33 volts across R2, as shown in B. This is what a perfectly accurate meter would read.

Now, if a 20,000-ohms-per-volt meter is used instead, the voltmeter resistance (still assuming a 100-volt scale) is 20 times as large as R2, so the effect on the total resistance is small. The meter now reads 48.7 volts, again quite accurately, but the indicated voltage still isn't quite what the *actual* voltage would be with the meter disconnected. A 10-megohm voltmeter reduces the error still more, as shown at D.

Observe, however, that if R2 had been connected directly to a 50-volt source, such as a battery, having very low internal resistance, the added current taken by the voltmeter would have only a negligible effect on the actual voltage. In that case all three instruments would have the same reading, 50 volts. It is the presence of a large *series*

resistance, R1, that is responsible for the error. Nevertheless, if the resistance of the voltmeter is very large compared with the resistance across which it is measuring voltage, the error will not be large even if the series resistance is high. "Very large" here means at least ten times (which may cause an error as large as 10 percent in the reading) and preferably at least 20 times (which cannot cause more than about 5 percent error in the worst case).

A comparable error in current measurement results when the resistance of a milliammeter is large compared with the series resistance of the circuit in which it is inserted. A 50-ohm instrument introduced into a 25-ohm circuit obviously would reduce the current by a very considerable amount. But this isn't so likely to happen in practice with ordinary instruments. A 50-ohm instrument would be a low-range one, and therefore would be used in low-current circuits — which are usually ones having fairly high resistance, at least as compared with the meter resistance. But "not likely" doesn't mean "never"; so don't take it for granted that current measurements will always be free from instrument effect.

### Electronic Voltmeter

The ohms-per-volt rating of a VOM means that the voltmeter resistance is relatively low on low-voltage ranges, although it may be quite high when measuring high voltages. For example, a 1000-ohms-per-volt meter has a resistance of only 1000 ohms if the range is

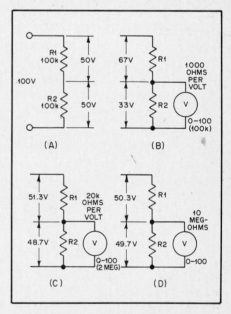

Fig. 8 — Effect of voltmeter resistance on indicated voltage in a typical case. Although all three meters may be equally accurate, each indicates a different voltage because the presence of the meter itself changes the voltage across R2.

0-1 volt. On the other hand, its resistance is 1 megohm on a 1000-volt range. This limitation can be overcome with the *electronic voltmeter*, which has constant resistance on all ranges.

The electronic voltmeter uses an amplifier having very high input resistance. As you learned in chapter 2, either a negative-grid vacuum tube or field-effect transistor has essentially an infinite input resistance. The change in drain or plate current is a measure of the voltage present at the grid or the gate. Both the grid and the gate require a dc path, however, so it is necessary to connect a resistance across the volt-meter input terminals. This resistance can be quite high, though, and common practice is to use a total of 11 megohms on all ranges. For most measurements this is such a high resistance that its presence can be ignored.

Electronic voltmeters also have several resistance-measurement ranges, and in general are considerably more accurate in this field than the VOM, as well as capable of measuring much lower and much higher resistances. The instrument usually also is provided with a rectifier so it can be used for ac measurements. On ac, it measures the *peak* value of the voltage (although the calibration is nearly always in rms values). You can't expect ac readings with the electronic voltmeter to agree with those made with a VOM, for this reason, unless the voltage being measured is a pretty good sine wave.

The most economical way to get a good electronic voltmeter is to buy one of the many kits available. It would cost you a good deal more to buy the individual parts, and you would not have the calibrated scales that go with the commercial jobs. If you do much testing and experimenting, you'll find the electronic voltmeter an invaluable part of your measuring equipment.

# Frequency Measurement

Literally, you can comply with the FCC regulations governing your transmitter frequency without actually measuring it. The regulations don't require you to know the exact frequency on which you are sending. They *do* require that it be within a *band* of frequencies, and you must have some way of telling whether or not you are operating inside an authorized band. The system for determining this must be independent of the transmitter itself. That is, you cannot depend on the frequency marked on a crystal used in your transmitting oscillator. It may be quite accurate, but in itself it isn't enough to satisfy the FCC.

It takes only simple equipment to locate the limits of these frequency bands with very high accuracy. Such equipment is based on using harmonics of a high-stability oscillator. The oscillator can be adjusted to exact frequency by using the government's standard-frequency transmissions over the National Bureau of Standards station WWV. It is something of a paradox, though, that while such a simple *frequency standard* will locate a band edge for you within a few hertz of the exact frequency, it gives you no assurance whatsoever that your transmitter is inside the right limits. You might actually be transmitting on the 80-meter band, for example, when you *think* your transmitter is "putting out" in the 40-meter band.

Adequate frequency checking, then, has to be done in two steps: First, it must be determined that the transmitter output is in the right band. Second, it must be established that the frequency is within the right limits *inside* that band. It is possible to do both without any auxiliary equipment at all, after you've gained a little experience. But it's a help to have simple frequency-measuring gear on tap.

### The Wavemeter

The very simplest device for measuring frequency is a resonant circuit — a coil and capacitor. You learned in chapter 1 that the current in such a circuit will be largest when the circuit is tuned to the frequency of the rf energy introduced into it. If you hook a coil and variable capacitor in parallel, Fig. 9, the circuit can be tuned over a range of frequencies by varying the capacitance from maximum to minimum.

Parenthetically, the name wavemeter dates back to the time when radio was known as "wireless" and it was the universal custom to think in terms of wavelength instead of frequency. The remnants of this practice are still with us — we speak of the "80-meter" and "40-meter" bands, for instance. But no one seriously thinks of measuring wavelength. Frequency can be specified and measured much more accurately.

The wavemeter is used by coupling its coil to a circuit carrying rf energy. Besides its tuned circuit, the wavemeter needs some system for indicating whether or not energy is present in the circuit being checked. The indicator used in the wavemeter shown in Fig. 10 is a miniature 0-1 milliammeter. L1 is tapped appropriately for delivering maximum power to the meter, and the rf output is rectified by CR1. C2, C3 and RFC1 function as a filter, which prevents rf energy from reaching the meter. The circuit is built in a 2-1/8 X 3 X 5-1/4-inch Minibox, with C1 mounted so that the rotor tab and stator-support bar can be soldered directly to the coil-socket terminals. The meter, M1, is mounted at the end opposite C1.

The coils are wound on Millen type

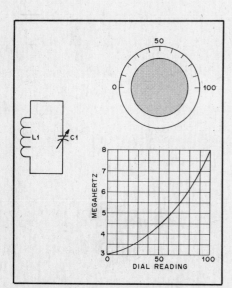

Fig. 9 — The wavemeter circuit and a typical calibration. L1C1 can be selected for any frequency range desired. The range covered with a single coil depends on the maximum/minimum capacitance ratio of C1; a 50-µF capacitor has a useful range of a little over 2 to 1; a 140-µF capacitor will tune over a bit more than 3 to 1.

Fig. 10 — Absorption frequency meter for 1.6-300 MHz.

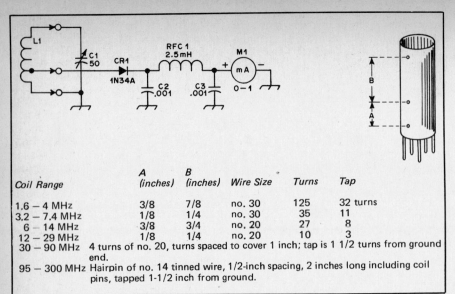

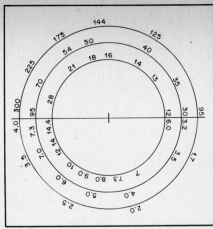

| Coil Range | A (inches) | B (inches) | Wire Size | Turns | Tap |
|---|---|---|---|---|---|
| 1.6 – 4 MHz | 3/8 | 7/8 | no. 30 | 125 | 32 turns |
| 3.2 – 7.4 MHz | 1/8 | 1/4 | no. 30 | 35 | 11 |
| 6 – 14 MHz | 3/8 | 3/4 | no. 20 | 27 | 8 |
| 12 – 29 MHz | 1/8 | 1/4 | no. 20 | 10 | 3 |
| 30 – 90 MHz | 4 turns of no. 20, turns spaced to cover 1 inch; tap is 1 1/2 turns from ground end. | | | | |
| 95 – 300 MHz | Hairpin of no. 14 tinned wire, 1/2-inch spacing, 2 inches long including coil pins, tapped 1-1/2 inch from ground. | | | | |

Fig. 12 — This dial chart may be copied full size and used as shown in Fig. 10 provided the tuned-circuit parts are exactly as specified in Fig. 11 and the construction duplicates Fig. 13.

Fig. 11 — Circuit diagram of the frequency meter.
C1 — 50-pF variable (Millen 20050).
C2, C3 — .001-μF disk ceramic.
CR1 — 1N34A germanium diode.

L1 — See coil table.
M1 — 0-1 milliammeter.
RFC1 — 2.5-mH rf choke (Millen 34000-2500).

45004 four-prong coil forms. Taps are made by doubling the wire back on itself at the appropriate point, feeding the double portion through the hole in the side of the form, twisting, and inserting the twisted pair into the coil-form pin. Clean off the enamel where the tap goes into the pin so that a good soldered connection can be made. The finished coils can be given several coats of clear lacquer for protection. Construction of the 95-300 MHz coil will be easier if 3/4 inch of the form is sawed off first.

### Frequency Markers

Now we come to the second step in frequency checking — determining the whereabouts of your transmitter *inside* an amateur band. For this some accurately located guideposts or *markers* are needed. These are signals whose frequencies are known very accurately, and which can be tuned in by your receiver.

Some receivers come equipped with a 100-kHz crystal-controlled oscillator just for this purpose. The *crystal calibrator*, as it is called, generates a harmonic at every multiple of 100 kHz. Some receivers employ calibrator circuits that are capable of generating markers every 25 kHz. The harmonics get weaker as we go higher in frequency, but they are strong enough to be used as marker signals on any amateur band through at least 30 MHz.

Harmonics are always *exact* whole-number multiples of the oscillator frequency. Therefore if the oscillator is set precisely on a known frequency, the harmonic frequencies also are known

with the same percentage accuracy. When the oscillator is on exactly 100 kHz, its 35th harmonic is 3500 kHz, the 36th is 3600 kHz and so on. The edges of most amateur bands also are multiples of 100 kHz, which is one reason why an oscillator on 100 kHz is useful. However, some subbands, including a few used by Novices, end with a 50-kHz figure. To check the edges of these bands it is desirable to have multiples of 50 kHz.

### A 50-kHz Frequency Standard

To be most reliable, the oscillator in a frequency standard or *marker generator* should be crystal-controlled. Crystals for 100 kHz are readily available at relatively low cost, but 50-kHz crystals are rather rare. To get around this, the standard shown here uses a 100-kHz oscillator followed by a frequency-dividing circuit which reduces the output frequency to 50 kHz. Semiconductor integrated circuits are used for both the 100-kHz oscillator and the frequency divider. Integrated circuits are ideal for this kind of application, and greatly reduce the number of parts required. Everything you need, aside from the 100-kHz crystal and a couple of resistors and capacitors, is in the "ICs" themselves, as you can see from the circuit of Fig. 14.

It would take a lot of space to explain the operation of the particular circuits used in this standard, so we won't attempt it in detail. The oscillator part is a "multivibrator," a rather unstable type of *RC* oscillator which, however, can readily be "locked" to a

given frequency by a stable circuit such as a quartz crystal. The frequency divider part uses a "flip-flop," a circuit which switches "on" in its output circuit when a pulse is applied to its input, and then switches "off" when a subsequent pulse is applied. This results in an output at one-half the input frequency, which is just what we want in this case. Furthermore, the output has quite strong harmonics right through the rf spectrum, and we have no trouble hear-

Fig. 13 — Inside the absorption frequency meter, showing placement of tuning capacitor and coil socket.

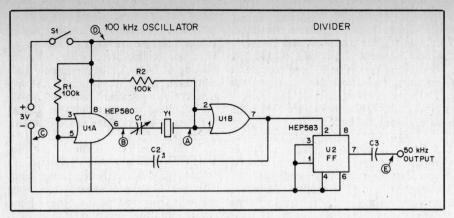

Fig. 14 — Schematic diagram of the 50-kHz frequency standard. The integrated circuits, HEP 580 dual gate and HEP 583 JK flip-flop, are made by Motorola.

C1 — 50-pF variable for panel mounting; 7-45 pF ceramic trimmer can be used if readily accessible control is not necessary.

C2 — 0.1-μF ceramic, 3 volts working, or more. Low-voltage paper capacitor can be substituted.

C3 — 100 pF or less, ceramic or mica; value depends on coupling to receiver.

R1, R2 — 100k, 1/4 or 1/2 watt.
S1 — Spst toggle.
Y1 — 100-kHz crystal.
This drawing also shows relationship of tab on IC case to the socket pin numbers, as viewed from the bottom. Pin 5 on the HEP 583 is not used.

ing them in a communications receiver.

Note that the crystal has a small variable capacitor in series with it. This is for adjusting the frequency to exactly 100 kHz. The crystal as furnished will have a small amount of frequency tolerance which you will want to compensate for. Also, its frequency changes a little with temperature and the oscillator supply voltage. C1 will take care of these discrepancies if you adjust it as described in the section on using the signals from WWV.

There is nothing especially critical about assembling the standard; you can use about any layout you please. In fact if your receiver already has a built-in 100-kHz oscillator of any type, all you need is the divider part of the circuit. Just couple it through C2 to the output lead from the existing oscillator and it will give you the 50-kHz harmonics.

Also, the crystal and C1 don't have to be mounted on the same circuit board or chassis as the two integrated circuits. C1 can be put on your receiver panel for convenient adjustment, if you want. The on-off switch, S1, also can be panel-mounted. The crystal, too, can be separated from the other parts, since the frequency is so low that a few inches of lead don't matter much.

If you want to make an etched circuit, Fig. 15 is one wiring plan you can use. Perhaps different circuit-board dimensions would be more suitable in your case; if so, it will give you some practice in etched-circuit design to try laying out your own. Chapter 7 describes an easy method.

The power supply for the standard may be two 1.5-volt dry cells in series. The current is only 6 mA at this voltage, which will put little strain on "C" — or

even penlite — cells in the intermittent use that a standard ordinarily gets. However, it is perfectly practical to make up a small power supply using a 3-volt Zener diode regulator as described in chapter 12. If the standard is to be incorporated in a receiver, the Zener and its series resistor are about all that is necessary, since the resistor can be chosen to drop the dc voltage from some suitable source in the receiver itself. We can't give details because everything depends on how much the voltage has to be dropped, but chapter 12 describes how to calculate the resistance. Alternatively, a 6.3-volt heater source in a tube receiver can be used to supply the rectifier-filter-Zener combination shown in chapter 12.

The output terminal of the standard should be connected to the "hot" antenna input terminal of the receiver. It may be worthwhile to experiment with different values of capacitance at C3, to regulate the signal level to a suitable value. If the signal is too strong, just bringing the lead from the standard close to the receiver antenna lead probably will be adequate.

### Using the Frequency Standard

The frequency standard gives you a series of signals of known frequency, and checking a transmitter frequency is simply a process of comparing the transmitter signal with the markers. Your receiver is an essential part of this process.

A marker signal by itself gives no indication of its frequency. All you actually know is that each such signal is an exact multiple of 50 kHz. Thus the first step is to *identify* a particular marker signal so you can be sure, for instance, that it is on 7150 kHz and not on 7300 or some other 50-kHz multiple.

This is done by comparing the markers with signals of known frequency. Government or commercial stations near the amateur bands, as well as amateur signals themselves, can be used for this. Examples of government signals that are useful are NSS on 4005 kHz and CHU on 7335 kHz. Suppose you want to use CHU to find the 7-MHz band. Tune in the time signal that this station transmits, turn on the frequency standard, and slowly tune *lower* in frequency until you run into the first marker. This must be 7300 kHz. Note the receiver dial reading and continue tuning lower until you hear the next marker, which will be 7250 kHz. Note this dial setting and then go on in the same way until you finally reach 7000 kHz. At this point you have the dial settings for each 50-kHz point throughout the band. Now you can easily spot the exact limits of the Novice 7100-7150-kHz band, for example. Any signal that appears on the dial between

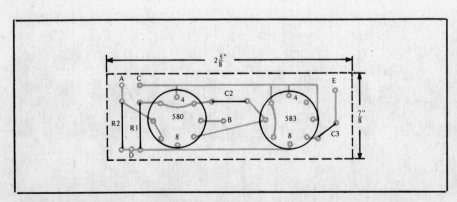

Fig. 15 — Wiring plan for etched circuit, viewed from foil side of board. This plan assumes that C1, S1 and Y1 will not be mounted on the board. Lettered holes are for external wire leads; lettering corresponds to that shown in Fig. 14.
See chapter 7 for method of using a wiring plan of this type. Dashed line represents outer edge of circuit board.

those two points must be in the Novice band — and conversely, a signal either higher or lower in frequency than those two markers must be *outside* the Novice band.

The same method is used on any band you need to calibrate. In many cases you can tell where the extreme ends of an amateur band should be because you won't find amateur signals outside those limits. The marker at that point will give you the exact band-edge frequency.

In calibrating a receiver in this way, it is desirable to have a reasonably strong marker signal, but not one so strong that it tends to overload the receiver. (This can happen on the lower-frequency bands if the coupling between the standard and the receiver is too great.) Tinker with C3 until you get a marker of a bit greater strength than the average amateur signals you hear on that band.

### VFO Calibration

The application of this and similar methods to calibrating other equipment, such as a VFO, should be obvious. In the case of a VFO you may be able to get calibration points at smaller intervals than 50 kHz. For example, if your VFO covers 3500-4000 kHz, you may be able to hear its fourth harmonic by tuning your receiver over 14,000-16,000 kHz. The frequency standard will give you signals at 14,000, 14,050, 14,100 and so on. If you tune in the *harmonic* of the VFO in each case, the calibration points at the *fundamental* frequency of the VFO will be one-fourth of 50 kHz, or 12.5 kHz, apart.

By using higher-order harmonics of the VFO, the calibration points will be still closer together. Using the fifth harmonic, you can get points exactly 10 kHz apart on the fundamental by this method.

### Checking Transmitter Frequency

To check your own transmitter fre-

quency, tune it in on your receiver and see which marker signals are on either side of it. The frequency will be somewhere between those two marker frequencies. You don't need to know anything more than that it is between 7100 and 7150 kHz, say, if you're a Novice; the FCC only requires you to be safely inside the band.

Making a frequency comparison of this sort is simple in principle, but in actual practice it can be confusing if you don't go about it properly. Receivers will give all kinds of spurious responses when hit by extremely strong signals such as the one from your transmitter. One of the easiest things to do is to tune in one of these spurious signals — which *won't* be on the right spot on the dial — and make the mistaken assumption that you're listening on your actual frequency. If you've used an absorption wavemeter to check the transmitter, you'll know you're in the right *region*. To get the right *frequency*, disconnect the antenna from the receiver, turn down the rf gain, and then tune around where you know the signal should be. Under these conditions it will be the strongest signal you pick up, and if the receiver is well shielded, this signal will be the *only* one you'll hear in that region. Keep the receiver rf gain down to the level where your own signal is about the same in strength as ordinary signals with the antenna connected. Then compare the frequency with the markers.

### How to Use WWV

Thanks to standard-frequency transmissions by the Bureau of Standards, your crystal frequency standard can be checked any time. This is done by comparing a harmonic of the standard with any of the WWV or WWVH transmissions that may be receivable at the time. These transmissions are continuous on 2.5, 5, 10 and 15 MHz. Time ticks and various types of modulation, including voice announcements and

standard audio frequencies of 500 or 600 hertz, are used.[1] Only the carrier frequencies are of interest to us in checking radio frequencies, and in making such checks the modulations are confusing rather than helpful. Fortunately, during much of each five-minute period there is no modulation except for the one-second time ticks. These are not bothersome.

WWV is at Fort Collins, Colorado, and WWVH is in Hawaii. Any carrier frequency you can hear can be used. The best one will depend on your distance from one or the other of the stations and the time of day. In general, the lower frequencies are better at short ranges and during evening hours. In daytime it may be necessary to listen for one of the higher frequencies if you are a few thousand miles from either station. If your receiver is one having continuous tuning throughout the high-frequency spectrum, finding the best signal at any time is simply a matter of trying them all. The receiver calibration should put you in the right frequency region, and the signal itself is easily recognized because of the modulation and the time ticks.

To adjust your crystal calibrator, first tune in WWV with the calibrator off. Turn off the receiver beat oscillator. Wait for the tone on WWV to stop, leaving nothing but the time ticks and the usual background noise that you hear on any unmodulated carrier. Then turn on your crystal standard. If it is not exactly on frequency, you will hear either an audio tone or a "whoosh-whoosh" pulsation in the background noise. The tone or pulsation is the beat between WWV's carrier and the harmonic of your crystal standard. The presence of such a beat indicates that your standard is off-frequency by the

---

[1] Complete details can be found in the chapter on measurements in *The Radio Amateur's Handbook* published by the American Radio Relay League.

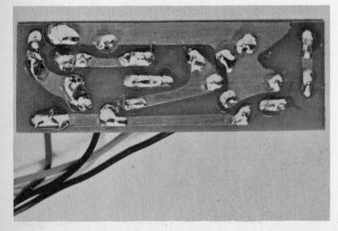

Fig. 16 — Etched circuit of the frequency-marker generator made using the plan shown in Fig. 15. Oscillator is at the left in both views; frequency divider at the right.

Fig. 17 — Exterior view of the dual-gate MOSFET dip meter with plug-in coils.

The result is the same in both cases — the meter reading dips when the oscillator is turned to resonance with the circuit to which it is coupled.

A primary requirement for the dip meter is that it should have continuous coverage of a wide frequency range — the wider the better, for maximum usefulness in experimental work. Also, it should have no pronounced "holes" — individual frequencies at which the amplitude drops below normal to be expected on a given frequency range. These holes are often caused by internal resonances which "suck out" the energy and cause confusion in using the instrument for circuit checking.

Dip meters usually have plug-in coils so a wide frequency range can be covered. You can build such a meter from a manufactured kit, several brands of which are available. The kits compare favorably in cost with the cost of equivalent new parts and in addition have the calibration scales supplied.

In using the dip meter for checking the resonant frequency of a circuit, the coupling should be set to the point where the dip in current is just perceptible. This reduces interaction between the two circuits to a minimum and gives the highest accuracy. With too-close coupling the oscillator frequency may be "pulled" by the circuit being checked, in which case different readings will be obtained when resonance is approached from the low side. If you get no dip on one coil, try another; the circuit being investigated may not tune to the frequency you think it does.

Transmitter or receiver rf circuits can be pretuned by this method, either during construction or after completion. Knowing that the circuits are tuned properly gives you a head start in getting a new piece of equipment working.

Because it generates an rf signal, the dip meter also is useful as a *test oscillator* — an oscillator that provides a steady signal of known frequency for receiver circuit alignment and similar jobs. The output is great enough so that no special coupling to a receiver is needed. Whenever a small amount of rf is called for — and you will run into plenty of such cases — the instrument is a convenient signal source.

The dip meter also can be used as an absorption wavemeter if the voltage to the oscillator is turned off. If the meter uses a vacuum tube, the heater power has to be left on so the grid-cathode circuit can act as a rectifier, letting the meter read when the coil is coupled to a circuit carrying rf current — provided, of course, that the circuit is tuned to resonance. The diode loads the tuned circuit to some extent, so the circuit is not as selective as it is in the simple

number of cycles per second in the beat tone or pulsation. Now adjust C1, Fig. 14, to bring the oscillator frequency into zero beat (no tone or pulsation) with WWV. A very slow pulsation — one or two per second — may be the best you can hold. This is plenty good enough. WWV's transmissions are accurate to about 1 hertz in 100 *megahertz*. If you can get within a cycle or two per second at, say, 5 megahertz and hold it there, your standard is doing very well indeed. However, crystal oscillators do drift with temperature and other factors, so it is a good idea to check against WWV every now and then.

This same procedure can be used with any crystal calibrator, homemade or manufactured. Most of them will have some built-in provision for adjusting the frequency, corresponding to C1 in Fig. 14.

The beat between your crystal calibrator and WWV will be most easily observed if its harmonic and the WWV signal are about the same strength. If one is very much stronger than the other, the beat may be hard to detect. Use the WWV signal that comes closest to matching the strength of the calibrator harmonic, or adjust the coupling between the calibrator and the receiver to match the strength of the WWV signal.

### The Dip Meter

When you construct any equipment with tuned-rf circuits in it, such as a transmitter, receiver, transmatch or the like, it is helpful to be able to determine

in advance whether these circuits are capable of being tuned over the intended range. Until you have the equipment actually working, the absorption wavemeter doesn't help, because there has to be rf current in the circuit before the wavemeter can function. For checking a "dead" circuit the measuring device has to supply its own rf and must also have some sort of built-in indicator to tell when it is in resonance with the tuned circuit being checked.

The *dip meter* or "dipper" is just such an instrument. It is a low-power oscillator having an indicator which shows when some of the oscillator power is being absorbed by the resonant circuit being checked. Maximum absorption will occur when the two circuits, that being checked and the dip-meter oscillator circuit, are tuned to the same frequency. Since the indicator in the dip meter usually responds to the amplitude of the oscillation, its reading takes a "dip" or becomes smaller when the meter is tuned through resonance with the unknown circuit, because the oscillation amplitude is least under this condition.

Dip meters can be built with both tubes and transistors. In the tube versions the indicator is usually a dc milliammeter or microammeter which measures the oscillator grid current. These instruments have traditionally been called *grid-dip meters* or *grid-dip oscillators (GDO)*. Transistor oscillators ordinarily have a separate rectifier which converts a little of the rf to dc, which is then measured by a dc meter.

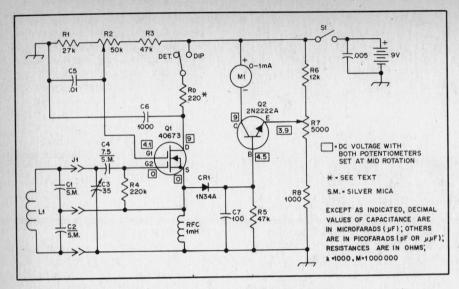

Fig. 18 — Schematic diagram of the dual-gate MOSFET dip meter. All resistors are 1/2-watt composition type. Capacitors are disk ceramic unless noted otherwise.

C1 — See Fig. 20.
C2 — See Fig. 20.
C3 — Variable capacitor, 35 pF, Millen 20035 or equiv.
J1 — Socket, Amphenol type S4.
L1 — See Fig. 20 for values. All coils wound on Millen 45004 coil forms.

M1 — Edgewise panel meter, 0-1 mA, Calectro DI-905 or equiv.
Q1 — Dual-gate MOSFET, RCA 40673.
Q2 — Npn transistor, 2N2222A.
R2 — Potentiometer, 50 kΩ.
R7 — Potentiometer, 5000 kΩ.
S1 — Spst on-off switch mounted on R7.

wavemeter. However, if the power supply is shut off completely, the circuit can be used as a plain absorption wavemeter; the method is the same with the Band-Finder.

### A Dual-Gate MOSFET Dip Meter

Described here and shown in Fig. 17 and 21 is a simple to build dip meter that covers the frequencies from 2.3 to 200 MHz. By opening switch S2 the circuit will function as a wavemeter, eliminating the need for two separate test instruments. The layout is not especially critical; however, you should try to keep the leads from the coil socket to the remainder of the circuitry as short as possible. This will help prevent unwanted resonances in the higher frequency ranges. Such parasitic

resonances can cause false dips and erratic operation.

### Circuit Details

The circuit shown in Fig. 18 is a grounded-drain Colpitts oscillator employing an RCA n-channel, dual-gate MOSFET. The oscillation level, detected by a diode and amplified by a 2N2222A transistor, is displayed on a 0- to 1-mA meter. Transconductance of the MOSFET, and hence the output signal, is controlled by potentiometer R2 and reaches a maximum of 10-volts peak to peak at the source when $V_{G2}$ (voltage from gate 2 to source) is set to +5 volts. The meter is adjusted for the desired deflection by R7. R8 must be selected according to the meter used and should be 1 kΩ for a 1-mA meter movement.

Frequency of oscillation depends on C1, C2, C3 and L1, and may reach 250 MHz or so when L1 is reduced to a hairpin.

Higher frequencies may be obtained by using a uhf D-MOSFET, such as a Signetics SD300, and by placing C3 and L1 in series in a Clapp-oscillator configuration. The circuit is designed to operate from a 12-volt supply, but it also works fine with a 9-volt transistor-radio type of battery if the drain resistor ($R_D$) is shorted. In either case the unit draws approximately 20 mA.

### Construction

Most of the components that comprise the oscillator and meter-driver circuits are mounted on a circuit board that measures approximately 1-1/4 × 2-1/2 inches. The foil pattern is shown in Fig. 19. A minibox that measures 5-1/2 × 3 × 2-1/2 inches contains the circuit board, variable capacitor, meter, controls and 4-pin coil socket. Nine plug-in coils are used to cover the frequency range from 2.3 to 200 MHz. The coils are wound on Millen 45004 coil forms to which L brackets are mounted for the dial scale. Epoxy cement holds the aluminum brackets to the forms. The use of nine separate coils instead of five or six greatly expands the calibration scales so more accurate frequency measurements may be made. To reduce the fast tuning rate of the variable capacitor, a reduction vernier is used. It was removed from a Japanese vernier dial assembly. An aluminum bracket supports the variable capacitor inside the box. A rectangular piece of thin Plexiglas is used for the dial. A thin line is scribed down the center of the dial and is colored with a permanent-marking felt pen.

### Alignment

A general-coverage receiver or an-

Fig. 19 — Here is the circuit board pattern for the dip meter — foil side of board. Grey areas represent the unetched copper pattern.

**Fig. 20**
Listed here are the values for C1, C2 and L1.

| Freq. Range MHz | C1 pF | C2 pF | L1 Turns |
|---|---|---|---|
| 2.3-4 | 15 | 15 | 71-1/2 |
| 3.4-5.1 | 33 | 10 | 39-1/2 |
| 4.8-8 | 10 | 33 | 25-1/2 |
| 7.9-13 | 10 | 33 | 14-1/2 |
| 12.8-21.2 | 10 | 33 | 6-1/2 |
| 21-34 | 10 | 33 | 4-1/2 |
| 34-60 | 10 | 33 | 2-1/2 |
| 60-110 | 10 | 33 | * |
| 90-200 | Not used | Not used | ** |

*denotes a 1-1/2-turn coil of no. 18 enam. wire wound on a 1/2-inch form spaced 1/8 inch between turns. It should be placed so that the coil is near the top of the coil form.
**denotes a hairpin loop made from flashing copper, 3/8-inch wide × 1-7/8-inch total length.
All other coils are wound with no. 24 enam. wire.

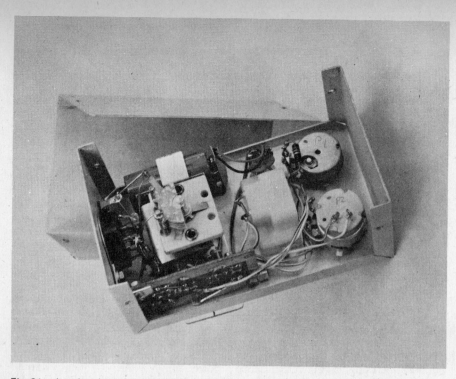

Fig. 21 — Interior view of the MOSFET dip meter. Just to the right of the variable capacitor is the edgewise panel meter. The battery can be seen just above the variable capacitor.

other dip meter (calibrated) will be required to align the instrument. Plug in the appropriate coil for the range to be calibrated and turn the power switch to the ON position and advance R7 to approximately one-third scale. If a receiver is being used to calibrate the instrument, tune it to the lowest frequency covered by the particular coil in use. With the coil of the dip meter in close proximity to the receiver antenna terminal and the variable capacitor fully meshed, the dip-meter oscillator should be heard somewhere close to that frequency. Start by marking this frequency on the paper or thin cardboard dial attached to the plate. Next tune the receiver higher in frequency (approximately 100 kHz on the lower range coils and 1 MHz on the higher frequency ranges) and mark this frequency on the dial. Continue this procedure until the complete range of the particular coil has been marked. Do the same for each of the other coils. If another dip meter is used for the calibration process, it should be placed in the DETECTOR mode and used in a similar fashion as that of the receiver outlined above.

# Other Measurements

The measurements described in this chapter are the most important one for the beginner. The more experienced amateur will find many other types of measurements useful, but these are outside the scope of this volume. You can find more information in *The Radio Amateur's Handbook*, if you want to pursue the subject. It is worth while to do so, because measurement of the performance of circuits and equipment is a vital part of the technical side of radio. Examples of other measurements that are frequently needed in amateur work are finding values of inductance, capacitance, rf resistance, impedance and similar circuit constants; audio-frequency voltage, power and frequency measurements; rf power and voltage; and the standing-wave ratio on transmission lines.

Measuring SWR with good accuracy requires special care. The Monimatch circuit described in chapter 11, although inherently capable of SWR measurement, is seldom reliable for this purpose in practice. (But the instrument is quite satisfactory for impedance-matching adjustments, as well as giving relative indications of rf output.) Fortunately, there is seldom a real need for accurate measurement of SWR unless you are experimenting with antennas and transmission lines.

A most versatile instrument for many kinds of testing and measurement

is the *cathode-ray oscilloscope*. Eventually you may want to own one, but whether you do or don't you should have at least a general idea of what the "scope" can do and how it works.

### The Oscilloscope

The oscilloscope is built around a cathode-ray tube much like the one that gives you the picture in your TV receiver. The tube isn't as big — a seven-inch diameter display face is about the largest ordinarily used — and its internal construction is different.

You've probably read enough about television to know that the picture is drawn on the face of the tube by a rapidly moving spot of light. The bright spot is formed when the fluorescent material on the glass face of the tube is struck by a narrow beam of electrons projected from a "gun" in the neck of the tube. An oscilloscope tube has the same kind of gun and a similar *fluorescent screen*. The fluorescent material belongs to the same family as that used in fluorescent lamp tubes that you see everywhere.

The electron beam can be made to change its course inside the tube if it is subjected to a magnetic field. In the TV tube the magnetic field is set up by a current flowing through a "deflection coil" wound around the neck of the tube. Actually, two such coils are used, one for moving the beam sidewise and

the other for moving it vertically.

A different method is used in the oscilloscope tube. The beam is deflected by subjecting it to an *electric* field. To do this a pair of *deflection plates* is placed inside the tube so the beam has to pass between them. When a voltage is applied to the plates, the beam is attracted toward the plate with the positive charge and repelled by the one having the negative charge. With two pairs of plates at right angles, the beam can be moved both sidewise and up and down. This *electrostatic deflection* has the advantage, over the magnetic method, that very high frequencies — far up into the radio-frequency region — can be applied to the plates. Also, the power required for deflection is insignificant.

In the absence of deflection voltages the oscilloscope controls are adjusted so that a small bright spot appears in the center of the screen. Then, if the tube is properly oriented, an ac voltage applied to the "horizontal" plates will cause the spot to move from side to side, as in Fig. 22. If a similar voltage is applied to the "vertical" plates, with no deflection voltage on the horizontal plates, the spot will move up and down, also as shown in the figure. The speed at which the spot moves is exactly proportional to the rate at which the voltage is changing. In the course of one ac cycle the spot will move in one direction, say

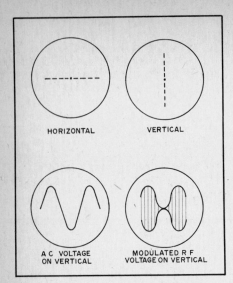

HORIZONTAL          VERTICAL

A C VOLTAGE          MODULATED R F
ON VERTICAL          VOLTAGE ON VERTICAL

Fig. 22 — With an alternating voltage applied only to one set of deflection plates of the oscilloscope, the moving spot traces a straight line as shown in the two upper drawings. With voltages applied to both sets of plates, a pattern is formed because the position of the spot then depends upon the instantaneous values of the voltages on both sets. The two lower drawings show typical examples.

to the right, while the voltage is increasing from zero. When the positive peak of the cycle is reached and the voltage begins to decrease, the spot will reverse its direction and go to the left. It will continue in this direction, passing through the center of the screen at zero voltage, until the negative peak of the voltage is reached. Then it will reverse again. This continues as long as the voltage is applied to the deflection plates. The action is the same if the voltage is applied to the vertical plates, except that the spot moves up and down.

The oscilloscope becomes useful when deflection voltages are applied *both* horizontally and vertically. Suppose the spot is made to move at a uniform rate of speed horizontally, while an alternating voltage is applied to the vertical plates. Then the moving spot traces a pattern of the voltage just like those you've seen earlier in this book. This is shown at the lower left in Fig. 22. You can actually look at the waveform of the voltage and tell whether it is a sine wave or some other form.

One final example from among the innumerable things that the oscilloscope can show is found at the lower right in the figure. This is the kind of pattern that results when a modulated rf signal is applied to the vertical plates while the spot is moving horizontally at uniform speed. The outline of the pattern traces the modulation envelope of the signal.

From it you can tell what the percentage of modulation is and whether the signal is distorted. Inside the modulation envelope the pattern appears to be filled with light. This is because the beam actually is moving up and down with each rf cycle. As there are usually many hundreds — or thousands — of rf cycles in each audio-frequency cycle of the modulation envelope, their traces on the screen blend together, forming a solidly lighted area.

The oscilloscope tube requires a number of auxiliary circuits — power supply, amplifiers for the voltages applied to the horizontal and vertical deflection plates, special circuits for generating deflection voltage, and so on — if its full capabilities are to be exploited. As a general rule, building such a scope from one of the several varieties of kits now available is far preferable to assembling parts and building from scratch. On the other hand, a scope used just for modulation checking takes little more than the power supply (which frequently can be taken from the transmitter itself) and a few resistors, in addition to the cathode-ray tube. You can easily put together an oscilloscope of this type; suitable circuits, along with the method of using the finished scope, are given in *The Radio Amateur's Handbook.*

# Chapter 14

# Antennas and Masts

All the basic information you need for putting up a workable antenna system is contained in chapter 6. It will pay you to digest the principles discussed there, because antennas and transmission lines, like transmitting and receiving circuits, will be found to act quite rationally when you know how they're supposed to work.

This chapter contains a few concrete suggestions for putting up simple antennas, the kinds of transmission lines (if any) to use with them, and the methods of supporting them.

## The Center–Fed Dipole

The center-fed antenna is the "old stand-by" for amateurs who work the lower-frequency bands — 3.5 and 7 MHz especially. If there is room to run one in a straight line and it can be erected at a height of 30 feet or more, you can count on its doing an excellent job for you. It's just as capable a radiator at the higher frequencies, too, and many amateurs have done eminently good long-distance work with it on 14, 21 and 28 MHz, with power under 100 watts. On these bands you can't expect to jump in and compete for the "rare" DX with stations running high power and beam antennas. Nevertheless, you can work just as far, in actual distance, and get your share of good signal-strength reports.

We pointed out in chapter 6 that you don't have to measure the length of a center-fed dipole to a fraction of an inch if you use an open-wire transmission line, plus a transmatch. It's the most flexible system there is. You can use the same antenna on practically any frequency, even frequencies for which it is considerably shorter than a half wavelength. It is shown in practical form in Fig. 1.

The antenna or "flat-top" part of the system should be about a half wavelength long at the lowest frequency you want to use, if that is possible. But if the length has to be shorter, just put as much in the air as you can.

### Multiband Operation

For working on all bands from 3.5

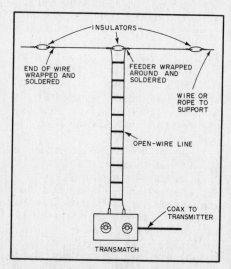

Fig. 1 — Center-fed dipole with open-wire feeders. The total antenna length preferably should be in the neighborhood of one-half wavelength at the lowest frequency to be used, but if space doesn't permit such a length it can be reduced to as little as one-quarter wavelength. See text.

to 28 MHz there are even some advantages in using a length somewhat less than a half wavelength at 3.5 MHz. A good all-around length for this purpose is 100 feet, because this length will tend to be nondirectional on 14 MHz. On this band it is a 1-1/2-wavelength antenna having the directional pattern shown in chapter 6. On 7 MHz the antenna will be somewhat directional *broadside* — that is, at right angles to the direction of the wire. On 3.5 MHz it will be almost nondirectional. Directional effects on 21 and 28 MHz will not be clearly evident with an antenna of this length, unless you have some way of comparing it with another antenna. For practical purposes, it is an "all-around" system on all bands.

It should hardly need saying that an antenna will have the best chance of working well if it is up in the air by itself. Nearby wires, metal gutter piping, and similar conductors won't give it much assistance in getting your signal out, and may do considerable harm to the radiating properties of the antenna. Steer clear of them if you can. Nevertheless, a poorly located antenna is better than none at all!

### Feeder Installation

The feeder is in the strong electromagnetic field around the antenna, since it has to run right to the antenna in order to connect to it. This field will induce an rf voltage in the feeder wires, and in turn the voltage will cause a current to flow in the wires. This current is not related to the transmission-line current discussed earlier. In fact, the induced current flows in the *same* direction in both wires, because both wires are in the same field. For this current the wires simply act as though they were in the same conductor, or two conductors in parallel. This *parallel current* will cause radiation just as current in the antenna itself causes radiation.

We want the antenna to do the radiating, not the feeders. To minimize current of this type the feeder must be placed where the voltage induced in it

---

**Quarter Wavelength in Feet and Inches at Various Amateur Band Frequencies.**

| Frequency | Length |
|---|---|
| 3500 kHz | 66 feet, 11 inches |
| 3600 " | 65 " 0 " |
| 3700 " | 63 " 4 " |
| 3800 " | 61 " 7 " |
| 3900 " | 60 " 0 " |
| 4000 " | 58 " 6 " |
| 7000 kHz | 33 feet, 6 inches |
| 7100 " | 33 " 0 " |
| 7200 " | 32 " 6 " |
| 7300 " | 32 " 1 " |
| 14.0 MHz | 16 feet, 8 inches |
| 14.15 " | 16 " 6 " |
| 14.3 " | 16 " 4 " |
| 21.0 MHz | 11 feet, 2 inches |
| 21.2 " | 11 " 0 " |
| 21.4 " | 10 " 11 " |
| 28.0 MHz | 8 feet, 4 inches |
| 28.4 " | 8 " 3 " |
| 28.8 " | 8 " 2 " |
| 29.2 " | 8 " 0 " |
| 29.6 " | 7 " 11 " |

Fig. 2 — Some suggested dimensions for center-fed dipoles. These antennas can be used on all bands from 3.5 to 30 MHz, but the lower one is a little shorter than desirable for 3.5 MHz.

---

will be least. If the system is perfectly symmetrical, mechanically and electrically, the pickup will be zero when the feeder is exactly at right angles to the antenna. Such perfection is rare, if it ever exists at all, but certainly the induced voltage will be least when the feeder leaves the antenna at right angles to the antenna wire. If it is at all possible, the feeder should continue in a straight line for a quarter wavelength before any turns or bends are made in it. Do the best you can in this respect. In any case, don't have the feeder parallel to one side of the antenna and close to it; this is the worst condition.

**Feeder Length**

At this point you're probably won-

dering what length of feed line you should use. The most obvious answer is long enough to reach from the antenna to the transmitter or transmatch. Feeders can always be made to work, regardless of their length.

However, open-wire feeders will make a better load for a transmatch if the impedance they present to it is close to being a pure resistance. For this to be so the whole system — not just the antenna — must be resonant, or not very far from resonance. We've discussed this a little in chapter 6. It's less confusing to consider the length to be that of *one* half of the antenna plus the length of *one* of the feeder wires. The sum of these two should be some whole-number multiple of a quarter wavelength.

Fig. 2 gives the length of a quarter wavelength in feet and inches for various frequencies in the bands from 3.5 to 28 MHz. If you want to use the antenna on all these bands it is best to choose 3600 kHz as your "basic" frequency. Lengths based on this frequency will be reasonably close to resonance in some part of each of the five bands.

To see how the table works out, suppose that you've selected an antenna length of 100 feet. The total length of half the antenna plus one feeder wire will be some multiple of 65 feet (a quarter wavelength at 3600 kHz). Since half the antenna length is 50 feet, the shortest length of feeder you would use would be 65 − 50 = 15 feet. This feeder length probably would be too short to be practical, so you might take the next length, 2 × 65 feet or 130 feet. Then 130 − 50 = 80 feet is the feeder length.

As another example, suppose you're principally interested in cw work on 7 MHz and up. Since this kind of operation is in the low ends of the bands, a reasonable choice for the basic frequency would be 7050 kHz. Interpolating in Fig. 2, the length would be 33 feet, 3 inches for one side of the antenna (the total length would be 66 feet, 6 inches). Since one side of the antenna is a quarter wavelength, the feeder length itself can be any multiple of one-quarter wavelength. Thus, you could use a feeder 33 feet, 3 inches long, or one 66 feet, 6 inches long, or 99 feet, 9 inches, and so on.

In passing, we might point out that the 100-foot antenna mentioned above can be scaled down for use on 7 MHz instead of 3.5 MHz as the lowest frequency. Then it will have a total length of 50 feet — 25 feet on a side. This length will be substantially nondirectional on 28 MHz but will be somewhat directional broadside on 14 MHz with a small gain over a half-wave dipole on that band. The various examples given here are shown in Fig. 3.

Physically, you may not need all the

feeder length that Fig. 2 shows to be optimum. If not, there are two things you can do. One is to make the feeder take a path from the antenna to the transmatch that does use up all its length. It should not be rolled up in a coil, but any path that doesn't bend it back sharply on itself will be satisfactory. Part of it can even be strung up around your operating room if some of the length has to be used up indoors.

The second thing you can do is to cut the feeder to the length you need for coming into the station. As we said earlier, any feeder length can be made to work. Some lengths will give difficulty; it may be hard, or even impossible, to find taps on the transmatch that will give you proper loading if you happen to hit one of the "bad" lengths. These are in the region around lengths that represent a multiple of an eighth wavelength instead of the quarter-wavelength multiples we have recommended. Avoid lengths of this order and you should have little trouble.

In determining feeder length, include the section inside the station — right up to where the line connects to the transmatch. This should be the same type of line that you used outside.

**The End-Fed Dipole**

Another antenna system which is not inherently a one-band system is the end-fed dipole. As you saw in chapter 6, any dipole a half wavelength long at one frequency will resonate as a one-

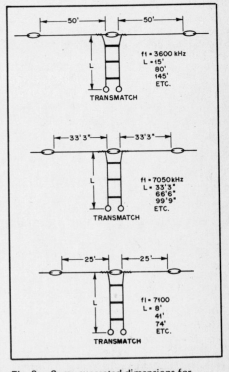

Fig. 3 — Some suggested dimensions for center-fed dipoles. These antennas can be used on all bands from 3.5 to 30 MHz, but the lower one is a little shorter than desirable for 3.5 MHz.

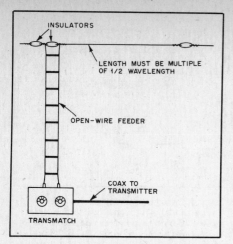

Fig. 4 — End-fed antenna with open-wire feeders. This system requires that the antenna length be resonant at the operating frequency, either on the antenna fundamental (half wavelength) or its harmonic resonances. For operation in the Novice bands the following lengths are recommended.

| Band | Antenna | Feeder |
|---|---|---|
| 3.5, 7, 21 MHz | 130 ft | A multiple of 65 ft |
| 7 and 21 MHz | 65 ft | A multiple of 33 ft |
| 21 MHz | 22 ft | A multiple of 11 ft |

wavelength (full-wave) antenna at approximately twice that frequency, as a 1-1/2-wavelength at three times the frequency, and so on. Thus, an antenna resonating as a half-wave dipole at, say, 3600 kHz will resonate again at approximately 7200 kHz, at 14,400 kHz, and on up the scale. It doesn't matter whether such an antenna is fed at the center or the end, so far as resonance goes. The end-fed system is shown in Fig. 4.

However, you can't take liberties with the antenna length, as you can with center feed. If the antenna itself isn't resonant, the feeder currents will be unbalanced, and the line won't act wholly like a real transmission line. Imbalance will cause it to radiate, too, so it becomes part of the antenna. Also, only one line wire is connected to the antenna; the other simply stops between two insulators, as shown in the drawing. This unsymmetrical termination for the line is itself enough to cause a parallel current to exist on the line, even when you're operating on the exact resonant frequency of the antenna.

Aside from this, the system is much like the center-fed arrangement. Open-wire feeders should be used, because the standing-wave ratio is high and the power loss in any other type of line would be excessive. Although the feeder can be any length, multiples of one-quarter wavelength are preferred. Such lengths will make the line look like a pure resistance, or nearly so, to the transmatch circuit. The considerations

here are the same as those outlined in the discussion on feeder length for the center-fed antenna. Suitable feeder lengths can be taken from Fig. 2. The figures in that table also can be used for the length of the antenna itself, except that for any given frequency the length given must be multiplied by 2. That is, an antenna for 3600 kHz (plus the multiples of that frequency) should be 2 × 65 = 130 feet long, one for 21.2 MHz should be 2 × 11 = 22 feet long, and similarly for other frequencies.

With end feed, the antenna has somewhat different directional characteristics when operated on harmonics, as compared with the center-fed wire. However, the differences are not likely to be very evident in practice. Also, the direction toward the open end of the wire is favored slightly, as compared with the opposite direction.

Adjustment of the transmatch for coupling to the transmitter is the same as with center feed.

## Matched Dipoles

The center-fed dipole with open-wire feeders is the most versatile system you can use, since it lets you work on several amateur bands with negligible loss of rf power in the feeders. However, there are several other dipole arrangements, some of which may be better suited to the physical conditions existing at your station. Most of these are basically one-band systems, but there are ways in which they can be adapted to multiband operation.

The advantage of matching the antenna and transmission-line impedances is that the feeder length has no effect on the input impedance of the line. Strictly speaking, this is true only when the match is perfect. In practice, the match isn't perfect — except possibly at one single frequency. Therefore, there is some change in line input impedance with length. However, the change is small enough so that the pi-network tank circuit in the transmitter can be adjusted for full loading on the final amplifier, over the range of frequencies for which the match is reasonably close, with any length of line you may use.

In return for this convenience your operation is restricted to a relatively small range of frequencies around the one for which the dipole is resonant. A range of about 200 kHz is representative on the 3.5-MHz band; that is, you can work up to 100 kHz above or below the resonant frequency with no intolerable increase in standing-wave ratio. On 7, 14 and 21 MHz, the whole band can be covered (a separate dipole must be used for each band, of course). On these three bands it suffices to make the antenna resonant at the midfrequency; there is no need to choose a particular part of the band unless you have no

interest in working anywhere else in it. On 28 MHz you can also cover the band with a single antenna cut for the center, but with a higher SWR at the ends than on the three next lower bands.

Two common types of matched antennas are the single-wire dipole shown in Fig. 5 at A and the folded dipole shown at B. In each case the length of one-half of the antenna should be one-quarter wavelength at the selected frequency. This length can be taken from Fig. 2.

## Single-Wire Dipole

Since the center-fed dipole is a balanced antenna, it should be fed with balanced — that is, parallel-conductor — line if at all possible. To keep the system balanced throughout, a transmatch should be used at the input end. It should be connected and adjusted as described in chapter 11.

Actually, the transmatch could be omitted and the line could go directly to the output terminals on the transmitter. This would work essentially the same as the coaxial-cable system shown at A, but would sacrifice the balance that can be maintained by using twin line.

The principal reasons for using coax (Fig. 5A) instead of twin line are three: coax is easier to find in radio stores, the operator doesn't want to use a transmatch, and he fondly believes that all the rf will be inside the cable. Unfortunately, the outside of the cable is

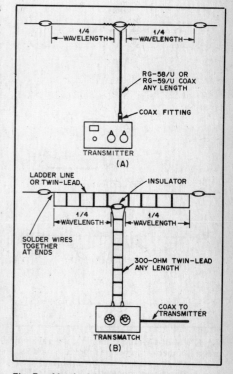

Fig. 5 — Matched antennas. These are generally useful only on the band for which the antenna's length is a total of one-half wavelength. The dipole must be resonant.

inherently part of the antenna with this method. If you're lucky in your choice of cable length and in your grounding system, this may give you no obvious difficulties. If you're unlucky, there may be rf feedback troubles in addition to the other undesirable effects that go with a radiating feeder.

### The Folded Dipole

The folded dipole, Fig. 5B is a little more complicated to construct than the single-wire dipoles. Two wires are needed in the antenna itself. Open-wire line can be used for the dipole part. As an alternative, solid-dielectric twin line can be used. The heavy-duty twin line is best mechanically, especially if the antenna is fairly long as at 3.5 and 7 MHz. Twin line of the ordinary TV variety can be used for the feeder. The folded dipole is a balanced system and the power should be fed to the transmission line through a transmatch in order to keep it balanced. Chapter 11 describes the transmatch adjustment.

The folded dipole is a good single-band antenna. Its frequency coverage, for a given SWR at the ends of the range, is a bit better than that of the single-wire dipole. The reason for this is that the two dipole wires tend to act like a single thick conductor. A thick antenna is always broader tuning than a thin one.

Regular TV stand-offs can be used for supporting the 300-ohm line along a

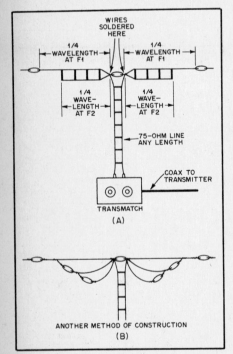

Fig. 6 — Multiple-dipole antenna. This system uses a number of half-wave dipoles in parallel. The one that is resonant at the operating frequency takes practically all the power. The remaining ones affect the impedance match to some extent, but not seriously enough to cause the SWR to be excessively high.

building or at other points where an anchorage can be used. The line should not be allowed to get closer than an inch or so to other conductors that it has to pass, and should not be parallel to such conductors if it can be avoided. Also, the line should go away from the dipole at right angles, to avoid rf pickup from the antenna field.

### Multiple-Dipole Antenna

A number of schemes have been advanced for using one antenna system for operation in several bands, with acceptable impedance matching between the antenna and line on the frequencies for which the system is designed. Probably the simplest of these is the multiple-dipole antenna shown in Fig. 6A. This system merely uses a number of dipoles, one cut for each band, connected in parallel at the feed point. Only two are shown in the drawing, but three or even more can be used.

A two-dipole antenna can be built quite easily from open-wire line. The longer of the two wires takes all the mechanical strain. The shorter one is made by cutting the second wire at the proper lengths from the center. At the center insulator the two wires on each side are joined together and connected to the transmission line. The unused wires and insulators beyond the ends of the shorter dipole should be clipped off.

Separate single-wire dipoles can be used instead of the ladder line as shown at Fig. 6B. The dipoles do not have to be parallel to each other. The shorter ones can be suspended from the longest one by letting them form loops as shown. A separation of a few inches is ample; the principal thing is that the outer ends of each dipole must be insulated from the other wires. The wires can be pulled off separately to the supports, making enough of an angle with each other so they cannot touch. Separate supports, not necessarily in the same line, can be used if available.

Such an antenna does not match the line equally well on all the bands for which the dipoles are cut. In fact, it does not result in as good a match on *any* band as you could expect from a single dipole on that same band. However, it does well enough in this respect to let you use any convenient length of feeder, and the feeder losses will not be large at frequencies close to the resonant frequencies of the dipoles. The range of frequencies, on each band, over which the SWR on the feeder will be low is smaller than is the case with the systems shown in Fig. 5.

The preferable type of feeder for this antenna is 75-ohm twin line, since the antenna itself is symmetrical about the center. The transmatch will help maintain line balance. However, the

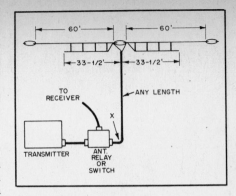

Fig. 7 — Two-dipole antenna for three Novice bands. Although a coaxial feeder is shown, 75-ohm twin line can be used instead. Coaxial feeder may be either RG-58/U or RG-59/U.

antenna will work with 75-ohm or 50-ohm coaxial line, with the same limitations as discussed earlier.

The advantage of such an antenna — that it will operate on a number of bands — is also a disadvantage. It will not reject harmonics of the transmitting frequency that happen to fall in the range of one of the dipoles. The transmatch will help discriminate against these.

### Three Novice Bands with Two Dipoles

The antenna shown in Fig. 7 combines the multiple-dipole idea with harmonic operation to give three-band operation with only two dipoles. We mentioned in chapter 6 that a center-fed antenna working at the third harmonic (three times its fundamental frequency) has an impedance in the vicinity of 100 ohms. This is not too bad a mismatch for coaxial cable or 75-ohm twin line. If the antenna length is adjusted so that the third harmonic is in the Novice 21-MHz band, the antenna also will work well in the 7-MHz band. The feeder can be any length.

The system shown here uses a 7-MHz

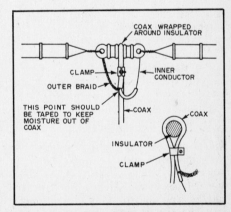

Fig. 8 — Suggested method of anchoring coax at the center insulator. The same type of cable support can be used with any of the coaxial-fed antennas shown earlier.

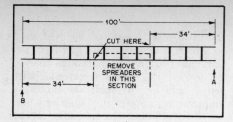

Fig. 9 — How to cut a 100-foot length of ladder line to make the two dipoles of Fig. 7.

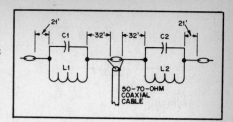

Fig. 11 — Here are the dimensions for the Novice bands. The traps are resonant at 7150 kHz. For details on the trap construction see the text and photograph.

antenna in this way and has a 3.5-MHz dipole in parallel with it. The lengths of the two dipoles have been experimentally adjusted for optimum results in the three low-frequency Novice bands.

You have your choice of three kinds of transmission line for the feeder: 50-ohm coax (RG-58/U), 75-ohm coax (RG-59/U), or 75-ohm twin line. The advantages and disadvantages of coaxial and parallel-conductor line are the same as with other balanced systems described earlier.

The dipoles are made from open-wire line having 1-inch spacing. Fig. 8 shows how the inner ends are connected to coaxial line, together with a method of anchoring the coax to the insulator so there is no mechanical strain on either the inner conductor or the braid.

A single 100-foot roll of ladder line is enough for the two dipoles. Cut the roll as shown in Fig. 9. The outside ends of the roll go to the center insulator of the system. After using six inches for bending back through the insulator and wrapping, one half-dipole is 33-1/2 feet long. It needs no support at the open end. The remaining piece should be cut down so the length between the holes in the inner and outer insulators is 60 feet, as in Fig. 7.

Like other multiband systems designed to match the antenna to the feeder, this one will radiate any harmonic power that may get out of the transmitter. When the feeder is 75-ohm twin line, a transmatch should be used for the sake of maintaining line balance, and the selectivity of the transmatch will be adequate for suppressing the undesired frequencies. A transmatch

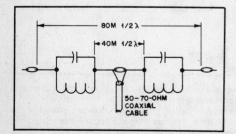

Fig. 10 — Basic configuration of the trap dipole.

also can be used with coaxial cable (chapter 11).

## A Trap-Dipole for 80 Through 10 Meters

Whenever coaxial feed lines are used to feed an antenna, it is important that the lines be matched at the antenna to keep the SWR low. The SWR on a feed line is always dependent on the impedance of the antenna. If we use 50-ohm line, and the antenna impedance is 50 ohms, then the coax will be "matched" and the SWR will be 1 to 1. If the antenna impedance were 100 ohms, the SWR would be 2 to 1. The worse the mismatch, the higher the SWR will be. And, the higher the SWR, the more losses you will have in the feed system. Even more important, the SWR may be too high to allow proper tuning and loading of the final amplifier stage in the transmitter. For this reason, we want the antenna to have an impedance as close as possible to that of the coax.

If we were to take an average of how high amateurs install antennas, we would probably find that the average height of 80-meter antennas would be about 30 feet. This would put the "average" impedance somewhere between 40 to 70 ohms. This being the case, you could feed the antenna with either 50- or 70-ohm coaxial cable and have a reasonably good match on 80 meters.

Let's suppose we switch our rig to 40 meters, and attempt to use the 80-meter dipole for the antenna. What happens to the impedance of the antenna on 40 meters? Instead of a value of 40 to 70 ohms, the impedance will be on the order of 4000 ohms. With 50-ohm coaxial feed, the mismatch would be about 80 to 1 — quite a bad mismatch. If we want to use the 50-ohm coax, and use the antenna on both 80 and 40, our problem comes down to making the antenna look like a match on both bands.

One method of doing the job is to insert traps in antenna as shown in Fig. 10. The traps are parallel tuned circuits. When an 80-meter signal is fed to the antenna, the overall electrical length works out to be a one-half wavelength and be a good match for the 50-ohm coax. When a 40-meter signal is fed to the antenna, the traps act to divorce the outer parts of the antenna and the antenna looks like one-half wavelength on 40 meters and also is a fairly good match for the coax.

On the 20- through 10-meter bands, the antenna works out to be close to odd multiples of half wavelengths and has a low impedance, providing a fairly good match on these bands also.

### Making the Trap Antenna

Fig. 11 is a circuit drawing of the trap dipole. These dimensions will pro-

vide a good match for either 50- or 70-ohm coaxial cable in the Novice portions of the 80- and 40-meter bands. For General class operation, the antenna as shown will provide a reasonably good match on any of the bands from 40 meters down. However, for 80-meter operation, it is best to change the outer lengths of the antenna (those portions from the traps out) to make the antenna resonant in the desired section of 80 meters. As shown, the antenna will provide a good match from 3700 to 3750 kHz with the SWR rising sharply toward either band edge. More about this in a moment.

The traps shown in Fig. 12 are made from B&W coil stock; a single length of the 3905-1 will be adequate for both traps. The coil stock has 6 turns per inch, is 2-1/2 inches in diameter, and comes in 10-inch lengths. The capacitors are a transmitting type, Centralab 850S-50Z. Using this type coil stock and capacitor, the traps will easily handle the amateur legal power limit.

Fig. 12 shows the construction method. Allow several inches of lead length at each coil end so that the wires can be fed through the support insulator. This will take any strain off the coil ends. Of course the antenna wire should also be fed through the insulator ends. Use no. 12 or 14 solid copper wire for the antenna because if the antenna is supported at the ends it must also support the weight of the coaxial feed line. In order to reduce the strain on the

Fig. 12 — Here is a photograph of one of the traps. It's a good idea to coat the entire assembly with clear lacquer or enamel.

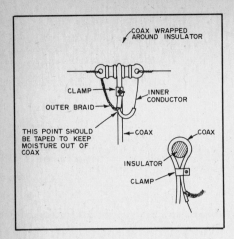

Fig. 13 — To provide adequate support for coax at antenna feed point, the coax should be installed as shown in this drawing.

coax at the center insulator, the coaxial end should be mounted as shown in Fig. 13. Wrap the coax around the insulator as shown and clamp the two sections together and also tape the exposed end of the coax to prevent moisture accumulation inside the coax. Be sure to clean any enamel away from the antenna wires before soldering the coil and capacitor leads to the antenna wires.

As mentioned earlier, the antenna shown is cut for the Novice band on 80. For General class operation, the amateur should select that portion of 80 he plans to use more than others and cut the antenna accordingly. The inner portions of the antenna, up to and including the traps, should be the same dimensions as shown in Fig. 11. For operation on the low end of 80, near 3500 kHz, make the outside lengths 30 feet long. Insert an SWR bridge in the line and then "prune" the ends for lowest SWR reading.

### 40-Meter Loop

An effective but simple 40-meter antenna that has a theoretical gain of approximately 2 dB over a dipole is a full-wave closed loop. A full-wavelength closed loop need not be square. (See Fig. 14.) It can be trapezoidal, rectangular, circular or some distorted configuration in between those shapes. For best results, however, the builder should attempt to make the loop as square as possible. The more rectangular the shape, the greater the cancellation of energy in the system and the less effective it will be. The effect is similar to that of a dipole, its effectiveness becoming impaired as the ends of the dipole are brought closer and closer together. The practical limit can be seen in the "inverted-V" antenna, where a 90-degree apex angle between the legs is the minimum value ordinarily used. Angles that are less than 90 degrees

cause serious cancellation of the rf energy.

The loop can be fed in the center of one of the vertical sides if vertical polarization is desired. For horizontal polarization it is necessary to feed either of the horizontal sides at the center.

Optimum directivity occurs at right angles to the plane of the loop, or in more simple terms, broadside from the loop. Therefore, one should try to hang the system from available supports which will enable the antenna to radiate the maximum amount in some favored direction.

Just how the wire is erected will depend on what is available in one's yard. Trees are always handy for supporting antennas, and in many instances the house is high enough to be included in the lineup of solid objects from which to hang a radiator. If only one supporting structure is available it should be a simple matter to put up an

A frame or pipe mast to use as a second support.

The overall length of the wire used in a loop is determined in feet from the formula 1005/$f$ (MHz). Hence, for operation at 7125 kHz the overall wire length will be 141 feet. The matching transformer, an electrical quarter wavelength of 75-ohm coaxial cable, can be computed by dividing 246 by the operating frequency in MHz, then multiplying that number by the velocity factor of the cable being used. Thus, for operation at 7125 kHz, 246/7.125 MHz = 34.53 feet. If coax with solid polyethylene insulation is used, a velocity factor of 0.66 must be employed. Foam-polyethylene coax has a velocity factor of 0.80. Assuming RG-59/U is used, the length of the matching transformer becomes 34.53 (feet) × 0.66 = 22.79 feet or 22 feet, 9-1/2 inches.

This same loop antenna may be used on the twenty- and fifteen-meter bands,

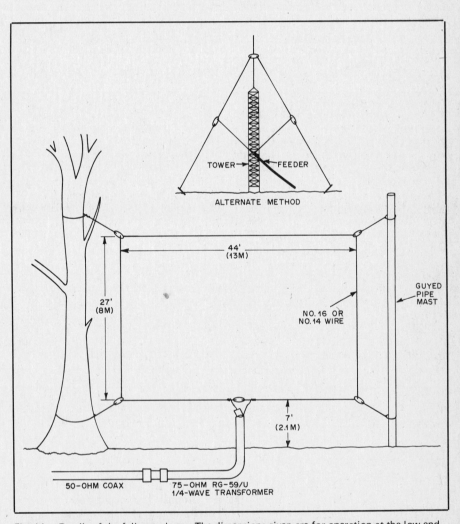

Fig. 14 — Details of the full-wave loop. The dimensions given are for operation at the low end of 40 meters (7050 kHz). The height above ground was seven feet in this instance, though improved performance should result if the builder can install the loop higher above ground without sacrificing length on the vertical sides. The inset illustrates how a single supporting structure can be used to hold the loop in a diamond-shaped configuration. Feeding the diamond at the lower tip provides radiation in the horizontal plane. Feeding the system at either side will result in vertical polarization of the radiated signal.

although its pattern will be somewhat different than on its fundamental frequency. Also, a slight mismatch will occur, but this can be overcome by a simple matching network. When the loop is mounted in a vertical plane, it tends to favor low-angle signals. If a high-angle system is desired, say for 80 meters, the full-wave loop can be mounted in a horizontal plane, thirty or more feet above ground. This arrangement will direct most of the energy virtually straight up, providing optimum sky-wave coverage on a short-haul basis.

# Materials and Construction Techniques for Wire Antennas

Use no. 14 or no. 12 copper wire for the antenna. It can be either bare or enameled. It is worthwhile to use the hard-drawn variety, if available. Although it is harder to handle because it tends to be springy, it has greater strength.

For center feed cut two equal lengths, one for each of the two halves of the antenna. Scrape the ends clean for at least 12 inches. Feed the ends through the eyes of the insulators and wrap five or six inches of end around the wire. See Fig. 15. Solder this wrapped joint. Wrap the ends of the feeder wires around the inner antenna ends, on each side of the center insulator, and solder them, too. A heavy (100 watt or larger) iron or soldering gun should be used for this job. Because the wire conducts the heat away rapidly, a small iron won't make a good joint. Do your soldering indoors where there won't be any breeze to cool the iron and joint. Also, in cold weather it's almost impossible to solder outdoors with an ordinary iron.

The insulators in the antenna should be the "strain" type, in which the wires go through holes ("eyes") in the ends. Don't use the "egg" type here; egg insulators are fine for use in guy wires but there is considerable capacitance between the wires fastened in them. This capacitance is undesirable in the antenna itself. Either glass or ceramic is suitable, and the size doesn't matter a great deal at the rf power levels we're concerned with in this book. At one time you could find antenna insulators in every hardware and "5 & 10" store, but most broadcast receivers today use built-in antennas, so insulators aren't as commonly available. You'll probably have to get them through an outlet that handles radio components.

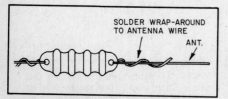

Fig. 15 — Securing the antenna wire to an insulator. The support wire, at left, is generally stranded steel wire, obtainable at hardware stores, and does not need soldering.

The most convenient type of open-wire transmission line is the TV "ladder" line. Use the kind that has the widest spacing between wires — 1 inch. Ladder line comes on a reel, when you buy a standard length of 100 feet. Don't unroll it until the antenna has been put together and is ready to be pulled up. If you're careful in unrolling it then, the line will have relatively little tendency to twist. It can't be prevented from twisting a little, though, unless it is pulled up really tight, with individual tension adjustment on each wire. This isn't possible when the line hangs from the center of the antenna. A gradual

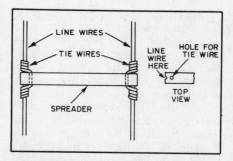

Fig. 16 — Method of fastening feeder wires to line spreaders. It is best not to solder these joints because a slight amount of slippage will be helpful in aligning the feeder wires for uniform separation when the antenna is put up.

twist doesn't matter, as long as the wires maintain their spacing throughout the length of the feeder.

An open-wire line also can be made up using spreaders. Porcelain ones are available having lengths of two, four and six inches. The four-inch size is probably the easiest to use for runs of moderate length. The line wires can be no. 12 or no. 14 copper and should be fastened to the spreaders as shown in Fig. 16. The tie wires don't have to be quite as thick as the line wires, although the same size can be used for both. Don't solder these joints. Just wrap the tie wires tightly. Then you can slide the spreader along the wire to adjust the spacing for a shipshape job.

## Location and Supports

The antenna can be supported at the

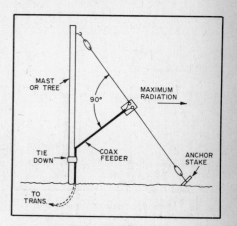

Fig. 17 — Method of supporting a half-wave dipole from a single upright such as a tree or wooden mast. Maximum directivity will be in the direction of the arrow, and the signal will be vertically polarized at a fairly low radiation angle. By having anchor stakes at different compass points, the directivity can be changed to favor different DX regions.

ends by buildings, trees or anything you may be able to use. Later in this chapter, there is information on putting up poles and masts. A mast may be the real answer to holding up at least one end of the antenna. Many operators fasten one end of the antenna to the house, or to a short pole on the roof, and build a mast far enough away to permit using the desired antenna length. The spot for the mast can be chosen so the antenna will be in the clear.

You can slope the antenna wire if your two supports aren't the same height. A sloping antenna usually will radiate best in the direction of the downslope. You can take advantage of this effect by deliberately sloping the wire to get a desired "best" direction. A sloping dipole that requires only one support is shown in Fig. 17. The directivity is not so marked that you'll lose out too badly in the opposite direction, except possibly on the highest frequency bands.

## Trees as Antenna Supports

From the beginning of amateur radio, trees have been used widely for supporting wire antennas. Trees cost nothing, of course, and will often provide a means of supporting a wire antenna at considerable height. However, as an antenna support, a tree is

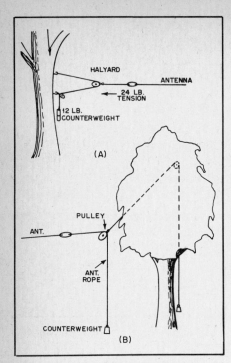

Fig. 18 — Methods of counterweighting to minimize antenna movement. The method at A limits the fall of the counterweight should the antenna break. It also has a 2 to 1 mechanical advantage, as indicated. The method at B has the disadvantage that the point of support in the tree must be higher than the end of the antenna.

highly unstable in the presence of wind, unless the tree is a very large one, and the antenna is suspended from a point well down on the tree trunk. As a result, the antenna must be constructed much more sturdily than would be necessary with stable supports. Even with rugged construction, it is unlikely that an antenna suspended from a tree, or between trees, will stand up indefinitely, and occasional repair or replacement usually must be expected.

There are two general methods of securing a pulley to a tree. If the tree can be climbed safely to the desired level, a pulley can be wired to the trunk of the tree, as shown in Fig. 18. If, after passing the halyard through the pulley, both ends of the halyard are simply brought back down to ground along the trunk of the tree, there may be difficulty in bringing the antenna end of the halyard out where it will be clear of branches. To avoid this, one end of the halyard can be tied temporarily to the tree at the pulley level, while the remainder of the halyard is coiled up, and the coil thrown out horizontally from this level, in the direction in which the antenna will run. It may help to have the antenna end of the halyard weighted. Then, after attaching the antenna to the halyard, the other end is untied from the tree, passed through the pulley, and brought to ground along the tree trunk in as straight a line as

possible. The halyard need be only long enough to reach the ground after the antenna has been hauled up, since additional rope can be tied to the halyard when it becomes necessary to lower the antenna.

The other method consists of passing a line over the tree from ground level, and using this line to haul a pulley up into the tree and hold it there. Several ingenious methods have been used to accomplish this. The simplest method employs a weighted pilot line, such as fishing line or mason's chalk line. Grasping the line about two feet from the weight, the weight is swung back and forth, pendulum style, and then heaved with an underhand motion in the direction of the tree top. Several trials may be necessary to determine the optimum size of the weight for the line selected, the distance between the weight and the hand before throwing, and the point in the arc of the swing where the line is released. The weight, however, must be sufficiently large to assure that it will carry the pilot line back to ground after passing over the tree. Flipping the end of the line up and down so as to put a traveling wave on the line often helps to induce the weight to drop down if the weight is marginal. The higher the tree, the lighter the weight and the pilot line must be. A glove should be worn on the throwing hand, because a line running swiftly through the bare hand can cause a severe burn.

If there is a clear line of sight between ground and a particularly desirable crotch in the tree, it may be possible to hit the crotch eventually after a sufficient number of tries. Otherwise, it is best to try to heave the pilot line completely over the tree, as close to the center line of the tree as possible. If it is necessary to retrieve the line and start over again, the line should be drawn back very slowly, otherwise the swinging weight may wrap the line around a small limb, making retrieval impossible.

Stretching the line out in a straight line on the ground before throwing may help to keep the line from snarling, but it places extra drag on the line, and the line may snag on obstructions overhanging the line when it is thrown. Another method is to make a stationary reel by driving eight nails, arranged in a circle, through a 1-inch board. After winding the line around the circle formed by the nails, the line should reel off readily when the weighted end of the line is thrown. The board should be tilted at approximately right angles to the path of the throw.

Other devices that have been used successfully to pass a pilot line over a tree are the bow and arrow with heavy thread tied to the arrow, and the short

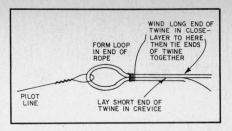

Fig. 19 — In connecting the halyard to the pilot line, a large knot that might snag in the crotch of a tree should be avoided, as shown.

casting rod and spinning reel used by fishermen. Still another method that has been used where sufficient space is available is to fly a kite. After the kite has reached sufficient altitude, simply walk around the tree until the kite string lines up with the center of the tree. Then pay out string until the kite falls to the earth. This method has been used successfully to pass a line over a patch of woods between two higher supports, which would have been impossible using any other method.

The pilot line can be used to pull successively heavier lines over the tree until one of adequate size to take the strain of the antenna has been reached. This line is then used to haul a pulley up into the tree after the antenna halyard has been threaded through the pulley. The line that holds the pulley must be capable of withstanding considerable chafing where it passes through the crotch, and at points where lower branches may rub against the standing part. For this reason, it may be advisable to use galvanized sash cord or stranded guy wire for raising the pulley.

Especially with larger sizes of line or cable, care must be taken when splicing the pilot line to the heavier line to use a splice that will minimize the chances that the splice cannot be coaxed

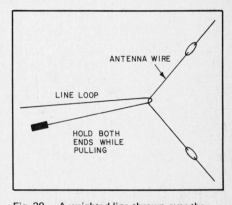

Fig. 20 — A weighted line thrown over the antenna can be used to pull the antenna to one side to avoid overhanging obstructions, such as branches of trees in the path of the antenna, as the antenna is pulled up. When the obstruction has been cleared, the line can be removed by releasing one end.

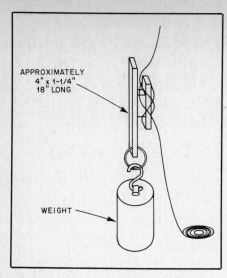

Fig. 21 — The cleat avoids the necessity of having to untie a knot that may have been weather-hardened.

through the tree crotch. One type of splice is shown in Fig. 19.

The crotch which the line first comes to rest in may not be sufficiently strong to stand up under the tension of the antenna. However, if the line has been passed over, or close to, the center line of the tree, it will usually break through the lighter crotches and finally come to rest in one sufficiently strong lower down on the tree.

Needless to say, any of the suggested methods should be used with due respect to persons or property in the immediate vicinity. A child's sponge-rubber ball (baseball size) makes a safe weight for heavy thread line or fishing line.

If the antenna wire becomes snagged in lower branches of the tree when the wire is pulled up, or if branches of other trees in the vicinity interfere with raising the antenna, a weighted line thrown over the antenna and slid along to the appropriate point is often helpful in pulling the antenna wire to one side to clear the interference as the antenna is being raised, as shown in Fig. 20.

## Wind Compensation

The movement of an antenna suspended between supports that are not stable in wind can be reduced materially by the use of heavy springs, such as screen-door springs under tension, or by a counterweight at the end of one halyard, as shown in Fig. 18. The weight, which may be made up of junk-yard metal, window sash weights, or a galvanized pail filled with sand or stone, should be adjusted experimentally for best results under existing conditions. Fig. 21 shows a convenient way of fastening the counterweight to the halyard. It avoids the necessity for untying a knot in the halyard which

may have hardened under tension and exposure to the weather.

## Man-Made Supports

In practice, a height of 30 to 60 feet is in the optimum region for *any* band above 7 MHz where the ionosphere plays a part.

You can get by with even less than 30 feet if you have to. However, nearly everyone can put an antenna at least 25 feet or so in the air. This height puts it in the class where, usually, at least one end can be supported by your house. The other end can be held up by another building (if you have permission to use it) far enough away, or by a tree, or if necessary by a pole you put up yourself. The pole doesn't have to be an elaborate structure, especially if it can be erected on top of something. A detached garage makes a good base. It should give you a start of 12 to 15 feet, and generally will have enough roof area to let you put guys on a simple wood pole that can be up to 20 feet tall. It is important to realize that antennas with horizontal polarity should be one-half wavelength or more above ground for best results in long-distance communications.

## Anchoring

Wire antennas are not heavy, and even when pulled up tight the strain can easily be supported by a husky screw eye or hook, if it can be sunk 1-1/2 or 2 inches into good solid wood. Screw eyes can be used similarly for anchoring guy wires from light poles up to 20 feet long. Often other anchorages for guy wires offer themselves; use anything that seems solid enough and which gives you the opportunity for wrapping the wire around a couple of times so it won't slip.

A length of 2 X 3 makes a good pole for heights up to 20 feet or so. It isn't heavy, but with three solidly anchored guys it will hold any wire antenna you may use with it. Fig. 22 shows a simple type of construction, using fittings that you can buy at a hardware store. The pulley and halyard make it possible to raise and lower the antenna easily. With the antenna up, only two guys are really necessary, placed 90 to 120 degrees apart back of the antenna, as shown at B and C. The third guy, A, can be part way down the pole so it will be out of the way of the pulley and halyard, and should pull off in about the same direction as the antenna. Its purpose is to hold the pole up when the antenna is down.

The guys can simply be wrapped around the pole near the top. One is shown in the drawing. To keep them from slipping down they can be run through a screw eye as shown. This avoids putting any strain on the screw

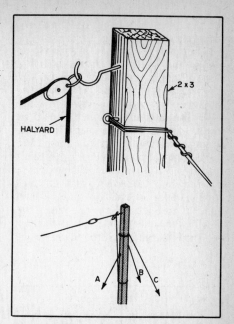

Fig. 22 — Using a length of 2 X 3 as a support for a horizontal antenna. Lengths up to 20 feet can be used with a single set of guys arranged as shown.

eye. Stranded steel wire such as you can buy in a hardware store (a typical type has four strands of about the same diameter as no. 18 copper) has ample strength for guying a pole of this type. Guy wire also is available from radio supply houses.

Plastic clothesline can be used for the halyard. The plastic kind stands the weather better than ordinary cotton clothesline. If you do use cotton, get the type having a steel core; it has greater strength and lasting qualities. But whatever type you use, be sure to use enough. Remember that you need to be able to reach the free end of the halyard when the antenna is down!

## Simple Wooden Mast

If you have to set a mast on the ground, the structure shown in Fig. 23 is easy to build and erect. Three 22-foot lengths of 2 X 3 are used to make a mast 40 feet tall. It makes a sturdy support for a horizontal-wire antenna when properly guyed. The mast is pivoted at the base for ease in raising (and lowering, if necessary), the pivot being the lower carriage bolt (A) shown in the drawing.

The base is a length of 2 X 4 set solidly in the ground. The 2 X 4 should be buried to a depth of about three feet and should extend at least three feet above the ground level. Use a plumb line to make sure that it is vertical when setting it. Pack rocks around it before refilling the hole with dirt; this will make a solid foundation which is helpful when the mast is being raised. After it is up and the guys are in place, the stress on the base is practically all straight down, so there is really no need for an elaborate footing.

The mast should be assembled on the ground (with the antenna halyard affixed; the method shown in Fig. 22 can be used for this) and fastened to the ground post with the lower carriage bolt. The guy wires, which should be made long enough to reach their anchorages while the mast is down, also should be attached. Push the mast straight up at the middle, letting it pivot on the bolt. When it gets up high enough, have an assistant slide a ladder under it to hold it. Keep working it up, moving the ladder down the mast as you go. Stop now and then to pull up on the

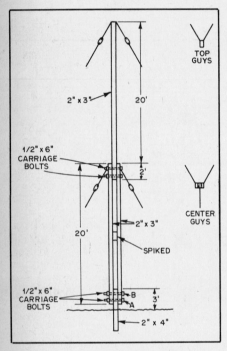

Fig. 23 — This mast construction is suitable for heights up to 40 feet, for supporting a horizontal antenna. Pivoting the mast on the lower bolt, A, simplifies the job of raising and lowering.

guys. Keep the front guy short enough so the mast won't swing all the way over and come down on the other side, but leave it loose enough so it can't interfere as the mast goes up. When the mast approaches the vertical, pulling on the top guys will bring it up the rest of the way. Slip in the upper carriage bolt (B) and the mast will stand by itself (if the base is solid) while you adjust the lower set of guys. Don't give the top guys their final tightening until the antenna is up, as they must work against the pull of the antenna.

The guy wires should be anchored about 20 feet from the base of the mast, for a height of 40 feet. If shorter 2 × 3s are used so that the completed mast is

less tall, this distance can be correspondingly reduced.

## Insulating Guy Wires

Guy wires are like antenna wires — if their length happens to be near resonance at your operating frequency, they can pick up energy from the antenna field and re-radiate it. This may do no harm, but then again it might distort the radiation pattern you hope the antenna will give.

To circumvent this, guy wires are often "broken up" by inserting insulators at strategic points. The idea is to avoid letting any section of guy wire have a length that is near resonance at any operating frequency or harmonic of it. Egg type insulators are generally used as a safety measure. With these insulators the wires are looped around each other so that if the insulator breaks the guy will still hold.

General practice is to put an egg in each guy a foot or so from where it is attached to the pole or mast, and another a foot or so from the point where it is anchored. Whether any more are needed depends on the remaining length. In most cases it is sufficient to insert insulators in such a way that no section of the wire will have a length that can be divided evenly by either 16 or 22.

## Guy Anchors

Trees or buildings at the right distance from the base of a mast can be used for anchoring guys. However, they don't always "just happen" to be present. In such a case a guy anchor can be sunk into the ground.

A six-foot length of 1-inch iron pipe driven into the ground at about a 45-degree angle makes a good anchor. It should be driven toward the mast, with 12 to 18 inches protruding from the ground for fastening the wires. Fig. 24 shows the general idea, with a suggested way of fastening the guy so it can't slip off the anchor.

## Weather Protection

A wooden mast or pole needs the same protection against weather as the exterior woodwork on a dwelling. New wood should be given three coats of a good paint made for outdoor use, with the first coat thinned so it sinks in well. Follow the directions on the paint container.

Masts made from several pieces of lumber, such as the one shown in Fig. 23, should have their individual parts painted separately before assembly. The heads of nails or screws should be sunk into the surface far enough so they can be puttied over. These, too, should be painted — after assembly.

Hooks, screw eyes and similar hardware should likewise have a coat of

paint to prevent rusting.

## Other Types of Masts

Amateur ingenuity has conjured up all sorts of mast and tower designs over the years. It is possible, for example, to make a satisfactory pole, 40 feet or so high, out of lengths of metal downspouting. Wooden lattice construction has long been a favorite for masts and towers. A number of such designs will be found in *The ARRL Antenna Book*, and new ones keep coming along regularly in *QST*. Then there are TV masts, built up in sections of metal tubing and provided with guy rings and other hardware — readily available and not at all costly. These can be run up to heights as great as 50 feet, with proper guying.

In fact, anything you can put up, and which will *stay* up, will be satis-

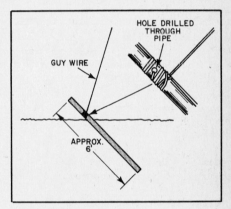

Fig. 24 — Pipe guy anchor. One-inch or 1-1/2-inch iron pipe is satisfactory for a mast such as is shown in Fig. 23.

factory. Never forget that you can't afford to take any chances with safety. A falling mast can result in accidental injury, or even death, to anyone that happens to be in its path. The taller and heavier the mast, the more necessary it becomes to build in plenty of safety factor — in size of guy wire, type of anchorage, and in the strength and cross section of the materials used in the mast or tower itself.

## A Trap Vertical for 40 Through 10 Meters

The multiband concept can be applied to verticals as well as to horizontal systems of the kind described earlier in the chapter. Such an antenna is illustrated in Fig. 25, and is designed for use from 7 to 30 MHz. It operates with an SWR of less than 2:1 and can be used for DX and local work.

Other construction techniques are possible, but the method shown is simple and inexpensive. The trap assembly should be protected from the weather by enclosing it in a plastic housing, possibly a refrigerator jar or similar.

The trap is built from a section of 2-1/2-inch diameter Miniductor stock, no. 12 wire, 6 turns per inch (B&W 3900-1). The coil has 10 turns, but should be adjusted for resonance, with the capacitor shunted across it, at 14.1 MHz with the aid of a grid-dip meter. This is done before the trap is installed in the antenna system. The capacitor is Centralab 850S-25Z.

Though it is common practice to cut the radials for *each* band of operation, one set (4) can be cut to the lowest operating frequency as shown in the sketch. Performance will not differ markedly from a similar antenna using multiband radials. Here the radials are drooped at a 45-degree angle to raise the feed-point impedance of the antenna to approximately 50 ohms. The radials also serve as guy wires.

### A Two-Element Beam for 15 Meters

We discussed the merits of beam

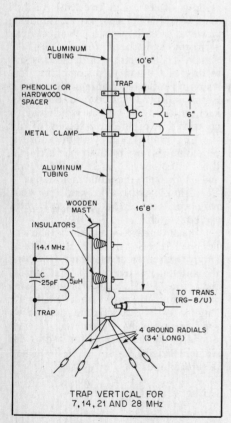

Fig. 25 — Diagram of the multiband trap vertical. A wooden mast supports the system, and the driven element is mounted on the mast by means of stand-off insulators. An insulator plug isolates the two sections of tubing. It can be made to fit inside the sections, then secured with screws. Or, it can be bored out for the OD of the tubing and slipped over the outside. If hardwood is used it should be boiled for half an hour in paraffin wax.

antennas in chapter 6. Anyone who has used a Yagi, cubical quad or other type of directional array will likely testify to the effectiveness of the antenna. Even the beginner can appreciate the gain and directivity of such an array especially for the higher frequencies. A rotatable array for 15 or 10 meters is not prohibitively large and, in many cases, can be turned with a heavy-duty TV rotator.

This antenna can be built with aluminum to make it lightweight, and mounted up in the air and rotated so that the signal can be beamed in the most favorable direction. The gain of this antenna is approximately 5 dB over a half-wave dipole alone.

To give you an idea of what 5 decibels means, let's assume you are running 75 watts input and getting 50 watts output. The 5 dB would increase your effective radiated power about three times in the favored direction, or to something slightly more than 150 watts! Additionally, the beam will have a property known as front-to-back ratio with about 20 dB of attenuation of signals arriving from the rear of the antenna. This is helpful in cutting down QRM.

### Finding Suitable Materials

Some hams may be fortunate to live near junk yards where aluminum tubing is available and at reasonable prices. However, many hams live in areas where there are no surplus or junk markets. Fortunately, there is one source that is available to all hams and that is the Reynolds "Do-It-Yourself" material available in practically any hardware store and in most Sears retail stores. The Reynolds stock may be slightly more expensive than surplus aluminum but the ease of procurement makes up for the price difference.

The Reynolds tubing that is used to make up the elements in our beam comes in eight-foot lengths. The readily available sizes are 1-inch and 3/4-inch diameters. A single element consists of one of the larger diameter lengths and two of the 3/4-inch diameter sections. When the smaller diameters are telescoped into the larger piece, the fit is very loose. Reynolds manufactures a 7/8-inch diameter stock for the primary purpose of telescoping their other two sizes together. The average dealer may not know this stock exists mainly because his catalog doesn't show it or isn't up to date.

We've included a bill of materials to make your shopping easier. The boom is 1-1/4-inch diameter, eight-feet long and Reynolds has such an item available or you can get a TV mast section from any TV store.

### Constructional Information

Fig. 26 provides all the dimensions

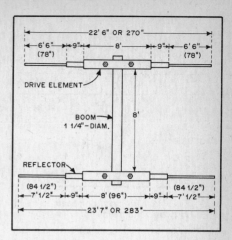

Fig. 26 — Dimensions for the two-element beam.

of the completed beam. The 7/8-inch diameter stock is six feet long and this should be cut into four equal lengths, 18 inches long. This will provide the required sleeves for joining the other two sizes of stock together. In order to mount the one-inch tubing to the 1-1/4-inch boom the smaller stock must be drilled to take the U bolts as shown in Fig. 27 at B. Take extra precautions when measuring the one-inch stock for drilling the U-bolt holes. The stock that we used was exactly eight feet long but don't take that for granted; measure each piece yourself and be sure the U-bolt holes are drilled exactly each side of center so that the element will be balanced when mounted to the boom.

After you cut the 7/8-inch diameter stock into four lengths, carefully deburr and smooth off both the inside and outside of the cut ends with a file or knife blade. The fit between the two

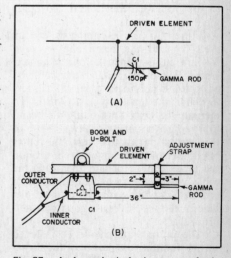

Fig. 27 — At A, method of using gamma feed and at B, constructional details of gamma. The coaxial feed line should be taped to the boom and then down the supporting mast, allowing enough free line at the mast to permit rotation of the beam.

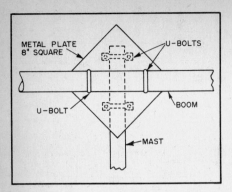

Fig. 28 — Details for mounting beam to mast. All U bolts are TV-antenna hardware type.

size tubings is quite precise and if the sleeves aren't smoothed, you are liable to "lock" up the pieces when sliding them together and have a nasty job trying to separate them.

With a pencil, carefully mark off the tubing at the dimensions shown in Fig. 26 and recheck the lengths about three times to be sure they are correct *and then* drill holes to take no. 6 metal tapping screws. The holes are drilled about one inch in from where the tubing meshes. When the metal tapping screws are screwed in, all "looseness" in the elements disappears.

A freezer container of the nonrigid plastic variety is used to house and protect the gamma capacitor, C1. Either no. 12 or no. 14 solid copper wire can be used to connect from the stator and rotor to nuts and bolts mounted on the side of the plastic box. Incidentally, a good source for short lengths of no. 12 or 14 solid wire is ordinary house-wiring cable. Any hardware store will sell you whatever you need and you'll find it a lot cheaper than buying a whole roll of wire. The plastic container is mounted to the boom via the U bolt that holds the driven element.

Either 50- or 70-ohm coax can be used to feed the beam and we used 50-ohm in our installation. It is suggested that the larger-diameter cable be used, RG-8 polyfoam type, as it has less loss than the smaller type, RG-58/U. To prepare the coax for feeding the beam, first remove about six or seven inches of the insulation that covers the outer braid. Separate the braid from around the inner conductor and then tape the cable where the two conductors separate in order to weatherproof the cable. Electrical tape makes a good weatherproof seal.

The outer braid should be fastened to the boom at the center of the driven element. You can do this by clamping the braid under one of the U-bolt nuts that holds the plastic box. The inner conductor of the coaxial line should be connected to one of the nuts and bolts

that connect to one side of C1. The other nut and bolt connecting to C1 is used to support one end of the gamma rod, the other end of the gamma rod is supported by the adjustment strap, see Fig. 27.

There are so many ways in which a beam can be mounted that we won't go into great detail here. However, a couple of hints may help. First, this entire beam weighs less than ten pounds so a TV rotator will easily handle the antenna. Along the same lines, TV hardware and masting could be used for supports. The only real problem is mounting the boom to a supporting pipe. One of the simplest methods is the device shown in Fig. 28. This consists of four TV U bolts and a metal plate, aluminum or steel, 1/16- to 1/8-inch thick, and eight inches square. Two of the U bolts hold the boom and the other two bolts hold the plate to the mast.

Fig. 29 — Here's the gamma match, driven element. Note the coax dressed along the boom.

### Adjusting the Gamma

In order to adjust the gamma match you'll need an SWR indicator of the type shown in chapter 11. This device, when installed in the feed line, will show when the antenna end of the line is properly matched. Also, it will serve as a constant monitor or output indicator and tune-up device.

If it is possible to adjust C1 and the gamma adjustment strap with the antenna in its normal location, then do so. However, in many cases, it won't be possible to reach the antenna to make adjustments so they will have to be made with the antenna near the ground, on a garage or on a step ladder. Try to get the antenna as high above earth as possible and still be able to reach the gamma adjustments. The closer the antenna is to its normal location, the less

change there will be in the match. The feed-point impedance of an antenna changes with its height above ground. Hence, we want it as high as possible so we'll get the least change after it is once adjusted.

While the dimensions given for the gamma settings in Fig. 26 may be the same for your beam, it is quite likely that because of construction differences, height above ground, and so forth, you will probably have to make some adjustments in the gamma. The object in adjusting a gamma is to have your reflectometer read zero in the reflected position versus full scale in the forward position. This would indicate a matched condition and an SWR of 1 to 1.

For a trial setting, place the gamma adjustment strap at the dimensions shown in Fig. 27 and set C1 near maximum capacitance, 95 percent meshed. Tune up the rig on 21,200 kHz and feed enough power through the system to get a full scale reading and it is a good idea to make your adjustments at as low a power level as possible. Switch the reflectometer to read reflected power and note the reading. Any reading of less than one-tenth of full scale would indicate an excellent match. However, you'll probably want to experiment and shoot for a "perfect" match. Try increasing or decreasing the setting of C1 and then comparing forward and reflected readings to see if the match improved or worsened. Be sure to keep notes so you'll know which way to go with C1, or the new setting of the shorting strap. Try moving the shorting or adjustment strap about one inch at a time, either out or in from the boom, and go through the adjustment range of C1 again. Eventually, and if your patience doesn't wear out; you'll get a perfect match.

The antenna shown in the article was designed to resonate at 21,200 kHz at about the center of the band. However, the antenna was essentially "flat" across the entire 21-MHz band. For those hams who want to work both ends, the lengths for 21,200 kHz are ideal. However, if you want the antenna for just phone or cw the formula for finding the element lengths for any given frequency is quite simple.

$$\text{Driven element length} = \frac{473}{f}$$

where $f$ equals the frequency in megacycles, and the answer will be in feet. The reflector should be made five percent longer than the driven element.

### A 10-Meter Swiss Quad

Basically, the Swiss Quad is a two-element array with both elements driven. One element is longer than the

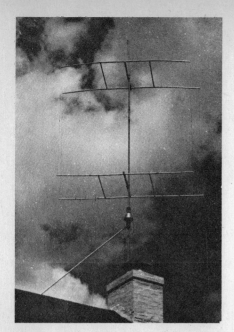

Fig. 30 — This is the completed Swiss Quad. As can be seen, there is very little sag in the antenna.

other, and to simplify our discussion of this antenna we will call the longer one the "reflector," and the shorter one the "director." Spacing between elements is usually 0.1 wavelength. As determined by the originator,[1] the impedance of the antenna, using the 0.1-wavelength dimension, is approximately 50 ohms.

Fig. 31 is a drawing of the components of the beam. In its usual form, lengths of aluminum or copper tubing are bent to form the horizontal members. The element perimeters are completed with vertical wires. At the crossover points (X, Fig. 31), which are connected together, voltage nodes occur.

These formulas only apply to the use of horizontal members of aluminum or copper tubing. Using the PVC tubing and wire elements, the overall lengths of

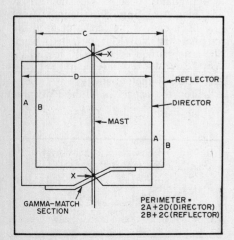

Fig. 31 — General arrangement for the Swiss Quad.

the perimeters are different and the correct lengths were determined experimentally as will be shown.

One of the advantages of this antenna over the more conventional quad type is that Plumber's Delight type construction can be used. This means that both elements, at the top and bottom of the beam, can be grounded to the supporting mast. In my antenna, the structure is lightweight but strong, and an inexpensive TV rotator carries it nicely. Another feature is the small turning radius, which is less than half that of a three-element Yagi.

### How to Build It

If your mechanical skills include the ability to form precise bends in aluminum or copper tubing, the original design[1] presents no great challenge. But if your talents are limited to using the saw, screwdriver and pliers, you might want to build your Swiss Quad in the manner shown. The antenna in the photograph is made entirely of wire which is supported by two insulating

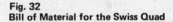

**Fig. 32**
**Bill of Material for the Swiss Quad**

Four 10-ft lengths 1/2-inch rigid PVC pipe.
Two 10-ft lengths 3/4-inch rigid PVC pipe.
One 10-ft length 1-inch rigid PVC pipe.
Twelve feet 1-1/8-inch or larger steel or aluminum tubing.
Epoxy cement (equal parts of resin and hardener).
100 ft annealed copper wire, 14 or 15 gauge.

frames constructed from rigid plastic water pipe. It can be built in a few evenings with minimal mechanical skills and a very modest cash outlay for materials. Rigid polyvinyl-chloride (PVC) water pipe is readily available from plumbing supply houses and from the large mail-order firms. The standard 10-foot lengths are just right for building the 10-meter Swiss Quad. You can cut and drill PVC pipe with woodworking tools. PVC plastic sheds water, an advantage where winter icing is a problem. Heat from the intense summer sun has not softened or deformed the quad structure at the author's station.

To build the wire version of the Swiss Quad, you will need the materials listed in Fig. 32 plus some wood screws and U bolts. Also required are a few scraps of wood-dowel rod and some old toothbrushes. A catalog order to Montgomery Ward resulted in the delivery of

[1] Baumgartner, "The Swiss Quad Beam Aerial," *R.S.G.B. Bulletin*, June, 1964.

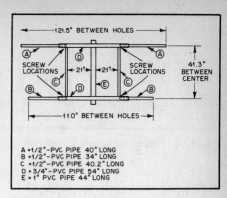

Fig. 33 — Dimensions and layout of the insulating frame.

white PVC pipe marked "Cresline." Each size telescoped neatly into the next larger size. If you select another brand, be sure that the 1/2-inch size will slide into the 3/4-inch pipe.

Cut the PVC pipe to the lengths shown in Fig. 33. Also cut several short lengths of dowel rod for reinforcement at the points indicated. These are held in place by means of epoxy cement, mixed thoroughly and applied generously. The bond is improved if the PVC surface is roughened with sandpaper and wiped clean before the cement is applied. A tack inserted through a tiny hole in the pipe will hold each dowel in place while the epoxy cures (about 24 hours at room temperature).

Reasonable care is required in forming the boom end joints so that the two sections of 3/4-inch pipe are parallel. The joining method used is illustrated in Fig. 34. Parallel depressions were filled near each end of each boom with a half-round rasp. These cradles are about 0.4 inch deep and their centers are 41.3 inches apart. Holes are drilled for the U bolts and the joints are completed with the U bolts and epoxy cement. Draw the bolts snug, but not so tight as to damage the PVC pipe. Final assembly of the insulating frames should be done on a level surface. Chalk an outline of the frame on the work surface so that any misalignment will be easy to detect and correct. If the 1/2-

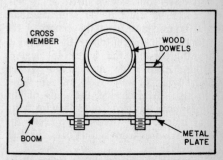

Fig. 34 — Boom end-joint detail.

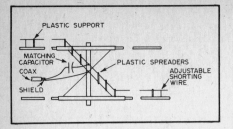

Fig. 35 — Details of the double gamma match.

inch pipe sections fit too loosely into the lateral members, shim them with two bands of masking tape before applying the epoxy cement.

Supports for the gamma-matching section can be made from old toothbrush handles or other scraps of plastic. Space the supports about 10 inches apart so that they support the gamma wire 2.5 inches on top of the lower PVC pipe. See Fig. 35 and photograph. Attach the spacers with epoxy cement. Strips of masking tape can be used to hold the spacers in place while the epoxy is curing.

There are several ways to attach the frames to the vertical mast. The mounting hardware designed for the larger TV antennas should be quite satisfactory. Metal plates about five inches square can be drilled to accept four U bolts. Two U bolts should be used around the boom and two around the mast. A piece of wooden dowel inside the center of the boom prevents crushing the PVC pipe when the U bolts are tightened. The plates should not interfere with the element wires that must cross at the exact center of the frame. A 12-foot length of metal tubing serves as the vertical support. The galvanized steel tubing used as a top rail in chain-link fences would be satisfactory.

When the epoxy resin has fully cured, you are ready to add the wire elements to produce the configuration shown in Fig. 31. Start on the top side of the upper frame. Cut two pieces of copper wire (no. 15 or larger) at least 30.5 feet long and mark their centers. Thread the ends downward through holes spaced as shown in Fig. 33 so that the wires cross at the top of the upper frame. Following the detail in Fig. 36, drill pilot holes through the PVC pipe and drive four screws into the dowels. The screws must be 41.3 inches apart and equidistant from the center of the frame. With the centers of the two wires together, bend the wires 45 degrees around each screw and anchor with a short wrap of wire. Now pull the wires through the holes at the ends of the pipes until taut. A soldered wire wrap just below each hold will prevent the element wires from sliding back through the holes.

Attach the wired upper frame about

two feet below the top of the vertical mast. Make a bridle from stout nylon cord (or fiberglass-reinforced plastic clothesline), tying it from the top of the mast to each of four points on the upper frame to reduce sagging.

Now cut two 11.5-foot lengths of wire and attach them to the bottom of the lower frame. Also, cut a nine-foot length for the gamma-matching section. If insulated wire is used, bare six inches at each end of the gamma wire. Details of the double gamma match are shown in Fig. 35. Attach the wired lower frame to the mast about nine feet below the upper frame and parallel to it. The ultimate spacing between the upper and lower frames, determined during the tuning process, will result in moderate tension in the vertical wires. Join the vertical wires to complete the elements of your Swiss Quad. All vertical wires must be of equal length. Do not solder the wire joints until you have tuned the elements. Connect the Swiss Quad to a grounded metal mast exactly at the

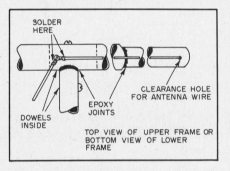

Fig. 36 — Details of the frame and wire assembly.

voltage nodes (crossover points) of the elements.

## Tuning and Adjustments

For tuning and impedance matching you will need a "dipper" (e.g., grid-dip oscillator), a VSWR indicator, and the station receiver and exciter. Stand the Swiss Quad vertically in a clear space with the lower frame at least two feet above ground. Using the dipper as a resonance indicator, prune a piece of 50-ohm coaxial cable to an integral multiple of a half wavelength at the desired frequency. (RG-8/U and RG-58/U with polyethylene insulation have a velocity propagation factor of 0.66. At 28.6 MHz, a half-wavelength section (made from the above cables) is approximately 11.35 feet (3.46 m) long. Connect one end to the midpoint of the gamma section and the other to a two-turn link. Couple the dipper to the link. You may observe several dips. Look for two pronounced dips near 26 MHz and 31.4 MHz. Measure the fre-

quencies at which these dips occur using your receiver to double-check the grid-dip meter. Then multiply the frequencies and take the square root of this product; that is $\sqrt{f_1 \times f_2}$. If the result is less than 28.6, shorten the vertical wires equally and repeat the process until $\sqrt{f_1 \times f_2}$ lies between 28.6 MHz and 28.8 MHz. Your Swiss Quad is now tuned for the 10-meter band.

Remove the link and connect the VSWR bridge in its place. Connect your exciter to the input terminals of the bridge, tune to 28.6 MHz and apply just enough power to obtain a full-scale forward voltage indication. Measure the VSWR. Now slide the two shorting wires of the matching section to new positions, equidistant from the center of the wire elements, and measure the VSWR. Continue adjusting the shorting wires until minimum VSWR is obtained. Insert a 100-pF variable capacitor between the center conductor of the coaxial cable feeder and the midpoint of the gamma wire. Adjust the capacitor for minimum VSWR indication. It may be necessary to readjust both the shorting wires and the capacitor to obtain a satisfactory impedance match. With patience, a perfect match (VSWR = 1:1) can be achieved. Solder the shorting wires.

The matching results obtained with the Swiss Quad are presented in Fig. 37. The adjustments were made with the antenna near ground level.

The variable capacitor may be replaced with a short length of RG-59/U coaxial cable. Each foot of this cable has a capacitance of approximately 20 pF. Measure or estimate the value to which the variable capacitor was finally set, add 10 percent, and cut a corresponding length of RG-59/U. Solder the shield braid to the midpoint of the gamma wire and the center wire to the center conductor of the 50-ohm transmission line, leaving the other end of the coaxial-cable capacitor open. You will probably observe that the VSWR has increased. Snip short lengths from the open end of the capacitor until the original low VSWR is obtained. When the antenna was raised to 40 feet (12.2 m), the VSWR was less than 1.5:1 over the entire 10-meter band.

Tape the capacitor to the PVC pipe

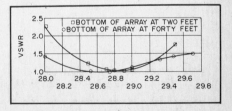

Fig. 37 — Plot of VSWR vs. frequency.

boom, then wrap a few bands of tape around the sections where the wires run along the sides of the pipes. Check the soldered joints and mechanical connections. Coat the soldered joints and the cable ends with a weatherproof sealing compound (e.g., silicone bathtub caulk) and hoist your new Swiss Quad up the tower.

# When Space Is Limited

So far in this chapter we've taken it for granted that you'd have all the space you need for putting up a half-wave dipole at a reasonable height above ground. Only too often, though, what the city dweller sees from the station window isn't exactly in the "ideal location" class.

Don't let yourself be discouraged by such a situation. It has been faced — and licked — by plenty of other amateurs. Makeshift antennas often work surprisingly well. Here's something you can take comfort from: Almost any antenna you put up will be at least as efficient as the *best* antenna you could install on a car for mobile operation. And even at the Novice power limit you have quite a bit more power than the average mobile transmitter. But in spite of inefficient antennas and lower power, thousands of hams have had lots of fun operating mobile.

The principle to follow, when you can't put up a half-wave dipole, is to get out as much wire as you can, as high as you can. Then add loading to the system to make it resonant at your operating frequency. That's about all there is to it. In this section we have a few suggestions that may be useful to you, but in the end they boil down to applications of the first two sentences of this paragraph.

### The "Random-Length" Antenna

The term "random length" is used to describe any antenna that simply consists of a wire running out of the station to whatever length is feasible. No special feeder is used; the rf power is applied at the station end of the wire.

A ground connection is essential, so the system as a whole corresponds to the grounded antenna described in chapter 6. As an antenna of this type has already been discussed at some length in that chapter, we don't need to go into it further except to repeat that it is a good idea to make the wire about a quarter wavelength long at the lowest frequency you want to use. This is in the neighborhood of 60 feet for the 3.5-MHz band. Don't worry if you can't get the entire length in a straight line; bend it if you have to, but don't make the bends at acute angles if there is some way to avoid it. Also, the wire doesn't have to be horizontal; it can slope either up or down away from the point where it enters the station. The main thing is to get as much of it as high in the air as possible.

Loading and coupling circuits for use with antennas of this kind are discussed in chapter 6, and you will find an example of one in chapter 11. The construction of the antenna — wire, insulators, lead-in and so on — should be the same as recommended for dipoles earlier in this chapter. And do your best about that ground connection — see chapter 6.

### The Vertical Antenna

Although you may have very little ground space available you often can find room to go up. A vertical antenna is the answer in that case. Electrically, it is practically the same as the random-length antenna. You use the same method of coupling power into it, and use the same method of grounding.

Reams have been written about the radiation patterns and other characteristics of vertical antennas. These discussions are all based on an antenna sitting on perfectly conducting ground, with nothing nearby to disturb the pattern. Your antenna won't be like that. Most likely it will have houses, wires, pipes and probably trees right within arm's length, and the ground below it will act more like a resistor than a conductor. The chances are, too, that the bottom of the antenna won't even be close to the earth. So don't look for anything approaching the theoretical performance of a vertical antenna. It will be more accurate to think of it as a random-length antenna that goes up instead of sidewise.

Make it as tall as you can. Thirty feet is a good length, but requires guying. The antenna can be made out of aluminum tubing, about an inch in diameter, but a good substitute can be found in the TV mast sections that are readily available at radio supply houses. These are usually 1-1/4 inches in diameter and have one end swaged for fitting into another section as the mast is built up. Ten feet is a standard length, so two such sections will give you a 20-foot antenna and three sections will make up 30 feet.

If the construction of your house permits, the bottom of the antenna can be fastened to the wall just outside the window of your operating room. Fig. 38 shows how TV wall brackets can be used for supporting it. If the upper bracket can be high enough to hold the top section you will need no guys. Just fit the sections together and, if possible, drill them for self-tapping screws in the part that overlaps. This will add some mechanical strength and will help the electrical contact. However, if any joints come above the upper wall bracket, use rope guys at the top. It isn't safe to have a section supported only by the joint at its lower end. Plastic clothesline makes a good guy rope and needs no insulators. The guys should be anchored at some solid point that will let them make at least a 30-degree angle with the antenna.

When brackets are used as in Fig. 38, the antenna should be insulated from them. One simple way is to strip the wires out of a length of 300-ohm twin line, leaving a polyethylene tape that you can wind around the antenna where it is held by the U bolt. Make the wrapping as thick as the width of the U bolt will permit, to reduce the stray capacitance introduced by the wall bracket.

Since you're treating this vertical as a random-length antenna, you don't need to worry about the length of the wire that goes from the bottom of it to your loading and coupling apparatus. It's more important to get the antenna up in the air as much as you can.

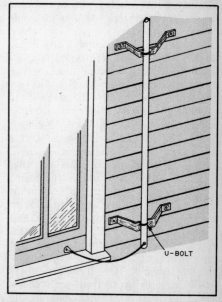

Fig. 38 — Using TV wall brackets for supporting a vertical antenna made of metal tubing. The antenna should be insulated from the brackets as described in the text.

# Chapter 15

# Setting Up a Station

Somewhere, sometime, there must have been an amateur who went through the trials of studying for his license, and the tribulations of taking the examination, but who *didn't* get "on the air" at the very earliest possible minute after the mailman rang the door-bell with the "ticket" in his hand. We're still looking for that chap, and some day we may meet him!

The impatience to get going as soon as the bare minimum of equipment is at hand is human. It denotes real interest and enthusiasm — and these you should have. But unless you've had your apparatus well in advance of the license, and have had plenty of time to plan your layout, you'll quickly realize that there's more to a station than just a collection of workable gear. So after the buck fever of the first few QSOs has worn off, sit down and do a little thinking about getting the various and sundry items to work together harmoniously.

Your amateur equipment may be all factory-built, but there is still opportunity for the individual touch in the way you arrange your station. No two operators have exactly the same ideas about it. Nor are any two confronted by exactly the same conditions. One may have a whole room available, another a corner of the bedroom or kitchen, another a spot in the cellar or attic. Each station presents its own problems — what sort of operating table, how to run in antenna leads, where to pick up ac power and how to control it, and others like them. In these matters you're pretty largely on your own. The suggestions we have here will help you get started, but if you're like others you'll develop you own preferences. Then, too, part of the pleasure in having a station is the privilege of rearranging it when the mood strikes.

If you do much operating — as no

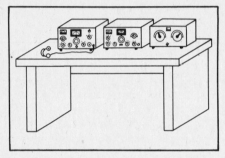

Fig. 1 — If you build your own operating table, here is a simple design. The top can be an unfinished flush type door cut to a convenient size. The supports are rectangles 2 X 3, with internal cross-bracing if necessary, covered by 1/4-inch plywood. The rear support apron ties the whole structure together and makes it rigid. Wood screws can be used for fastening, or the sections can be bolted together if there is any thought of having to take it apart.

doubt you will in the first phase of your amateur career — the thing to concentrate on is convenience. The controls you use all the time, such as the receiver tuning knob, want to be within easy reach. Working them for a period of a few hours shouldn't lead to fatigue. Also, you should be able to send and receive with a minimum of lost motion in changing from one to the other. Having to throw a half dozen switches each time doesn't make for snappy contacts!

### The Operating Table

In picking out a table or desk on which to set your equipment, don't be stingy with space. You need to have room for writing, both for keeping your log and for jotting down notes during a conversation. Although this can be done with only a foot or so of depth, it's a lot more comfortable if you can have more. The receiver panel should be about 18 inches from the front edge of the operating table. You also need about

that same depth for mounting your key for code work; anything less makes sending a rather tiring chore. As a general rule, the equipment itself won't be more than a foot or so deep, so a table depth of about 30 inches is adequate. A few extra inches, though, make a world of difference in roominess, and are worth having if there's nothing to prevent it.

The table width needed depends, of course, on how much gear has to be accommodated. A three-foot width will give *you* enough elbow room, but is rather small for the transmitter, receiver and the accessories that are bound to accumulate. Standard office-desk width — about 60 inches — will take care of the average low- or medium-power station. In fact, such a desk makes a very good operating table. The drawers can be put to good use, obviously.

### Homemade Table

An operating table can be built at a relatively small cost. An example is shown in Fig. 1, with the constructional details given in Fig. 2. The top of the table is made from an unfinished flush type door, measuring approximately 30 X 84 inches. Side members for supporting the top are made from ordinary 2 X 3 lumber which comes in standard lengths of 8 and 12 feet. Making legs that are good and solid isn't the easiest job in the world, and if the table isn't solid it will be a poor operating desk. You can get around this by using the construction technique shown in Fig. 2A and D. The 2 X 3s are formed into a square or rectangular format, as shown at A. Each joint should be glued and screwed together. Nails will not provide the sturdiness that we are looking for.

Once the glue holding the 2 X 3s together has completely dried (several hours is sufficient with most types of glue), these assemblies can be drilled and made ready for mounting. If you are planning to cover the top and edges of the door with a plastic laminate, such as Formica, holes should be drilled through the door and countersunk as shown in Fig. 2B. After the holes in the door have been drilled, place the pieces in the position shown in Fig. 1. Drill through the 2 × 3s at the four bolt locations. After these holes have been drilled, the four bolts should be inserted in the holes, through the 2 × 3s and secured by means of flat washers and nuts. With the bolts securely in place,

fill the gaps between the bolt heads and wood with epoxy cement. See Fig. 2C.

Once the epoxy has hardened (it's a good idea to let it set over night), the nuts can be removed and the three sections taken apart. If you are planning on having the top laminated, now is the time. Most kitchen cabinet shops can do this for you, as they have all of the necessary tools. Pick a color that compliments the rest of the shack!

The table is now ready for assembly. Place the table top on its good surface with the bolts sticking up. Now the side

members can be slipped over the bolts and held in place with flat washers, lock washers and nuts. Make sure to tighten the nuts securely.

At this point, the side coverings can be attached to the leg assemblies. Ordinary 1/4-inch plywood or Masonite can be used if you plan on painting this portion of the table. An alternative would be to use oak-, walnut-, birch- or teak-veneered plywood. Although this material is a bit more expensive than ordinary plywood it yields a quality furniture-like appearance The wood can be stained and coated with clear lacquer to preserve the finish. Another alternative would be to use pieces of wood paneling for the side coverings. In any case, the coverings on the outside of the table should be glued and tacked to the frame. The inner side coverings should only be tacked to the frame so they can be removed and the table taken apart should the need arise. The front face of the side members should be covered with a wide strip of veneer or plastic laminate of the same color used for the top of the table.

A rear-apron brace can be made from a 2 × 4. By painting this brace flat black it will not detract from the appearance of the table even if a small amount of its surface shows.

### Arranging Equipment

Having ample table-top space doesn't always solve completely the problem of having everything within easy reach. Many amateurs find it useful to spread the equipment vertically as well as horizontally. A low shelf, supported above the table, will let you put your key or keyer paddle, log book and other accessories of this type under the receiver and transmitter, thus doubling the area within arm's reach. Obviously, in doing this you need to give some thought to the position of the receiver controls: Can they be operated comfortably when the receiver is set up above the table in this way? A shelf height of six inches or so will accommodate many accessories, and also offers a place for mounting small panels for control switches.

One thing is essential for code work. The key or keyer paddle should be fastened down so it can't move, especially if it doesn't have a heavy base of its own. You can't send decent code if the key or paddle keeps sliding away from you every time you bear down on it: It should be at the right distance from the edge of the table, so your arm can rest comfortably while you send.

### Transmit-Receive Control

A certain amount of coordination is needed in the control of the receiver and transmitter, for smooth transition from send to receive and back again.

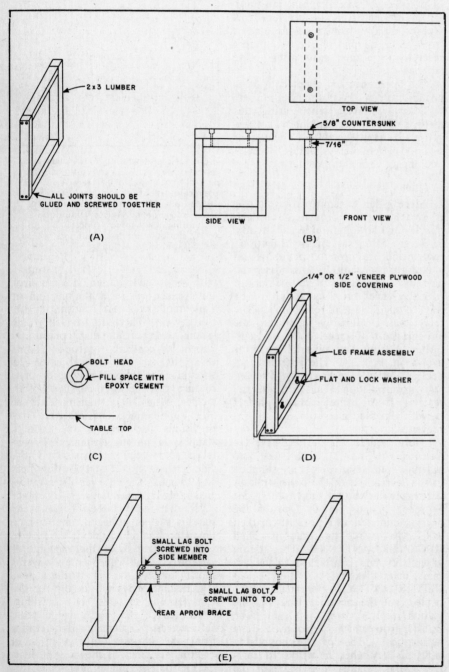

Fig. 2 — (A) 2 X 3 lumber is used to form the two side supports. Each joint should be glued and then screwed together. (B) Front, top and side views detailing the method of fastening the side supports to the top. (C) Completely fill the space around the bolt head with epoxy. (D) Table assembly and side covering information. (E) The rear-apron brace should be attached to both side members and the top of the desk.

Here, a great deal depends on the actual equipment you have and the kind of operating you want to do. There are basically two areas of concern — antenna switching from transmitter to receiver, and receiver muting during transmit.

The simplest system of all involves *no switching*. Separate antennas are used for the transmitter and receiver. As was pointed out in chapter 6, the use of separate antennas may not be altogether desirable, but it does simplify the send-receive changeover function. In many low-power cw transmitters, the oscillator is keyed along with the final amplifier. Thus, with the key open the transmitter is not generating a signal, and so it will not interfere with reception. To send, you merely operate the key.

The success of this method depends a good deal on your receiver. It is bound to be badly overloaded when you have the key down. This causes blocking — a shift in the operating conditions of the active devices in the receiver — and loss of sensitivity, especially near the transmitting frequency. Some receivers don't recover rapidly from blocking, and it may be a couple of seconds before reception is normal again after you've stopped sending.

As mentioned in chapter 6, it is possible to ruin the rf amplifier in some solid-state receivers when using this method. If you are planning to use this system it might be wise to read that section of chapter 6 before actually hooking up your equipment.

### Antenna Changeover

Some older transmitters have a pair of switch contacts brought out to terminals for controlling external circuits. These are often part of the "function" switch and are open on stand-by and closed for transmit. In some cases the contacts operate a 117-volt circuit which is "live" on transmit and can be used to operate a send-receive relay. The relay is used ordinarily for shifting the antenna from the receiver to the transmitter. A typical circuit arrangement is shown in Fig. 3A. The antenna connection on the receiver is grounded when transmitting. This protects the receiver from being damaged by rf power from the transmitter, and usually prevents blocking.

Most modern transmitters have the antenna relay built in. In this case, two antenna connection points are supplied at the rear apron of the transmitter. A system similar to that shown in Fig. 3A is usually incorporated. One of the antenna connections is normally marked ANTENNA while the other is called RECEIVER ANTENNA. The station antenna system is attached to the terminal marked ANTENNA and the RECEIVER ANTENNA terminal is connected to the antenna jack on the station receiver via a short cable. The transfer from transmit to receive is done automatically. The operator simply activates the key when he wishes to transmit — the circuitry takes care of the rest.

### Receiver Muting

On phone, if you try to transmit

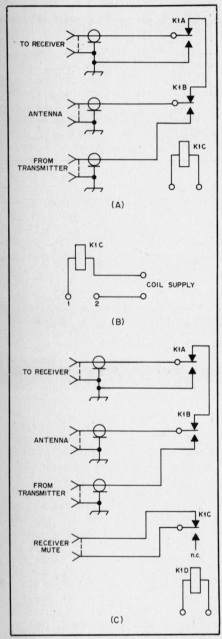

Fig. 3 — Using an antenna changeover relay with coaxial lines. The circuit at A can be used if the transmitter offers a controlled 117-volt circuit for operating the relay. If the transmitter has only a pair of contacts for relay control, but no power, the circuit at B can be used. The antenna changeover part is the same as in A. C shows how an auxiliary relay or an extra set of contacts can be used with the basic circuit of B, in cases where automatic muting of the receiver is wanted.

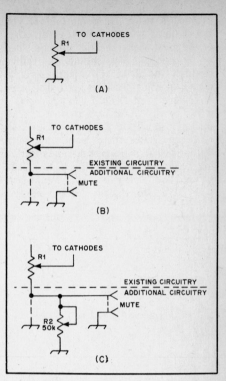

Fig. 4 — Receiver muting for a vacuum-tube type receiver. At A is a conventional rf-gain control circuit used in most receivers. In B the receiver is cut off completely during transmit periods. The circuit at C allows the receiver to operate at reduced gain, for cw monitoring, while transmitting. In both B and C, short-circuiting the muting terminals restores normal reception.

with the receiver turned on, sound from the speaker will reach the microphone. This modulates the transmitter and starts a howl. The audio-frequency oscillation arising from that condition is known as *acoustic feedback*. The receiver has to be silenced when you transmit. The simplest way to do this is to turn off one or more stages of the receiver when your transmitter is on. Most communications receivers have provisions for this (in the form of standby or muting terminals). For the receiver to function normally you provide a short circuit at these terminals, and to mute the receiver the terminals are simply left open.

If your receiver doesn't have such a standby system, either the one shown in Fig. 4 or 5 should work. If the receiver you are using is of the vacuum-tube variety, you will want to use the system shown in Fig. 4. R1 is the manual rf-gain control resistor in the receiver. One terminal of this control will be connected to the chassis in practically all receivers. Disconnect this terminal from the chassis and run it to an external terminal, as shown at B. When the muting terminals are open, the receiver is inoperative; shorting them puts it back in normal operation.

The system at Fig. 4C is useful if you're operating cw and want to listen

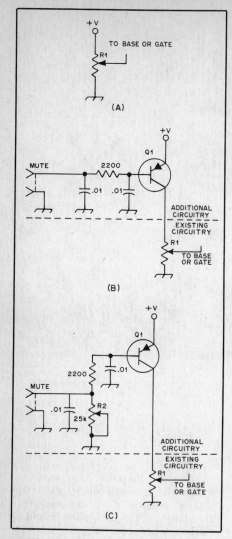

Fig. 5 — Receiver muting for a solid-state receiver. The conventional rf-gain circuitry is shown at A. The circuit shown at B will mute the receiver entirely, while C will provide a variable level sidetone for cw work.

to your sending. Although you can leave the receiver completely on, as mentioned earlier, it isn't likely that you'll get a good sidetone for monitoring your code, because the receiver will block. However, by cutting back on the rf gain it is possible to make most receivers give a good tone. The gain can be reduced automatically if an extra control, R2, is installed as shown at C. Adjust it for a good-sounding signal while sending. It is shorted out and the receiver comes back to normal when a short is supplied at the mute terminals.

Fig. 5 illustrates a system that is usable with most solid-state receivers. Unfortunately, we cannot simply open the ground connection on the control as we did with the previous circuit. Positive voltage would still be supplied to the receiver circuits and they would remain operative. Instead, we must break the positive lead to the rf-gain

control, R1, as shown at B. With the mute terminal open circuited, the transistor will not conduct and no voltage will be present across the rf-gain control. This effectively shuts off the receiver. When a short appears across the mute terminals, Q1 conducts, voltage is applied to the rf-gain control, and the receiver functions normally. This circuit, as is, will not enable you to monitor your sending.

The circuit shown at Fig. 5C will let you listen to your sending. R2 is adjusted for a good-sounding note. During receive conditions R2 is shorted via the mute terminal, and the receiver functions as normal.

## Other Methods

Control schemes such as those described are well suited to the types of equipment many beginners use when they first get on the air. More elaborate ones have been devised, and you will no doubt run into them in your reading. You'll appreciate better what they're designed to do after you've had some operating experience. We'll mention only one here: the electronic *T-R (transmit-receive) switch.*

The T-R switch is an active circuit that replaces the mechanical relay for antenna change-over. Information on how to build one is given in chapter 11. It lets signals through from the antenna to the receiver whenever the transmitter isn't turned on. But whenever any rf from the transmitter reaches it, it in effect disconnects the receiver from the antenna. Since there is no mechanical motion the action is practically instantaneous.

## CW Break-in

The electronic T-R switch is fine for cw *break-in* operation, since it lets you use the same antenna for both transmitting and receiving. Break-in, strictly speaking, is a send-receive system that lets you hear other signals while you're sending. The advantage of this is that if the operator at the other end has trouble copying you, or wants you to stop sending for any reason, he can simply press his key and you'll hear him.

It doesn't usually work quite as ideally as this in ordinary rag-chewing, unfortunately. When the band is crowded, anyone is likely to open up on the same frequency, so you'll often get an apparent break from some quite different operator who may not even know there's a QSO going on. This can be confusing, both to you and the fellow at the other end. However, real break-in is a useful technique in many circumstances, such as net operating.

What most rag-chewers mean by "break-in" is that they have no switches to throw when they go from receive to

send. Separate antennas for receiving and transmitting provide this species of break-in. It isn't real break-in, though, unless the receiving operator can attract the attention of the transmitting operator *while* he's transmitting. For this, the receiver has to be in full operating condition at least between letters in a transmission, if not actually between dots and dashes.

## Safety

Your station should offer no hazards, either to you, your family, or to your friends, or to property. There are reasons for every accident involving radio apparatus, but never a *good* reason. Take no chances with electricity. Even a low-voltage shock can be serious — sometimes fatal. Practically all manufactured equipment is built so that you can't get your fingers on any "hot" points unless you deliberately take off covers or remove a chassis from a cabinet. But that doesn't mean there cannot possibly be any hazard in using it. There can be, unless you take measures to prevent it.

The worst condition is one where the equipment is seemingly safe but actually isn't, should there be a breakdown inside. Most radio gear is enclosed in metal containers. These offer excellent protection against shock, *provided the cabinet is connected to a good earth ground.* The 115-volt wiring inside the cabinet is normally isolated from it, but there *could* be a breakdown that would cause the hot side of the line to make contact with the metal. This is dangerous, if there is no external ground connection on the cabinet. With such a connection a fuse may blow, but there can't be any voltage lying in wait for you.

The first rule, then, is this: Enclose all equipment in metal so that no "hot"

An unusual space-saving arrangement, with the equipment housed in a built-in bookcase. Since the writing desk is part of the normal room furniture this station, W2URP, literally makes no demands on the living room area.

points can be reached, and ground all such cabinets or shields. Do this for *all* your equipment. This goes for microphones, too. Also, one side of the key — the terminal having the most exposed metal — should be grounded. And don't use a keying circuit that has more than a few volts on it.

## Grounds

The general idea is shown in Fig. 6. If you live where there is water distribution, make your ground connection to a cold water pipe. These almost invariably go right to ground, and you get a good earth connection through the underground piping. The electrical-system ground is usually made to this same piping. In rural districts where there is no such water system you may have to go to the alternative of a driven ground rod. This is also shown in the figure. Use one at least six feet long (the kind made for television use is satisfactory) or, preferably, two or three spaced several feet apart and connected together. Grounds of this type do not always have as low resistance as might be wished, depending on the kind of soil, and several rods are better than one. Be sure to tie this system to the power company's ground connection at your service entrance, because there can be an appreciable voltage between two such grounds.

Don't depend on the cables that go from one piece of equipment to another for completing your ground connections. Make sure that each piece of equipment is *separately* connected to the ground system. The external ground connection should be the *first* one made when installing a piece of equipment, and the *last* one removed when taking it out of service.

## Pull the Plug!

One final point about safety — *never* take a cabinet or dust cover off a piece

This neat station belongs to WN2AUD. The equipment pictured is a Heath HR-10B receiver, a DX-60B transmitter and an HG-10B VFO. The major equipment is mounted above arms level thereby doubling the space within easy reach.

of equipment, or raise a lid that gives access to the live circuits, without first pulling the power plug. Better a dead circuit than a dead operator.

## Fire and Lightning Protection

So far as the equipment itself goes, the same methods that are effective against accidental shock usually will reduce the hazard of fire. If the equipment is in metal cabinets and an internal breakdown causes overheating, the chances are small that the cabinet temperature will get high enough to set fire to anything outside the set. It is a good idea to fuse all 115-volt circuits, since a breakdown generally will cause a fuse to blow and thus — in many cases but not always — will shut off the source of heating power before the faulty component gets dangerously hot.

The lightning hazard from an antenna is much exaggerated; ordinary amateur antennas are no more likely to be hit by a direct stroke than any other object of about the same height in the vicinity. However, an ungrounded antenna system can pick up quite a large electrical charge from a storm in the neighborhood. This can damage your equipment (receiver front ends are particularly susceptible) if you take no precautions against it. The best thing is a grounding switch, as shown in Fig. 7. A small knife switch will allow you to ground the feeders when you're not on the air. It will not disturb the normal

operation of the feeders (with the switch open, of course) if the lead from the line to the switch contact is no more than a couple of inches long. The grounding switch preferably should be installed where the feeder enters the building. It should be on the outside of the wall, if possible, and should be protected from the weather.

An alligator-jaw clip can be used instead of the switch, if a few inches of flexible lead are allowed for making the ground connection. Whether you use the switch or the clip, don't forget to

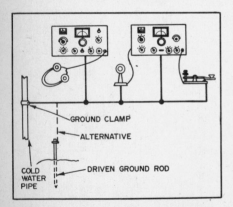

Fig. 6 — Each piece of equipment should be connected to a good ground external to the equipment itself. The cold water pipe can be used where there is underground water piping. This grounding is an important safety measure.

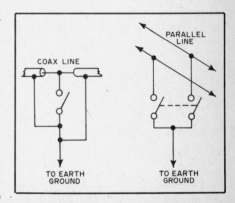

Fig. 7 — Methods of grounding antenna feeders for protection against surges caused by lightning in the vicinity. A flexible clip can be substituted for the switches. The earth ground should be of the type shown in Fig. 6.

Here is another Novice station, this one belonging to WN9SBC. Note the efficient use of space in the arrangement of the equipment.

disconnect the ground when you try to do any transmitting.

### Station Accessories

Although the real essentials of the indoor part of an amateur station are the transmitter and receiver (and of course a key or microphone, or both), most hams don't stop with these two alone. Other instruments can contribute mightily to efficient operation and to the satisfaction you get out of having a station.

A certain amount of measuring gear is useful. Making measurements can be a hobby in itself — and don't make the mistake of thinking that there's nothing more to it than reading a number on the face of a meter. Measurements tell you what's going on and whether your transmitter and receiver are performing as they should. One thing the FCC regulations require, for example, is a means for determining whether your transmitting frequency is within the proper limits, *and it must be independent of the transmitter itself.* The best way to meet this is with a simple *frequency standard.* A *wavemeter,* which is a "coarse" frequency-measuring instrument, is a worthwhile supplement to the frequency standard, but is not a substitute for it.

As an aid in the adjustment of a transmatch for maximum power to the antenna, a device for measuring standing-wave ratio is extremely handy. The *SWR bridge* or *Monimatch* does this.

If you do any building, an instrument for measuring voltage, current and resistance is very helpful. It is also the first thing you reach for when servicing equipment that has developed some fault. Either a VOM *(volt-ohm milliameter)* or an *electronic voltmeter* (EVM) is a worthwhile investment. Many amateurs find both practically indispensable Then, too, an oscilloscope is an instrument no advanced station would omit from the list of needed measuring devices. The list could go on and on. You won't need many of those named right away, but as your interests develop along technical lines you'll turn to them sooner or later.

There are lots of other useful auxiliaries — gimmicks for improving reception, monitoring, testing, extending frequency coverage — almost anything you can think of that will help you do better what you're now doing or help you extend your activities into new fields. Your interests in amateur radio need never be static!

# INDEX

# Schematic Symbols Used in Circuit Diagrams

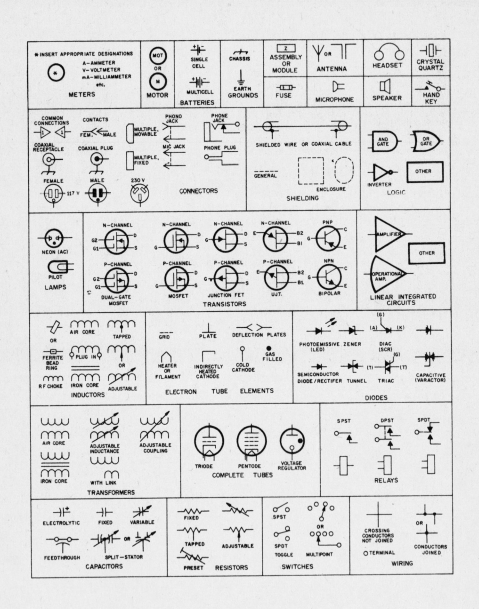